366 BIBLE STORIES

Retold by
Roberto Brunelli

Illustrated by
Chris Rothero

Translation by
Colin Clark

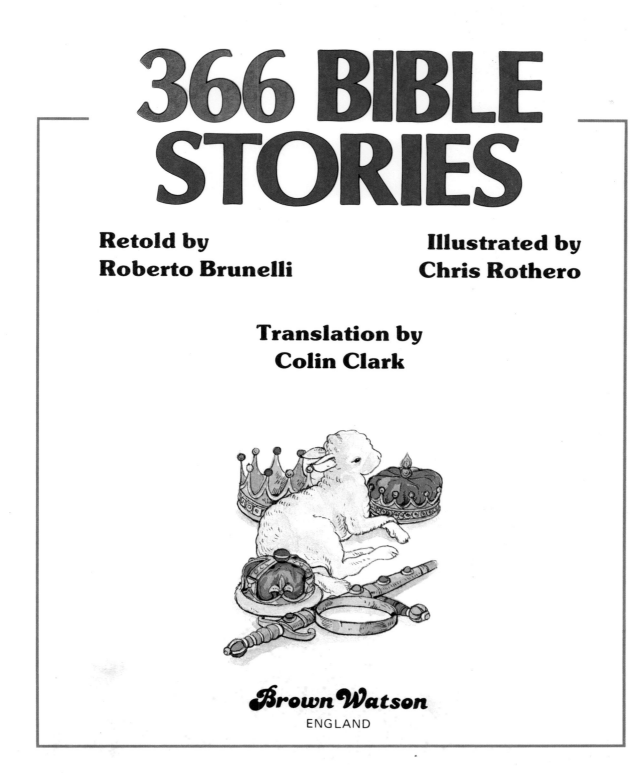

Brown Watson
ENGLAND

BIBLE STORY OF THE MONTH

God Creates the World and its Inhabitants

Along, long time ago, the sky, the earth, and all living things did not exist. There was nothing of what we now see all around us: there was only God, and it was he who created everything we see around us.

This is how it all happened. First, God said, "Let there be light!" And light began to shine. God saw that the light was good and decided to separate it from the darkness. He called the light "day" and he called the darkness "night." And it was morning and then evening: this was the first day.

Then God made the firmament over the waters, and it was like a great vault, transparent and clear. God called the firmament "sky." A morning passed and evening came, and this was the second day.

God then said, "Let the waters gather under the sky and let dry land appear:" And thus it was. God called the dry land "earth" and the waters he called "sea," and he saw that they were good. He spoke again, saying, "The earth shall produce buds, grasses, flowers, and trees that bear fruit, each according to its species!" And thus buds and shoots appeared from the earth, and grasses and flowers and fruit trees grew, each according to its species. And God saw that all of these things

were good, and night came and that was the third day.

God said, "Let there be lights in the firmament of the sky, to distinguish day from night; they shall serve to indicate the passing of days, of seasons, and of years and they shall also illuminate the earth!" And thus it happened. God made two great lights. The larger was to illuminate the day, and the smaller was to brighten the night, and he then made many tiny lights. In this way God created the sun, the moon, and the stars, and he placed them in the firmament of the sky so that they might illuminate the earth, measure

day and night, and separate the light from the darkness. God saw that all of this was good, and it was the end of the fourth day.

God said, "The waters of the sea shall be full of living things, and in the sky over the earth many kinds of birds shall fly." In this way God created all the creatures of the seas and oceans, from the enormous whale to the smallest fish, and also all the winged creatures, and set them to fly. At the end of the fifth day, God saw that this was good.

There were still no inhabitants of dry land and God said: "The earth shall be populated by living beings

of many different kinds: animals that are good to eat, wild beasts, reptiles, and every other species that moves on the land." This happened, and thus God created all the species of animals. And he saw that they were good.

At this point, God said: "I shall make man and he shall be different from all other creatures! I shall make him in my own image and likeness, and he shall reign over the fish of the sea, over the birds of the air, and over the animals on land!"

And so God created man in his own image and likeness, and he divided man into male and female

and he blessed them, saying: "Give birth to other men and populate the earth; subject the earth to your will and rule over the fish of the sea and over the birds of the air, and over every other living thing that I have made!" And God continued: "I give you also all the plants that grow on the earth and all the fruit trees so that you may eat them. All green grass I give to the animals of the land and the birds of the air as food." And thus it was. When he had created man in his own image and given him the earth as his domain, God looked at everything he had made and he saw that it was

good. Thus ended the sixth day.

The sky and the earth were thus finished and all their inhabitants completed. Therefore, on the seventh day God rested from his work, and he blessed the seventh day and made it holy. For this reason men do not work on the seventh day, which we call Sunday, but rest and worship God instead.

Oh Lord, Our God,
How great is thy name
In all the world:
Your magnificence
Crowns the heavens.
When I look at your sky,
The work of your hand,
The moon and the stars that you
    created,
I wonder why you remember
To take care of man.
And still you have made him
Little less than the angels.
And you have crowned him
With glory and with esteem.
You have given him power
Over the works of your hands,
And you have placed the world at
    his feet:
All the flocks and the herds,
All the beasts of the countryside,
The birds of the air
And the fish that swim in the seas.
Oh Lord, Our God,
How great is thy name
In all the world!

Genesis 1–2; Psalm 8

1 A Name for Every Animal

This is how the Lord God created man. He took dust into his hands from the earth and shaped it into the form of a man. Then God blew a breath of life into the nostrils of his creation and man became a living being.

God called him Adam.

Then the Lord created a magnificent garden in Eden, and it was full of beautiful trees which produced fruits that were good to eat. A great river watered the garden and then divided into four and flowed over the earth.

And there, in the Garden of Eden, God set down the man he had created, and nurtured and cared for him, for he wanted him to be happy.

God made all of the beasts of the earth and the birds of the air come before Adam, for he wished to see what name the man would give to them; whatever the man chose to call the living things was to be their name.

Thus Adam gave names to every animal of the earth and every bird of the air, and the name Adam gave to each has remained the same for all men since.

2 God Creates Woman

God had given the beautiful Garden of Eden to Adam. This, however, was not enough, for God wanted him to be happy.

Thus God said: "It is not right for man to be alone; I will make him a mate who will be like him." God made sleep fall on the man and then he removed one of his ribs and from it he shaped a woman.

God then led the woman to Adam, who greeted her with joy, saying: "This is flesh of my flesh and bone of my bones; she is just like me!" And he called her Eve.

4

3 The Serpent in the Garden

Adam and Eve were living happily in the Garden of Eden. Everything was beautiful to behold and they did not have to work, for the trees bore every type of fruit that was good to eat.

The Lord God had given everything to Adam and Eve, with one exception. He said: "You may eat the fruit of every tree in the garden except for one special tree in the middle. It is the tree of the knowledge of good and evil; and you must not eat of its fruits or you will die."

The most cunning of all the creatures that God had created was the serpent, and it did not like the man and the woman. Indeed, the serpent sought their downfall for, in reality, the serpent was the devil, the enemy of man.

One day, in the Garden of Eden, the serpent spoke to the woman saying: "Is it true that God has forbidden you to eat the fruit of the trees in the garden?"

"No," replied Eve. "We can eat every fruit except the fruit from the tree of knowledge. God told us not even to touch that fruit or we will die!"

"It is not true that you will die," lied the serpent. "On the contrary, God has forbidden you to eat from that tree because he knows that if you do then you will be like him and know good and evil."

Eve then looked at the fruit of the forbidden tree and found it desirable. She picked an apple from the tree and ate half, then gave the rest to Adam, and he too ate.

In that instant, their eyes opened, they realized they were both naked, and they covered themselves with fig leaves. Then Adam and Eve felt great shame and they understood the evil they had done. The Lord had given them everything and, in return, they had disobeyed him.

4 The Sin Is Discovered

Genesis 2–3

Adam and Eve, in the Garden of Eden, had disobeyed the Lord God by eating the fruit from the tree which he had forbidden to them.

A short time later they heard the Lord God walking in the garden and they hid themselves among the trees. The Lord called to the man: "Where are you?" and Adam replied: "I heard your footsteps and I hid myself in fear, for I am naked."

"Who told you that you are naked?" asked the Lord. "You have eaten the fruit which I commanded you not to eat!" And the man said:

"It was given to me by the woman whom you created and placed at my side."

"What have you done?" God asked Eve. "The serpent gave me the fruit," replied the woman. "It deceived me and I ate it."

And God then pronounced punishment. To the serpent he said: "You shall crawl on your stomach forever, as punishment for having done this." And to Adam and Eve the Lord God said: "You can no longer stay here in the garden; go forth and earn food to eat with the sweat of your brow." He then placed an angel with a flaming sword to guard the gates of Eden.

5 Cain and Abel

Genesis 4

Adam and Eve had two sons and they were called Cain and Abel. Cain was a farmer and Abel was a shepherd. One day the two brothers offered a sacrifice to God: Cain offered him the best fruits from his fields, and Abel his best lamb.

Abel made his offering with a sincere heart; this pleased the Lord. But Cain was angry and jealous of his brother, so his gift did not please the Lord. The Lord warned Cain, saying: "Why are you angry? Why do you glower? You must conquer your jealousy."

6 Cain Murders Abel

Genesis 4

Cain was jealous of his brother Abel because his gifts pleased the Lord, whereas those offered by Cain did not. His rage grew until one day he invited Abel into the fields and killed him there.

God, who saw everything, asked him: "Where is your brother?" and Cain, adding dishonesty to his crime, replied, "How should I know. Am I my brother's keeper that I should know where to find him?"

"The voice of your brother's blood cries out to me," said the Lord, "and for this reason you must flee from this place, and for the rest of your life you shall wander over the face of the earth."

Cain, then, was very much afraid that somebody would kill him because he was a fugitive. The Lord, however, did not desire anyone's death—even for sins as great as Cain's, so he marked Cain with a sign of warning so nobody would hurt him.

Thus Cain went away from the Lord and went to live in the land of Nod. After Cain had murdered Abel, God gave Adam and Eve another son and they called him Seth, and their descendants became ever more numerous on the earth.

7 Three Skillful Brothers

Genesis 4–5

In those days there lived three brothers named Jabal, Jubal and Tubalcain. They became famous because they taught the skills of their trades to those who followed. Jabal raised animals; Jubal played the lyre and the flute with great skill; and Tubalcain was a smith and a master of working iron and copper.

Early men behaved very badly, more like Cain than Abel. One of them, Lamech, father of the first three, was so evil and violent that he took revenge for every little wrong done to him.

8 Noah's Ark

Genesis 6–7

All the men living on the face of the earth were bad, for they did that which was evil in the eyes of the Lord. The only exceptions were the members of Noah's family.

God grew weary of so much evil and decided to rid the earth of all the wicked people. He therefore appeared to Noah and said to him: "I shall send a deluge, a great flood that will sweep away all life on the earth, except for the few whom I shall save." And he gave Noah this order: "You must build an ark, a great ship. It must have three levels, windows and a roof." And God told Noah exactly how long, how wide, and how high to build the ark.

Noah set to work with his three sons, Shem, Ham, and Japheth and his wife and the wives of his sons gathered food and clothing for their life in the ark.

Many laughed at Noah for trying to build a ship on dry land, a long way from the sea. But Noah paid no attention to them and went on with the work. When he had finished the building of the ark, Noah gathered together two animals of every species and made them enter the ark and then, finally, he and his family also went on board.

9 After The Flood

Genesis 8–9

A week passed and then it began to rain. As the Lord had foretold to Noah, it rained so much for forty days that a great flood came and covered everything—the houses, the trees, and then the mountains themselves. The ark floated, and when Noah looked out of the window he saw only the waters, but the people and the animals inside the ark remained safe, just as the Lord had promised.

At last the winds began to blow and the waters which had covered the earth began to ebb. The highest peaks began to appear above the water and the ark came to rest on Mount Ararat.

After forty days had passed Noah opened a window he had made in the ark and said: "I shall send out a dove to discover if there is dry land anywhere." But the dove, returned, having found nowhere to land.

Noah waited another seven days and then sent the dove out again. This time, too, it returned, but in its beak it carried a small olive branch, which was a sign that the waters had receded. Seven days later, Noah once again released the dove, and this time it did not return.

Four more weeks went by and then God said to Noah: "You, your wife, your sons and their wives, and all the animals of every species that you have with you must now leave the ark. All of you leave the ark, spread over the earth and multiply."

Obedient to the Lord, who had spared him and his family, Noah came out of the ark and he immediately built an altar to offer a sacrifice of gratitude to the Lord.

The Lord was pleased with Noah's sacrifice and he blessed him and his children and said to them: "Behold, life returns to the earth, and everything that is to be found on the earth, I now give to you and your children."

10 The Sign of the Rainbow

Genesis 8–9

When Noah, who had been saved from the flood with his family and the animals in the ark, set foot on the ground, he immediately gave thanks to the Lord, who had been so good to him. And the Lord then said to him: "From this day on, for as long as there is life on the earth, there will never be another flood like this one; there shall always be sowing and reaping, heat and cold, summer and winter. I make this pledge to you and your descendants, and to seal this promise, I place the rainbow in the sky."

11 The Tower of Babel

Genesis 11

After the days of the deluge, men had returned and multiplied on the earth and they were like a great family, with all of them speaking the same language. They lived on the plain of Shinar and thought themselves very important. "Let us build a great city," they said, "with a tower that is so high it will touch the sky. This will keep us united and well-remembered."

How proud they were of their idea! But they gave no thought to the Lord God and did not consider if their plan was in accordance with God's will. They believed that they had no need of God. For this reason, he intervened.

When the building work was already well advanced, the Lord changed the language of the people so that they could no longer understand each other and had to stop the work on the building of their great tower. Those who could understand each other came together and left the city to go and live in other countries, and thus spread all over the earth.

The city that they left behind, where every person spoke a different language, was named Babel, which means "confusion."

12 God Calls Abraham

Genesis 12

Abraham was born at Ur, an ancient city in Mesopotamia, the fertile land between two rivers. He moved to Haran, a city in the north, with his father and his family, where he earned his living as a shepherd and a breeder of livestock.

It was at Haran that an extraordinary thing happened to him: the Lord God spoke to Abraham. At that time men had forgotten God and they worshiped many different idols which they had invented and passed down from father to son. But Abraham recognized the voice of the one true God, the Lord, when he spoke to him.

The Lord appeared to Abraham and said: "You must leave here, leave your homeland and the house of your father, and go to the country I have chosen for you. From you and your descendants I shall make a great nation and I shall bless you. I will make your name great, and through you I shall give great gifts to mankind and all the earth."

Abraham trusted the Lord's word and, despite his great sadness at leaving Haran, he immediately set out for the south. He took with him his wife Sarah, his nephew Lot, his servants and his flocks.

13 Abraham's New Homeland

Genesis 12

Abraham followed God's instructions and arrived in the land of Canaan, later called Palestine.

Once there, he heard che voice of God again and it promised him: "This land I will give to your descendants." As a sign of his thanks and of his faith, Abraham at once built an altar to the Lord on that place.

He then began to travel around his new homeland. From Sichem, where the Lord had spoken to him, he moved to Bethel, where he built another altar, and then he went, eventually, to live in the south.

14 God Promises Descendants to Abraham

Genesis 14–17

Abraham owned a great number of beasts of the field and so, too, did his nephew Lot. Since the area they farmed was not large enough, they decided to split up. Lot took his flocks and his shepherds and went to live near Sodom, and Abraham remained in Canaan.

A short time later, during a war being fought by four kings against Sodom, Lot and his family and servants were taken prisoner and carried off. As soon as Abraham learned of this, he gathered his people together and set off in pursuit of the four kings. He caught up with them, fell on their camp by night, defeated them, and liberated Lot.

Upon his return Abraham met with Melchisedech, king of Salem and high priest of God, who gave him his blessing.

The Lord God had promised to give the land of Canaan to the descendants of Abraham. But Abraham and his wife Sarah were already old and they had no children. Where were these descendants? Abraham did not understand, but the Lord insisted, saying: "Look up at the sky and count the stars— there are not as many as shall be your descendants."

15 Three Strange Visitors

Genesis 17, 21

Abraham had set up his tents at the oaks of Mamre. One day, at the hour when the sun was at its height, he was sitting at the entrance to his tent when he raised his eyes and saw three men before him. At once he ordered that water be brought so that they might wash their feet, according to the custom of his people. He then went into his tent, told Sarah to prepare some cakes quickly, then ran to his herd and chose a tender young calf and had it cooked. When everything had been prepared, he invited his three mysterious guests to eat with him.

When the three men had finished their meal, they said: "We shall return in time and you and your wife, Sarah, will have had a son."

When Sarah, who was listening from inside the tent, heard these words, she gave a little laugh. For she believed that she had grown too old to bear a child. But the Lord—and the three strange visitors were sent by him—said to Abraham: "Why did Sarah laugh? Is there anything that is impossible for God?"

And, in fact, everything took place exactly as the Lord had foretold. Abraham and Sarah had a child and they gave him the name of Isaac.

16 Fire from the Sky Falls on Sodom

Genesis 18–19

The inhabitants of Sodom and its nearby cities behaved with great wickedness in the eyes of the Lord.

The Lord grew tired of such great evil and told Abraham that he intended to destroy the city of Sodom. Abraham, however, spoke to the Lord, saying: "Perhaps in Sodom there are fifty righteous men. You, Lord, would not want to slay the righteous with the wicked. This would not be just." The Lord replied: "If I find fifty just men in Sodom, then for their sakes I shall spare the whole city." But Abraham went on, saying: "Perhaps there will not be precisely fifty righteous men . . . perhaps there will only be forty." And, again, the Lord agreed.

"Lord, do not be angry with me," persisted Abraham, "but perhaps there will only be thirty . . . or twenty . . . or ten righteous men!" And at each of these figures the Lord promised to spare the city out of love for these few. But in Sodom there were not even ten just men and the Lord sent his angels to warn Lot to save himself and his family. And God then made fire and sulphur rain down from the sky over Sodom and the nearby cities, which were completely destroyed.

17 Abraham Is Put to the Test by God

Genesis 22

One day God said to Abraham: "You must offer me Isaac, your only son, in sacrifice." In those days it was not unusual for men to kill their own children in homage to their gods. Perhaps Abraham thought that the Lord was the same in this as all the other gods, but he was still very surprised, because God had promised that he would have many descendants and now required that Abraham sacrifice his only son. Abraham was very old and knew that he could not father any more children. How then did God intend to keep his promise?

Abraham did not understand, but he knew that he had to obey. One day he loaded his donkey with wood and set out with his son Isaac. When they reached Mount Moriah, Abraham loaded the wood onto Isaac's shoulders, and together they climbed the mountain. At the summit Abraham prepared an altar on which he laid first the wood and then his only son. Abraham took out his knife and was about to strike with it, when an angel of the Lord stopped his hand and said: "Do not kill the boy! Now God knows that you love him even above your only son."

18 A Bride for Isaac

Genesis 24

When Isaac came of an age to take a wife, his father, Abraham, called his most trusted servant and sent him to Haran to seek out a bride. Haran was the city from which Abraham himself had come.

The servant took ten camels and many precious things and set out. When he reached the city of Haran, he stopped outside the city walls, near the well where the women came to draw water in the evening, and he prayed to the Lord: "O Lord, I do not know how to find the maiden that you have chosen for Isaac. When I ask for some water let her be the one who not only gives me a drink, but also my camels."

A little later a beautiful girl approached with her water jar on her head. "Will you give me a drink?" asked the servant, and the maiden at once replied: "Of course, as much as you want; and your camels must be thirsty too."

The maiden's name was Rebecca and she was from the family of one of Abraham's relatives. When the servant explained to her father the reason for his journey, the girl was asked if she wished to become Isaac's bride. She consented and returned to Canaan.

19 The Veiled Bride

Genesis 24–25

The caravan had now arrived in the land of Canaan. The young Rebecca gazed at the land that was to become her home. Toward evening she saw a young man approaching the caravan. When she learned that it was Isaac, her husband-to-be, Rebecca dismounted from her camel and covered her face with a veil. Her husband, according to custom, should only see her face on their wedding day.

Isaac and Rebecca celebrated their wedding, and some years later they had twin sons, Esau and Jacob.

20 For a Mess of Pottage

Genesis 25

The Lord God had made a covenant with Abraham: Abraham had agreed to obey the Lord as the one true God, and in return the Lord had promised Abraham that he would give him the land of Canaan and that he would have descendants as numerous as the stars in the sky and the grains of sand by the sea. When Abraham died, this covenant held good for his son Isaac, and then for Isaac's firstborn son, Esau.

But Esau's twin brother, Jacob, wanted the rights for himself.

One day Esau came home tired and hungry from hunting and found that Jacob had cooked a mess of pottage. "Give me some to eat, for I am very hungry," demanded Esau. Jacob was ready with his reply: "In exchange you must hand over to me the rights of the firstborn." "I am dying of hunger, what use are the rights of the firstborn to me? You can have them," replied Esau. "You must swear it!" insisted Jacob.

Esau gave his solemn promise then ate. Thus, he showed how little he valued the covenant which God had made with his grandfather and it was only later that he realized how much he had lost with such a thoughtless action.

21 Jacob Deceives His Father

Genesis 27

Esau had thoughtlessly given up to his brother Jacob his rights as the firstborn. However, for this to have any real meaning it required the blessing of their father, Isaac. But everyone knew Isaac would never give this blessing to Jacob, because the firstborn son was Esau, whom he had always loved best anyway.

Rebecca, on the other hand, preferred Jacob to Esau, and she suggested a way for Jacob to find a way to obtain his father's blessing by trickery.

Isaac was now very old and his eyesight was failing. "He called Esau to him, and said, "I don't know when my death will be, but I know that I must offer my blessing to the firstborn. Therefore, take your bow and go out and hunt some deer for my meal, for you know that meat is the meal I enjoy most. When I have eaten the meal you have gotten for me, I will bless you before I die."

When Esau departed, Rebecca put into action her plan to have Isaac give his blessing to Jacob rather than Esau. She sent Jacob to fetch two kids from the herd of goats. When he brought them to her, she had them prepared for a meal for Isaac.

Next, she dressed Jacob in Esau's best clothing. Only, Jacob's arms were hairy, whereas Esau's were smooth. To make sure Isaac was fooled, Rebecca wrapped the smooth kidskins around Jacob's arms. Then Jacob carried in the meal to his father and asked for the blessing that rightfully belonged to his brother.

"Your voice sounds like Jacob's," said Isaac, "but the arms you hold out to me are definitely those of Esau." And so the deception worked. Isaac failed to recognize Jacob and he gave to him the blessing of the firstborn that was his favorite son Esau's by right.

22 Isaac Blesses His Son

Genesis 27

"Come and kiss me, my son," old Isaac said. Jacob obeyed. Isaac smelled the fragrance of Esau's clothes and gave him his blessing. With this, the covenant, made by the Lord with Abraham and then Isaac, now passed on to Jacob.

Isaac said: "Behold the fragrance of my son is like the smell that rises from a fertile field full of fruit, a field blessed by the Lord. The Lord will grant you dew from heaven and an abundance of the fruits of the earth. And all will respect you and bow down before you."

23 The Deceit Is Discovered

Genesis 27–28

With the help of his mother, Rebecca, Jacob had deceived his father. Pretending to be his brother Esau, Jacob had received Isaac's blessing, the right of the firstborn that also fulfilled the covenant made with the Lord God.

When Esau, who had been hunting, returned home with his catch, he prepared a meal and took it to old Isaac. The old man, who was by now almost blind, immediately asked him: "Who are you?" "I am your firstborn son," replied Esau. "Then who was here before you?"

Isaac went on, "And to whom have I already given my blessing?"

Thus, the deception was discovered. Esau was furious and vowed: "When our mother is dead, I will kill Jacob."

Rebecca became fearful at this threat and called Jacob to her, saying: "Go away from here until your brother has calmed down. Go to Haran for a while, to the house of my brother Laban. We will tell your father that you have gone to seek a bride at your relatives' home."

Old Isaac agreed that Jacob should do as he had done and should not take a bride from among the women of Canaan.

24 A Ladder from Earth to Heaven

Genesis 28

Jacob was in flight from his brother Esau, from whom he had deceitfully gained the rights of the firstborn, and so, also, inherited the promises that God had made to Abraham. Esau, naturally, was furious with Jacob. Who knows if even God had forgiven Jacob his deception?

One night on his journey, Jacob lay down on the ground to sleep with a stone for his pillow. After he fell asleep, he had a dream in which he saw a ladder that started from the earth and reached up to heaven. The angels of the Lord were going up and down the ladder. Then the Lord himself appeared before Jacob and said, "I am the Lord, God of Abraham and of Isaac. As I promised to them, so I do to you; you will have descendants as numerous as the stars and to them I will give the land on which you lie. I shall protect you wherever you go and I shall bring you back to this land."

Jacob, awed, awoke and said, "The Lord is present here and I did not know it! This is the house of God; this is the gateway to heaven." He then took the stone he had used as a pillow and blessed it and named the place Bethel, which means "House of God."

25 Jacob Is Also Tricked

Genesis 29

Laban, Jacob's uncle, had two daughters: Leah, the eldest, and Rachel. Jacob asked for Rachel as his wife; Laban agreed on the condition that Jacob work for him for seven years. But then Laban tricked Jacob into marrying Leah instead, saying, "It is our custom that the older daughter be married before the younger. If you want to marry Rachel, work seven years more."

At that time men often had more than one wife. And so Jacob worked another seven years to get Rachel because he loved her very much.

26 Peace between the Brothers

Genesis 32–33

Jacob remained with his uncle Laban for fourteen years, and during this time he worked for him and for himself as well, and he grew very rich. Then he decided to return to the land of Canaan, which God had promised to give to his descendants; so he gathered together his wives, his sons, and all his belongings, and he set off.

Along the way he grew afraid because of his brother Esau, whom he had tricked and whose revenge he feared. So he sent ahead to his brother a present of two hundred she-goats and twenty he-goats; two hundred sheep and twenty rams; thirty camels with their young; forty heifers and ten bulls; and twenty female and ten male donkeys.

The next day he saw Esau approaching him with four hundred men. Since he did not know if his brother was pleased with his gift, it was with great fear that he prostrated himself seven times on the ground before his brother to show the greatest respect. But Esau ran to meet him, hugged him and kissed him, and they were both moved to tears. And after the two brothers had spent some time together, they each went their separate ways.

27 Jacob Changes His Name

Genesis 32

A strange event once happened to Jacob. He was journeying with his family and his flocks, but at this moment he found himself alone on the banks of the River Jabbok. It was night when a man approached him and wrestled with him until daybreak. Then as the stranger prepared to leave, Jacob realized that perhaps this opponent was a messenger from God. So he said to him, "I will not allow you to go until you have blessed me." And the stranger blessed him, saying, "From this time on, your name will be Israel."

28 The Twelve Sons of Jacob

Genesis 35

While he was away from the land of Canaan, Jacob, who was also called Israel, became the father of many sons; he then had others when he returned to Canaan, the land that God had promised to his descendants.

These are the names of the twelve sons of Jacob-Israel: the firstborn Reuben, then Simeon, Levi, Judah, Issachar, Zebulun, Dan, Naphtali, Gad, Asher, Joseph and Benjamin. All together, with their wives and sons, they settled in Canaan as nomad shepherds.

29 Joseph the Dreamer

Genesis 37

Jacob loved Joseph more than all his other sons, because he was born during his old age of the wife Jacob cherished above all else, Rachel.

Then, Joseph was his youngest son, because at the time of these events Jacob's final son, Benjamin, was not yet born.

Jacob had given Joseph a coat with long sleeves which was a princely garment compared to the short coats of the Shepherds. When Joseph's brothers saw that Jacob favored Joseph so much they became jealous and no longer treated him kindly.

Once, when Joseph had grown to boyhood and had gone with his brothers to take the flocks to pasture, he had a dream and he told his brothers about it: "I dreamed that we were all working in the fields, tying bushels of corn, and while my bushel remained upright, I saw that your bushels bowed down, on all sides of mine."

The brothers understood what the dream meant and, in great anger, they replied: "Do you think that you will become more important than all of us, and that we will bow down before you?"

30 Joseph Dreams Again

Genesis 37

Joseph, who was seventeen years old at that time, had another dream, and on this occasion he spoke of it to his father and his brothers. "Listen," he said, "I dreamed that the sun, the moon, and eleven stars bowed down before me."

The meaning of this dream was also clear. This time it was his father who spoke up: "What sort of dream is this? Shall I and your mother and your brothers bow down before you? Do you, the youngest, believe that you will become more important than the rest of your family?"

31 Joseph is Sold by His Brothers

Genesis 37

One day, when Joseph was seventeen years old, his father sent him to see how his brothers were, for they were grazing their flocks a long way from home. The brothers did not love Joseph, for they knew that he was the one their father loved best and they were convinced that he considered himself more important.

Joseph walked a great distance and at last found his brothers with their flocks at Dothan. The brothers saw Joseph approaching from far off and they plotted among themselves. Here was the perfect opportunity to

be rid of him, and they decided to put him to death. "We will throw him in a well," they said, "and then we will tell our father that a wild beast has torn him apart."

But Reuben, the eldest brother, tried to save him. He said to the others, "He is our brother and we should not kill him. Let us throw him in a well, but not put him to death." Secretly Reuben intended to return later and save Joseph. So when Joseph reached them, his brothers stripped off his beautiful coat and threw him into an empty well. Then they saw a traders' caravan approaching and thought, "What do we gain by killing him? It

would be better to sell him to these merchants."

And that was what they did: Joseph was sold to the passing merchants as a slave for twenty pieces of silver. Then his brothers took his coat, killed a goat and having dipped the coat in the blood of the slaughtered animal, they took it to their father. "We found this," they told him. "Do you think it could be Joseph's coat?" Jacob took the coat in his hands and, recognizing it, began to weep in the belief that his youngest son had been torn to pieces by a wild animal. The merchant caravan was bound for Egypt and it carried Joseph there.

August

BIBLE STORY OF THE MONTH

Joseph in Egypt

Joseph, the young man who was sold into slavery by his brothers, was taken into Egypt and resold to Potiphar. Potiphar was an important man in Egypt; he was the chief of the pharoah's guards. He came to like Joseph because he could see that the young man was trustworthy and did his work well, and so he entrusted him with the running of the household.

Now that he was a slave in a foreign land, Joseph often thought of his own home and his father. But his situation became even worse when the wife of Potiphar turned against him, and before her husband she accused Joseph of behaving dishonestly. It was not true, but Potiphar believed his wife and had Joseph thrown into prison.

Some time later, both the chief cup bearer of the pharoah and his chief baker were thrown into prison with Joseph. One night each of his two companions had a dream, but they could not interpret its meaning. It was Joseph who explained it to them.

The chief cup bearer told him; "I dreamed of a vine with three shoots with bunches of grapes on them; I took the grapes, I squeezed the juice from them into a cup and gave it to the pharoah." Joseph explained: "The three shoots are three days; in

three days' time the pharoah will free you from prison and give you back your previous position. Then, I beg you to remember me: tell the pharoah that I am innocent."

Then the chief baker also recounted his dream: "I was carrying on my head three baskets of white bread and sweets for the pharoah, but then birds came and attacked the baskets and ate up their contents." Joseph said to him: "The three baskets are three days: in three days the pharoah will decide your fate, and he will have you executed." Everything happened exactly as Joseph had foretold. But the chief cup bearer forgot all about

Joseph and did nothing to have him freed from prison.

Two years passed, then one night the pharoah also had a dream. He dreamed that he was beside the Nile, the great river on which the very life of Egypt depended. Out of the river there came first seven fat cows, which began to graze; then out came seven lean cows, which promptly devoured the fat ones. Then he dreamed of seven big fat ears of wheat all growing on the same stalk; but afterward along came seven empty husks which swallowed up the full ears.

When he awoke the pharoah called upon all the wise men of his

kingdom, so that they might interpret his two dreams, but no one knew what they meant. Then the chief cup bearer remembered Joseph, and said to the pharoah, "In prison I met a young Hebrew who succeeded perfectly in interpreting one of my dreams."

The pharoah had Joseph brought before him. He told him of his dream, and Joseph said to him: "The two dreams have the same meaning: God is telling you what is going to happen. The land of Egypt will enjoy seven years of abundance, after which will follow seven years of famine. So take care to find someone able and intelligent, who will store up enough food during the first seven years, so that it can be distributed during the seven years of famine, when otherwise there will be nothing to eat."

The pharoah replied: "You have answered well, and God must be with you because he has revealed all these things to you. You are the right man. I hereby give you full powers, and all of Egypt will obey you; after me, you will be the most important man in the kingdom."

And so Joseph became the viceroy of Egypt; the pharoah gave him his ring, he dressed him in rich clothes, and around his neck he hung a golden chain of office.

During the seven years of plenty, Joseph amassed enormous quantities of grain and other supplies, so that when the seven years of famine arrived, no one in Egypt went hungry. In fact, people even came from countries all around to buy grain. Joseph's brothers also came, because the famine had struck the land of Canaan. They did not know what fate had befallen Joseph, and when he came before them, dressed as an Egyptian, they did not recognize him. Joseph, however, recognized them and, without giving himself away, he made inquiries about them and found out how his father was.

When they all came before him, Joseph was deeply moved and decided to make himself known to them. He said: "I am Joseph, your brother whom you sold into slavery. But do not be ashamed, because it was the Lord who brought me here before you, in order that our whole family might survive the famine."

The brothers then grew afraid that Joseph would now seek revenge. But he reassured them again, and said: "The famine will last another five years; therefore go and fetch my father, your wives, and your children, and bring them into Egypt: I will give you land where you can live in peace."

Genesis 39—45

August

1 The Hebrews Move to Egypt

Genesis 46

Joseph, the viceroy of Egypt, wanted all his family to be saved from the famine: For this they had to move from the land of Canaan, where they lived, to Egypt where Joseph, who was the favorite of the Pharoah, could guarantee them everything they needed to live on.

His father, Jacob, asked himself if it was good to leave the land of Canaan, the land that God had promised to him and his descendants.

He did not know what to do; but God came to his aid. In a dream, Jacob heard the Lord speak to him: "I am the Lord God, your father. Do not be afraid to go down into Egypt, because there I will make you a great people, and one day I will make your great people return to this land."

Then Jacob gathered all his sons, their wives, and their children, with their flocks and the other riches they had acquired in the land of Canaan, and they went down into Egypt. The number of the tribe of Hebrews who went down into Egypt was seventy in all.

And Jacob sent his son Judah on ahead to announce to Joseph the arrival of his whole family and their worldly possessions.

2 Jacob and the Pharaoh

Genesis 47

Seventy people, the entire family of Jacob, arrived in Egypt. Joseph, who had not seen his father for many years, had his chariot prepared and went out to meet them.

As soon as he saw Jacob he threw his arms around his neck and wept for a long time. Jacob was no less moved and he said: "Now I can even die, because I have seen that you are alive and well."

Joseph said: "Now I will go in person and announce to the pharoah the arrival of my father and my brothers with their wives and their children."

The pharaoh said to Joseph: "The land of Egypt is at your disposal. Have your father and brothers move into the richest part, into the fertile valley of Goshen."

Then the old man Jacob was brought into the pharoah's presence. "How old are you?" asked the king of Egypt. "One hundred and thirty," replied Jacob. "My years have been spent in wandering and hardships."

Jacob and his sons settled into the land of Goshen, in Egypt, where they continued to be shepherds and breeders of livestock. And Joseph took care of their every need.

3 The Lord Will Have You Return to Canaan

Genesis 48

One day Jacob-Israel sent for his son Joseph, viceroy of Egypt, and told him of a vision he had had many years before.

Israel said to Joseph: "When I was in the land of Canaan, the Lord appeared to me, blessed me, and made me a promise saying: 'You will have a large number of descendants, the sons of your sons will become a great people, and to that people I will give this land.'

"So remember, the Lord has promised you the land of Canaan and one day you will return there."

4 Jacob Foretells the Future of his Sons

Genesis 49

The old man Jacob, also called Israel, called all his sons to him one day and said: "Gather together, because I must tell you what will happen in future times."

One by one, his sons passed before him, and to each of them he foretold developments that would occur once they had all returned to the land that the Lord had promised them.

To Issachar, Jacob said: "You are as strong as a donkey, and you will be able to survive in spite of the domination of your enemies."

To Naphtali, he said: "You are as graceful as a doe, and you will also know how to use words gracefully."

To Benjamin, his last born, he said: "You will resemble the wolf which devours its prey."

To Zebulun, he said: "You will live by the sea in a place where the ships will shelter safely."

To Asher, he said: "You will live in a fertile region, rich in grain, with which you will bake bread fit for a king."

To Joseph, Jacob said: "You are like the sapling of a tree, growing up strong and green because its roots are near a spring of water. Almighty God will bless you."

5 Judah, the Young Lion

Genesis 49

Before he died, Jacob-Israel foretold his sons' futures.

He called together Simeon and Levi to tell them that they would be separated and dispersed, because they had been cruel.

But the most surprising predictions he made were to Reuben and Judah.

To Reuben, he said: "You are my oldest son, proud and strong, with blood that boils like water. But you will not be the most important among your brothers, because at one time you offended your father."

To Judah, Jacob said: "You will be the most important. You are like a young lion: you will overcome your enemies, and even your brothers will bow before you. You will be the ruler and the scepter will remain in your hands, until the one to whom it belongs will come, the one who all the peoples will obey."

After these predictions, people wondered who was this descendant of Judah, to whom the scepter of command belonged, who it was who would guide all the peoples. Only many centuries later was it realized that Jacob was speaking of the Messiah, the Lord Jesus, sent by God to save the whole world.

6 Ephraim and Manasseh

Genesis 48

After he had settled, with his whole family, in the land of Goshen, Jacob sent for his son Joseph, the viceroy of Egypt, to thank him again for the good that he had done.

As a sign of his gratitude, Jacob wished to adopt Joseph's two sons, Ephraim and Manasseh, who were still only boys. "They shall be sons of mine," Jacob said, "and their inheritance shall be equal to that of my other sons; the inheritance of the land that the Lord has promised to give to my descendants."

He then asked the two boys to approach him. Jacob embraced them, he kissed them, and he blessed them. In his blessing he placed his hands on their heads: crossing his arms he placed his right hand on the head of Ephraim who was the younger one, and his left hand, the less important one, on Manasseh, the firstborn son.

Joseph tried to correct his father, pointing out to him that he should change hands, so that the right hand was placed on the head of the older son. But Jacob refused. "Even though he is the younger son, Ephraim's descendants will be more numerous, prosperous, and powerful."

7 "Take Me away from Egypt"

Genesis 47–50

Jacob now knew that he had reached the end of his earthly life. He called Joseph to him and said: "When I am dead, take me away from Egypt to the land of Canaan and bury me in the tomb of my ancestors."

"I will do as you wish," replied Joseph. But Jacob wanted to be certain, so he added, "Swear it to me," and Joseph swore it.

The tomb of Jacob's ancestors was the cave of Machpelah, in the land of Canaan. It was a cavern that Abraham had bought as a burial place for his wife Sarah, and then Abraham himself had been buried there, as were Isaac and his wife Rebecca, and Jacob's first wife Leah.

When Jacob-Israel died, the whole of Egypt went into mourning because the father of their viceroy was dead. When some time had passed, Joseph asked the pharoah for permission to bury his father in the land of Canaan. With Joseph went his sons and his servants, his brothers with their families, the ministers and counselors of the pharoah, along with the war chariots and the cavalry. A mighty caravan accompanied the body of Jacob into Canaan, and then returned.

8 "Am I in the Place of God?"

Genesis 50

After Jacob was buried, his other sons became afraid of their brother Joseph. When they had sold Joseph into slavery he had suffered greatly. Afterward he had become an important man—no less than the viceroy of Egypt—but, the brothers thought, he certainly would not have forgotten the wrong they had done to him. The fact that he had refrained from punishing them, in fact had saved them from famine, they attributed to the respect Joseph had for their father. But now that Jacob was dead, the brothers thought that nothing was going to stop Joseph from taking revenge for the wrongs he had suffered.

So his brothers sent him a message saying: "Before he died, our father asked you to pardon us." Then they went and threw themselves at his feet, saying: "We are your slaves."

Joseph was deeply moved and said to them: "Do not be afraid. It is up to God to hand out rewards and punishments: am I in the place of God? Rather, the Lord our God has brought good out of bad, because he has used me to save your lives and make it possible for you to prosper!"

9 A Baby in the Bulrushes

Exodus 1–2

Many many years had passed since the Hebrews had come to Egypt. They had grown in number, they had become a great people, and had grown very strong in that land.

In fact, they became so powerful that the king of Egypt, the pharoah, began to grow worried: "These sons of Israel could take up arms and fight against us," he thought; "we have to stop them from growing any greater in numbers."

And to do this, he first made them into slaves, forcing them to work in the fields and build great cities. In his fear he then ordered that every male child born to a Hebrew family be put to death immediately by drowning it in the river Nile.

A short time after this cruel order was given, a male child was born to a Hebrew family, and its parents sought to save its life; so they kept it hidden for three months after its birth.

When they could no longer keep it hidden, the mother took a reed basket, and coated it with tar and pitch so that the water would not enter. Then she put the baby in the basket and placed it among the bulrushes on the riverbank.

10 Moses Is Rescued from the River

Exodus 1–2

A short time after his mother had placed the basket with little Moses in it in the water of the Nile, the pharoah's daughter came down to the river with her handmaidens to bathe. She saw the basket and sent one of her maids to get it. Inside she found the baby crying. "It is a child of the Hebrews," she realized, and she was filled with pity for the infant. The child's sister, who had been hiding, went up to her and said, "Do you want me to find a Hebrew nursemaid to look after the baby?"

The pharoah's daughter agreed and the young girl went away and brought back her mother, without revealing to anyone that she was the baby's mother. "Nurse this child for me," the princess said to her, "and I will pay you well."

And so the baby was raised safely by its own mother. When he was weaned, his mother brought him back to the princess, who adopted him as her own son and gave him the name Moses, a name which means "saved from the waters."

Moses remained at the pharoah's court, where he studied and became an important and respected man: in this way God prepared Moses for great tasks.

11 The Flight into the Desert

Exodus 2

The Hebrews lamented their condition as slaves in Egypt. Moses was in anguish to see his people so oppressed. One day he came across an Egyptian beating a Hebrew. Moses saw that there was no one else watching, and killed the Egyptian and hid his body.

The next day, he came across two Hebrews fighting among themselves, and when Moses tried to make them stop, one of them said to him: "You are not our judge. Perhaps you would like to kill me, just as you killed the Egyptian?"

Moses grew afraid because he thought: "Many people now know my secret!" In fact, the pharoah came to hear of it and tried to arrest Moses, so that he would be put to death. So Moses escaped from Egypt and fled into the desert.

After much wandering he came to a well, where he protected seven sisters, who had come there to water their flocks, from the bullying of the other shepherds. In gratitude, the sisters took him back to the camp of their father, Jethro, who welcomed Moses warmly, and gave him one of his daughters as a bride. So Moses remained with Jethro, and spent his days grazing his flocks.

12 A Fire That Does Not Burn

Exodus 3–4

Out in the desert Moses was grazing the flocks of Jethro, his father-in-law, when he witnessed a strange sight: a bush was burning, but although it burned the flames did not consume it. "I must go closer and look at this wonderful happening," cried Moses in amazement.

As he drew near the bush, he heard a voice coming out of the flames: "Moses, Moses." "Here I am," Moses replied. "Come no closer. Remove your sandals, because the place on which you are standing is holy ground."

So Moses did so, and the voice continued: "I am the Lord God. I have seen the misfortunes of my people in Egypt, and I have chosen you to free them. You will go to the pharoah and tell him to let my people go."

13 The Name of God

Exodus 3

"You command me to go to my people and tell them that you wish to free them from slavery," said Moses to the Lord, "but they will not believe me, and they will ask me who has sent me. What shall I say?"

The Lord answered him: "You will say this to the people of Israel: I have been sent by Jehovah, the God of your fathers, the God of Abraham, of Isaac, and of Jacob, to lead you out of Egypt, into the promised land."

The name Jehovah means "the true God, the only God."

14 Moses and the Pharaoh

Exodus 4–12

Moses set off toward Egypt, to carry out the difficult mission that God had entrusted to him. Along the way, he was met by his brother Aaron, and together they went to announce to the people of Israel that the Lord had taken pity on their tribulations, and had decided to lead his people back to the land of Canaan, the Promised Land, so rich and fertile that it was as if its rivers flowed with milk and honey.

But first Moses had to persuade the pharoah, who did not wish to let the Hebrews go because he used them as slaves to build his cities.

Through the mouth of Aaron, Moses warned the pharoah that many punishments would be sent by God to force him to free the people of Israel. These punishments, "the plagues of Egypt," soon came to pass. The waters of the River Nile were changed into blood, the land was invaded by frogs, by mosquitoes, then by flies. All the livestock died off, the Egyptians were stricken by ulcers, the fields were destroyed first by hailstones and then by locusts, and for three days there was only darkness.

As each plague arrived, the pharoah sent for Moses and promised him that he would let the people of Israel go free; but as soon as the plague was over, he changed his mind again. Then the Lord foretold the worst plague of all: the death of every firstborn child of the Egyptians, from the firstborn child of the pharoah, to that of the humblest servant.

And so it came about: on the ordained night all the firstborn of the Egyptians died, while the people of Israel were untouched.

Then the pharoah hastily called Moses before him and told him to leave at once, he and all his people, and to go out from the land of Egypt forever.

15 The Sign of Blood

Exodus 11–12

In order to free his people from slavery, the Lord had to bring about the death of all the firstborn of the Egyptians. So that the firstborn of the Hebrews might be saved, the Lord ordered his people to mark the doors of their houses with the blood of a lamb.

He then ordered that the lamb should be roasted on the fire and eaten quickly, along with bitter herbs, while the people were standing up, with sticks in their hands, all ready to leave as soon as the pharoah gave his permission.

This meal was called the Passover, and the Lord ordered that it be held every year from then on, in memory of the miracles he did for his people: to remind them of the *passing* of the Lord who, seeing the sign of the blood, spared the lives of his people.

The meal was also to be held in memory of the passing of the people of Israel from slavery in Egypt to freedom in the Promised Land.

And as soon as the Passover meal was consumed the people of God left Egypt forever and, with the help of God and under the guidance of Moses, set off toward their new homeland.

16 And the Sea Divided . . .

Exodus 14–15

The people of Israel were on their journey through the desert. After years of slavery in Egypt, Moses, sent by God, was at last leading them to the land that God himself had promised to the descendants of Abraham, Isaac, and Jacob.

The pharaoh had granted the Hebrews permission to leave, but he soon regretted it. He gathered his war chariots together and set off to bring them back. He caught up with them near the Red Sea.

Moses and his people were caught in a trap: the sea was in front and the pharaoh's army behind.

All seemed to be lost, until God intervened with one of the most incredible miracles: for a whole night a strong wind blew. It swept back the waves of the sea, and the waters divided, leaving a dry path across which the people of God could travel to the other shore, without even getting their feet wet.

The pharaoh's chariots raced to pursue them across the same pathway, but when they were out in the middle, the waters surged back into their proper place, and swept them away. The Hebrews were saved and together they all sang a hymn of praise to God.

17 Miracles in the Desert

Exodus 15–17

With his mighty hand, the Lord had freed his people from slavery in Egypt, allowing them to cross the sea without getting wet.

The Lord performed many other miracles for his people, as they journeyed across the desert toward the land he had promised them.

After three days of marching, the Hebrews reached the waters of Mara, hoping to be able to quench their thirst there, only to discover that the water was as salty as the sea. But, through Moses, the Lord made it drinkable again.

Later it seemed that they would die of hunger, and they protested bitterly to Moses. On the very next day, around their camp, they found a great flock of quails, so numerous that they could catch them with their hands. And on the ground was a sweet, white substance, good to eat and very nourishing. This was manna and from then on it was found wherever the chosen people of God wandered on their journey to the Promised Land.

At another time, God made water flow out of a rock for his people, and when they were attacked by the Amalekites, God granted Moses the victory he prayed for.

18 The Ten Commandments

Exodus 19–20

The people of Israel had long been journeying in the desert toward the Promised Land, when they put up their tents at the foot of a high mountain called Mount Sinai. There, God summoned Moses onto the mountain for forty days, and then gave to him two stone tablets on which were written the ten laws, the Ten Commandments.

The Lord said to Moses: "I will make a pact with all my people. If they observe these ten commandments, I will guide them to the promised land, and I will make them a prosperous and mighty people."

These are the ten laws:

1 You shall worship no other God
2 Do not take the name of the Lord thy God in vain
3 Remember to keep the Sabbath; the seventh day is holy to God
4 Respect thy father and thy mother, and you will live long
5 You shall not kill
6 You shall not commit adultery
7 You shall not steal
8 You shall not tell lies
9 You shall not covet anyone's wife or husband
10 You shall not covet anyone's possessions

19 The Golden Calf

Exodus 32–34

When Moses came down from the mountain, he found that the people had not waited for his return. They had done a great wrong, and had made a statue of God in the form of a golden calf. They were worshiping it, saying: "Here is our God who brought us out of Egypt."

Moses was outraged; in his anger he threw the two tablets of the laws onto the ground, and they broke into many pieces. Then he destroyed the golden calf and punished those who had made it, for it was forbidden to make images of him.

The next day Moses went back up the mountain and the first thing he did was to beg God to forgive the grave sin of his people. Out of his goodness, the Lord granted his pardon, and gave Moses another two tablets of the laws, as well as other instructions for the people.

After another forty days Moses went back to the camp. In the presence of all his people he spoke of the pact that the Lord had proposed, and he read out the laws that the people were to respect in exchange for God's mighty help. The people listened to him and promised that they and their descendants would be obedient.

20 Listen, Israel

Deuteronomy 6

In the desert Moses explained the laws of God to his people; and then he spoke these words.

"Listen, O Israel. The Lord is our God, there is only one Lord. You shall love the Lord your God with all your heart, with all your soul, and with all your strength. Let these laws that I give you today be fixed in your hearts; you shall teach them to your children, you shall speak of them when you are sitting in your home, when you walk on your way, when you lie down to sleep, and when you rise up in the morning."

21 The House of God

Exodus 35–40

The Ten Commandments that God gave to Moses on Mount Sinai were written on two stone tablets.

Moses commanded the people to make a magnificent chest to contain the tablets, out of acacia wood covered in gold. This chest holding the tablets was called the Ark of the Covenant. The Ark of the Covenant had a golden top surmounted by two cherubs: it represented the throne of God, who was invisible but present among his people.

In the desert there was no temple to which the people could go to worship the Lord, so Moses had a special tent constructed, to take down and put up at every resting place on their journey.

This special tent was made of the finest purple hemp, and divided into two rooms: one room contained the Ark, and the other, precious objects like the golden candelabrum with seven arms and a golden altar on which scented incense was burned.

Outside this tent on special occasions a sacrificial altar was set up, where Moses and the Hebrews offered burnt sacrifices of the best meat and the best crops.

22 A Land Flowing in Milk and Honey

Numbers 13

Before leading all the people into Canaan, Moses sent ahead a group of men to scout out the land. This group was made up of one man from each tribe, and with them was Moses' right arm, a man called Joshua.

After forty days they returned and reported to the people: "We have found a land so rich and fertile that it seemed to be flowing with milk and honey: look at some of its fruits," and with that they held up a bunch of grapes so large that it had to be carried on a pole by two men.

23 Forty Years in the Desert

Numbers 14

"The land of Canaan is very fertile," the scouts reported to the people, "as these wonderful fruits we have brought back will prove. But the land is inhabited by powerful nations who have built huge, fortified cities. Moreover, some of the people who inhabit the land are as big as giants."

When they heard these words many of the Israelites were afraid and said: "We will never conquer this land. It would be better for us to return to Egypt; otherwise we will die in the desert."

Moses and Joshua tried to calm the people by saying: "This is the land that the Lord has promised us. He is with us and without doubt he will give us the strength to conquer it." But the rebellious people did not want to listen and began complaining again.

Then, above the tent which held the Ark of the Covenant, the glory of God appeared to all the Israelites. And the Lord said: "You yourselves will not enter this land: I will give it to your children." And so it was that the people of Israel remained in the desert for forty years, before they were able to enter the Promised Land.

24 The Conquest of the Promised Land

Deuteronomy 34; Joshua 1

Moses, the beloved of God, who had spoken face to face with the Lord, was not permitted to lead the people of Israel in their conquest of the Promised Land. He was one hundred and twenty years old when the Lord, from the summit of Mount Nebo, allowed him to see the full extent of the Promised Land: from Dan to Jericho, from the river Jordan to the Mediterranean Sea.

Then Moses died and his place as leader of the people was taken by Joshua. The Lord said to Joshua: "Be strong and brave because you are to lead my people in the conquest of the land I promised them. If you obey all the laws I gave you through my servant Moses, then you need not fear, I shall be with you!"

Joshua commanded the armies of the people in many expeditions and victorious battles and conquered the land of Canaan. Then he divided the land into many parts, and he gave one to each of the tribes that made up the people of Israel.

However, he did not give any land to the tribe of Levi, because this tribe was to serve the Lord in the tent which was his dwelling place; it had no land because its only wealth was the Lord himself.

25 Rahab and the Spies

Joshua 2

To enter the Promised Land, the first city that Joshua had to conquer was Jericho, a mighty place with strong walls. To find out more about its fortifications, Joshua sent two men to spy inside the city.

The king of Jericho found out about this and ordered that the gates be closed and the spies, hunted down and captured. The two Israelites went into the house of a woman, Rahab, who hid them on her terrace. When the guards came to look for them, Rahab said: "They have already fled. Run and perhaps you can catch up with them!"

Then she returned to the terrace and said to the two Israelites; "I know that the Lord is with you, and you will certainly conquer this city. When you enter into it be kind to me and my family." The men reassured her: "When we enter the city, keep your family in the house with you; tie a red rope to your window, so that our warriors recognize your house and spare you."

Rahab's house overlooked the wall of the city, so the woman lowered the two Israelites out of the window with a rope, and they returned to their camp.

26 Over the Jordan

Joshua 3

Joshua struck camp on the other side of the Jordan, crossed over the river, and thus entered the Promised Land. The whole people moved, preceded by the Ark carried on the shoulders of the priests.

As soon as the priests' feet touched the water, the flow of the river was interrupted: the waters rose up, leaving a dry passage. Everyone was able to cross to the other side before the river began flowing again. This was another of the great miracles that God performed for his people.

27 The Walls of Jericho

Joshua 6

Joshua and his warriors were outside Jericho. Faced with the arrival of the Israelites, the city had closed the gates in its mighty walls. How were they to conquer it?

Once again the Lord intervened to help his people, who followed his instructions and succeeded in the conquest of the city. This is how it came about.

For six days, in complete silence, a procession wound its way around the walls: at the front were seven priests carrying trumpets, then came the Ark of the Covenant, then Joshua and the warriors.

On the seventh day, the people arose at dawn, and they walked around the city seven times: then the priests sounded their trumpets and all the warriors uttered a great shout. At this sound, without a hand being laid on them, the walls of Jericho collapsed, and the warriors swarmed in, overcame their enemies, and took the city.

The Israelites took no spoils of war from the city that the Lord had given over to them; the gold, silver, bronze, and iron that they found within were kept for the Lord and placed in the treasury of the house of the Lord.

28 The Day the Sun Stood Still

Joshua 10

The Israelites conquered the cities of the Promised Land one after another. So the inhabitants of Gibeon thought to themselves: "It would be better to seek peace with the people of Israel than fight them and suffer defeat the way the others have done." And they made an alliance with Joshua.

Five kings of nearby cities then decided to declare war on Gibeon; they gathered their armies and besieged the city. Its inhabitants sent messengers to Joshua to beg for his aid.

Joshua hurried to the place with his warriors, and did battle with the armies of the five kings. He attacked them by surprise, causing panic among their soldiers; but the night was beginning to fall and the battle had not yet been decided.

Then Joshua invoked the aid of the Lord, and said: "Sun, stop above Gibeon!" And to everyone's amazement, on that day the sun did not set until the people of Israel had won their victory. Never before had it happened, nor has it happened since, that the sun stood still in the sky. And Joshua became famous throughout the land, as a great war leader, and as a friend of the Lord.

29 Joshua Speaks in the Valley of Shechem

Joshua 24

When he had conquered the Promised Land and had divided it among the people of Israel, Joshua called representatives of all the tribes of Israel to Shechem. They came in great numbers, their elders, their leaders, their judges, their families, and Joshua spoke to them.

He reminded them of the history of their ancestors, of Abraham, Isaac, and Jacob. He reminded them of their slavery in Egypt and the great things God had done to liberate his people. He reminded them of the laws that God had handed down through Moses, the Ten Commandments, and of God's goodness in giving them the land they now inhabited.

Speaking in the name of the Lord, Joshua preached to them: "I have given you a land which you have not worked with your own hands; you live in cities which you did not build with the sweat of your own brow. You eat the fruit of vines and olives you did not plant."

"Now," Joshua went on, "you must decide if you wish to serve the Lord, or if you prefer the gods of the other races we have encountered. As for myself, and my family, we wish to serve the Lord."

30 The Israelites Choose the Lord

Joshua 24

Great was the crowd that had gathered in the valley of Shechem, and it was with close attention that they listened to the speech made by their leader, Joshua.

Joshua had invited the people of Israel to choose: either to serve the Lord forever, or to abandon him and worship the strange gods that they had found in the Land of Canaan.

The people of Israel answered Joshua with a great shout: "We will serve the Lord, our God, forever, and we will obey only his voice."

31 Deborah and the Iron Chariots

Judges 4–5

The people of Israel lived in peace in the Promised Land, but often they had to confront nations nearby who waged war against them. When this happened, the chiefs of Israel, who were called judges, would pray to the Lord for his help and call the warriors together to defend them from their enemies.

A woman named Deborah was a judge of Israel once, when the northern territory was attacked by the powerful army of Sisera. The men of Israel were all foot soldiers and feared they could do little against an enemy who possessed nine hundred iron chariots. Deborah, however, rallied the warriors and gave them hope, saying: "The Lord will give us victory, because he leads us into battle."

The enemy was crossing the plain in its iron chariots when it began to rain. So much rain fell that the plain was flooded and the chariots were bogged down and remained stuck in the mud. The enemy fled, pursued by the warriors of Israel, who had won a great victory.

After the battle, Deborah sang a hymn of praise and thanks to the Lord, who had fought for his people by sending the providential rain.

September

BIBLE STORY OF THE MONTH

BIBLE STORY OF THE MONTH

The Story of Samson

Because the people of Israel had been oppressed for so long by their enemies, the Philistines, they raised up their voices in prayer to the Lord to ask him to come to their aid.

The Lord heard their prayers and from among the Israelites he set apart a child at the moment of his birth. His name was Samson and the sign that showed he was chosen by the Lord was that he was to allow his hair to grow and never cut it. In return, the Lord would give him extraordinary strength to fight the Philistines.

His strength was truly great: one day, when he was out in the countryside, Samson was attacked by a roaring lion. Although unarmed, he wrestled with the lion and killed it.

Some time after, he was passing by and decided to go and look at the remains of the lion. He discovered that a swarm of bees had made its home inside the carcass and had already begun to produce honey. There was so much that Samson was able to gather enough to satisfy his hunger.

It was the lion and the honey that inspired Samson to put a riddle to thirty young Philistines. He said to them: "If you can solve this riddle within seven days, I will give you thirty bed sheets and thirty changes of clothes."

The Philistines accepted the chal-lenge and Samson put the riddle to them: "Out of the eater came forth meat, and out of the strong came forth sweetness."

The Philistines went to great lengths to solve the riddle, but they only succeeded by resorting to a trick at the end of the seventh day. Then they answered Samson: "What is sweeter than honey? What is stronger than a lion?"

Samson was obliged to give each of them a bed sheet and a change of clothes: these he obtained by killing thirty other Philistines, and in this way he began to fight his enemies.

On a later occasion, at the time of the corn harvest, Samson burned not only the Philistines' corn, but also their vines and their olives. The Philistines, in their fury, sent a great army against the people of Israel, who were filled with fear. So Samson said to the Israelites: "Do not be afraid. Bind me and hand me over to the Philistines, and then they will depart." The Israelites did as Samson commanded, but no sooner did he find himself alone among the Philistines, than he broke free from the bonds which restrained him and began to strike out at the enemy, killing a thousand of them.

On yet another occasion, Samson went into Gaza, a Philistine city. The enemy soldiers found out where he was staying and made plans to surprise him and kill him. But Samson

rose up at midnight and, since the gates of the city were barred, he used his mighty strength to lift up the great doors and the two posts, put them on his shoulders, and carry them off to the top of a hill nearby.

Since they could capture Samson in no other way, the Philistines decided to resort to trickery. It so happened that Samson was in love with a Philistine woman by the name of Delilah. She secretly made a bargain with the leaders of her people. Then she asked Samson again and again what the secret of his great strength was. He did not want to reveal this to her, but she insisted to such an extent that finally Samson explained: "My strength comes from

the Lord, my God; as proof of my love for him I have never cut my hair, and therein lies my strength."

Then, at night, while Samson slept, Delilah had his hair cut off and had him bound with strong ropes. When he awakened, Samson thought that he could break free but since his hair had been cut off, his strength had left him.

Then the Philistines led Samson away and they gouged out his eyes and chained him to the grindstone in the prison in Gaza.

Slowly, however, his hair began to grow again and his strength started to return. Some time later, on the day of a feast in honor of Dagon, their god, the Philistines

gathered in great numbers at their temple. There was great rejoicing among the Philistines that they no longer had to fear their great enemy, Samson. They decided to bring him out so that they might be amused by the spectacle of his defeat.

Samson was sent for and was brought from the prison to the temple, where a little boy led him by the hand because he was blind. Around the inside of the temple and on the roof were all the leaders of the Philistines and a huge crowd of about three thousand men and women. They laughed with delight at the man of whom they had been so afraid.

In his blindness, Samson asked the little boy who led him to guide him to the two pillars which supported the temple so that he could lean against them. He then prayed to the Lord: "Lord, remember me! I pray thee, only this once, to give me strength, O God!"

As soon as he had finished this prayer, he braced himself between the two pillars of the temple and began to push, crying out: "Let me die with the Philistines."

Then Samson pushed over the two pillars and the temple collapsed and fell upon all the people who were gathered there. In this way, Samson killed more enemies at his death than he had killed in his life.

Judges 13–16

1 The Lord Calls Gideon

Judges 6–7

For years the people of Israel had lived in fear of the Midianites, who stole or destroyed their crops and their livestock.

One day a messenger of the Lord appeared to Gideon and said to him: "The Lord is with you, mighty man of valor, and sends you to free his people from the Midianites."

"How do I know that it is the Lord who speaks? Show me a sign," Gideon asked the messenger. "Meanwhile, stay here while I go home to prepare food to offer you." Gideon went away and returned with bread and a pot of meat broth.

"Pour the broth over the bread," the mysterious visitor told him. Gideon obeyed, and then the messenger touched the meat and bread which were soaked in broth with the stick he held in his hand. At once they were consumed in flame and the visitor disappeared.

Then Gideon knew for certain that this mysterious visitor had been an angel of the Lord. The Lord himself then spoke directly to Gideon and commanded him to free his people from their enemies. Gideon now felt himself to be full of strength and when the Midianites returned, he gathered together a great army.

2 The Dew on the Fleece

Judges 6

Gideon wished to be certain that the Lord intended him to lead the army of Israel. So he prayed: "O Lord, tonight I shall lay a fleece of wool on the ground. If, tomorrow, I find dew only on the fleece, I will know that you will save Israel by my hand."

The next morning the fleece was soaked with dew while the ground around it was dry. "Help me to be certain, Lord," prayed Gideon, "and let it tomorrow be dry only on the fleece while the ground is bedewed." At dawn, he found the ground damp and the fleece dry.

3 The Victory over the Midianites

Judges 7

Gideon had gathered together his army to fight the Midianites and was camped at the well of Ḥarod.

"The warriors who are with you are too numerous," the Lord said to Gideon. "They might think that the victory is a result of their own strength and not of my support. Therefore tell those who are afraid to leave and return home."

Gideon did this and twenty-two thousand men went home, leaving only ten thousand soldiers. "They are still too many," said the Lord. "Bring them to the well to slake their thirst. Keep with you those who drink by cupping their hands to their mouths and send home those who go on their knees to drink."

Gideon did as the Lord commanded and was then left with only three hundred men. "With these few men I will save the people of Israel and free them from the Midianites," the Lord assured Gideon.

When night was falling, Gideon divided his three hundred warriors into three companies and to each man he gave a trumpet and an empty pitcher containing a torch. He gave them precise orders and then, in the middle of the night, he led them to the enemy camp.

The three hundred silently positioned themselves around the camp where the Midianites were sleeping. Then, at a given signal, they smashed their pitchers and let their torches burn in the night, and they blew their trumpets and cried: "For the Lord and for Gideon!"

The Midianites awoke in surprise; when they saw the torches and heard the trumpets and the shouts, they were terrified. They too began to scream and fight among themselves confusedly, until they fled. Without using their arms and without even moving from their positions, the Israelites gained the victory, recognizing it as the work of God.

4 The Story of the Trees

Judges 9

The people of Shechem had chosen Abimelech, a cruel and ambitious man, as their leader. His brother, Jotham, warned the people, saying: "You have behaved as the trees did when they chose a king. They asked the olive to reign over them, but the olive replied: 'Should I stop producing oil, which is so useful to men, only to be king over you?'

"So the trees then asked the fig tree to come and be their king. But the fig replied: 'Should I forsake my sweetness and my lovely fruit only to reign over you?'

"The trees then asked the vine to be their sovereign. The vine, however, replied: 'Should I stop producing wine, which so cheers mankind, only to come and be your king?'

"Finally all the trees went and asked a mere bramble to be their king. The bramble accepted their offer at once, saying: 'I shall be your king, and if you are not good subjects I shall have you devoured by fire!' "

Jotham's parable turned out to be true. Abimelech showed himself to be wicked and inept, and some time later the people of Shechem had to rebel against him to free themselves from his dominion.

5 Ruth, the Faithful Daughter-in-Law

Ruth 1

In the days when the judges ruled the people of Israel, a great famine fell upon the land. For this reason, a certain man of Bethlehem went, with his family, to live in Moab.

His sons found wives among the women of Moab, but some time later they died and so did their father. Then the mother, whose name was Naomi, called her two daughters-in-law and said: "I can no longer look after you; therefore you should return to your families. I shall return to Bethlehem, my native city, to live among my own people."

One of the daughters-in-law returned to her own family, but the other did not wish to abandon her elderly mother-in-law and said to her: "Where you go, I will also go; and where you live, I too will live. Your people shall be my people and your God shall be my god. Only death shall separate me from you."

Naomi insisted, but when she saw her daughter-in-law was determined, they both gathered their belongings and left Moab for Bethlehem. The faithful daughter-in-law, willing to leave behind her own land and customs so as not to abandon her elderly mother-in-law, was called Ruth.

6 In the Fields of Boaz

Ruth 2–4

Everyone in the city of Bethlehem admired the young stranger, Ruth, who had risked so much and endured such hardship so as not to abandon her elderly mother-in-law.

Life was hard for the two women; they often had difficulties in finding enough food to eat. One day, at the time of the barley harvest, Ruth went out to gather grain and, without knowing it, she wandered into the fields of Boaz, who was a distant relative of Naomi's.

Ruth worked tirelessly for the whole day; Boaz noticed this, admired her, and wished to help her. He said to his men: 'Let some sheaves fall deliberately, so that the young woman may gather more."

On another occasion, Boaz made her a gift of six measures of barley and finally, moved by her unselfish manner to Naomi, he asked Ruth to marry him. Life was no longer hard for the two women, since Boaz was rich. But the marriage of Boaz and Ruth was also important for another reason: they had a son who was a great comfort to the aging Naomi and she gave him the name of Obed. He became the father of Jesse, who, in turn, was father to David.

7 A Child Is Offered to the Lord

1 Samuel 1–2

At that time a woman named Anna lived among the people of Israel and she was much loved by her husband. She, however, was very sad because the Lord had not granted her any children.

In those days, the Ark of the Covenant was kept at Shiloh and the priest Eli and his two sons served the Lord there in the sanctuary.

Many Israelites went there to pray, and one day, in tears, Anna offered up the following prayer and promise: "Lord," she said, "if you give me a son, I will consecrate him to you and he shall serve you all his life."

The Lord God heard Anna's prayer and she gave birth to a boy whom she called Samuel. She raised him with love and, years later when he was old enough to leave home, she took him to the sanctuary and entrusted him to the priest, Eli, to be trained in the service of the Lord.

Anna then offered up a sacrifice to the Lord, sang a hymn of praise, and returned home. Afterward the Lord rewarded Anna by blessing her with three more sons and two daughters.

8 God Speaks to Little Samuel

1 Samuel 2–3

Samuel lived in the sanctuary of the Lord, with the priest Eli and his two sons. These two sons behaved badly and carried out their work in a manner which offended the Lord.

Samuel was still a child when, one night, he heard a voice calling him: "Samuel! Samuel!" He thought it was the voice of Eli, sleeping nearby. Quickly, Samuel got up and ran to him. "Here I am," he said. But Eli replied: "I did not call you. Go back to sleep." A short time later, Samuel again heard his name called. He went back to Eli who again told him to go back to sleep.

When this occurred a third time Eli understood and said to the child: "If you hear your name being called again, you must say 'Speak, Lord, for your servant is listening.'"

Samuel went back to sleep, and when he heard his name being called a fourth time, he replied: "Speak, Lord, for your servant is listening." And it really was the Lord who had called him, for he gave Samuel a message: "I shall punish the sons of Eli for their wicked deeds," said the Lord, "for they have done evil in the eyes of the Lord and Eli has not restrained them. Tell Eli what I have said."

9 Samuel, the Prophet of the Lord

1 Samuel 3–4

The priest Eli knew that the Lord had spoken to Samuel and he asked the boy what the Lord had said to him.

Samuel told him that the Lord was angry at the way in which the two sons of Eli behaved in his temple and had decided to punish them.

Not long afterward, the two wicked sons were both killed in battle and everyone then realized that the Lord had chosen Samuel as his chosen prophet, as a man to speak on his behalf.

10 The Ark in the Hands of the Philistines

1 Samuel 5–6

It happened that the people of Israel were attacked by the army of the Philistines and the Lord allowed his chosen people to be defeated, for the Israelites had frequently ignored his will, and he wished to remind them to be faithful to him again.

When the Israelites realized that they were about to lose the battle, they sent for the Ark of the Covenant, which held the invisible presence of the Lord. They said: "If the Lord is among us, the victory will be ours."

But the Philistines were victorious instead, and they captured the Ark and carried it off to the temple of their god, Dagon.

The next morning the Philistines found that the statue of Dagon had fallen face down before the Ark of the Lord. They put it back in its place, but the following day they found that it had fallen down again and broken. Then strange diseases started to spread among the Philistines and they began to fear the Lord.

So they decided to return the Ark to the Israelites. They placed it on a new carriage, adding gifts of gold, and sent it back to the Lord's chosen people.

11 The Ark Returns to the People of Israel

1 Samuel 6

The Philistines, who had taken possession of the Ark of the Lord, sent it back to the Israelites on a carriage drawn by two oxen, without a driver. Despite having no one to guide them, the oxen went straight to the land of the Israelites, straying neither to the left nor to the right.

It was the season of the grain harvest and the Israelites were at work in the fields. When they saw the Ark passing on the carriage they were filled with joy that the Lord, present in the Ark, was returning to be with his chosen people.

12 The Road to Salvation

1 Samuel 7

Once again, when the Philistines returned to threaten the Israelites, it was Samuel, the priest of the Lord, who showed his people the road to salvation. "Cast away all the false gods and turn your hearts completely to the Lord. If you serve only him, the Lord will deliver you from the Philistines."

The Israelites did as their wise priest had told them and succeeded in defeating the Philistines as well as their other enemies and recaptured the cities which had been taken from them.

13 The People Ask for a King

1 Samuel 9–10

One day the elders of the people of Israel came to Samuel with a request. "We," they said, "do not wish to be different from the other peoples. We, too, wish to have a king to keep us united, to give us just government, and to lead our armies into battle."

Samuel, however, replied: "We already have a king. The Lord God rules over us!" But they insisted and Samuel prayed to the Lord for guidance. "Listen to their request," the Lord told him. "Let a king reign over them. Appoint as king the man whom I shall choose for you, and I shall bless him."

Some time later it happened that a young man by the name of Saul was journeying from village to village in search of some of his father's donkeys which had been missing. Since he was passing close to the house of Samuel, he decided to go and ask the prophet whether or not he should continue to search for the donkeys.

Samuel saw that Saul was a tall and handsome young man. Samuel invited Saul to stay in his house for the night and the next day he was certain that he had found the man chosen to become king. Then Samuel took a jar of oil and poured it over Saul's head; in this way he blessed him and made clear what the Lord intended for him.

Samuel then said to Saul: "As for your donkeys, cease to trouble yourself, for they have already been found. Now you must go home; I will follow you and together we will offer up a sacrifice to the Lord. Then I will tell you what you must do."

On the road home Saul encountered a group of prophets with harps and flutes as Samuel had predicted. Then Saul knew that he really was chosen by the Lord and with the prophets he began to praise God.

14 Saul Is Proclaimed King

1 Samuel 10

Samuel had anointed Saul as king of Israel, but only in secret; now it was time to make the Lord's choice known to the people.

To do this, the prophet Samuel called the people together at Mizpeh. He made the men stand together according to their tribes, and then according to their families. Then he told the tribe of Benjamin to stand apart. From the tribe of Benjamin, Samuel then told the family of Matri to come forward. From this family Samuel chose a young man to stand forward and this was Saul.

They all looked for Saul and found him hiding among the baggage. He was brought before everyone and Samuel announced: "Here is the man whom the Lord has anointed." The whole assembly shouted: "Long live the king."

Sacrifices were offered to the Lord and a great feast was celebrated. Samuel then told the people what it meant to have a king and reminded them that all of them, both king and people, should seek above all else to do what was pleasing to the Lord. He then wrote all these things down in a book so that they should never be forgotten.

15 Saul Disobeys the Lord

1 Samuel 15

King Saul had decided to wage war on the Amalekites, so the prophet Samuel went to him and said: "The Lord will be with you and he will grant you victory, but all the spoils must be offered to the Lord. Neither you nor any other soldier must keep anything for yourself."

Saul went away to war and he defeated the Amalekites; but he disobeyed the Lord because he and his soldiers kept the best part of the spoils for themselves, instead of offering them to the Lord.

God then spoke to Samuel and said to him: "I regret having chosen Saul as king for he does not listen to my word."

Samuel went back to Saul and told him what the Lord had revealed to him. Saul then realized that he had acted against the will of God and asked for Samuel's forgiveness. "I cannot forgive you," replied the prophet, "for the Lord has rejected you and has already chosen another man to reign after you." He then turned to leave and Saul tried to detain him by grasping at his mantle, but it ripped. Samuel cried out: "Behold! In the same way the Lord will tear from you the kingdom which he gave you."

16 A Young Shepherd with a Kindly Face

1 Samuel 16

The Lord said to the prophet Samuel: "Go to Bethlehem to the house of Jesse. For it is from among his sons that I have chosen the king who will succeed Saul."

Samuel departed and when he arrived at the house of Jesse, he asked Jesse to let him see all of his sons. Jesse presented the eldest, Eliab, and Samuel wondered if he was perhaps the one that the Lord had chosen. But the Lord answered Samuel, saying: "Do not consider his stature, for I have refused him. Men look upon appearance, but I look upon the heart."

Jesse then presented his second, third, and fourth sons, and so on, until he had presented seven sons to Samuel. Samuel then asked him: "Are all your sons now here?" "There is still the youngest," replied Jesse. "Send for him now," said Samuel. The young shepherd was brought before them, and Samuel looked at him. He was golden-haired, with a beautiful face.

"It is he whom I have chosen," the Lord said, and so Samuel anointed him in front of his brothers. The young shepherd was called David and was to become the greatest king of Israel.

17 David at the Court of Saul

1 Samuel 16

King Saul knew that the Lord was not pleased with him, for he had disobeyed his command. Even the prophet Samuel no longer came to see him and no longer gave him advice. Saul was full of concern and from time to time he even had moments of madness.

His counselors advised him: "Find someone who plays the lyre well; when you feel agitated have him play and it will calm you." Saul accepted their advice and said: "Find me someone suitable."

"I know the right person," said one of the advisers. "He is David, the youngest son of Jesse. He has a handsome countenance, is strong and courageous, skilled in the use of arms, and wise in argument. What is more, he is an excellent player of the lyre."

David was sent for, and afterward he came often to the court of Saul, particularly when the king felt ill at ease. At these times, David would calm him by singing and playing his lyre.

Saul did not know that the young man had already been chosen by the Lord to become king of Israel after him, instead of Jonathan, his eldest son.

18 David Fights the Giant Goliath

1 Samuel 17

The Israelites were at war with the Philistines. The soldiers of Israel were terrified because every day a gigantic man strode out of the camp of the Philistines to challenge them. Each day, for forty days, the giant shouted: "Israelites: Send out one of your men to fight me. If he wins, the Philistines shall be your servants; if I win, then you become our slaves."

Then David came and said: "I will fight him!" He ran down quickly to the nearby stream, and picked up five stones and put them in his shepherd's bag. Then, with his sling, he moved toward the giant.

When Goliath saw this unarmed youth coming toward him, he began to laugh, but David said to him: "You come to me armed with your sword, your lance, and your club. I come to you in the name of the Lord, who will defeat you!"

When he was at the correct distance, David took a stone from his bag, fitted it into his sling, and threw it. He struck Goliath full in the forehead, and the giant fell to the ground unconscious. With a leap David, with Goliath's own sword, cut off the giant's head. At that, all the Philistines fled, pursued by the soldiers of Israel.

19 The Triumph of David

1 Samuel 18

With the help of the Lord, the young and unarmed David had defeated the giant Goliath, and had gained a great victory for the army of Israel, and put to flight the ranks of their enemies, the Philistines.

David returned home with King Saul from the field of battle and in all the villages and cities they passed through the women came out to praise them and sang and danced around them. As they danced for joy, they sang: "Saul has slain thousands of the enemy, but David has killed tens of thousands!"

20 Saul Tries to Kill David

1 Samuel 18–19

The people of Israel admired and loved David after he had killed the giant Goliath and put their enemies to flight. But King Saul became jealous of David and sought to kill him.

The king had promised the hand of his daughter in marriage to the man who overcame Goliath, but now he said: "I will give her to him, but first he must kill one hundred Philistines." Saul believed that if David had to fight one hundred enemies, then one of them would surely kill him!

But David, well within the allotted time, returned with proof of having killed not one hundred, but two hundred Philistines. And so David took as his bride Michal, the daughter of the king.

But Saul had not given up the idea of killing David. One day when Saul was at home and feeling ill at ease, David took up his lyre and began to play to calm the king. Suddenly Saul picked up his spear and threw it at David. If it had struck him, David would surely have been killed, but he avoided it and fled from the palace. Each time Saul made an attempt on David's life he was unsuccessful, for David was protected by the Lord.

21 Michal Helps David

1 Samuel 19

Michal, the daughter of King Saul, greatly loved her husband, David. When Saul tried to kill David with a blow from his lance, David escaped to his own home. Michal, however, warned David, saying: "I fear that my father will not change his mind; he will seek to kill you even here. You must flee tonight."

David listened to his wife's advice. She lowered him from a window and David ran off to hide in a nearby field. Then Michal made up David's bed as if he were still in it; she stuffed clothes under the blankets to look like his body.

Just as Michal had foreseen, men sent by Saul arrived the following morning to take David and kill him. Michal said to them: "Tell the king that David cannot come for he is sick," and she allowed them a glimpse of the bed, which seemed to be occupied.

"Bring him and his bed to me!" Saul ordered. Thus the trick was discovered and Saul was very angry with his daughter. He said to her: "Why did you deceive me and allow him to escape?"

And Michal, in her great love for David, lied: "He threatened to kill me if I did not help him to flee."

22 Jonathan, the Faithful Friend

1 Samuel 20

Jonathan, the son of King Saul, was a great friend to David and was very unhappy because his father wanted to put David to death.

David went in secret to Jonathan to ask him to find out what the king's intentions were. Jonathan promised he would try to tell him within three days. They agreed on a time and place to meet.

Saul said to Jonathan; "I know you are a friend to David! But if he lives you will not be king after me." Angrily, he added: "He must die!"

Jonathan tried to defend David and reminded his father that he had never done anything wrong; but Saul was unyielding. Then Jonathan took his bow and his arrows and, accompanied by a boy, he went out into the countryside.

At the place where he had agreed to meet David, Jonathan began to shoot arrows just as if he were practicing with his bow. Each time, the boy went to recover the arrows. At a certain moment, Jonathan shouted out to the boy: "Run! The arrow is farther away than that!"

This was the agreed signal. David, who was watching and listening from a hiding place, knew then what Saul's decision had been.

When Jonathan had sent the boy home with the arrows, David came out of hiding, walked up to Jonathan and embraced him. The two friends wept together. Then, when the moment of parting came, Jonathan said: "Now you must flee and hide; but do not be afraid, because the Lord is with you wherever you go. I beg you not to hate me for the wrong my father does you; be my friend always, as I have been and always will be a friend to you. Swear to me that, when you have defeated all your enemies, you will be kind to my children and their descendants." And David, moved by his friend, made a solemn promise.

23 The Sword of Goliath

1 Samuel 21

Under threat from King Saul, who wanted to put him to death, David fled. First, he went in secret to the sanctuary of the Lord, where he explained to the priest that he had to leave in haste, without arming himself. Immediately, the priest said to him: "We hold here the sword of Goliath. Use it if you wish."

David took the sword and went off to live in the desert. Many men gathered around him and together with them David fought against the enemies of his people.

September

24 David Flees from Saul

1 Samuel 23

David was living in the desert with his men. He did not declare war on King Saul, who planned to put him to death, but fought instead against the Philistines, the enemies of his people.

But Saul hated David so much that he wanted to kill him at any cost. One day some spies came to the king and informed him that David and his men were living in a certain part of the desert. Saul called up his army and set out.

He arrived near where David was and almost caught him in a trap. He would certainly have succeeded if David had not been under the Lord's protection, for the Lord had already chosen David to be the new king.

At one point during the pursuit the two armies were close enough to see each other. They had both entered a steep mountain gorge, and Saul and his men were on one side, David and his men on the other.

There would have been no escape for David if a messenger had not come unexpectedly to Saul to inform him that the Philistines had invaded the kingdom again, and the king had to hurry back to defend the land and his people.

25 Abigail, a Clever Woman

1 Samuel 25

David and his men were in the desert, preparing to fight the enemies of the people of Israel when David sent several of his young men to Nabal. Nabal was a very rich man whom David had helped. David sent a messenger to say to him: "Help me and my men, for it is difficult to find sustenance in the desert." But Nabal's reply was cold, for he did not want to give anything to David.

A servant spoke to Abigail, the wife of Nabal, and told her what had happened. She immediately realized the danger they were in: insulted by this reply, David and his men could easily take revenge on Nabal and his people. Without saying a word to her husband, Abigail hurriedly gathered two hundred loaves of bread, two bottles of wine, five cooked sheep, five measures of parched corn, a hundred clusters of raisins, and two hundred cakes of figs, and loaded it all onto the backs of donkeys. She sent servants to David with the laden donkeys, and she herself followed behind them.

When she came before David, she prostrated herself at his feet, saying: "Accept these gifts and forget the wickedness of my husband. The Lord will look on you favorably if you don't take revenge on him."

"Blessed be the Lord that has sent you to me," replied David, "for he has prevented me from taking vengeance with my own hands. You are a wise and clever woman."

Abigail returned home, where she found her husband feasting like a king. When she told him what had happened, he was so overcome with the thought of the risk that he had run that he became paralyzed with fear, and some days later he died.

When David learned that Nabal had died, he remembered how wise Abigail was and sent for her and married her himself.

26 David Spares the Life of Saul

1 Samuel 26

Saul, the king of Israel, was still determined to put David to death and prevent him from becoming king in his place. The king and his army were camped in the desert when David and one of his young men came down to their camp one night. They came to Saul's bedside and, everyone slept, so did not notice David. The man with David said: "Here is your chance to kill your enemy!"

"I will never do that," replied David, "even if Saul wishes my death, for he is the Lord's

anointed!" Then he took the spear and the water jug which stood by the king's bedside and moved off. He climbed to the top of a nearby hill and shouted in a loud voice: "I am innocent. Why do you persecute me? I could have killed you and did not do so. If you do not believe me, send a man to fetch back your spear and your water jug."

Saul was overwhelmed by David's generosity and called: "I have sinned against you. Return and I will do you no further wrong." However, David did not trust him, and he replied: "Just as your life was sacred to me today, so is mine in the eyes of the Lord."

27 David Weeps for Saul and for Jonathan

1 Samuel 31; 2 Samuel 1

The king of Israel died on Mount Gilboa during a battle against his enemies, the Philistines. Many soldiers died with him, and among them was Jonathan, the son of the king and a great friend to David.

When David learned the news, he gave no thought to all the wrongs that Saul had done him. Instead he raised a cry of lament and said: "Neither dew nor rain shall fall again on Mount Gilboa, for heroes have perished there. Sons of Israel, weep for Saul! I am filled with anguish for you, Jonathan, my friend!"

28 David Becomes King

2 Samuel 2, 5, 8, 12

After the death of Saul and his son Jonathan, the people of the tribe of Judah, to which David belonged, came to him and proclaimed him their king.

David established himself in the city of Hebron, and there he reigned over the tribe of Judah for seven years. After seven years the men of the other tribes also recognized him as king and David reigned over all the people of Israel. He was thirty years old when he was made king and his rule lasted forty years.

During that time he fought many wars against his enemies. He subjugated many peoples and expanded the kingdom and amassed great wealth. He was a good king; he administered justice with wisdom; he praised the greatness of the Lord, composing beautiful prayers called psalms; and he ordered that the history of the people of Israel, the people whom the Lord had shaped, protected, and helped on so many occasions, be recorded in writing.

David had many wives, as was the custom then, and many children. Among these children was Solomon, the son of Bathsheba, and David promised Bathsheba that Solomon would be his successor.

29 The Conquest of Jerusalem

1 Chronicles 11

In the middle of the land of Israel there was a city inhabited by foreigners, the Jebusites. It was the city of Jerusalem, which stood on a hill and was surrounded by walls. It was a city that was impossible to conquer, and its inhabitants would say: "The blind and the lame would be enough to repel the attacks of our enemies."

David, who had become king over all the people of Israel, saw that Jerusalem was the ideal city for the capital of his kingdom. But how could he conquer it?

When he made a close study of how it was built, he noticed that the Jebusites had dug a deep well inside the city so that the water from the spring outside would reach the city. So David said to his men: "If there are any volunteers who will follow the spring up through the well, I will reward them greatly. Moreover, the first man to enter the city in this way will become a captain of my army."

A band of men went up through the well, entered the city, and took it by surprise. The first man among them was Joab, and David proclaimed him head of his army. In this way, Jerusalem became the capital of Israel.

30 The Ark Is Brought to Jerusalem

2 Samuel 6

The Ark of the Covenant, the golden chest which contained the tablets of the law given to the people of God through Moses, was the most precious to the people of Israel. On its lid stood God's two cherubim.

When David had conquered Jerusalem and made it the capital of Israel, he began to think about bringing the Ark of the Lord to the city, for until then it had remained in various places in the countryside.

The procession would have to be very solemn, thought David, to be worthy of the majesty of the Lord. For this reason he called all the people to celebrate at the Ark with music and songs, while he himself removed his royal garments and went dancing before it.

His wife Michal saw him from her window and when he came back into the palace she scorned him for having danced in front of everyone like a common man. David, however, said to her: "In this way, I chose to respect the Lord. And it was right, because he has been so good to me. I was a mere shepherd, a man of no importance, and he has made me the king of his chosen people!"

BIBLE STORY OF THE MONTH

Absalom, Son of David

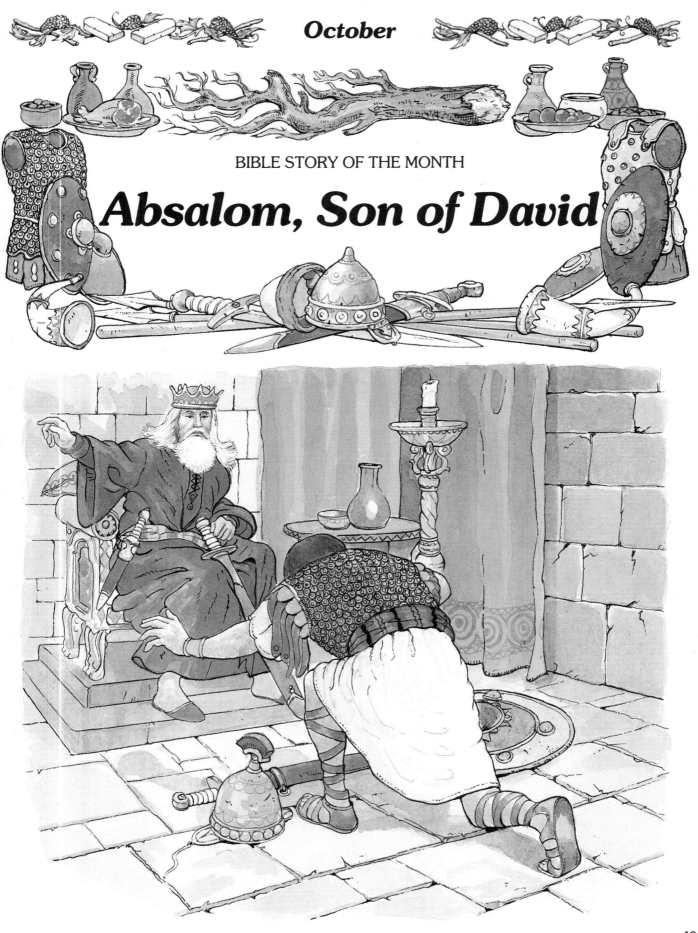

King David was a good and just man, whose actions pleased the Lord; and even when David committed a sin, he asked the Lord's pardon immediately.

The same could not be said for his sons, who were often violent and selfish. Absalom was one of them: he was young, handsome, and brave, and many people thought well of him; but his heart was full of treachery. Absalom felt he had been offended by his brother Amnon. So, without showing his anger, he invited Amnon to a banquet and there he ordered his servants to kill him. Then he fled, to escape the wrath of David.

Absalom had a friend close to the king: Joab, the commander of the army. After three years, Joab found that the king had stopped mourning for his murdered son, Amnon, and he managed to obtain permission from David for Absalom to return to the land of Israel, as long as the king did not have to see him. Once he was back, Absalom tried so hard and insisted for so long, that in the end David agreed to pardon him and see him.

From that time, Absalom assumed an air of great richness and importance, and went with his men outside the gates of the city. When anyone came to the city to receive justice, Absalom said to him: "You are in the right, but no one will recognize your rights; no one will listen to you on behalf of the king. Oh, if only I could be named Judge of Israel: Then everyone who had suffered a wrong would receive justice."

Then Absalom would hold out his hand and hug and kiss the person, pretending to be very sorry for him. In this way young Absalom's popularity continued to increase throughout the land.

When the right moment arrived, Absalom went before David and said: "Let me go to Hebron, because I promised the Lord I would offer him sacrifices in that city." In reality his intentions were very different. Accompanied by some of the most important men in the kingdom, Absalom went to Hebron and sent out messengers to all the tribes, to announce that he was the new king.

When David was informed that Absalom had begun to plot against him, that he had proclaimed himself king and had a large following, David cried out: "Hurry, we must flee, otherwise none of us will escape the hand of Absalom."

Immediately, surrounded by his guards and his faithful friends, David set out from the palace, and a great number of the people of Jerusalem

went with him. He set off toward the desert, and in the valley of Cedron he stopped and waited for all of his followers to come to him. Then he saw that the priest Zadok was coming with the Levites, bearing the Ark of the Lord. David ordered him: "Return the Ark to the city! If the Lord is with me, he will allow me to return there and see it; if the Lord does not wish that I return, then his will be done."

Then David went off up the Mount of Olives. He went weeping, with his head covered and his feet bare, as signs of great suffering. Along the way a man insulted him. David's guards would have killed this man, but David held them back saying: "My own son would take my life; what are the insults of this stranger compared to that? Leave him alone. Perhaps God will see the wrongs that I must suffer and repay me with a greater kindness."

Meanwhile Absalom had moved into Jerusalem and taken over the palace. His advisers then counseled him to chase after David, in order to kill him and all those who were with him. Absalom listened to them, called together his army, and set off after David.

David, too, was preparing for battle. He gathered all those who had remained faithful to him, organized them into groups and, before all of them, he ordered the leaders to treat his young son Absalom with respect.

The battle took place in the forest of Ephraim, and David's soldiers overcame Absalom's. Absalom also fled, on a mule. All of a sudden the mule passed under the low branches of a great oak tree, and Absalom's head got wedged in the branches. The mule went on, leaving Absalom suspended in the branches. A man saw him and ran off to tell Joab, the army commander. "Why did you not kill him at once?" asked Joab, and the man answered: "With my own ears I heard the king's order that the life of his son be spared." But Joab killed Absalom himself.

David was sitting by the gates of the city, when a messenger arrived to announce the victory. "Is young Absalom well?" asked David. The man answered: "Would that all the king's enemies be as he!"

So David understood that his son was dead, and he began to shudder and weep. Through his tears, he cried: "Absalom, my son, if only I were dead instead of you, oh, my son Absalom."

And thus the victory was transformed into mourning; all the people were moved by the king's sorrow over his son, even though Absalom had betrayed him.

2 Samuel 13–19

1 The Lord Is My Shepherd

Psalm 23

Throughout his whole life, King David continued to compose poems (or psalms), which he sang to the music he played on his lyre. There is one psalm that is full of joy for the protection that the Lord grants to those who trust in him: "The Lord is my shepherd, I shall not want. He makes me to lie down in green pastures; he leads me beside the still waters. He restores my soul; he leads me in the paths of righteousness for his name's sake. Though I walk in the dark valley, I fear no evil, for he is at my side."

2 A Prophecy for David

2 Samuel 7

David lived in peace in Jerusalem, where he had taken the Ark of the Covenant. One day he called the prophet Nathan to him and said: "Look. I live in a beautiful palace, while the Ark of the Lord is still in a humble tent. I want to build a great house, a temple suitable for the Lord, to enshrine the Ark."

Nathan, who, like all the other prophets, spoke in the name of God, said to him: "Do not worry about building a temple; the Lord has not asked you for it. The temple will be built by your son Solomon, who will be king after you; and after Solomon, Jerusalem will still be ruled by your descendants. Your throne will endure forever."

Then David went and stood before the Ark, in the presence of the Lord, and said: "Who am I, Lord, that you cover me with so many favors? And still you do not consider this enough: you now guarantee my descendants far into the future. You are truly great, O Lord, my God."

Nathan's prophecy came true with Jesus, the descendant of David and the Son of God: he is the King of the Universe, and his kingdom is without end; his throne will endure forever.

3 The Gratitude of David

Psalm 139

God knows the heart of man. David was aware of this, and so he sang his gratitude: "Lord you watch me and you know me, you know when I sit down and when I arise, when I walk along my path and when I rest. Where can I go to get away from you? If I go up into the sky, you are there, if I descend into the abyss, there you are. If I fly on the wings of the wind to go and live at the ends of the sea, it is your hand that guides me. For you the shadows are light and the night is clear as the day."

4 For Love of Jonathan

2 Samuel 4, 9

David ruled over Jerusalem, loved and respected by his subjects and feared by his enemies. He was very powerful, but he did not forget those who had helped him. In particular he did not forget Jonathan, the son of King Saul; nor did he forget his promise to Jonathan to treat his descendants with respect.

But were there any left? The king sent servants to find out, and they told him that only one of Saul's sons had survived. He was called Meribbaal, now a grown man, but he was crippled in both feet. He had been five years old when the news had arrived of the defeat of Saul and Jonathan; his nursemaid had picked him up to flee with him, but in her haste she had dropped him, leaving him crippled.

When David sent for Meribbaal he came, but full of fear, because he thought David wanted to take revenge on him for the wrongs he had suffered at the hands of Saul. But the king said to him: "Do not be afraid! I wish to be kind to you, out of love for Jonathan, your father. I will give you back all the fields taken away from you, and you will always feast at my table. For love of Jonathan."

5 Solomon Is Crowned King

1 Kings 1–2

King David had grown very old, and his eldest son, Adonijah, thought he would declare himself king. The most important men in the kingdom were on his side.

However, King David had decided a long time ago that on his death his place should be taken by another son, Solomon. So Nathan the prophet sent Solomon's mother to David, to remind him of his promise and tell David of Adonijah's intentions.

When he heard about Adonijah, David called the prophet Nathan and the priest Zadok to him, and said to them: "Take my guard at once, tell Solomon to go down to the well at Gihon: there you must consecrate Solomon as king; then sound the trumpets and shout: 'Long live King Solomon.'"

All this was done and Solomon became king of the people of Israel. When he felt that his time to die was near, David called Solomon to him and said: "Be strong and wise. Observe the laws of the Lord and you will succeed." Then the great King David died; Solomon took his place, and his kingdom grew prosperous and mighty, because the Lord was with him.

6 Solomon's Dream

1 Kings 3

King Solomon went to Gibeon to offer a great thanksgiving sacrifice to the Lord. And that night the Lord appeared to him in a dream and said to him: "Tell me what you desire from me."

Solomon replied: "O Lord. you have been so good to me to allow me to become king in the place of my father, David. But I am like a child, lacking in the experience to rule over your people properly. Help me to become wise."

The Lord was pleased by this request, and replied to Solomon:

"You did not ask me for a long life, nor riches, nor the defeat of your enemies, but you have asked me for the wisdom to rule over my people fittingly: so, I grant you a wise and intelligent heart, and I also grant you that which you did not ask for. Together with wisdom, I will grant you riches and glory and a long life for yourself."

Solomon awoke, returned to Jerusalem and went before the Ark of the Covenant, in the presence of the Lord. There he offered other sacrifices to the Lord, and the Lord kept his promises: Solomon ruled for forty years, and his rule was wise, rich, and glorious.

7 The Judgment of Solomon

1 Kings 3

Solomon was such a wise king that his judgments became famous all over the world.

On one occasion, two women came before him. The first one said: "We live in the same house and each of us had a child within a few days of each other. One night this woman's child died; and so she substituted it for mine: the child that she carries in her arms is mine!"

However, the second woman protested and said: "No, this child is mine. The one that died was yours!"

So Solomon had a sword brought and ordered his servants: "Cut the child in two and give half to each of these women!"

When she heard these words, the first woman said: "No, my lord, do not kill the child: I would rather have you give it to the woman who holds it in her arms than see it die!"

The second woman said: "Very well, let it be divided: so it be neither mine nor yours."

The wise King Solomon had given this order deliberately: he did not want to put the child to death, but he knew that the real mother would prefer to lose it rather than see it die. And he then gave the little baby to the real mother.

8 A House for the Lord

1 Kings 5–6

Solomon ruled in peace over the people of Israel, and he decided that the time had come to fulfill his father David's wish and build a permanent house for the Lord.

Until that time, the Ark of the Covenant, over which hung the invisible presence of God, had been housed in a tent which had been moved many times from the desert of Sinai until it reached Jerusalem. Now the Lord would have a permanent dwelling place among his people, a temple worthy of him.

For this reason, Solomon sent ambassadors to Hiram, the king of Tyre in Lebanon, and they spoke in the name of Solomon: "You know that my father, David, was not able to build a temple to the name of the Lord, because of the wars waged against him by all his enemies. Now that the Lord has granted me peace, I have decided to build a temple to his name. Order, therefore, that cedar trees of Lebanon be cut."

When Hiram heard these words, he sent a messenger back to Solomon saying: "I have received your message. I will do as you wish about the cedar and fir wood. My servants will take it down from Lebanon to the sea; I will have it loaded onto rafts and carried to the place you ask. Then I will have it unloaded and you can take it away."

After this agreement was reached, Solomon called upon thousands and thousands of workers from his people and sent them to dig out stone from the mountains and then he took skilled architects into his service. And in the fourth year of his reign, on the hill to the north of Jerusalem, Mount Zion, he began the construction. The building work lasted seven years, and the result was so magnificent, it became famous not only among the people of Israel but also in foreign lands.

9 The Temple on Mount Zion

1 Kings 6–7

The temple that Solomon raised to the Lord on Mount Zion was huge and magnificent.

An enormous terrace was raised high by thick walls on all its sides.

In the middle of the terrace was the sanctuary, made of nothing but marble embossed with gold, and of bronze, and precious wood like the cedar from Lebanon.

On the sides of the sanctuary there were wide courtyards, all covered in marble and surrounded by noble porticos on columns of pure marble.

10 The Sanctuary of the Temple

1 Kings 6

The main part of the great temple built by Solomon was the sanctuary. It rose up above the other buildings of the temple and it could be seen from afar in all its glory. It was made up of three rooms: the entrance, the sanctuary, and the Holy of Holies.

In the sanctuary there was a large elaborately carved seven-branched candelabrum and a table on which were laid twelve loaves, one for each of the twelve tribes of Israel. In the sanctuary there was also a small gold altar, the altar for holding incense.

11 The Holy of Holies

1 Kings 6

The third room in the sanctuary was the most sacred part of the whole temple; in fact it was the most sacred place in the whole world. This room was called the Holy of Holies, and contained the Ark of the Covenant, above which hovered the invisible presence of the Lord. The Ark of the Covenant was placed between two giant cherubs made of olive wood covered in gold. The two cherubs were taller than the height of two men, and their wings, which touched in the middle of the room, spread out over the Ark.

12 Offerings to the Lord

1 Kings 6

Outside the sanctuary of the temple of Jerusalem, in the open air, there was everything necessary to offer up to the Lord the sacrifices that the king and the people brought to the temple: animals without blemish or the choicest of the crops.

They were offered on the altar, a huge square piece of stone with a ramp on one side to allow access.

Not far from the altar there was a large washbasin of bronze, supported by twelve bronze oxen; it was full of water and was used for the purification of the priests.

13 Priests and People in the Temple

1 Kings 6–7

In the great temple of Jerusalem, built by Solomon, the main tasks were undertaken by the high priest and the other priests; the less important tasks were carried out by the Levites.

The priests wore special clothes while carrying out their tasks in the temple. Out of respect for the holy place, in the presence of the Lord, they went barefoot. They remembered that the Lord, when he spoke to Moses from the burning bush, out in the desert, commanded him to take off the sandals that he wore, because any place where the Lord is present is sacred.

Only the priests could enter into the sanctuary; only they could offer sacrifices. The people were not even allowed to approach the altar, but the men could watch the ceremonies from behind a screen. The women were only permitted as far as the courtyard before the one that admitted the men.

Foreigners, all those who did not belong to the people of Israel, could only enter the external courtyard of the temple, where notices in various languages warned them that, if they went beyond it, they risked certain death.

14 The Lord Enters into His Temple

1 Kings 8

The great temple built by Solomon on Mount Zion, in Jerusalem, was ready. It was a noble building, magnificent in its construction and furnishings. It was ready, but it lacked the essential element for which it had been built: the Ark of the Covenant, over which hovered the invisible presence of God. From the time of King David, the Ark of the Covenant had been in its tent in Jerusalem. When the temple was finished, King Solomon called together the elders, the princes, and the chiefs, and had them carry the Ark of the Covenant into the temple.

The priests and the Levites lifted it up, and amidst great exultation, the Ark was carried inside the temple, to the Holy of Holies. As soon as they left the temple, the glory of the Lord, in the form of a cloud, entered to fill up the temple: the Lord took possession of his house among men.

The king then went before the altar and, in front of all the people, he made a prayer to the Lord. He said: "Lord, listen to us when we come to this place to pray to you. You, from the sky, listen to our prayers and pardon our sins." Then Solomon offered a sacrifice to the Lord and blessed the people.

15 Pilgrims on the March

Psalm 84

Wherever Israelites lived, no matter how far away from Jerusalem, their greatest desire was to go to the holy city, to the temple of the Lord.

What could have been more important? That is why the Israelites composed this song:

How lovely is your house,
Lord, God of the universe!
My soul is sad because
it is far from your temple.
Even sparrows make their home
and swallows build their nests
there, near to your altar.
O Lord, my king and my God;
happy are those
who live in your house:
always singing your praise!
Happy are those who can make the
holy journey.
Along the way their strength grows
until they come before you.
For me a day in your temple
is worth more than a thousand days
elsewhere.

The journey that is spoken about in this song is the one that the Israelites made at Passover and on other major feast days, to Jerusalem, on the hill of Zion, where the temple of the Lord stood.

16 The Gratitude of the Pilgrims

Psalms 121, 130, 124.

The pilgrims who made their way to Jerusalem used to recite some psalms along the way:

"I raise up my eyes to the mountains: where will my help come from? My help comes from the Lord who made the sky and the earth."

The pilgrims prayed in this way, to ask for help with the dangers of the journey.

In order to go before the Lord they had to repent of their sins; and that is what the pilgrims did with this psalm:

From the depths I cry out to you Lord: Lord, listen to my voice.
If you look upon our sins,
then who could stand before you?
But we can find pardon in you!
I put my hope in the Lord;
my spirit awaits him
more than the watchmen await
the morning light.

After they had obtained his pardon, the pilgrims thanked the Lord with this psalm:

"If the Lord had not been with us, the waters would have swept us away, a torrent would have drowned us. We have been freed like a bird from the hunter's snare: the rope has been broken and we have flown away!"

17 The Pilgrims' Departure

Psalm 133; 134

The pilgrims journeyed in groups, and it was good for them to find themselves among other people with the same faith: good and sweet like the dew which comes down from mount Hermon.
Look, how good and right it is, that brothers should live together!
It is like the dew of Hermon which falls on the hills of Zion!

Hermon is the highest mountain in the land of Israel, and its snows were a symbol of coolness and delight for the inhabitants of that sun-parched land.

After the days spent near the temple, the pilgrims got ready to depart. First, however, they asked the priests, who had the good fortune to remain in the temple of Jerusalem, to continue to pray for them:
Bless the Lord,
All of you, servants of the Lord;
who pass your nights in
the house of the Lord.
Raise your hands up to the temple and bless the Lord.

In reply, the pilgrims received a last blessing from the priests: "The Lord who made the sky and the earth and all creatures great and small blesses you from atop Mount Zion."

18 The Feasts of Pentecost and the Day of Atonement

Leviticus 16, 23

Along with Passover, two major feasts were celebrated in the temple of Jerusalem.

Fifty days after Passover came the feast of Pentecost, when thanks were given to the Lord for the gifts of the earth, and the choicest of the crops were offered up in sacrifice.

And they also celebrated the Day of Atonement, when the Lord was asked to pardon the sins of the people. On that day, they would choose two goats. Through a random choice, one of them was put aside for the Lord; the other for the devil.

The high priest then performed a ceremony, during which he transferred all the sins of the people onto the second animal, which was then turned loose into the desert, to be consigned to the devil.

The other goat was offered up in sacrifice in the temple. Then the high priest took a little of its blood, and on this one day out of the whole year, he went into the Holy of Holies and poured it over the Ark of the Covenant.

This strange rite meant that the goat offered in sacrifice represented the people of Israel, and through this animal the whole population offered itself to the Lord.

19 The Feast of the Tabernacles

Leviticus 23

One of the main feasts celebrated by the chosen people of the Lord was the feast of the huts, or the tents, or the Tabernacles.

It was so called because on this day all the people left their houses to go and live in tents or temporary huts.

This was in memory of the forty years during which the people of Israel lived in the desert, after their flight from slavery in the land of Egypt.

During the eight days spent in the tents nobody worked; everyone meditated on the great miracles performed by the Lord for his people. He had kept his people fed and defended them from their enemies; he had made an alliance with them; he had given them his laws so that they would know how to behave in any circumstances in life; and last of all he had given them a fertile land in which to live.

Remembering how good the Lord had been also brought to mind all the other gifts that the Lord had given to his people, and they all praised him and thanked him, promising to repay him in the only way he desired: by loving him and observing his laws.

20 The Ships of Solomon

1 Kings 9–10

Solomon was a very wise and able king. His people were great traders and he levied a tax on all the merchant caravans which crossed his kingdom.

With the help of his friend Hiram, king of Tyre, Solomon also built a fleet of ships at Eloth, on the shores of the Red Sea.

Hiram sent his servants, sailors who knew the sea, onto the ships, and they went to the land of Ophir, along with Solomon's servants and sailors, to get gold and take it back to King Solomon.

21 The Greatness of Solomon

1 Kings 9–10

The greatness of Solomon spread over the whole kingdom of Israel. The fleet, loaded with gold from the city of Ophir, also brought back precious sandalwood with which pillars were made for the temple and the palace, as well as lyres and harps.

Kings from near and far paid homage to Solomon: visitors to his royal palace brought gifts of gold and silver, cloth, arms, rare perfumes, horses, and mules. It was said that during Solomon's reign silver was as plentiful as stone!

Solomon had gathered a great number of horses and chariots, which his merchants brought from the Hittite kings and from the kings of Aram. He owned one thousand, four hundred chariots and twelve thousand horses, which were distributed among Jerusalem and the other cities in the kingdom of Israel.

One day the Lord appeared to Solomon for the second time and said to him: "I have heard your prayer and your supplication and I have blessed this temple which you have built for me. If, however, you turn away from me to go and serve false gods, then I will destroy the temple which has been blessed in my name."

22 A Throne of Gold and Ivory

1 Kings 10

Solomon had also embellished the royal palace, which was built next to the temple of the Lord, and had enriched it with precious stones and golden ornaments.

Inside the palace Solomon had had his throne built: it was made of ivory and overlaid in pure gold; it had two armrests and beside these stood two lions.

The throne had six steps on which stood twelve more lions, six on each side. No other king on earth had a throne to equal the one King Solomon ruled from.

23 The Queen of Sheba's Caravan

1 Kings 10

King Solomon was richer and wiser than any king on earth. People from all over the world came to Solomon to listen to the wisdom with which God had filled his heart and which guided his decisions.

When the queen of Sheba, in Arabia, heard of the fame of Solomon she came to visit him in Jerusalem. She left her own country with a great caravan of camels loaded with gifts fit for a king: gold, precious stones, spices, and rare perfumes which she intended to give to Solomon.

24 Solomon and the Queen of Sheba

1 Kings 10

Having left her kingdom in Arabia, the queen of Sheba arrived in Jerusalem after a long journey. She presented herself to King Solomon and offered him the gifts she had brought. Then she wished to put his wisdom to the test: She put many difficult questions to him; when Solomon answered them all, she was filled with admiration. Solomon then showed the queen the temple of the Lord that he had built and the royal palace. He explained to her the laws of his kingdom and the work of his ministers.

The queen of Sheba was left breathless when she admired all of Solomon's wisdom and everything he had built. At last she said to Solomon: "Everything that I have heard in my own country, then, is true, concerning you and your wisdom! I would never have believed all that I heard unless I had come here and seen it with my own eyes. And still I have not even heard one half of the truth! Blessed are your ministers who benefit from your wisdom; blessed are the people that you govern, and blessed is your God who made you King!"

After this Solomon, too, gave many gifts to the queen.

25 The Kingdom Divided

1 Kings 11–12

Solomon reigned in wisdom and in glory for forty years—until in his later years his foreign wives attracted him to their gods and Solomon did evil in the eyes of the Lord.

For this reason the Lord said to Solomon: "You have not behaved as your father, David, did; you have not observed the covenant with me. Thus I shall now take away the kingdom which I have given you. But out of my love for your father, David, I shall leave one part of the kingdom for your descendants."

When Solomon died, his son Rehoboam became king in his place. He behaved in a foolish and evil way and a large number of the people rebelled against him. In this way, the kingdom was divided in two. The southern part remained under Rehoboam; it was called the kingdom of Judah and Jerusalem was its capital. The northern part became the kingdom of Israel, its capital Samaria and the first king was one of Solomon's ministers, Jeroboam.

Jeroboam did not wish his subjects to go to Jerusalem to pray in the temple of the Lord, so he built two other temples to the Lord in his own kingdom, one at Bethel and one at Dan.

26 The Prophets of the Lord

1 Kings 14–16; Amos 7; Jeremiah 1

The kingdom of Saul, of David, and of Solomon, had been divided into two. In Jerusalem, the descendants of David ruled one after the other. But they often behaved badly and had little faith in the Lord, and they often turned away from him to worship the false gods of other peoples.

The kings of Israel who reigned in Samaria behaved in exactly the same way. The people followed the bad example set by their kings and they too behaved wickedly.

The Lord saw how his people had betrayed him, but he never tired of inviting them to abandon their wicked ways and return to his love.

He did this in a number of different ways. For example, he permitted the enemies of his people to win in their wars, in order to make his people understand that they could only live in peace if they remained true to the Lord.

The Lord also sent special men to speak on his behalf: the prophets.

There were many prophets sent by the Lord, both in the kingdom of Judah and in the kingdom of Israel, but often neither the king nor the people listened to them; indeed they treated them badly, chased them off, or even killed them.

The Lord chose his prophets from among the people and it did not matter to which group they belonged. It was enough that they had a great love for the Lord in their hearts. Amos, for example, was a simple shepherd in the kingdom of Judah: the Lord sent him into the kingdom of Israel to warn the people of the grave punishments awaiting.

Jeremiah was a shy young man; when the Lord called to him, he replied: "Lord, I am not a good speaker, for I am young!" But the Lord said to him: "Do not say that you are young. You must only repeat that which I tell you to say."

27 The Lord Appears to the Prophet Isaiah

Isaiah 6

Isaiah was one of the great prophets of the kingdom of Judah. He discovered one day that he had been chosen by the Lord while he was in the temple in Jerusalem where he had a magnificent vision.

He saw the Lord on a high, raised throne and the hem of his gown reached down to the temple. All around him stood seraphim who proclaimed: "Holy, holy, holy is the Lord God of the universe; the heavens and the earth are full of his glory."

When he saw this vision Isaiah was filled with great fear and he said: "Woe is me! I am lost. For I am but a man and a sinner and yet my eyes have seen the Lord!"

At this, one of the seraphim flew toward him and seemed to touch his mouth with a glowing coal, saying: "Behold! Now your lips are pure and your sins are forgiven."

Isaiah understood at once what this gesture meant; the Lord had removed every obstacle and Isaiah could now speak in his name. Thus, when Isaiah heard the voice of the Lord asking: "Whom shall I send? Who will go and speak for us?", he replied at once: "Here I am, Lord. Send me!"

28 Amos the Prophet

Amos 5

There was once a prophet by the name of Amos. He was a shepherd in the kingdom of Judah, but God told him to go and speak in his name in the kingdom of Israel: Amos went, obedient to the command of the Lord.

One of the sins that Amos most condemned was the way in which the rich men in Israel treated their fellow men. Often the rich were very concerned about going to the temple and offering magnificent sacrifices while they behaved very badly with other people, cheating them and exploiting the poor.

All of this was very different from what the Lord had willed. He wanted them to help the poor and treat everybody with justice. Therefore, speaking through the mouth of his prophet Amos, the Lord said: "I detest your ceremonies, and your assemblies do not please me. You offer me animals in sacrifice, but I do not even pay them a glance. I would rather see your righteousness run like the water in a river. Do good, not evil, if you wish to live."

But the words Amos preached only annoyed them. "Go back to your own town," they said. "The words you say are of no interest."

29 Amos Speaks of Salvation

Amos 9

The prophet Amos warned the people of Israel that if they did not repent of their sins, then the Lord would punish them severely, and would go as far as to destroy the temple built by Solomon. But if they mended their ways, then God would love them once again.

Everyone had to learn to do the will of God. When that happened, Amos said, then the harvests would be rich and plentiful once again, wine would flow in streams from the hills, and the gardens would be rich in fruit.

30 The Trials of Jeremiah

Jeremiah 10

Jeremiah was a prophet born near Jerusalem. Speaking in the name of the Lord, he often chastised the Jewish people because, instead of worshiping the one and invisible Lord, they preferred the gods of other nations.

Jeremiah often said: "These false gods do not exist, even if they are represented in statues. They are only wood, cut in the forest and shaped by a carpenter. They are adorned with silver and gold but they cannot speak; and they must be carried everywhere. They are like scarecrows in a field of watermelons! You should not fear them for they can do you no harm. And it is useless to pray to them, for they can do no good either!"

Jeremiah also saw that the nearby nations were stronger than the Israelites and realized that God would make use of them to punish his chosen people. Jeremiah tried in every possible way to convince the people of Israel that if they continued to worship these false gods then they would be defeated by their enemies. Jeremiah repeated tirelessly: "God wishes you to return to him!" But the people of Israel did not listen to him.

31 Jeremiah Goes to the Potter

Jeremiah 18

The men of Israel made it clear that they did not believe the prophet Jeremiah, who feared that the Lord would punish all the Jews if they did not decide to worship the true God once again and renounce all the false gods.

One day, the Lord told Jeremiah to explain this to the people by way of a practical example. He said to Jeremiah: "Go down to the potter's workshop and there you will hear my words." Jeremiah obeyed: he went to the potter's workshop and found the potter making some clay vases on his wheel. Whenever he was not satisfied with the vase he would mix the clay all over again to shape a better vase.

"Behold!," the Lord spoke through the mouth of Jeremiah, "I could do with you, O people of Israel, just as the potter does with his vase. You are like clay in my hands; if you worship false gods you are like the badly-formed vase that must be reshaped."

These words of Jeremiah did not please the elders of the city and they complained to the king. But Jeremiah, like all the other prophets, continued to say what God ordered him to say.

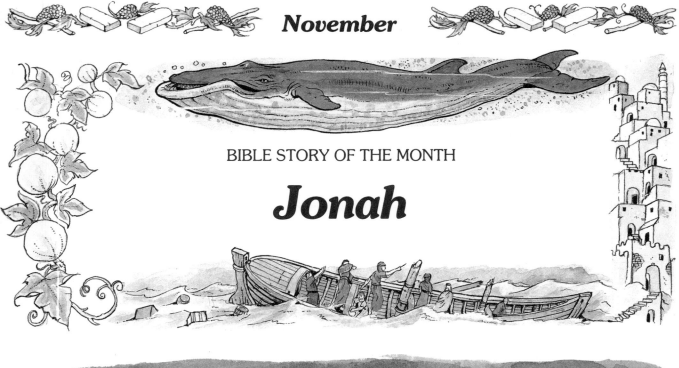

November

BIBLE STORY OF THE MONTH

Jonah

At one time, the Lord chose as his prophet a man by the name of Jonah. "Get up," he told him, "and go to the great city of Nineveh and warn the inhabitants that they must cease their wicked deeds, for their evil has grown and is offensive to my eyes."

Nineveh was not a Jewish city, which showed that the Lord is God not only of his chosen people, but of all other people as well, and that he cares for everyone. Jonah, however, was afraid to go to this foreign city: what if the people should answer him with violence? Jonah, therefore, fled the Lord; he went down to Joppa and embarked on a ship going in the opposite direction from Nineveh.

During the voyage, however, while Jonah was fast asleep below deck, a great wind blew up and filled the sails and such a great storm began to rage that it endangered the ship. Each of the sailors cried out to his own god and they began to throw the cargo overboard so that the ship would be lighter and float better. When they found Jonah fast asleep, they asked him why he too was not praying to his god. Finally the sailors said to each other: "let us draw lots to see who has caused this disaster." So they drew lots and the lot fell to Jonah.

"Who are you?" they asked him. "Where are you from? Where are you going? With what evil are you tainted?"

"I am a Hebrew, and I fear the Lord, the God of heaven, who has made the sea and the dry land," replied Jonah. "Now, however, I am fleeing from his presence because I have disobeyed his command."

"What can we do to calm this storm?" the sailors asked him.

"Take me and throw me into the sea, and this great storm will subside, for I know that it is because of me that it rages," replied Jonah.

At first, the sailors did not want to do this, but when they saw the sea grow even more tempestuous they threw Jonah into the sea. The storm subsided at once!

The Lord then caused Jonah to be swallowed by a great fish and there, in the belly of the fish, Jonah prayed ardently to the Lord. He repented for not having followed the Lord's command and asked for his forgiveness.

After three days and three nights the Lord spoke to the fish, and the fish threw Jonah up alive and well, on the shore of his own land, from which he had departed.

Jonah had tried to avoid obeying the Lord's command, but in vain. He now made up his mind to do

what the Lord wanted and he went to the city of Nineveh to speak to the king and the inhabitants.

As he walked through the streets, Jonah cried out: "Forty more days and then Nineveh will be destroyed. If you do not change your ways, then you will not survive."

The people of Nineveh believed the words which God spoke through Jonah, and from the oldest to the youngest they dressed themselves in sackcloth as a sign of repentance and to show that they wished to change their evil ways.

Even the king of Nineveh dressed in sackcloth and said: "Who can tell if God might not have pity on us, and put aside his anger at our behavior? This is our only hope of being allowed to continue to live!"

And, in fact, God saw the works of the king and the people of Nineveh; he saw that they had repented of their evil ways and he had pity on them and did not destroy the city.

Jonah should have rejoiced that the men of Nineveh had repented and so had been saved. Instead, he was angered by this because he thought that they would consider him a fool for having warned of a destruction which had not taken place. So Jonah complained to the Lord, saying: "I already knew that this would happen, from the first moment that you ordered me to come to Nineveh. For this very reason I sought to flee to Tarshish. For you are a gracious and merciful God, and even when you threaten punishment you are always moved to pity afterward. Therefore take my life from me, for it is better for me to die than to live!"

"Do you think that it is right that you should be so angry?" the Lord asked him. Jonah, however, remained sullen and went out of the city and stopped a short distance away. He made himself a shelter from branches and sat down outside the walls to wait and see what would happen to Nineveh.

Then the Lord made a vine grow near Jonah so that he could take shelter in its shade, and Jonah was very grateful for this generosity. But the next day the Lord sent a worm to gnaw at the plant and it died. Jonah was left exposed to the sun and he said: "It is better for me to die than to live!"

"Do you think it is right for you to be so upset for a simple vine?" the Lord asked Jonah. And then he went on: "You feel pity for the vine which you did not plant and for which you had to do no work; should I not then feel pity for Nineveh, where one hundred and twenty thousand people live?"

Jona 1–4

1 King Ahab and the Prophet Elijah

1 Kings 16–17

Among all the kings of Israel, Ahab was the one who did most evil in the eyes of the Lord. As his wife, he took Jezebel, the daughter of the king of Zidon, a foreigner. Because of her, in the city of Samaria, a temple was built to Baal, a false god. Jezebel supported a great number of the prophets of Baal and was the enemy of all who remained true to the Lord.

In an attempt to change the hearts of the king and all those who had taken to worshiping Baal, the Lord sent the great prophet Elijah into the kingdom of Israel.

But Elijah's repeated calls went unheard, so, at the Lord's command, he presented himself to King Ahab and said to him: "I am the servant of the Lord. In his name I tell you that from this day forth neither dew nor rain shall fall on your kingdom, until I give the word."

And that is what happened. Without either dew or rain, the fields began to wither and gave no more fruit; the situation grew desperate and the king gave an order for Elijah to be found. However, with the help of the Lord, the prophet was able to remain in hiding.

2 Elijah Is Fed by the Ravens

1 Kings 17

Elijah, the prophet, was in danger. King Ahab and the wicked Queen Jezebel searched for him everywhere since he had announced the Lord's punishment to them: famine throughout the kingdom.

The Lord himself, however, hid his prophet and provided for him. First of all, he sent Elijah to hide near the brook Cherith, and said to him: "You shall drink the water from the stream and I will command the ravens to bring you food." And that is what happened. The ravens brought him nourishment in the morning and evening.

3 The Widow's Flour

1 Kings 17

The Lord was careful to keep his prophet Elijah hidden, because he was threatened by King Ahab. In order to keep him safe, the Lord sent him to another country. He said to Elijah: "Get up and go to Zarephath in Zidon: behold, I have commanded a widow of that town to feed you."

Elijah went to Zarephath. When he came to the gate of the town, he saw a widow: he recognized that she was a widow by the clothes she was wearing. The prophet called out to her: "Bring me a little water to drink, and also a bit of bread!" The woman replied: "All that I have left is a handful of flour and a little oil; I was gathering a few sticks so that I could cook the flour for myself and my son. We shall eat it and then we shall die, for nothing else remains to us!" But the prophet reassured her: "Do not be afraid. Use the oil and the flour to make me a cake and bring it to me; and then prepare something to eat for yourself and your son, because the Lord says that the jar of flour will not be empty, nor will the jar of oil run out." Thus, Elijah, the widow, and her son had food to eat, for the flour and oil lasted.

4 Elijah and the Widow's Son

1 Kings 17

Elijah was in hiding near Zidon, in the house of the widow who had taken him in and given him food.

After some time, the woman's son fell ill and the illness grew more and more serious, until the boy died. The poor widow began to weep and wail, suspecting in some way that the prophet was the cause of her son's death. In her great grief, the woman shouted at the prophet: "Did you come here to punish me by causing the death of my son?"

But the prophet lifted her son out of her arms and carried him to the loft where he slept and laid him on his own bed. Then Elijah called on the Lord, saying: "O Lord, my God, help this widow who keeps me in her house. I pray you to let the child's soul return to his body!"

The Lord heard Elijah's prayer; the boy's soul returned to his body and life returned. Elijah took the child in his arms again, carried him back downstairs and handed him over to his mother, saying: "Behold your son is alive!"

At this, the woman felt great joy and said to Elijah: "Now I am certain that you are a man of God; now I understand that when you speak, you speak in the name of the Lord."

5 The Faith of Obadiah

1 Kings 18

For three years now the famine had lasted in the entire kingdom of Israel, because, just as the prophet had warned King Ahab, neither rain nor dew had fallen on the land.

The time had come, however, to put an end to this punishment and the Lord said to Elijah: "Rise and go to Ahab, for I have decided to give rain to the earth."

Ahab had betrayed the Lord, but he had one minister, Obadiah, who had always been faithful to the Lord and had secretly helped all those who were opposed to the false for-eign gods. Obadiah was in the countryside when he met the prophet Elijah and recognized him as the man of God.

Elijah said to him: "Go and inform King Ahab that I have come to speak with him." Obadiah was surprised and replied: "The king has searched for you for a long time, in every corner of his kingdom. If I go and give him your message, and you disappear again before he comes here, then he will punish me by putting me to death!"

"Have faith: I shall not move from here," replied Elijah. Obadiah trusted him and went off, returning to Elijah with King Ahab.

6 Elijah Challenges the Priests of Baal

1 Kings 18

"You and your family are the ruin of Israel," the prophet Elijah told King Ahab, "because you have turned away from the Lord to worship the false god Baal. Now I will show you who is the true god. Call all the people to Mount Carmel, together with the prophets of Baal."

When all were gathered at Mount Carmel, Elijah spoke: "For how much longer will you limp on both feet? You must make up your minds: you cannot worship both the Lord and Baal. Behold: I am the only prophet of the Lord here, while the prophets of Baal, whom you see before you, number more than four hundred. And still, I challenge them: I shall offer a sacrifice to the Lord, and they will offer one to Baal. We shall not, however, light fires to burn them. The true God will send fire from heaven to burn the sacrifice offered to him. Let the followers of Baal begin, for there are many more of them."

The prophets of Baal built an altar, then they took a bull calf and placed it on top of the wood; then they began to call upon their god. They called on him for so long that Elijah began to laugh: "Call on him a bit louder: perhaps your god is asleep."

Midday came and went and nothing had happened. Then Elijah too built an altar, and he too placed a bull calf on top of the wood. Then, in a loud voice, he prayed with these words: "Lord, God of Abraham, of Isaac, and of Jacob, today everyone will see that you are the Lord God and your people will return to you." These words had hardly passed his lips before fire fell from heaven onto the altar Elijah had built and burned the sacrifice, the wood, and even the altar stones.

At this, everyone fell to the ground and proclaimed: "The Lord is our God! The Lord is God!"

7 The Return of the Rain

1 Kings 18

It had not rained for three years in the kingdom of Israel; but now this punishment would end because the king and the people recognized the Lord as the one, true God.

The prophet Elijah spoke to King Ahab: "Rise and go and eat and drink and be glad, for I hear the sound of torrential rain." Elijah then went to Mount Carmel, by the sea, where he sat down on the ground and began to pray.

He had taken with him a boy with very sharp sight and, after praying for a while, he called the boy and told him to look carefully out to sea.

"There is nothing there," the boy told him. "Go and look seven more times," the prophet ordered.

The boy obeyed, and after he had looked for the seventh time, he said: "There is a cloud as big as a man's hand rising from the sea." Elijah then said to him: "Run quickly to the king and tell him to fasten his horses to his chariot and hurry to the palace so that he will not be caught out in the rain."

And it happened that the sky darkened immediately with clouds, a strong wind blew up, and the rain began to pour down. The drought was over.

8 Elijah in Flight

1 Kings 19

Queen Jezebel worshiped the false god Baal, and because of that she persecuted Elijah.

In view of this danger, Elijah was forced to flee in order to save himself. From the kingdom of Israel he went down into the kingdom of Judah, crossing the desert. He walked next into the wilderness, and stopped and sat down under a juniper tree, to pray: "It is enough now, Lord; I am too tired. Take my life from me." Then he slept.

All at once an angel of the Lord touched him and said: "Get up and eat!" Elijah looked around and saw a cake baked on hot coals and a jug of water nearby. He ate and drank and then went back to sleep.

A short time later, the angel returned and invited Elijah to eat again, saying: "You have a long journey ahead of you!" Elijah got up and ate and drank. With the strength he got from this food, he walked for forty days and forty nights until he arrived at the mount of God in Sinai.

This was the same mountain on which Moses had met the Lord and where he had been given the tablet of the Ten Commandments.

9 Elijah Meets the Lord

1 Kings 19

Elijah arrived at the mountain of God, where Moses had already encountered the Lord. He had gone into a cave to spend the night, when he heard a voice that said to him: "Go outside and wait on the mountain, and the Lord will come." And the Lord did come.

A wind blew that was strong and fierce enough to break the rocks on the hills; but the Lord was not present in the wind. After the wind there was an earthquake, but the Lord was not in the earthquake. After the earthquake there was a fire, but the Lord was not present in the fire. After the fire, there was the whisper of a light breeze. As soon as he heard it, Elijah understood that the Lord was passing! He heard a voice which asked him: ."What are you doing here, Elijah?" He replied: "The people of Israel have abandoned you, to follow false gods. I, alone, speak for you, Lord, and they seek to take my life!"

"I know those who have remained faithful to me," said the Lord. "Do not be afraid; retrace your steps and return to the land of Israel. There you will find Elisha, whom I have chosen as my prophet after you. Greet him."

10 The Vocation of Elisha

1 Kings 19

Elijah had been told to greet Elisha, who would become his successor. Elijah came across Elisha when he was working in his fields with a plow pulled by twelve pairs of oxen. Elijah went up to him and threw his cloak over him. This meant that he was passing onto Elisha his tasks and his responsibilities. Elisha stopped his oxen and ran after Elijah, who had already moved off, and said: "Allow me to go and kiss my mother and father good-bye, and I will follow you." Elisha then went with Elijah and became his disciple.

11 Naboth's Vineyard

1 Kings 21

A man by the name of Naboth owned a vineyard near the palace of Ahab, King of Israel. One day, Ahab said to Naboth: "Give your vineyard to me. It is close to my palace and I would like to make it my herb garden. In exchange, I will give you a better vineyard or, if you prefer, I will pay you in money."

Naboth, however, replied: "That vineyard has belonged to my family for many generations: the Lord forbids me to sell my inheritance."

King Ahab returned home, both sad and indignant at Naboth's reply.

He lay down on his bed and refused to eat. His wife, Jezebel, asked him: "Why are you angry? Why do you refuse to eat?"

Ahab told her what had happened: "I am angry because I said to Naboth, 'sell me your vineyard, or, if you choose, I will give you a better vineyard instead.' But his reply to me was: 'I will not give up the inheritance of my forefathers!'"

When she heard this, the wicked Queen Jezebel said,: "Are you or are you not the king of Israel? Do not despair! Get up, eat, and be merry! I shall find a way of obtaining Naboth's vineyard for you!" And Jezebel began to scheme.

12 The Prophet Elijah Confronts King Ahab

1 Kings 21

In order to possess Naboth's vineyard, the wicked Queen Jezebel wrote a letter in the name of King Ahab. She sealed it with the king's seal and sent it to the elders and chiefs of Naboth's city. The letter ordered that Naboth should be falsely accused, tried, and condemned to death.

And so it happened. After the unjust death of Naboth, Jezebel said to Ahab: "Behold! The vineyard that was Naboth's now belongs to you."

The Lord, however, spoke to the prophet Elijah and when Ahab went to visit his new vineyard the prophet was awaiting him. "The Lord knows that you killed Naboth to take possession of his vineyard!" the prophet told the king. "And since you have committed this great sin, a curse shall fall upon you, and Jezebel will die as Naboth has died!" At this, Ahab tore his clothes and began to fast and beg for forgiveness from the Lord for the sin he had committed. God spoke to Elijah and said to him: "Since Ahab has repented I shall forgive him." Jezebel, on the other hand, who had never repented, was later killed in a revolt and thus she suffered the Lord's punishment for her sin.

13 Into Heaven on a Chariot of Fire

2 Kings 2

Elijah was walking toward Jericho with his faithful disciple Elisha. That day Elisha knew that the Lord would take his master, the great prophet. When they arrived at the banks of the Jordan, Elijah took his cloak, rolled it up, and struck the water with it. The waters divided and the two prophets crossed the river without getting wet.

When they had reached the far bank, Elijah said to Elisha: "Ask me what you would like, before I am taken from you." "I wish that two thirds of your spirit would pass to me," replied Elisha, to show that he was ready to take the place of Elijah.

"God will grant this to you," said Elijah. And as they were speaking, a whirlwind came between them, and Elijah rose into heaven on the whirlwind as if borne on a flaming chariot pulled by horses of fire. When Elisha saw this, he cried: "My father, my father, the guide of the people of Israel."

Elisha then picked up the cloak of Elijah, which had fallen to the ground; with this he struck the waters of the river Jordan, which divided to let him pass. Thus, the spirit of Elijah lived on in Elisha; and with God's help he performed miracles.

14 The Spirit of Elijah Remains with Elisha

2 Kings 2

The prophet Elijah had been carried into heaven in a chariot of fire, while Elisha, his disciple, was watching.

When Elijah had disappeared from his sight, Elisha picked up the mantle that had fallen from Elijah's shoulders. Elisha said, "Where is the God Elijah served so faithfully?" He wanted a sign. Then, when he returned to the River Jordan, he used Elijah's mantle and smote the waters repeatedly until they parted before him, allowing him to cross, just as Elijah had done before him.

The prophets of Jericho witnessed this from a certain distance and they ran out to meet Elisha and bowed down before him. Then they urged Elisha to look for his former master, the prophet Elijah. They feared he had gotten lost in the mountains and some bad deed had befallen him.

The Prophets of Jericho offered to send fifty servants to look for Elijah, equipped with pack animals.

Elisha knew his master had gone to serve the Lord, but he could not stop the prophets from their search. At last they came back empty-handed, and avowed that Elijah's spirit had passed into Elisha.

November

15 The Healing of the Waters

2 Kings 2

The prophet Elisha was in Jericho when the people came to him and said: "Behold, this is a beautiful city, but the waters that feed it are polluted and make the land barren."

Elisha then said to them: "Bring me some salt." They brought him the salt and he went to the source of the water. He poured the salt into the spring and pronounced these words: "The Lord says: 'I have healed these waters and from this day forth the water will be good to drink and will enrich the fields.'" And that came to pass.

16 The Widow's Oil

2 Kings 4

One day a woman came to the prophet Elisha and said to him: "My husband is dead. As you know, he always heard and obeyed the word of the Lord. Now, however, one of our creditors has come to take my two sons as slaves in repayment of our debt to him."

Elisha asked her: "What can I do for you? Tell me what you have in your house."

"The only thing I have at home is a pot of oil," replied the woman sadly.

"Go and ask to borrow pots from all your neighbors," the prophet told her, "and ask for a great many. Then go home and pour oil from your pot into all the other pots."

The woman did as she had been told; her sons held the pots while she filled them all with oil. And her pot only became empty when all the other pots were full. She then went back to the man of God and told him that her oil had multiplied.

"And now what shall I do?" the woman asked Elisha. The prophet replied; "Go and sell the oil in the pots and with the money you receive you will be able to pay off your debt. There will be enough left over to support you and your sons."

17 The Breath of Life

2 Kings 4

One day the prophet Elisha went to the home of a rich woman who always gave food to both him and his servants when they passed. Elisha knew that the woman had no children and very much wanted a child, so he said to her: "For all your kindness the Lord will grant you a son."

In due course, the woman had a son who grew up into a healthy boy. One day, however, when he was in the fields with his father, the boy suddenly felt a great pain in his head. He was taken home and there his mother held him on her knees

until midday, when the boy died.

The mother laid him on his bed; then, saddling her ass, she hurried off to find Elisha. When he found out what had happened, Elisha accompanied the woman home at once. When they arrived, he went by himself into the room where the child lay and closed the door.

First, Elisha prayed to the Lord; then he lay down on the boy and put his hands and his mouth on the child's mouth and breathed his breath into the child. The body of the boy grew warm again and then his eyes opened. Elisha called the mother in and said to her: "Behold, your son is well again."

74

18 Naaman's Leprosy

2 Kings 5

Naaman, the captain of the king of Syria's army, was a valiant man who had been greatly honored by the king. Unfortunately, he had the terrible disease known as leprosy.

One day the servant of the wife of Naaman, an Israeli girl, said to her mistress: "If Naaman goes to my country, there is a prophet there who can cure him of his leprosy."

Naaman, with the permission of his own king, presented himself to the prophet Elisha. When Naaman arrived at the house of Elisha and stopped before the door, Elisha sent word to Naaman that if he went and washed himself seven times in the River Jordan, he would then be cured of his disease.

When he heard this, Naaman was furious and left saying: "I thought that the prophet would come out to meet me, pray to his God, then touch me where I am diseased and my leprosy would disappear. Instead he sends me to wash in the Jordan! As if the rivers in my own country are not better than all the waters of Israel! For what reason have I come this far?"

His advisers, however, said to him: "If the prophet had com-manded you to do something diffi-cult, would you not have done it? All the more reason to do this simple thing that he has commanded you to do!"

Naaman heeded this advice and went down to the River Jordan. There he bathed seven times and, behold, his leprosy vanished! When he saw this, Naaman said: "Now I know that there is no other god than the Lord, God of Israel!" He went back to the prophet and offered him great gifts as thanks for his cure. Elisha refused them, saying that if Naaman was cured then it was not the work of the prophet but the will of God.

19 The Ax Head in the Water

2 Kings 6

One day Elisha and his followers decided to build a house where they could meet. They went to the banks of the River Jordan and set to work. While one of the men was chopping down a tree trunk, his ax head fell into the river. The man went to Elisha and explained what had happened and the prophet made him point out where the ax head had sunk. Elisha then threw a piece of wood into the river at the very same spot, and immediately the ax head floated to the surface to be picked up.

20 Joash, the Little King

2 Kings 11

Although the king and the people of Judah and Israel kept on doing great wrongs in the eyes of the Lord, he always kept his word. On one occasion, the king of Judah, Ahaziah, was killed in battle. His mother, Athaliah, ordered that all the princes be killed so that she could rule as queen. But when she died a man from outside the family would become king. And that would break the promise the Lord made to David that his descendants would always reign on the throne in Jerusalem. So the sister of king Ahaziah saved one of the king's young sons, Joash, and hid him.

For six years little Joash remained in hiding in the temple of the Lord, while Athaliah ruled the country. During the seventh year, the priest Jehoiada called the elders and the captains of the guard to the temple and showed them little Joash, who was then proclaimed king according to the will of the Lord.

When she heard the noise of the celebration, Athaliah went to the temple. There she found the little king surrounded by singers and trumpeters and rejoicing. In this way, Joash, the descendant of the house of David, became king.

21 The Lesson of the Arrows

2 Kings 13

When Elisha fell sick, King Joash went to visit him and said: "Oh my father, oh my father, the protector of Israel!"

Elisha said to him: "Pick up your bow and arrows." When Joash had done this, Elisha said: "Put your hand on the bow." When the king had done this, Elisha placed his hand on the king's hand and said: "Open the eastern window."

Once the window had been opened, Elisha said: "Shoot!," and Joash fired his arrow. Elisha said: "The arrow of victory for the Lord, the arrow of victory over the Syrians. You shall defeat the Syrians."

Elisha then told the king of Israel to pick up his arrows. When Joash had done this, Elisha said to him: "Beat the ground with your arrows." And Joash struck the ground three times, but then stopped.

Elisha was angry with Joash and said: "You should have struck the ground five or six times with your arrows! Then you would have defeated the Syrians forever! Now, instead, you shall defeat them only three times."

Having said this, Elisha, the man of God, foretold the end of the kingdom of Israel, then died.

22 Josiah and the Rediscovered Book

2 Kings 22–23

There was a king named Josiah who reigned for thirty-one years in Jerusalem. In contrast with many other kings, he always did what was good in the eyes of the Lord. In the eighteenth year of his reign, Josiah gave orders that the temple of the Lord should be repaired. During this work, the high priest Hilkiah found a long-forgotten book and he had it brought to the king.

The book contained, in full, the law of God and the sayings of Moses, together with the counsel he had given to the people. When the king heard the words that were written in the book, he tore his clothes to show his great pain, for he knew that the kings who had preceded him had failed to keep the law of God. Josiah then called the elders, the citizens, and all the priests and prophets, to the temple and had the book read aloud.

When the reading was finished, the king rose to his feet and renewed the covenant with the Lord, and in the name of the whole people he promised to keep the law of God. Then he ordered the destruction of all the statues and temples to false gods and celebrated a memorable Passover.

23 The Temple Is Destroyed

2 Kings 17–25

Despite the many proofs of God's goodness to them, the people of Israel continued to offend him and do evil. And so the Lord allowed a grave punishment to fall on them so that the people would then turn back to him.

Thus the two kingdoms, first one, then the other, were conquered by enemies. Everything happened just as the prophets had foretold. Nebuchadnezzar, the king of Babylon, came with an immense army and laid siege to Jerusalem. The city resisted for months until, finally, its inhabitants had nothing left to eat. Then, through a gap in the wall, the Babylonians entered the city. The king was captured and many were killed.

The temple, which had been built by Solomon, was destroyed. The soldiers of Nebuchadnezzar took all of its treasures, and all of the objects and ornaments in gold, silver, and bronze. A great number of Israelites were made slaves and sent to work in Babylon. There, in that foreign land, they suffered greatly. But, as God had planned, it was there that they came to understand the evil they had done and turned back to the ways of the Lord.

24 Four Boys at the Court of Babylon

Daniel 1

Nebuchadnezzar, king of Babylon, ordered the superintendent of his palace to choose several boys from among the Israelites sent to his kingdom. They had to be good-looking and intelligent and were to be instructed to perform certain tasks.

Among the boys chosen were Daniel, Hananiah, Mishael and Azariah. They, like the others who had been chosen, were given food from the king's own table. But good Israelites did not eat the food of foreigners, so Daniel asked the superintendent not to force them to eat the king's food. "But if the king sees that your faces are less healthy than those of the other boys," said the superintendent, "he will blame me and condemn me to death!" "Put us to the test for ten days," Daniel begged him. "Give us only water and vegetables. Then compare our faces with the other boys and make your decision."

The superintendent agreed and at the end of ten days the four boys appeared healthier and more handsome than the others. They also seemed wise and intelligent and so, when their instruction was finished, Daniel, Hananiah, Mishael, and Azariah served the king.

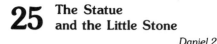

25 The Statue and the Little Stone

Daniel 2

One night, King Nebuchadnezzar had a dream. He saw an immense statue with a head of gold, the chest and arms of silver, the belly and the thighs of bronze, the legs of iron, and its feet partly made of iron and partly of clay. While Nebuchadnezzar was looking on, a stone flew from the mountain behind and struck the feet of the statue and broke the clay into pieces. When this happened, the entire statue crumbled, while the stone that had struck it grew and grew.

Since the wise men at the court of Nebuchadnezzar could not explain the dream to the king, a young Israelite named Daniel came forward. "My god has told me the meaning of your dream," said Daniel. "The golden head of the statue represents your glorious realm, O king. But after yours will follow other kingdoms, ever less glorious and strong, until God creates a kingdom which is greater than any other and it will grow until it covers the whole world and will endure forever."

The kingdom of which the prophet Daniel spoke was the one founded by Jesus, the Son of God and King of the Universe, when he came into the world.

26 Nebuchadnezzar and the Statue of Gold

Daniel 3

The king of Babylon, Nebuchadnezzar, had a statue of gold built, as high as a tower and very wide. He then called together all the important men in his kingdom, whereupon a herald announced: "At the sound of the musical instruments, you must all prostrate yourselves and pay homage to the golden statue. Whoever does not worship the statue will be thrown into a fiery furnace."

Hananiah, Mishael and Azariah, the three young Israelites at the Babylonian court, steadfastly refused to worship the statue. So the king had them arrested and asked them the reason for this refusal. "Only God is to be worshiped" replied the three young men. "You can have us thrown into the furnace, but if God wishes he will free us. And even if God does not save us, we will never act against his will."

Nebuchadnezzar was furious and ordered that the furnace be fired hotter than usual, and that the three youths be bound and thrown into it. To his amazement, he saw that they remained unharmed in the flames, praising God.

He had them brought out and saw that not a single hair on their heads had been singed by the fire.

27 The Fiery Furnace

Daniel 3

"Only God is to be worshiped" the three young Israelites, Hananiah, Mishael, and Azariah, had told King Nebuchadnezzar. For this the king had ordered them to be thrown into a fiery furnace. However, by the grace of God, they had been brought out again, unharmed.

The astonished king said: "These young men would not disobey their god, and he saved them. Therefore I now decree that no one in my kingdom speak against the god of these youths, since their god is so powerful."

28 The Writing on the Wall

Daniel 5

When Belshazzar became king of Babylon, he held a great banquet. A thousand nobles were invited and the king began to drink wine with them. The king ordered brought to him the precious cups and the vases of gold and silver which his father, Nebuchadnezzar, had brought from the temple of the Lord in Jerusalem. Belshazzar used them to drink to his false gods.

Suddenly, however, the fingers of a hand appeared and began to write on the wall of the banquet chamber. King Belshazzar was very afraid and

had his wise men brought to him but no one could make out what the writing meant, and the king and his counselors grew even more afraid. Then the queen spoke up and sent for an Israelite, who had been able to explain the dreams of the king. His name was Daniel and he was a prophet of the Lord.

Daniel said to King Belshazzar: "You have offended the Lord God, by using the cups and vases from his temple to glorify your false gods. These gods do not see, they do not hear, and they do not understand: they are nothing! But the Lord holds your life in his hands and you have

not worshiped him."

Daniel continued: "For this reason the Lord God has sent the hand to trace this writing on the wall. This is what is written: *Mene, Tekel, Peres.* And this is what these words mean: *Mene,* God has judged your kingdom and brought it to an end; *Tekel,* you have been weighed in the balances and you have been found wanting; *Peres,* your kingdom will be divided and will be given to the Medes and the Persians."

Just as Daniel had foretold, Belshazzar, king of Babylon, was killed that night. In his place, Darius the Mede became king.

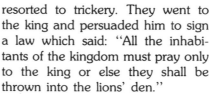
29 Daniel Prays

Daniel 6

Daniel, the prophet of the Lord, was living in exile in Babylon, where he was the wisest and most intelligent of the king's counselors. The king had given him a position of high responsibility and placed him above all the other governors.

These governors, however, grew jealous of Daniel, and began to look for some fault in him so that he could be discredited in front of the king. In this way, they hoped he would be dismissed. Since they could find no fault in Daniel, they resorted to trickery. They went to the king and persuaded him to sign a law which said: "All the inhabitants of the kingdom must pray only to the king or else they shall be thrown into the lions' den."

Daniel realized that this law had been designed to trap him. In fact, he did not try to hide his faith: three times a day, every day, he opened the window in his room, turned toward Jerusalem, and got down on his knees to pray and praise God, who lived among men in Jerusalem.

Without paying any attention to the new law nor to the punishment for breaking it, Daniel continued to pray openly to the Lord.

30 Daniel in the Lions' Den

Daniel 6

Although the king had passed a new law forbidding the people to pray to anybody but himself, Daniel went on praying to the Lord, his God.

His enemies had been spying on him so that they could accuse him of this very practice. They went at once to the king and told him that Daniel was disobeying his orders. The king was very unhappy because he had great trust in Daniel. But the law had to be observed. Those who broke it were to be thrown into a den of lions.

The king spent the whole day trying to think of a way to save Daniel. But there was no escape. As Daniel was lowered into the lions' den, the king said to him: "Your God will save you."

The king spent the whole night unable to sleep for worry. At dawn, he went straight to the lions' den and called out: "Daniel, servant of the Lord, has your god, whom you love, been able to save you?"

Daniel replied: "My god sent an angel to close the jaws of the lions, and they have done me no harm."

The king was delighted that Daniel was safe. He was brought out of the lions' den and everyone could see that he was not scratched.

December

BIBLE STORY OF THE MONTH

Esther the Queen

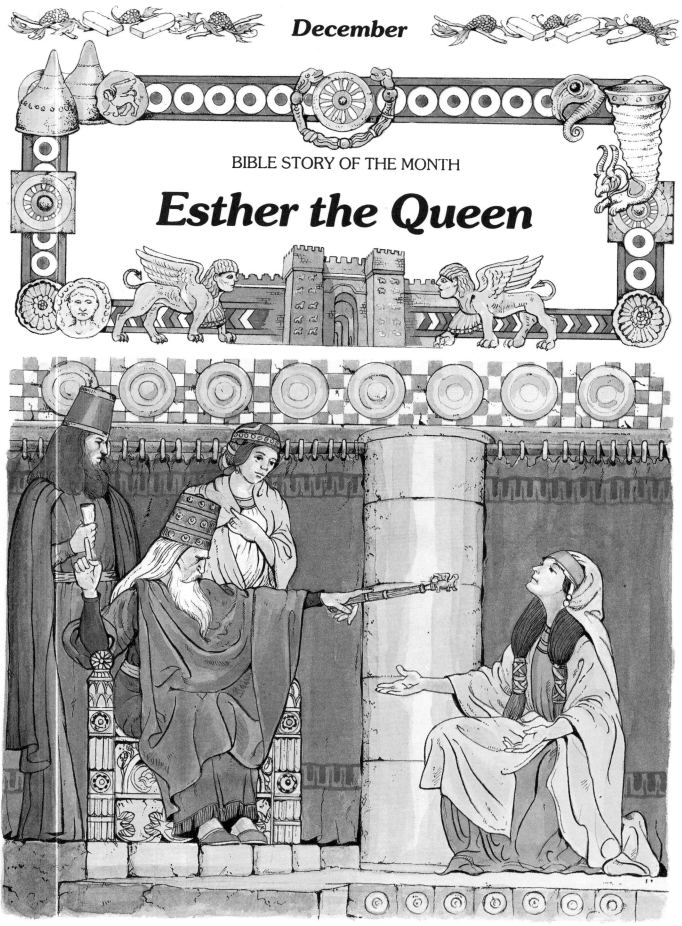

In the palace of Ahasuerus, the king of Babylon, there lived an Israelite named Mordecai. He was part of the group of Israelites that had been taken from Jerusalem into exile in the east, and now he was working in the court of the king.

Mordecai had a young niece, called Esther. The daughter of his brother, she had been left without parents, so he raised her. It happened that Ahasuerus preferred Esther to all the other women of his kingdom: he married her and named her queen. One day, Mordecai overheard two ministers plotting to kill the king. Mordecai told Esther, who then went to tell the king. Investigations proved the two ministers guilty and they were put to death.

Some time later the king placed a man called Haman at the head of all the princes who governed the kingdom. Haman hated Mordecai and all the people of Israel, so one day he went before Ahasuerus and said: "There is a people spread over all the provinces of your kingdom. Its laws are different from those of the other peoples, and they do not observe the laws that you have made. If it pleases you, give orders that they be destroyed and their properties confiscated. I will put a part of what is taken into the treasury."

Ahasuerus took off the ring with the royal seal and gave it to Haman, to show him that he was granting him full power in this matter, and then said: "Keep the money for yourself; and do what you will with that people; they are yours."

Then Haman wrote to all princes in the kingdom that on a certain day in the month of Adar, all the Israelites were to be put to death and their goods confiscated.

When Mordecai came to hear of this decision, he tore up his clothes and dressed in sackcloth as a sign of great sorrow, and with his head covered in ashes he wandered the city, crying in pain and sorrow.

In this way he also meant to attract the attention of Esther. He could not go directly to her, because no one knew that Esther, the queen, was one of the people of Israel.

When Esther was told that her uncle was behaving in this strange way, giving signs of great sorrow, she called a trusted servant of the king and secretly sent him to Mordecai to find out what had happened.

Mordecai told the servant of Haman's plan and asked him to beg Esther to go to the king and protect her people. But this was very dangerous, as Esther knew well. If anyone—man or woman, stranger or

 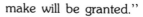

friend, even the ministers or the queen herself—went before the king without having been summoned, he would be put to death; unless the king pointed his scepter at the person, sparing his life and giving him permission to speak.

But Mordecai persisted in begging Esther to intervene, to try and save her people, even at the risk of losing her own life. The queen sent him this reply: "Go and gather all the Israelites who live in this city. Tell them to fast for me for three days; I and my handmaidens will also fast to ask for God's help. Then I will go before the king, and if I must die, I will die."

On the third day, after a long prayer to the Lord, Esther put on her royal gown and thus dressed, she went before the king.

The king was pleased by her and he pointed his scepter at her, saying: "What do you desire, Queen Esther? Anything you ask of me I will grant you, even if it be half of my kingdom."

"I ask that you come to the banquet today that I have prepared for you and for Haman," the queen replied.

So the king and Haman came to the banquet and Ahasuerus again asked: "What is it you desire, Queen Esther? Any request you

make will be granted."

Then Esther said: "If I have found favor in your eyes, oh king, my first wish is that you grant me my life, and my second is that you spare my people. Because I and my people have been condemned to be put to death, and all our belongings confiscated."

"Who is it and where is the person who would dare to plan such an act?" asked the king in surprise and fury.

"The enemy, our oppressor, is none other than that wicked man Haman!" Esther said bravely, pointing her finger at the king's minister.

Haman was gripped with fear; he tried to beg forgiveness for what he had done, but Ahasuerus would not listen and condemned him to death. Then he sent an order throughout his kingdom that the lives of all those belonging to the people of Israel be spared.

Later on Mordecai came before the king, because Esther had told Ahausuerus that Mordecai was really her uncle. And Ahasuerus took the ring with the royal seal, which he had taken from Haman, and gave it to Mordecai, ordering that his new minister be granted royal honors. On that day all the Israelites were filled with joy and thanksgiving because of Esther, the queen who had saved her people.

Esther 1—8

December

1 By the Waters of Babylon

Psalm 137; Ezekiel 11

Led away into a foreign land, the king and the inhabitants of the land of Israel suffered greatly.

Later on, they remembered that time with this song:
By the waters of Babylon,
we sat down and we wept
at the memory of Jerusalem.
There they asked us to sing,
those who had taken us away:
to sing songs of joy,
for them, our oppressors.
"Sing the songs of Zion for us,"
    they said.

But how could we sing the songs of the Lord
in a foreign land?
On the willows of that land
we hung up our lyres.

There in that foreign land, they realized that it was a bad thing to be far from the Lord. The Israelites understood that they had done wrong by abandoning the Lord, and so, just as the Lord desired, they turned back to him. They asked him to pardon the sins they had committed, and they begged him to give them back his love. And the Lord, who is good and pardons willingly, sent the prophets to them, to show them that he had not forgotten them.

2 The Visions of the Prophet Ezekiel

Ezekiel 11, 37

The Lord sent his prophets to give heart to his people who were suffering in exile and had repented of their sins. One of the prophets, Ezekiel, spent almost all of his life with the exiles. He remembered clearly the temple in Jerusalem and assured the Lord's chosen people that God would allow those who remained faithful to him to worship in the temple again. Ezekiel told them the Lord would change their very hearts, and instead of harboring evil, they would love the Lord.

Ezekiel explained to the people the visions which God sent him. One of these visions concerned the reuniting of the people of Israel. The prophet told them that God had led him into a valley full of dry bones and said to him: "Ezekiel, speak to these bones: Tell them that I will bring them back to life and all will know that I am the Lord!"

Hardly had he said this than he heard a great noise, and saw the bones coming together again. Ezekiel looked on astonished as the dead rose to their feet and life came back into them and they were as numerous as a great army.

God explained this vision to the prophet: "These bones are all the children of Israel. At the moment they are like the dead, like dry bones. In the exile in which they find themselves, they think there is no hope for them. But go now and tell them that I, the Lord God, will bring them back to life and take them to their homeland, the land that I have promised to Abraham and his descendants.

"My spirit will enter into them, and they will live again," the Lord continued to Ezekiel, "and they will know that I am the Lord. Thus I have spoken and thus I will do!"

3 The Return from Exile

Ezra 1–6

The people of Israel had had to pass many years in exile. But for the tribe of Judah this exile ended when Cyrus became king in the east.

In the first years of his reign, King Cyrus made the following proclamation: "The Lord, God of heaven, has told me to build a temple to him in Jerusalem. All of the people of the Lord in my kingdom are now free to return to Jerusalem to build the temple. Furthermore, I command that the people of God be given gold and silver, goods and livestock, over and above offerings for the temple to be built in Jerusalem."

Thus the Jews returned to Jerusalem and rebuilt the temple: in this way the promises that the Lord had made to his people through the prophets were fulfilled.

The rebuilding of the temple took a long time and there were many difficulties; in the end, however, it was completed and the occasion was commemorated with great joy by all of God's people. Everyone celebrated the Passover and sacrifices were again offered to the Lord in the temple. Hymns of praise were sung to God who had brought his people out of exile.

4 The Joy of the Returning Exiles

Psalm 126

The people who returned home from exile in Babylon commemorated the event with this song:
When the Lord led the prisoners home to Jerusalem, it seemed like a dream to us!
Our mouths opened with laughter, and our tongues sang songs of joy.
Even foreigners said God has done great things for them!
Indeed the Lord has done great things for us; he has filled us full of joy, like those who go out to sow and return home carrying sheaves!

5 Nehemiah and King Cyrus

Nehemiah 1–2

The Jews of the tribe of Judah rebuilt the temple as soon as they returned from exile. But the city of Jerusalem, which had been destroyed by their enemies a long time before, was still in a terrible state.

Nehemiah, who was one of the Jews who had remained in Persia, learned of the condition in which the city had been found. Saddened by this information, he went to the king. "Why are you so unhappy?" the king asked him, and Nehemiah replied: "Because Jerusalem, the city of my fathers, is ruined. Permit me, O king, to go and repair it!"

The king gave his consent and Nehemiah departed. When he reached Jerusalem, he rested for three days. Then, by night, he got up and went with a few men to inspect the walls. He saw that at many points there were open breaches and that the gates had been destroyed by fire.

Having seen this, Nehemiah went to the chiefs of the people and said: "You see clearly the situation we are in: Jerusalem is destroyed and the walls are useless. We must take heart and set to work!" And everyone replied: "We shall set to work at once. Jerusalem will be rebuilt!"

December

6 Nehemiah Rebuilds the Walls

Nehemiah 2-7

Under the direction of Nehemiah, the Jews had decided to rebuild the walls of Jerusalem. Some people laughed at them, but Nehemiah said: "Let us set to work and the Lord will see that we finish it!"

The work was begun. But enemies of the Jews in the surrounding region did not wish the Jews to become a powerful people again. These enemies united, planning to attack the city, stopping the rebuilding, and enslaving the Jews.

When Nehemiah learned of their plan, he divided his men into two groups. One half worked on the rebuilding of the walls, while the other half remained fully armed on guard. Those who were working also were ready to fight if necessary.

The work proceeded rapidly from dawn to dusk each day, and after fifty days it was finished. When it was done, Nehemiah declared: "The city gates shall be opened when the sun is already high in the sky, and they shall be closed while the inhabitants are still on their feet. Choose sentinels and guards from among you and make sure they are always at their posts."

The Lord had given great wisdom to his servant Nehemiah.

7 The Renewal of the Covenant

Nehemiah 7-13

The Jews lived in safety in the city of Jerusalem, now that the walls had been rebuilt and were well guarded.

Everyone thought that it was now time to give thanks to the Lord. All the men and women gathered together and told Ezra to bring out the book of the law of Moses, which the Lord had given to his chosen people. Ezra was a scribe and an expert in the explanation of the law.

Therefore Ezra brought the book out before the assembled people and stood up on a wooden pulpit which had been built for the occasion. He blessed the Lord and the people replied, "Amen." Then they listened to Ezra as he read and explained the law of God to them.

They all realized that they had often broken this law and said, "You, Lord, have not dealt with us as our sins deserve, but have showered us with blessings! We now promise to keep every commandment of your law."

Then, full of joy, and singing hymns and songs of praise, they made two great processions around the walls and came together in the temple. There, they offered sacrifices to the Lord and held a great feast in his honor.

8 Job Is Put to the Test

Job 1–42

By now, everyone clearly understood that if he was not faithful to the Lord, he would encounter great problems. But is this the only reason that we should be faithful? Should we avoid doing evil only to avoid God's punishment? Or should we always do good, no matter what happens? The story of Job gives us the answer to this question. . . .

In the land of Uz lived Job, who feared God and did no evil. He had three daughters and seven sons, and many herds of livestock. He was the most important of all the men of the east.

One day the Lord said to Satan: "Have you seen my servant Job? There is no man on earth as upright as he." But Satan replied, "Try taking some of his possessions from him, and he will curse you!" The Lord then said to Satan: "All that Job owns is in your power, but do no harm to his body."

And thus, one day soon afterward, a messenger came to Job and announced: "Marauders have attacked and carried off your oxen and your asses, killing your servants who were guarding them!"

He was still speaking when a second messenger arrived and said: "A fire has destroyed the sheep and the shepherds who were watching over them!" These words were barely out of his mouth when a third messenger arrived to say: "Robbers have killed your servants and stolen all your camels!"

Finally, yet another messenger arrived with the news: "Your sons and daughters were eating together when the house collapsed on them and killed them all!"

At this, Job threw himself to the ground and said: "All that I had was given to me by the Lord. Now the Lord has taken it away. Let his will be done."

9 Job Is Struck Again

Job 2–42

Through the will of the Lord, Job had suffered severe blows to his fortune and his family: his sons and his daughters were dead and he had also lost all of his possessions. And still Job accepted this as the will of the Lord: but he had never turned against God.

Satan, however, still was not satisfied: he wanted Job to turn away from God. Therefore Satan said to God: "I know why Job continues to praise your name: he is still alive and in good health. Strike him on his body and he will curse you!"

And the Lord replied to Satan: "Let Job be in your power, but his life must be spared. In this way we shall see if he truly does love me!"

Thus, Satan struck Job with boils all over his body. At this point, his wife said to him: "Do you still insist on accepting the will of God? After everything that has happened, you should curse his name!"

"You are speaking foolishly," replied Job. "If we accept the good things that God gives us, should we not also accept the bad things?"

Nevertheless, as Job endured his suffering he complained, "Perish the day that I was born! I have no peace, no comfort and no rest."

10 Job and His Three Friends

Job 1–42

Job had suffered every misfortune imaginable: his sons and daughters and all his wealth gone, and his body was covered with boils. Yet he remained faithful to the Lord.

One day, three of his friends came to visit him. They showed great sympathy for Job's pain, but they argued that if Job was suffering so much, then he must also have committed some great sin.

Poor Job replied that this was not true in his case. He had committed no great sin, and he suffered without knowing the reason why.

11 Job Questions God

Job 1–42

Tried by so much suffering, Job at last raised his voice up to God, to ask him the reason for his great misfortunes. But the Lord replied that men could not understand everything. Only God knew the reason for many things.

Moreover, the Lord said: "Who is this man that would try to teach me? Where were you when I laid in place the foundations of the earth? Tell me this, you who claim to understand so much! Who decided the dimensions of the world? Who made it strong? Have you ever ordered the morning to come or told the sun where to rise? Have you ever been to the source of the sea, or walked in the depths of the abyss? Which way do you go to arrive at the source of all light? Have you ever reached the place where the snow comes from or seen the home of the hail? Can you raise your voice to the clouds and order the rain to fall?"

When he heard this, Job replied to the Lord, saying: "I have spoken of things which are too great for me. Therefore, Lord, I ask pardon for having dared to request an explanation. I will ask no more and will not repeat my error. Instead, I will repent in dust and ashes!"

12 Job Is Rewarded

Job 42

Although he had been struck by many misfortunes, Job did not rebel against the Lord, and the Lord recognized and appreciated the patience and humility of Job, and gave back to him both his health and his wealth. All his friends came to congratulate him and to show their sympathy for his misfortunes.

In this way, the Lord blessed Job in later life even more than he had blessed him in his youth. He lived to see his children and his grandchildren as far as the fourth generation of his descendants.

13 Waiting for the Messiah

Daniel 7

Finally, at the time decided by God, there came the Messiah, whose arrival had been foretold for so long by the prophets and so long awaited by the people of Israel. Thus came true the prophecy made by Daniel, the last and greatest of the prophets who foretold the Messiah.

This prophecy, known as "the vision of the Son of man," is a vision of the Ancient of days, who is surrounded by angels. The Son of man comes before him and on him is bestowed eternal power and a kingdom with no end.

14 The Vision of the Son of Man

Daniel 7

These were the words of Daniel: "I saw thrones cast down, and the Ancient of days was seated. His garment was as white as snow, and the hair on his head was as pure as wool. His throne was like a flame.

"And in the night I saw visions more. I saw one, like the Son of man, appear on the clouds of the sky. He came before the Ancient and was given the kingdom, the power, and the glory. All nations shall serve the Son of man. His power is everlasting and his kingdom can never be destroyed."

15 The Long-Awaited One Is Here

Daniel 7

When the prophet Daniel wrote of the vision that he had of the Ancient of days and the Son of man it was as if he were putting forward a riddle: What could it mean?

All was made clear later when Jesus talked of his life on earth and his mission and on several occasions referred to himself as the Son of man. Jesus is God because he came down from heaven. He is man and, in fact, appears as a son of man. God the Father, the Ancient in Daniel's vision, has made him king of the universe for all eternity.

16 Zacharias and Elisabeth

Luke 1

At the time when Herod reigned in Palestine, there was a man named Zacharias among the priests who served in the temple. Both he and his wife, Elisabeth, were elderly.

Zacharias and Elisabeth were good people who were careful to obey the Lord's commandments in everything that they did. Only one thing made them sad: the Lord had not granted them any children, although they had both prayed a great deal for a child. Now that they were old, they had given up hope for such a blessing. When Zacharias was working in the temple, it was his duty to go into the sanctuary, the chamber which only the priests could enter, to offer incense to the Lord, while the people outside waited and prayed.

Zacharias was busy putting the incense on the brazier that stood on the altar, when the angel of the Lord appeared to him, standing to the right of the altar. Zacharias was filled with fear at this apparition, but the angel said to him: "Do not be afraid, Zacharias. The Lord has heard your prayer and will grant a son to you and your wife, Elisabeth, and you will call him John, which means 'God is favorable.'"

17 Zacharias and the Angel

Luke 1

The angel had spoken to Zacharias in the sanctuary of the temple and had told him that he and his wife, Elisabeth, although they were very old, would have a son. Zacharias could not believe this news, but the angel said to him: "You will feel great joy at his birth, and many will rejoice. For your son will prepare the people for the Lord who is coming. I am Gabriel and God has sent me to speak to you. Since you do not believe my words, behold, you shall be dumb until what I have foretold has been fulfilled."

18 Zacharias Returns Home

Luke 1

As the angel Gabriel had said, when Zacharias came out of the temple he could no longer speak and had to try to explain himself with gestures. When the people outside the sanctuary saw Zacharias gesturing, and moving his mouth in speechlessness, they understood that he had had a vision in the sanctuary. Quietly, Zacharias went among them, his head filled with the promise the angel Gabriel had brought that he would be father to a child that would grow to help to be a savior to all the world.

As soon as he had finished his priestly duties, Zacharias returned home. Some time later, his wife, Elisabeth, realized that the Lord's will was going to be fulfilled: she was going to give birth to a child. She knew that this was a great gift from God, and she thanked with all her heart the Lord who had answered her prayer.

That child, to whom the angel Gabriel himself had given a name, was John, and was later known as John the Baptist. To him the Lord had given the great task of preparing the people of Israel to accept Jesus, the Messiah whom the prophets had foretold.

19 A Young Woman Named Mary

Luke 1

The angel Gabriel was sent by God to a village called Nazareth in Palestine. A young woman named Mary lived there, and God knew that her heart was filled with faith and love for him.

For this reason, the Lord had already done an extraordinary thing for Mary: he had filled her with his grace and she had, therefore, always been full of his love.

God had done this because he had decided that Mary was the worthiest of all women to become the mother of his son.

20 Mary, the Mother of God

Luke 1

The angel Gabriel had been sent by God to the village of Nazareth. He entered Mary's house and said to her: "Hail Mary, full of grace, the Lord is with you."

This was an unusual greeting and Mary wondered what these words could mean. The angel went on speaking: "Do not be afraid, Mary: you have found favor with God. Because of this you will be the mother of a child and you will call him Jesus. He shall be great! He shall be called the son of the highest and God will give him the throne of David, his forefather. His kingdom will have no end."

Mary then asked: "How can I have a child if I am not married?"

"The Holy Ghost will descend upon you," explained the angel Gabriel, "and the power of almighty God shall overshadow you like a cloud. The child that is born to you will be holy, the Son of God. Know that your cousin Elisabeth is also expecting a child, despite her great age, because it is God's will."

At this, Mary said: "Behold, I am the handmaiden of the Lord; I wish to do his will: let it happen as you have said!"

21 Mary Goes to See Elisabeth

Luke 1

Mary had been told by the angel Gabriel that her elderly cousin Elisabeth was expecting the child she had wanted for so long. She knew that this child was a sign that God had listened to the prayers of Elisabeth and her husband, Zacharias.

Mary, therefore, decided to go and visit Elisabeth and tell her the wonderful news that she too would have a child, and that he would be the Son of God. Elisabeth, however, did not have to be told, for, when Mary arrived at her house and began to greet her, Elisabeth felt inspired by God and said: "Blessed are you among women and blessed is the fruit of your womb! What honor and what joy, that the mother of my Lord should visit me!"

Elisabeth then told Mary how her husband Zacharias had doubted the words of the angel who had told him that God would grant them a son, and how on account of this doubt he had been struck dumb. Mary, on the other hand, had never doubted, and so Elisabeth added: "Blessed are you Mary, because you believed that the Lord would fulfill all he has said to you." And Mary replied with a hymn of praise to God.

22 His Name Is John

Luke 1

Mary, who was to become the mother of Jesus, stayed with her cousin until Elisabeth gave birth to a baby boy—the same baby boy that the angel Gabriel had spoken of to the incredulous father Zacharias, who had been struck dumb.

Eight days after the birth of the child, according to custom, it was time to give the boy a name. Since the father could not speak, his relatives decided the child should be called Zacharias, but Elisabeth cried: "No! He will be called John!"

"John?" asked the puzzled friends and relatives. "Why? You have no relatives of that name." Then they made a sign to the boy's father, asking him how he wanted to name the child. Zacharias made signs requesting a tablet to write on and wrote: "His name is John." Hardly had he written the name of the child than his voice came back and he could speak again, just as the angel Gabriel had foretold. At once, Zacharias sang a hymn of praise to the Lord. The relatives and friends who were present were filled with wonder at these incredible events and asked: "What kind of child will this be?"

23 Joseph the Carpenter

Matthew 1

Mary was about to become the mother of the Son of God. She was engaged to be married to Joseph, a humble carpenter from Nazareth, a descendant of King David.

When Joseph found out that Mary, his bride-to-be, was going to be the mother of a child, he decided to free her from her promise to marry him. But an angel appeared to him and explained to him: "Joseph, do not hesitate to take Mary as your wife, for her child is the Son of God!"

The angel also told him the name of the child: Jesus, which means "God is the Savior," and the angel added: "This name is fitting, because this child, the Son of God, will save his people from their sins."

When he heard this, Joseph remembered many things which the prophets had said and written in the sacred books which were read every Sabbath day in the synagogue. In particular, he remembered that the prophet Isaiah had spoken of an unmarried woman who would bear a child called Emmanuel, a name which means "God with us."

Mary's child, then, was to be this Emmanuel, Joseph realized. God made man like us, to be with us!

Joseph felt his heart fill with the love of God. He realized what an important task God was entrusting to him: to be the guardian and protector of the Son of God on earth.

When he understood all these things, Joseph did not break off his engagement with Mary. He took her as his wife and he watched over her with great care. When the child was born, everyone thought it was Joseph's son. As far as the law was concerned, he was the son of Joseph and since Joseph was a descendant of the house of David, Jesus too was a descendant of the great king. This, too, was as the prophets had foretold.

24 The Journey from Nazareth to Bethlehem

Luke 2

At that time, the Roman emperor was Caesar Augustus and he also ruled over Palestine. Augustus wished to know how many people lived in his empire and he therefore ordered a census to be taken.

For the census, each person had to register in the place from which his family came. Since Joseph was a descendant of David of Bethlehem, Joseph had to travel from Nazareth to Bethlehem. And so he helped his pregnant wife, Mary, onto a donkey and they set off.

25 Jesus Is Born

Luke 2

Joseph and his wife, Mary, were traveling from Nazareth to Bethlehem. This was a long and difficult journey, especially because it was nearly time for Mary to give birth to her child. However, they had no choice, because the Roman emperor, who ruled in Palestine, had ordered everyone to return to his place of birth for the census.

In those days, when people had to make a journey, they would walk during the day and they would stop and spend the night in an inn along the way. To make the journey less tiring for Mary, Joseph made her travel on the back of a donkey.

After many days on the road, Joseph and Mary arrived in Bethlehem, the city of David, which was crowded with strangers who had also come for the census.

Joseph went to seek lodgings at the inn, but found that it was completely full. Mary was about to give birth, and shelter had to be found for her. At last Joseph found a cave which shepherds and farmers used as a stable. And it was there, in that cave, that Mary gave birth to Jesus, the Son of God. With great care, she wrapped him in swaddling clothes and laid him in a manger.

26 The Song of the Angels

Luke 2

In the fields around Bethlehem there were some shepherds who spent their nights out in the open, watching over their flocks.

One night, an extraordinary thing happened to them: all of a sudden they were surrounded by a great light and in the light they saw an angel of the Lord. The shepherds were filled with fear, but the angel said to them: "Do not be afraid: I bring you good news, news that will bring great joy to you and all men. Today, in Bethlehem, the city of David, is born the Savior, the Messiah foretold by the prophets, the Lord! Go and see him; he is wrapped in swaddling clothes and lying in a manger." And, suddenly, other angels joined with the one who had spoken and they began to sing in praise of God: "Glory to God on the highest and peace on earth and good will to men."

When they had finished their song of praise, the angels left the shepherds and disappeared back into heaven. The shepherds, who were still amazed by what they had seen and heard, said to each other: "Let us go at once to Bethlehem to see this thing which has happened and which God has made known to us."

27 The Good News Given to the Shepherds

Luke 2

The angel of the Lord had brought joyous news to the shepherds who were watching their flocks in the fields around Bethlehem. A child had been born in Bethlehem who was Christ the Lord, the Messiah of whom the prophets had spoken so often. And they now had the chance to see him. They, who were so poor and looked down on by everyone, had the honor of being the first to see him.

Truly, all men are equal in the eyes of God, and perhaps he even prefers the poor and humble.

28 Mary Praise the Lord

Luke 1

Mary, who was called by God to be the mother of his son, Jesus, praised the Lord with a great hymn that even today many people repeat as a prayer. This is the hymn that Mary sang to the shepherds and all who gathered:

My soul does magnify the Lord and
　my spirit rejoices in God my
Savior, who has looked on me, his
　humble handmaiden.
Henceforth all men to come shall
　call me blessed.
Almighty God has done great things
in me.
Holy is his name; he will be merciful
　to those that love him
　from generation to generation.
He has shown his great strength: he
　has caused the plans of
　the proud to fail
　and has brought to ruin
　the powerful;
And he has exalted the humble and
　filled the hungry with good things;
While he has sent the rich away
　empty-handed.
He has remembered to be merciful
　and has sent help to his people of
　Israel, according to the promise
　he made to Abraham and his
　descendants forever.

29 The Homage of the Shepherds

Luke 2

The shepherds had been told by the angel the news that the baby Jesus had been born in Bethlehem. They then hurried to Bethlehem and found the baby wrapped in swaddling clothes and lying in a manger in the stable where Joseph and Mary had found shelter. The shepherds immediately gave thanks to God, because the baby Jesus was the proof of the great love that God had for all mankind. Afterward, the shepherds did not keep their joy to themselves, but spoke to everyone they met of the miraculous events that had taken place.

30 Zacharias Gives Thanks to the Lord

Luke 1

When his son John was born, Zacharias sang a hymn of praise to the Lord.

Blessed is the Lord God of Israel; for he has visited and
redeemed his people.

Among the descendants of David he has caused a savior to
be born, as he had promised through the words of his holy prophets.

He has been merciful. Now we can serve him without fear;
faithful to him all our days.

And you, my son, will be the prophet of Almighty God: you will walk before the Lord himself and prepare the way for him.

You will announce to his people that God
will save them and forgive all their sin

The Lord will shine for us, like the sun among the shadows,
and he will guide our steps onto the path of peace.

And so it happened; the child who was born to him, and who was named John, grew in body and in spirit and prepared himself for the mission that awaited him. He was to be the last of the prophets, who was to proclaim that Jesus, the long awaited Messiah, had arrived.

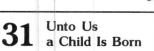

31 Unto Us a Child Is Born

Isaiah 9,11,35,62

The child born in Bethlehem was the Messiah, the Savior so long expected by the prophets and the people of Israel. This is the way the prophet Isaiah foretold his coming: The people who walk in darkness have seen a great light. Unto us a child is born! On his shoulders he wears the emblems of a king. Great will be his dominion and there will be everlasting peace in the kingdom which he establishes. In his kingdom all men will do what is good and right before God.

He, a descendant of David, will have the spirit of God in him. He will not judge according to appearances, but with justice, and he will have no respect for the powerful or the wicked.

In the kingdom he establishes, the wolf shall lie down with the lamb, the leopard with the kid; the calf and the lion shall go to pasture together and a small child will be able to watch over them. The cow and the bear will feed together, with their young. The lion will dine on straw and kill no more, and the child will play in safety with snakes.

In the whole Kingdom of God, no one will ever do evil again: everyone will live in peace and harmony.

Behold, the Savior is coming!

BIBLE STORY OF THE MONTH

Baby Jesus in the Temple

The angel of the Lord had said to Mary: "When your child, the Son of God on high, comes to be born, you will name him Jesus."

The baby was born in the stable in Bethlehem, and according to the Hebrew custom he was given his name eight days later. Naturally it was the name that the angel had indicated, Jesus, which means "God is the Savior." In fact, through this child, God intervened to save his people.

The prophets had foretold this centuries beforehand: one day God would send a Savior, and they had named him the Messiah, "the consecrated of the Lord." The name Christ means the same as Messiah: that is why Jesus was also later called Christ.

Jesus was Mary's first son, and Hebrew law stated that the firstborn son belonged to the Lord. So in a certain sense the child had to be bought back from the Lord, by an offer to exchange two doves or two wild pigeons.

For this reason, forty days after her son's birth, Mary and her husband Joseph took Jesus to the temple of the Lord in Jerusalem, and they also took two turtle doves to offer up to the Lord.

Inside the temple they met a man who was called Simeon. He was a good man, and all his life he had tried to please the Lord. Simeon remembered the words of the prophets, and he anxiously awaited the day when the Lord would send the Messiah.

And the Lord had promised him that before he died he would know the joy of setting his eyes on the long awaited Messiah.

The day that Mary and Joseph took Jesus to the temple, Simeon also felt inspired to go to the house of the Lord, and when he saw the child, God led him to understand that this was the Messiah.

So he picked the infant up, and thanking the Lord with all his heart, he said: "Now Lord, you can let me, your servant, go in peace, as you have promised, because my eyes have seen the Savior that you have sent.

You have placed him before all the peoples of the earth, like a light which illuminates all nations and all races of men and gives glory to your people, Israel."

Mary and Joseph were amazed to hear these words. Simeon blessed them and then turned to the mother of the child, Mary, saying: "This child will be the cause of the ruin or the salvation of many men from the people of Israel. He will be a sign from God, to reveal the intentions of

many people, those intentions which are kept hidden in their hearts. And for you Mary, a sword will pierce your soul.''

With these mysterious words, Simeon meant that in the future, Jesus was to be accepted by a part of the Jewish people, while the other part of his people would reject him.

Those who would accept him, believe in him, and love him, would be saved and go to heaven, while those who refused him would be ruined. As for Mary, she was to suffer upon seeing her son refused: She was to suffer as if she had been pierced by a sword.

That same day, in the temple, Mary and Joseph met a woman named Anna. She was very old, eighty-four, and since being widowed she had dedicated herself to God; she lived in the temple, and day and night she showed her most devout love for him with prayers and sacrifices.

When she saw the child, Anna, too, understood who he was; and so, like Simeon, she gave praise to God, and spoke of the child to all those who awaited the coming of the Messiah.

This was not the only time that Jesus' parents took him to the temple in Jerusalem.

Every year Joseph, with his wife, Mary, went to Jerusalem for the feast of the Passover, and they took Jesus with them.

When he was twelve years old it happened that, when the feast was over and Joseph and Mary were returning home, Jesus remained in Jerusalem.

Joseph and Mary were traveling with a large number of other pilgrims, the men divided from the women, as was the custom. During the first day of their journey, they did not realize that Jesus was missing: Joseph thought he was with Mary and the other children, and Mary thought he was with the group of men.

It wasn't till evening that they realized Jesus was missing, so they immediately left the others and returned to Jerusalem.

After searching for three days they found him in the temple, busy talking with the elders and teachers, who were amazed at his intelligence and the things that he knew.

Then his mother said: "You have made us very worried!" But Jesus answered: "Why are you looking for me? Didn't you know that I have to look after the affairs of my father?"

The child Jesus knew that his father was not Joseph, as everyone believed, but God himself.

Luke 2

1 The Wise Men from the East

Matthew 2

On the night Jesus was born, not only did the Lord send an angel to the shepherds, he also sent a message to three Magi (wise men) who lived in the east. This message was in the form of a bright star which suddenly began to shine in the sky.

When the Magi saw the star they knew, from all their studies, what it signified, and they said: "This star announces the birth of a very important person, the birth of a king, the king of the Jews. We must follow the star and find this child who is born, and worship him!"

2 They Will Bring Gold and Incense

Genesis 49; 2 Samuel 7; Isaiah 60

The birth of Jesus was, at first, an event of which very few people were aware. Later, when the people of Israel knew of him, many realized that in him the words of the prophets were fulfilled.

Through the words of the prophet Nathan, the Lord had promised to David of the tribe of Judah that one of his descendants would be king forever.

All of this was fulfilled in Jesus: He was a man born in the tribe of Judah, and a descendant of David. And he was God, a king who reigns forever, because he never dies!

There was, therefore, reason for rejoicing, as the prophet Isaiah had foretold: "Arise Jerusalem, bathed in light, for the glory of the Lord shines on you and illuminates you!

"Behold, shadows cover the earth, but the Lord shines on you and his glory covers you!

"The peoples of the world will move toward your light. Their kings will be drawn to you, led by he who illuminates you.

"Foreigners will bring you their treasure; a host of camels will be brought to your land; they will bring gold and incense and will come to praise the Lord."

3 The Journey of the Magi

Matthew 2

Large and bright, a new star had suddenly appeared in the sky to show that a new king of the Jews had been born, and the Magi of the east had decided to follow it. At once they prepared a great caravan of camels and chose the proper gifts for the newborn king.

After following the star for a long way, the Magi arrived in Jerusalem.

"Where is the king of the Jews who has been born?" the Magi asked. "We have seen his star rise, and we have come to pay homage to him!"

4 Herod, King of the Jews

Matthew 2

At the time when Jesus was born in Bethlehem, a cruel and bloody king called Herod ruled over the Jews.

He had come to the throne with the help of the Romans, who had conquered the whole land of Palestine and given him this kingdom so that they could keep better control over the country. Herod ruled over Palestine until a few years after the birth of Jesus. Out of spite, he had had many members of his own family put to death. His jealousy and suspicion caused him to persecute the infant Jesus.

5 King Herod and the Magi

Matthew 2

It was a common belief among the people of the east that a new star in the sky meant the birth of a great person. Thus, when King Herod learned that the Magi had arrived in Jerusalem following the star and seeking the new king of the Jews, he was filled with suspicion that this new king of the Jews would lay claim to his throne. What was he to do?

Herod called the high priests to him and asked them where this Messiah, of whom the prophets had spoken for centuries, should have been born. "In Bethlehem," he was told, "for the prophet Micah explained this clearly when he said these words 'And you Bethlehem, are certainly not the least of the cities of Judea, for in you will be born the ruler to lead my people, Israel!'"

Herod then secretly called the Magi to him and made them tell him precisely when the star had first appeared in the sky. He advised them to go at once to Bethlehem, with these false words: "Go to Bethlehem and carefully seek out the child. And when you have found him, come back and tell me so that I too can go and pay homage and worship him!"

6 The Adoration of the Magi

Matthew 2

King Herod wanted the Magi from the east to help him discover where to find the child whom they said would become king of the Jews. In reality, Herod had absolutely no intention of going to pay homage to a rival; he wished to know where to find Jesus in order to kill him!

The Magi departed from Jerusalem again and the star they had seen in the east shone over their heads and guided them. When they looked at it, they were filled with a great joy. The star finally stopped over the spot where Jesus lay with his mother, Mary. At once they went down on their knees and worshiped Jesus; then they offered their gifts to him. Opening a casket, one of them offered him gold, truly a gift fit for a king. Another brought from his casket incense, which would spread its sweet perfume when it was burned on the fire, and this also was a gift fit for a king. The third of the Magi opened his casket and brought out myrrh, a perfumed resin which was also precious for its medicinal properties; this too was a rare gift, and fitting. Thus, it was not only the humble shepherds who came to pay homage to Jesus, but also the illustrious wise men.

7 King Herod and the Children of Bethlehem

Matthew 2

The Magi, led by the star, had arrived at the cave in Bethlehem and worshiped the baby Jesus. It was now time for them to begin their journey back to their own country. The Lord, however, warned the Magi in a dream to say nothing to Herod of what they had seen and not to go back to him in Jerusalem. Thus the Magi did not return to Jerusalem, but went back home by another route. When Herod realized that the Magi had deceived him and had departed without telling him where the child was, he flew into a rage and sought another way to kill the infant whom he feared.

Thus, Herod sent his soldiers to Bethlehem and the surrounding countryside with orders to kill all male children under two years of age. This was the amount of time that had passed since, as the Magi had revealed to him, the star had first appeared in the sky.

Unfortunately, this cruel order was obeyed and the result was a massacre. All the male children in Bethlehem and the surrounding countryside who were under two years of age were put to death. However, even this cruel measure proved futile against Jesus.

8 The Flight into Egypt

Matthew 2

The cruel massacre of the children of Bethlehem, ordered by Herod, did not succeed in killing the baby Jesus. In fact, an angel of the Lord had appeared to Joseph in a dream and given him these commands: "Arise! Take the child and his mother with you and flee into Egypt, for Herod is seeking to kill the child. You must all stay in Egypt until I tell you to return!"

Joseph awoke at once and immediately did what the angel had ordered him to do; he took the child and his mother Mary and fled by night into Egypt, where he remained until the death of Herod. In this way the baby Jesus was saved and what the Lord had foretold through the prophet Hosea came true: "I have called my son from Egypt!"

When Herod died, Joseph was still in Egypt and an angel of the Lord appeared to him a second time and said: "Arise! Take the child and his mother with you and return to the land of Israel. For those who threatened the child are dead!"

Once more, Joseph did exactly as the angel had ordered him to do; he got up, took the baby Jesus and Mary with him, and set out from Egypt to the land of Israel.

9 Jesus in Nazareth

Matthew 2; Luke 2

From Egypt, where he had fled to save the life of the baby Jesus, Joseph returned to the land of Israel and, more exactly, to his home village of Nazareth.

There, Jesus grew up and became strong; he was filled with wisdom, and the grace of God was upon him. He lived in Nazareth, ever obedient to Mary, his mother, and to Joseph until he was about thirty years old. For this reason, although Jesus was born in Bethlehem, he was called the Nazarene. No one yet realized that he was the Son of God.

10 John Preaches Repentance

Luke 3

John, the baby born to Zacharias and Elisabeth a few months before the birth of Jesus, grew in body and in spirit. When he became a man, the Word of God came to him.

John would stand on the banks of the river Jordan and say: "The Messiah foretold by the prophets is soon to come among us! You must ask God's forgiveness for your sins and change your way of life."

Everyone held John in great respect, for he was the first to put into practice what he told others to do. He had spent many years in the desert, eating locusts and wild honey, and he dressed very poorly.

The people who were prepared to change their way of life came to him in the waters of the Jordan, and he poured water on their heads and thus baptized them. For this reason John was called the Baptist, which means "One who baptizes."

Some of the people asked him: "What must we do to become better people?," and John replied: "Whoever has two coats should give one to someone who has none. And whoever has more than enough to eat should do the same!"

Several tax collectors also came to be baptized and they, too, asked him: "Master, what must we do?" To them John replied: "Do not take a penny more than is due in taxes." Even the soldiers asked him the same question: "What should we do?" And John said to them: "Do not exploit your strength or take advantage of the weapons you carry. And do not maltreat anyone."

Everyone had so much admiration for John that they wondered if, perhaps, he himself was not the Messiah. But he explained to them: "No! The Messiah is much greater than I! I am not even fit to tie his sandals! I baptize you with water. But he, along with the water of baptism, will give you the Holy Spirit!"

11 John and Jesus: "Behold the Lamb of God"

John 1

Thus, John the Baptist stayed on the banks of the Jordan. He invited the wicked to change their way of life and to prepare themselves for the Messiah who was soon to come among them. Those willing to change were baptized by John.

His behavior was surprising and everyone wanted to know more about him. For this reason they asked him: "Are you, yourself, perhaps the Christ, the Messiah foretold by the prophets?" "No I am not the Messiah," replied John. "Then you must be Moses or the prophet Elijah, returned to this world?" "No," replied John.

"Well then, who are you?" To this question John replied: "As the prophet Isaiah foretold a long time ago, I am a voice that cries in the wilderness: prepare ye the way of the Lord who is coming among us!"

One day the Lord, Jesus, really did arrive. He had left Nazareth and come to the banks of the Jordan where John was baptizing people. When John saw who was coming toward him, he said to the crowd that surrounded him: "Behold the Lamb of God, behold he who will take away the sin of the world. He is the Son of God!"

12 The Baptism of Jesus

Matthew 3

Jesus had come to John, who was baptizing the Jews on the banks of the river Jordan. Like all the others, Jesus also went into the water as a sign that he wished baptism.

John, however, had not expected this at all: he baptized sinners, while Jesus was without sin. Moreover, he was the Son of God who had come into the world especially to take away the sins of mankind.

John, therefore, said to Jesus: "It is not you who should be baptized by me. It is I who should be baptized by you." But Jesus replied, saying: "Do as I ask, for there is a reason."

John understood the reason shortly afterward. Hardly had he baptized Jesus than he saw the spirit of God descend upon him like a dove and he heard a voice say: "This is my beloved son, in whom I am well pleased."

The voice of God the Father, while God the Son was before him, hardly out of the water, and God the Holy Spirit had come down upon him! The three persons of the Holy Trinity all present together! This was a solemn moment: Jesus was beginning the work for which he had come into the world.

13 Jesus Defeats the Devil

Matthew 4

Jesus' great task lay before him. To prepare himself well, he retired for forty days into the desert and did not eat in order to pray to his father in heaven and be ready for what he had to do. At the end of the forty days, he was very hungry. So Satan sought to tempt Jesus. He said to Jesus: "If you are truly the Son of God, then make these stones into bread." Jesus, however, replied: "Man does not live by bread alone, but also by every word that comes from God."

The devil then carried him to Jerusalem, to the highest pinnacle of the temple, and said to him: "If you are the Son of God, then throw yourself down. God will send his angels to protect you and prevent you from hurting yourself." But Jesus did not fall into the trap; he replied: "It is wrong to put yourself in danger and expect God to save you with a miracle."

The devil did not give up. He took Jesus to a very high mountain and showed him the whole world and all its wealth. "All that you see, I will give to you if you bow down before me and worship me." But Jesus replied: "Be gone Satan! Only God is to be worshiped."

14 Jesus Announces the Good News
Matthew 4

Jesus was about thirty years old when he began the task he had come into the world to accomplish. He had gone to be baptized by John, and his Father and the Holy Spirit had been present. He had meditated for forty days in the desert and had then defeated the devil who had come to tempt him into sin.

By now everything was ready and Jesus began to go around the cities and the villages of Palestine and to repeat to everyone he met: "Repent, for the Kingdom of Heaven is at hand!" He told the people to change their way of life and truly love God, and he would open the gates to his kingdom where happiness is eternal.

The words of Jesus constituted a happy announcement for the people of Palestine. This was the gospel, the "good news" that they had long awaited.

Hadn't the prophets spoken of this? Hadn't even John repeated it to those who came to him for baptism? The Christ, the Messiah had come to make true friendship possible between mankind and God. And the Messiah, the Christ, the Lord Jesus, had arrived!

15 The First Disciples
Luke 5

One day, Jesus was talking to the crowd by the lake of Gennesaret. Among the crowd there was a fisherman by the name of Simon, and Jesus said to him: "Launch out into the deep and let down your nets to fish." Simon replied: "Master, we have toiled and fished all night, and caught nothing. Nevertheless, if you say so, I will go out again."

And, together with his brother Andrew, that is what Simon did. When they pulled in their nets, they held such an enormous quantity of fish that the nets almost broke. They had to ask for help from their partners, the brothers James and John, who were on a nearby boat. They had caught so many fish that they filled both boats to overflowing.

Simon and the others were astonished, but Jesus said to Simon: "From this day, you shall be a fisher of men!" By this Jesus meant that Simon would bring men to accept the good news. In this way, Simon, Andrew, James, and John left their work in order to follow Jesus. They were his first disciples.

Simon, who lived in Capernaum, accepted Jesus into his house. Jesus changed the name of his disciple and called him Peter.

16 Jesus Calls Philip and Nathanael
John 1

One day, Jesus met a man called Philip and asked him to become one of his disciples. Philip consented and when, in his turn, he met his friend Nathanael, he said to him with great happiness: "We have found the Messiah, prophets foretold! He is Jesus of Nazareth."

Nathanael, however, was not impressed, and replied: "From Nazareth? Can anything good come from that tiny village?" But Philip insisted, saying, "At least come and see for yourself!" When Jesus saw Nathanael approaching, he said: "Behold a true Israelite, with no falsity."

Nathanael was surprised and said: "You know me? How is that?" Jesus replied: "Before Philip called you, I saw you beneath the fig tree."

It was true that, before his meeting with Philip, Nathanael had been in the shade under a fig tree. Thus, Nathanael realized, this was not a man like other men. He understood and exclaimed: "Master, you are the Son of God, you are the king!"

Jesus replied to him: "You believe only because I told you that I had seen you in the shade of the fig tree? You shall see much greater things than these!"

17 The First Miracle at Cana

John 2

A marriage was being celebrated in the village of Cana in Galilee. Jesus had been invited with Mary, his mother, and his disciples.

During the wedding feast the wine ran out and there was a risk that the celebration would be ruined. Mary realized this and said to Jesus: "They have no more wine." Jesus replied to her: "The hour has not yet come for me to perform miracles." Mary, however, said to the servants: "Do as he tells you."

In the house there were six large stone waterpots which could each hold two or three barrels. Jesus said to the servants: "Fill the jars with water." When the servants had done as Jesus asked, he said: "Now take a little of the contents to the head of the table."

The water had become wine, and the wine was excellent! When the head of the table had tasted it, he said to the bridegroom: "Normally, at a celebration, everyone gives the guests their best wine first. Then, when the guests have all had some to drink, they give them their poorer wine. You, on the other hand, have saved the best wine till last!"

In this way, in Cana in Galilee, Jesus began to perform his miracles.

18 Jesus Drives the Merchants from the Temple

John 2

The feast of the Passover was approaching and Jesus went to celebrate the holy day in Jerusalem. When Jesus entered the temple, in the courtyard he found a great number of merchants, dealing in foreign currencies or selling oxen, sheep, or doves to people who then offered them in sacrifice.

The temple, the Passover, and the sacrifices offered to the Lord all meant nothing to the merchants. They were only concerned with making as much money as possible. Jesus grew angry. He took small cords and made a scourge to topple the tables and drive out the merchants. "Take these things away," Jesus said. "You have transformed the house of my father, the temple, into a market!"

"Who are you to do these things?" they asked him. "Who has given you the authority?" Jesus replied: "Destroy this temple and in three days I will raise it up again."

At that time they did not understand, but his disciples were later to understand. Jesus was referring to the temple of his body. With these words he spoke of his own death and resurrection, his return to life after three days.

19 A Nocturnal Visit

John 3

A man named Nicodemus, one of the rulers of the Jews, felt a great desire to speak with Jesus. However, he did not want anyone to see him because he did not want to be considered a disciple of the person that the other rulers viewed with suspicion and distrust.

Therefore, Nicodemus decided to visit Jesus at night, and said to him: "Master, we know that you have come from God, because no one else can do what you do!" And in reply Jesus explained: "I tell you in truth, that if a man is not born again, then he cannot enter into the Kingdom of God."

"How can a man be born again when he is already old?" asked an amazed Nicodemus. And Jesus explained to him: "A man must be born of water and in spirit to enter the Kingdom of God."

With these words Jesus spoke of baptism. Whoever receives the holy water receives the life of God himself; the Lord adopts him as his son and opens the doors to his house to him.

"God loves the world so much," Jesus concluded, "as to send his only son, so that whoever believes in him shall have eternal life."

20 The Parable of the Sower

Matthew 13

"The sower went out to sow. And while he sowed, some of the seeds fell by the wayside and the birds came and ate them. Other seeds fell among stones, where there was very little earth; they grew up at once, but with shallow roots and, as soon as the sun came out, they withered away. And some of the seeds fell among thorn bushes which grew up and suffocated them. But other seeds fell upon good ground and gave fruit, some a hundredfold, some sixtyfold and some thirtyfold."

Jesus recounted this parable to his listeners one day. Parables are almost like riddles and those who listened to Jesus tried to understand them. Who is the sower? What are the seeds he is sowing? And the ground?

Sometimes, Jesus himself gave them the explanation. On other occasions his listeners understood the meaning by themselves. Jesus explained the parable of the sower in this way: "The seed is the Word of God; the different types of ground are the hearts of men.

When a man hears the Word of God and does not understand it, he is like the arid ground by the wayside; the seed does not take root, and the devil comes and takes it.

The word that falls on stony ground is like a man who hears it with joy, but he is inconstant and easily refuses the word of God which has no deep roots in his heart. The ground covered in thorn bushes is like the person attached to money and things of this world: these prevent the Word of God from bearing fruit.

The good ground, on the other hand, is like the heart of the person who listens seriously to the Word of God and accepts it gladly, so that he can put down healthy roots and produce the abundant fruits of good works."

21 The Kingdom of God and the Grain of Mustard Seed

Mark 4

To what can we compare the Kingdom of God? With what words can we describe it? This is what Jesus said about it:

"The Kingdom of God is like a grain of mustard seed. When it is sown it is the smallest of all seeds, so small that it is almost invisible. But, once it has been sown, the mustard seed grows and grows until it becomes the greatest of all the herbs. And the branches shoot out so large and strong that the birds of the air find shade beneath them and build their nests among them."

22 The Son of the Nobleman

John 4

Jesus was in Cana, in Galilee, the town where he had changed the water into wine, when he was approached in great haste by a nobleman who lived in Capernaum. The nobleman was very worried and distressed, and said to Jesus: "Master, my son is so ill that he is on the point of death. I beg you to come with me to Capernaum, to come and heal my son!"

"Go, your son is well again," Jesus said to him, without moving, to show to all those present that he could even perform miracles at a distance. The nobleman believed the words of Jesus and set off home. Before he even got there, his servants ran out to meet him and said: "Your son is well again!"

The nobleman wanted to know at what time his son had started to feel better again. The servants answered: "It was yesterday afternoon, about one o'clock, that the fever left him. And the nobleman realized that this was precisely the time at which Jesus had said to him: "Go, your son is well again!"

Jesus performed many miracles. He could do this because, although he was a man, he was also God and God has the power to do all things.

23 The Yeast and the Treasure

Matthew 13

In order to be sure that everyone understood him, Jesus explained himself with stories and comparisons. In this way, talking about the Kingdom of God, Jesus said: "The Kingdom of God is like a little yeast that a woman mixes with a large quantity of flour, until the whole mixture is leavened!

"The Kingdom of God is also similar to a treasure hidden in a field. A man finds it and hides it again. Then, filled with joy, he goes and sells everything he owns and buys the field!"

24 Jesus Heals a Leper

Mark 1

At the time of Jesus there were many lepers in Palestine. They suffered from a horrible disease of the skin and were forced to live far off. One day a leper approached Jesus and said to him: "If you want to, you can heal me!" Jesus was moved with compassion for him and stretched out his hand to touch him, saying: "Be healed!"

The disease left the man at once: He was healed! The man was so happy about this that he told everyone. And the fame of Jesus spread throughout the land.

25 Jesus Calls Levi Matthew to Him

Mark 2

In Palestine at the time of Jesus there was one group of people that everybody hated and tried their best to avoid. These were the tax collectors who were considered traitors and sinners by the people.

One day at Capernaum, Jesus passed near the stall where people went to pay their taxes. He saw among the tax collectors a man named Levi and he said to him: "Come with me." At this the man got up and followed Jesus.

Levi, the tax collector, is the disciple also known by the name of Matthew, and he is the same man who also wrote one of the Gospels.

Happy and moved that Jesus had actually chosen him, a man despised by everyone, Levi Matthew invited Jesus to dinner at his own house with his friends, the other tax collectors. Jesus accepted, and this caused several masters of the law to marvel. They asked some of the disciples of Jesus: "Why does your master eat with all those sinners?" But Jesus overheard these words and he himself replied: "Healthy people do not need the doctor. Those who are sick, on the other hand, do need him. I did not come to call the righteous, but to call sinners to me!"

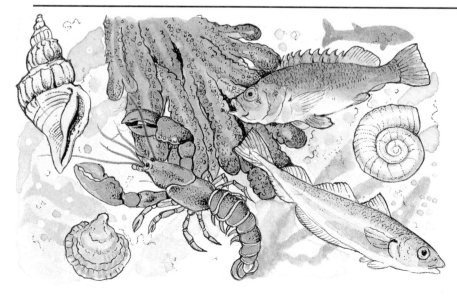

26 The Fishing Net

Matthew 13

To what can we compare the Kingdom of God? On one occasion Jesus said: "The Kingdom of God is like a net that is thrown into the sea and catches fish of every kind.

"When it is full, the fishermen draw the net to the shore and put the fish that are good to eat into baskets; the poor fish are thrown away.

"This is what will happen at the end of the world: The angels will separate the good men from the bad. The good will be carried into the Kingdom of Heaven, but the bad will be cast away."

27 The Man Lowered from the Roof

Mark 2

Jesus was in a house in Capernaum and the crowd had thronged to the door to listen to him speak.

Four men arrived carrying a paralyzed friend on a stretcher. They wanted to present him to Jesus and ask Jesus to cure him, but they could not get near the door of the house because of the crowd. Thus, they climbed onto the roof of the house and removed the straw covering over Jesus and then lowered the paralyzed man through the opening. When Jesus saw the great faith of these men, he said to the paralytic: "My son, your sins are forgiven."

When they heard these words, some of the learned scribes who were present thought, "What is he saying? Only God can forgive sins! This man is blaspheming!"

Jesus, however, knew what they were thinking and said: "Why do you think this? I will prove to you that I have the power to forgive sins. At this, Jesus turned to the paralyzed man and said: "Arise, take up thy bed, and walk!"

While everybody looked on, the paralyzed man stood up, lifted his bed, and walked off. Everyone was amazed and said: "We have never seen anything like this!"

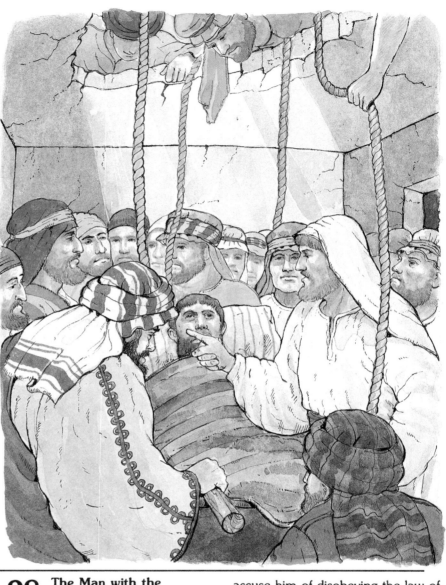

28 The Man with the Withered Hand

Mark 3

For the Jews, the Sabbath was a holiday, because they obeyed the commandment of the Lord which told them not to work on that day. For this reason, they did nothing on the Sabbath, not even good works.

One day Jesus taught them, with an example and a miracle, that the Lord had meant something else when he had given them this commandment. One Sabbath Jesus went into the synagogue at Capernaum and saw a man with a withered hand. The enemies of Jesus constantly spied on him, hoping to accuse him of disobeying the law of God, and now, too, they watched carefully to see what he would do.

Jesus was well aware that they were watching him and he said to the man with the withered hand: "Come here, to us." Then he turned to the onlookers and said: "Is it permitted to do a good work on the Sabbath? For example, is it permissible to save a life?"

They said nothing: these men would not even save the life of a man in danger on the Sabbath. Jesus was saddened by the hardness of their hearts. To the man, he said: "Hold out your hand!" The man stretched it out and Jesus cured it.

29 Jesus Chooses the Twelve Apostles

Mark 3; Matthew 5

One day Jesus chose twelve men from among all his disciples. They are the twelve apostles, which means "Those who are sent," and he gave them a very special task.

These were their names: The first was Simon, to whom Jesus gave the name of Peter. After him, Jesus chose his brother Andrew. Then came the two brothers James and John, whom Jesus called "the Sons of thunder." And then Jesus chose Philip, and Nathanael who is also known as Bartholomew, and Levi who is called Matthew. Then he chose Thomas and James the son of Alphaeus, Thaddaeus, Simon the Canaanite, and Judas Iscariot who was later to betray Jesus.

Jesus said to his disciples one day: "You are the salt of the earth. Be careful not to lose your flavor, for salt without flavor is good for nothing and has to be thrown away. You are the light of the world. A city built on a mountain cannot be hidden. Men do not light a lamp to put it under a bucket, but rather to put it up high so that it can give light to everyone. The light of your good works must shine in this way so that all can see the good that you do and give thanks."

30 A Group of Women Help Jesus

Luke 8; Mark 15

Jesus moved through the cities and villages to tell everyone the good news about the Kingdom of God. He was accompanied by the twelve apostles and there were also several women who helped him. Jesus had cured these women from various illnesses and they, out of gratitude, gave their goods and belongings to him. Among these women were Mary Magdalene, and Joanna, the wife of Herod's steward; Mary, the mother of the apostle James Alphaeus; and Salome, the mother of the apostles James and John.

31 The Parable of the Weeds

Matthew 13

One day Jesus recounted the following parable to his disciples: "The Kingdom of Heaven is like the man who sowed good seed in his field. But at night, while everyone was sleeping, his enemy came along and sowed weeds among the wheat, and then stole away. Thus, when the wheat began to spring up, the weeds also grew. The field workers then said to their master: "Do you want us to go and pull out the weeds?" But their master replied: "No, because you might root out the good wheat along with the weeds. Let them both grow together until harvest. Then we will gather the weeds and burn them and we will gather the wheat and store it."

After he had told this parable to the crowd, Jesus went into the house and his disciples asked him: "Explain the parable of the weeds in the field to us." And so Jesus said: "I am the man who sows good seed. The field is the world. The enemy is the devil. The harvest is the end of the world, when wicked and evil men, who are like the weeds, will be sent to the devil, while the men who have produced good fruits in their life will be gathered into the Kingdom of God."

February

BIBLE STORY OF THE MONTH

Jesus and his Disciples

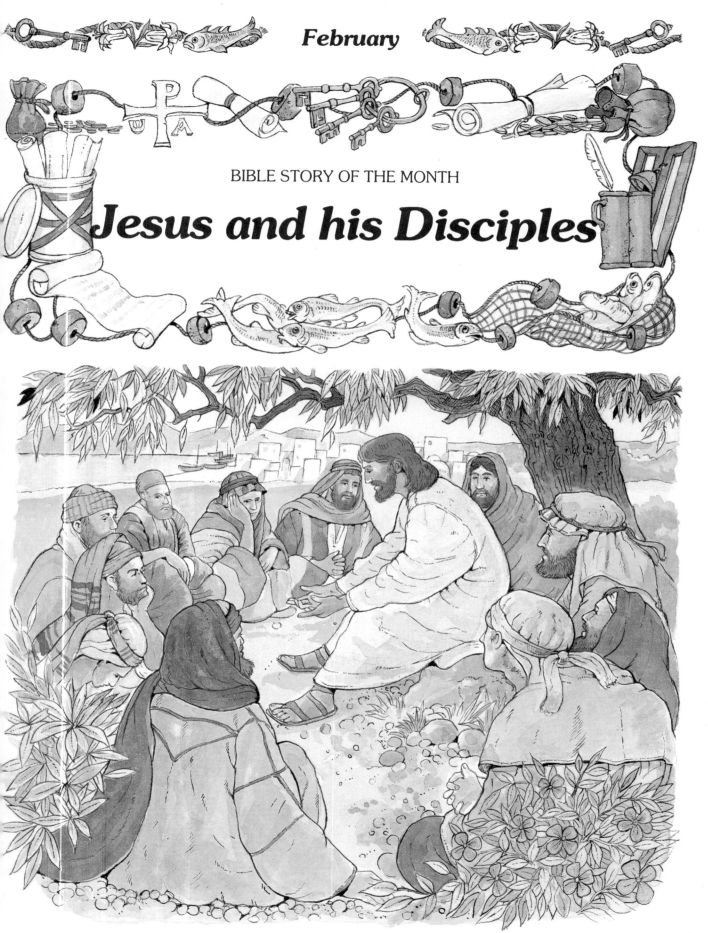

When it was time for Jesus to begin the work he had come down to earth to do, he left his native village of Nazareth and moved to Capernaum.

In Nazareth he had lived a quiet life, and no one knew that he was the Son of God; only his mother, Mary, was aware of it. So he went to live in Capernaum, an important city on the left shore of the Sea of Galilee. Here Jesus chose his first disciples from among the fishermen: one of them, Simon, whom Jesus later called Peter, welcomed him into his own home.

From Capernaum Jesus took to wandering through the villages of Galilee on foot, announcing the Gospel of the Kingdom of Heaven. In fact the word Gospel means "Good News." Jesus brought the good news that God the Father loves all men very much, and wants them to be happy with him.

One day Jesus went out from Capernaum and headed toward a nearby mountain. His disciples followed him. When he got to the top, he sat down with his disciples around him, and taught them the "Beatitudes," telling of those who will be blessed in the Kingdom of Heaven.

Jesus said: Blessed are those who are poor in the eyes of God, be-cause God will offer them the King-dom of Heaven.

Blessed are those who mourn, be-cause God will comfort them.

Blessed are the meek, because God shall reward them with para-dise.

Blessed are those who want to do God's will with all their hearts, be-cause God will fulfill their wish.

Blessed are those . who show mercy to others, because God will show mercy to them.

Blessed are the pure in heart, be-cause they shall see God.

Blessed are those who spread the word of peace, because God will welcome them like children.

Blessed are those who are per-secuted when trying to do the will of God: God will give them his king-dom. Rejoice if you are persecuted because you are my disciples: God has prepared a great reward for you!"

Sometimes Jesus would take a boat with his disciples to cross to the other side of the sea. On one occa-sion, being tired after a hard day, Jesus lay down in the bottom of the boat and fell asleep with his head resting on a cushion. It was evening, and the weather was calm. But all of a sudden, as happens on the Sea of Galilee, a great storm arose. The water became agitated. The waves

rose up higher than the boat, and the disciples began to feel frightened. When the water began to pour into the boat, they feared they were going to sink. So they went to Jesus, who was still sleeping, and they woke him, saying: "Lord, save us or we will all drown!"

So Jesus arose, and said to the wind: "Be silent!" and to the water he said: "Be calm!"

Suddenly the storm ceased, and Jesus said to the apostles: "Why are you so afraid? Do you have no faith in me?"

The disciples looked at each other with expressions of wonder and amazement, and they said: "Who,

then, is this man, this teacher of ours, whom even the winds and waters obey?"

The disciples began to understand. God created the winds and the water and everything that exists, and he has power over everything. If Jesus was able to command the forces of nature, then it meant that he had the same power and the same authority as God.

This experience, which had so frightened the apostles, helped them to get to know their master better, and to have more faith in him.

On another occasion, the disciples were out in their boat without Jesus when the wind picked up, making

the surface of the sea rough. The boat began to rock about in a dangerous manner.

Meanwhile, evening had fallen. The disciples rowed very hard in an attempt to get back to land as quickly as possible, but the shore was still a long way off.

Jesus, who was waiting for them on the shore, saw that his disciples were in danger and wished to help them. So he started off toward them, walking on the water.

When they saw a figure approaching them, walking on the water, the disciples grew fearful.

"Take courage, it's I, do not be afraid!" Jesus said.

"Lord, if it is truly you, command me to come to you by walking on the water!" Peter said to him.

"Come here!" Jesus ordered him.

Peter went out of the boat and began walking on the water. But he soon became afraid and began to sink. Then he begged Jesus to help him and he shouted: "Lord, save me!" So Jesus went to him, he took him by the hand and raised him up saying: "Why did you not have faith in me?" Then he climbed into the boat with Peter.

On seeing this, the other disciples went down on their knees before Jesus and exclaimed: "You are truly the Son of God!"

Mark 1; Matthew 5; Matthew 8; Mark 4;
Matthew 14

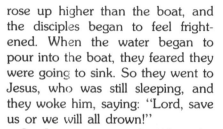

1 Jesus in the Synagogue

Mark 1

It was Saturday, the Sabbath, the feast day of the Hebrews. This was a day on which nobody worked, because it was completely dedicated to God. In the morning everybody went to the synagogue, the house of prayer. There, they read the Holy Scriptures, the Bible, and the teachings of Moses, or the prophets.

Then, anyone among the men who were present could explain or comment on what had been read.

Jesus, too, went to the synagogue, and after the readings he got up to give an explanation.

2 Jesus and the Man Possessed by the Devil

Mark 1

One day, in the synagogue of Capernaum, Jesus was explaining the Holy Scriptures, of the Bible, in a clear and precise manner. The people who were listening were amazed at his teachings.

At a certain point, however, Jesus' speech was interrupted. A poor man who had been taken over by a devil began to shout: "What are you doing here, Jesus of Nazareth? Have you come to ruin me? I know who you are: You are the saint sent by God!"

Then Jesus turned to the devil which was in this man, and shouted: "Be silent, you, and come out of that man!" At these words, the devil attempted to rebel and shook the poor man, making him scream. In the end, it left him and went away. The man was healed.

All those present grew even more amazed, and when they left the synagogue they went to tell everyone else: "We have seen amazing things! Jesus teaches with authority, not like the masters of the law. Jesus even commands the evil spirits, and they obey him!"

The news soon spread throughout the whole of Galilee, and everyone heard mention of Jesus of Nazareth.

3 Jesus Cures Peter's Mother-in-Law

Mark 1

One Saturday, in the synagogue in Capernaum, Jesus had explained the law of the Lord and cured a poor man who had been taken over by the devil.

Then Jesus left the synagogue and went to the house of Simon-Peter. Simon-Peter's mother-in-law was in bed with a fever. Jesus went up to the woman, took her by the hand, and made her rise up. At once her fever disappeared; the woman was cured! So she began to prepare a meal for Jesus and the other disciples.

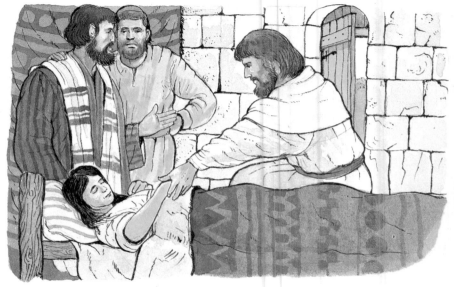

February

4 Jesus Cures Many Sick People

Mark 1

When the sun began to set and it was no longer too hot, people started to gather in front of Peter's house in Capernaum. Word had spread that Jesus had liberated a poor man who was possessed by the devil. A great many people came to ask Jesus to cure their illnesses, and they carried those unable to come alone. Soon there was a huge crowd. Jesus did not turn anyone away. He placed his hands on the sick, and cured them all: those who were paralyzed, blind, or possessed by the devil.

5 Where Is Jesus?

Mark 1

It was morning: a great crowd gathered outside Peter's house in Capernaum, where Jesus was living. Everybody wanted Jesus to cure his illness, or free him from evil spirits. Peter opened the door to let all the hopeful people in. Then he went to call Jesus, but his bed was empty. Where could he have gone?

Peter and the other disciples thought for a while, then they understood; they knew their master, and they knew where to go and look for him.

Peter and the disciples went out, and headed for a secluded place, up in the hills. And here they found Jesus, kneeling in prayer. Jesus was talking with his father in heaven.

Peter and his companions called to him: "Come! Everybody is looking for you!"

But Jesus replied: "We will go to the other villages so that I can take my message there too! This is why I came; I have to look after them as well!"

Thus began another day for Jesus. He traveled all throughout Galilee, followed by his disciples, and he preached in the synagogues, he cured the sick, and chased away the evil spirits.

6 Who is the Greatest?

Matthew 18

One day the disciples came to Jesus and asked him: "Who is the greatest in the Kingdom of Heaven?"

So Jesus called a child to him, stood him in front of the disciples, and said: "I tell you that if you don't become like children, you will not enter the Kingdom of Heaven.

"Anyone who becomes small like this child will be the greatest in the Kingdom of Heaven."

Jesus then added: "I dearly love little children; and whoever embraces and loves a child, embraces and loves me as well."

7 The Killing of John the Baptist

Mark 6

John the Baptist went around telling everybody what was right and what was wrong. And he even told the king.

At that time the king of Galilee was Herod Antipas, the son of the Herod who had tried to kill the baby Jesus. Herod Antipas had married Herodias, the wife of his brother, and this was evil in the eyes of the Lord. John had reprimanded him several times for this, and Herodias had sworn revenge. For this reason, John had been put in prison.

One day Herod had invited all the most important people of the kingdom to a feast. At a certain point during the feast, the daughter of Herodias, a young girl named Salome, entered the hall and began to dance. She danced so well that King Herod said to her: "Ask me what you wish and I will grant it to you!" Urged by her mother, Salome replied: "I want you to give me the head of John the Baptist."

Herod grew sad. He did not want to have John killed, but because he had made a promise before all the guests, he called a guard and ordered him to go and execute John the Baptist. In this way, the courageous prophet became a martyr.

8 The Rich Man and the Sinner Woman

Luke 7

A rich man called Simon invited Jesus to dine at his house. While they were eating, a woman entered who was well known for her many sins. She was carrying a jar of perfume. In silence she approached Jesus, she got down on her knees at his feet, and began to cry. Her tears fell on the feet of the Lord, and she dried them with her hair and sprinkled them with perfume.

When the owner of the house saw this, he thought to himself: "They say this Jesus is a prophet; but it can't be true, otherwise he would know this woman is a sinner and he would not let her touch him."

But Jesus, who had read his thoughts, said to him: "Simon, I have something to say to you." "Tell me, master," Simon replied. And Jesus continued: "A man lent five hundred coins to one person and fifty to another. As neither of them had the means to pay it back, he released them both from their debts. Which of the two do you think will love him the most?"

Simon replied: "I suppose the one who was pardoned the most." "You have answered correctly," said Jesus. Then, turning to the woman, he continued: "You see this woman? You did not welcome me into the house by washing my feet, as is done with guests. She, on the other hand, bathed my feet with her tears, and then dried them with her hair. You did not greet me with a kiss. She, on the other hand, has not stopped kissing my feet since I arrived. You did not pour perfume on my head, but she has sprinkled perfume on my feet."

Jesus concluded: "This woman has committed many sins, but they have all been pardoned, because by her behavior she has shown that she loves me very much." And turning to the woman, he said: "I forgive you your sins: go in peace."

9 The Brothers of Jesus

Mark 3

One day Jesus went into a house and a big crowd gathered outside. Then the mother of Jesus arrived with some relatives, but she was unable to enter the house because of the crowd around her son.

Someone told Jesus: "Your mother and your relatives have arrived. They are outside and they are looking for you." Then Jesus turned to the crowd and said: "I promise you that whoever listens to the Word of God and puts it into practice, is like my own family. And I will love them just as much."

10 The Son of the Widow

Luke 7

One day Jesus went to a village called Nain; he was accompanied by his disciples and a huge crowd followed him.

He had reached the first houses of the village, when he came across a funeral: on an open bier, as was the custom then, the body of a boy had been laid out, the only son of a woman who was a widow.

The poor woman, who was left all alone, followed the pallbearers and was accompanied by many of her fellow villagers. When he saw her, the Lord Jesus was moved to compassion, and said: "Do not cry!"

Then he went up to the bier, touched it, and bade the porters to stop. Then Jesus turned to the dead boy lying on the bier and said: "Boy, I am talking to you, arise!"

At these words the boy awoke, sat up, and began talking. Jesus took him by the hand and led him to his mother.

When all those present saw this incredible miracle they were amazed and began to praise God saying: "God has visited his people, sending a great prophet among us!"

They had still not realized that Jesus was not only a prophet: He was God himself.

11 Anger and Reconciliation

Matthew 5

One day Jesus gave the following lesson on how to treat people who offend us or do evil. Jesus said: "You all know the commandment that says "Thou shalt not kill." Whoever kills another man shall be brought to judgment. But I tell you now that whoever is angry with his neighbor shall also be judged.

"Therefore, if you bring an offering to the altar of the Lord and you remember that your brother has something against you, go first to make peace with him. Then return and pray and make your offering."

12 The Lost Sheep

Luke 15

One day Jesus said: "If a man has a hundred sheep and he loses one, he does not say: 'Ah, well, I still have ninety-nine.' Rather, he leaves the flock in a safe place and looks for the lost sheep. When he finds it, he lays it across his shoulders and returns home; he then calls his neighbors and friends and says: 'Rejoice, for I have found my lost sheep.'"

"In the same way there is great rejoicing in the Kingdom of Heaven over every sinner who repents, changes his way of life, and comes to love God."

13 A Woman Touches the Garment of Jesus

Mark 5

There was a woman who had been suffering from a loss of blood for twelve years. She had tried everything in an attempt to get better. She had gone to see many doctors and had spent all her money, but she had only grown worse.

One day she heard people talking about Jesus and his many miracles. At this, she thought: "I must go to him. Even if I only touch his garment, I am sure I will be healed."

She set off to look for Jesus and found him, as often happened, surrounded by the crowd who pressed against him from every side. With great difficulty, the woman made her way through the crowd and eventually touched Jesus' garment. Her loss of blood stopped at once and she was cured.

At that very moment, Jesus turned around and asked: "Who touched me?" The disciples immediately answered: "The crowd is thronging around you; how can you ask who touched you?"

Jesus, however, knew that the touch had been special, and when the woman knelt fearfully in front of him, as if to beg his forgiveness, he said to her: "Daughter, your faith has saved you: Go in peace."

14 The Precious Pearl

Matthew 13, 5

One day, Jesus described the Kingdom of Heaven: "The Kingdom of Heaven is like a merchant who searches for precious pearls. On the day he finds one of great value he sells everything he owns."

On another occasion Jesus taught the following lesson: "You have been told not to swear false oaths, and to keep your word once you have sworn. But I say to you that you should never swear oaths. You should simply say yes when it is yes, and say no when it is no. Anything more comes from the devil."

15 The Law of God

Matthew 5

One day Jesus said: "I tell you truly that for as long as heaven and earth exist, the law of God shall also exist. Not one word, not even a jot of the law of God shall ever in any way be abolished!

"Therefore, whoever breaks the commandments of God's law, even the least of them, and teaches others to do likewise, shall be the least in the Kingdom of Heaven. On the other hand, he who obeys all the commandments of the law of God, and teaches them to others, will be great in the Kingdom of Heaven!"

16 A Herd of Swine in the Lake

Matthew 8

One day, Jesus arrived in the country of the Gadarenes, but before he could go into the city he encountered two men possessed by devils. The two unfortunate men were in great distress; the devils made them leap and jump like furious madmen; so much so that nobody could pass any longer by that road or the two men would attack them.

When the devils saw Jesus they spoke through the two men they had possessed and said: "What do you want of us, Son of God? Have you come to torment us?"

The devils knew that Jesus, in order to heal the two men, would throw them out of the bodies they had possessed. Nearby a large herd of swine grazed. The devils, therefore, said to Jesus: "If you cast us out of here, then at least allow us to go into the herd of swine."

"Go," Jesus said and the devils at once left the bodies of the two men and entered the bodies of the pigs. At this, the whole herd of swine threw itself into the lake and died.

The two men were healed and the men who tended the swine ran to the city, full of amazement, to tell the story of the devils and the pigs who had drowned in the lake.

17 To Do Good in Secret

Matthew 6

One day Jesus said: "Be careful that you do not do good deeds for the purpose of being seen and admired by others, or you will have no reward from God.

"Therefore, when you give something to the poor, do not let everybody know; if you do this to be praised by other people then you have already received your reward. Instead, when you help someone, do not even tell your friends what you have done. It must be a secret: and your Father, who sees even that which is hidden, will reward you."

February

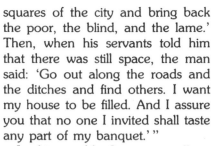

18 A Great Banquet

Luke 14

One day, Jesus told the following parable: "A man invited many of his friends to his house for a great banquet. Everything had been prepared when the guests began to make excuses for not coming.

"'I have bought a piece of land and I must go and see it,' said one.

"'I have bought five pairs of oxen and I must go and try them out,' said another.

"'I have only just been married, so I cannot come,' said a third.

"At this, the man said to his servants: 'Go out into the streets and squares of the city and bring back the poor, the blind, and the lame.' Then, when his servants told him that there was still space, the man said: 'Go out along the roads and the ditches and find others. I want my house to be filled. And I assure you that no one I invited shall taste any part of my banquet.'"

In this parable Jesus was talking about paradise, which is a place of celebration like a great banquet. The man who prepared the banquet is God. He invites everyone and it is a grave choice to refuse his invitation. Nothing is worth more than entering into the house of God to celebrate forever.

19 Love Your Enemies

Matthew 5

One day Jesus taught the following marvelous lesson about how to treat our enemies, the people who offend us or do us harm.

Jesus said: "Do not take revenge on those who do you harm. If somebody slaps you, then turn your other cheek toward him. If somebody wants to take your coat from you, then give him your cloak as well.

"Love your enemies and pray for them. In this way you will be children of your Father who is in heaven. For it is he who makes the sun rise on the evil and the good."

20 Jesus Resurrects the Daughter of Jairus

Mark 5

One day, a man by the name of Jairus approached Jesus and threw himself at his feet, saying: "My daughter is on the verge of death. Come and touch her so that she will be healed and live!"

Jesus set off with him. On the way they met a servant of Jairus, who said: "Your daughter is already dead!"

Jairus was about to burst into tears, but Jesus said to him: "Do not be afraid. Continue to have faith!"

When they reached the house of Jairus, Jesus said to the mourners: "Why are you crying? The little girl is not dead, but merely asleep!"

When they heard him talking like this, those present were astonished. Jesus, however, sent them all outside with the father and the mother of the young girl. With his three disciples—Peter, James, and John—he went into the room where lay the body of the dead girl.

Jesus went up to her, took her hand, and said: *"Talitha cumi,"* which means "Daughter, I say to you, get up!"

As soon as Jesus had said these words, the young girl arose and started to walk. Jesus' miracle had brought her back to life.

21 Like Sheep Among the Wolves

Matthew 10

Jesus moved from one village to another, announcing the good news, but he could not be everywhere. For this reason, he sent his disciples to some villages, after telling them: "Announce that the Kingdom of Heaven is at hand, but do not accept gold or silver or brass for this!"

Jesus went on to say: "I am sending you like sheep among the wolves: You must be as wise as serpents and as harmless as doves. But do not be afraid! Whoever receives you, receives me. And whoever receives me, receives our Father."

22 The Parable of the Merciless Servant

Matthew 18

One day, Peter asked Jesus: "Lord, you say that we must forgive those who offend us and do us harm. But how many times must I forgive the same person? Seven times?"

"Seventy times seven if necessary," replied Jesus. And to explain his words he told them this parable: "A king was doing his accounts with the servants who administered his kingdom. One servant arrived who owed the king the enormous sum of ten thousand gold coins. Since the servant did not have the money to pay the debt, the king gave orders, as was the custom at that time, that he and his family be sold as slaves so that the debt could be paid with the proceeds. The servant, however, threw himself at the feet of the king and said to him: 'Lord be patient with me and I will repay everything!'

"The king took pity on him. He had him released and even canceled his debt, making a gift of the money which should have been repaid.

"When that servant went out and met his fellow servants who owed him the small sum of one hundred coins, he threw himself upon him and shouted: 'Pay me what you owe me!'

"The poor servant fell at his feet and begged him: 'Be patient with me and I will repay you everything I owe!' But the first servant would not listen and had him arrested.

"Others went and told the king what had happened. The king called the servant to him and said: 'You are a wicked man. I canceled the enormous debt you owed me. You too should have had pity on your fellow and canceled his debt!' Then the king had his wicked and merciless servant thrown into prison."

After the parable Jesus added: "Your Father in heaven will deal with you in the same way if you do not forgive whoever does you harm and treat him as a brother."

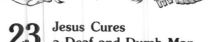

23 Jesus Cures a Deaf and Dumb Man

Mark 7

Jesus found himself in a foreign land, in the region of the Phoenician city of Sidon, when a deaf and dumb man was brought to him, in the hope that Jesus would cure him.

Jesus took the poor man to one side, placed his fingers on his ears, touched his tongue, then looked toward the heavens, gave a sigh, and said: *"Ephphatha,"* or, *"Open up."*

At once the man was healed. Everyone present was amazed and said: "Everything he does is wonderful! He is amazing! He makes the deaf hear and the dumb speak!"

24 You Are Peter

Matthew 16

Jesus was traveling with his disciples in the region of Caesarea. As they were walking along, he asked them: "What do the people think of the Son of man? Who do they say he is?" Jesus often called himself Son of man, as the prophet Daniel had named the mysterious person who appeared to him in his vision. The disciples answered: "Some think you are the prophet Elijah, others think you are one of the ancient prophets, returned to life."

"And what about you? Who do you think I am?," Jesus asked them. Simon-Peter said: "You are the Christ, the Son of the living God!"

And Jesus said: "Blessed are you, Simon, because what you have said did not come to you by itself, but was revealed to you by my Father in heaven. And I say to you: You are Peter, which means rock, and on this rock I will build my church, and not even the devil will be able to destroy it. I shall give you the keys to the Kingdom of Heaven, and anything that you declare forbidden on earth, God shall also consider forbidden. And anything you permit, God will permit."

25 The Blind Man of Bethsaida

Mark 8

One day, Jesus, accompanied by his disciples, arrived in the city of Bethsaida. There, the people brought a blind man to be healed.

Jesus took him away from the others, and put some of his saliva on the blind man's eyes. Then Jesus placed his hands on his head and asked him: "Do you see anything?"

"I see men," he replied. "At least I think they are men, because to me they look like walking trees."

Jesus again touched his eyes with his hands and the blind man's sight was completely restored.

26 The Laborers in the Vineyard

Matthew 20

One day Jesus told the following parable: "The Kingdom of Heaven is like the owner of a vineyard who went out early in the morning to hire laborers whom he sent to work in his vineyard after agreeing on a wage of a penny a day.

"At mid-morning the owner hired other laborers, more again at midday, others in the afternoon, and, finally he hired even more laborers an hour before dark: And to all of them he promised a fair wage.

"At the end of the working day, the owner began to pay the la-borers, starting with those who had arrived last. Those who had only worked the final hour came forward and received a penny each. And the same sum went to all the rest.

"Those who had worked the longest, particularly those who had been hired very early in the morning, began to complain: 'What? They have only worked for an hour and you pay them the same as us and we have worked the whole day in the heat!'

"The owner, however, replied: 'Friends, I am doing you no wrong. Did we not agree on the wage of one penny? Did I not pay you one penny? And if I choose to give the others the same wage as you, can I not do as I wish with money that belongs to me? Are you jealous because I am kind?'"

With this parable, Jesus meant to show that God is just, and gives to everyone the reward he has promised. He is also good, however, and he distributes his gifts as he sees fit.

The laborers hired earliest in the day are the Jews, who were the first to be called to enter the Kingdom of God. Then all the others came afterward; those called at the end of the day, for example, are the sinners who come to love God later in their lives, and the Lord calls them to him in paradise just the same.

27 Jesus Like Jonah

Matthew 12

One day a group of men said to Jesus: "Master, show us a miracle." They did not believe that Jesus was the Christ; they wanted a test.

Jesus was well aware of this and replied to them: "These sinners ask to see a miracle! They shall see the sign of Jonah. Just as Jonah remained three days in the belly of a fish, I shall remain for three days in the heart of the earth."

With these words, Jesus was speaking of the greatest proof he could give, that of rising from the dead on the third day.

28 The Faith that Moves Mountains

Matthew 17

One day a man approached Jesus and knelt before him, saying: "Lord, have mercy on my son! He is ill with epilepsy and suffers a great deal. When he has an attack, he often falls into the fire or into the water. I took him first to your disciples, but they could not heal him."

"Bring your son here to me," Jesus replied. When the boy came before him, Jesus spoke harshly to the devil that possessed the child and sent it away. The moment the devil left, the boy was healed.

Afterward the disciples approached Jesus, took him aside, and asked him: "Why were we not able to cast out the devil in the boy?"

And Jesus replied: "Because you have little faith. I tell you truthfully, if you had as much faith as a grain of mustard seed, you would be able to say to move this mountain. Nothing would be impossible for you!"

A short time later, Jesus again told his disciples about what was going to happen, saying: "Soon I shall be delivered into the hands of my enemies and they will kill me. But, on the third day, I shall rise up again."

This announcement made the disciples very sad.

29 The Transfiguration of Jesus

Matthew 17

One day, Jesus took his apostles Peter, James, and John with him to the top of a very high mountain. There, before their very eyes, Jesus was transfigured. His face shone like the sun and his clothing was as white as light. The prophet Elijah appeared to talk with Jesus, accompanied by Moses.

Peter then found the courage to speak and said: "Lord, it is beautiful to be here. If you wish, I will build three tabernacles: one for you, one for Moses and one for Elijah."

He was still speaking when a bright cloud overshadowed them and they heard a voice say: "This is my beloved son, whom I have sent. Listen to him well!"

When they heard the voice of God, the three disciples were filled with fear and fell facedown on the earth. But Jesus went to them, touched them, and said: "Get up and do not be afraid."

They raised their eyes and saw nothing out of the ordinary: only Jesus, looking as usual.

While they were coming down from the mountain, Jesus ordered them: "Tell no one what you have seen until I have risen from the dead."

BIBLE STORY OF THE MONTH

The Bread of Life

As Jesus moved from one village to another, a crowd often followed him. Everyone loved to listen to his wonderful parables and his other teachings, and they also sought to watch him cure the sick and work other miracles.

At one time Jesus went with his disciples to an isolated place in the hills around the sea of Tiberias, and a huge crowd followed behind them. They were a long way from any village, and Jesus asked: "Where can we buy enough bread for everyone?"

He asked this question of Philip, but only to draw attention to what he was about to do. Philip replied: "Two hundred loaves would not be enough to give everybody a piece!"

Andrew, the brother of Peter, added: "There is a boy here who has brought five loaves of barley bread and two fish; but what can this do for all these people?"

Then Jesus said to the disciples: "Make them sit down." Everyone sat down on the grass, perhaps five thousand people.

When everyone was seated, Jesus took the bread from the boy, and raising his eyes to heaven he blessed it, then he broke it up and gave it to his disciples to distribute among the crowd. They all ate as much as they wanted, and did the same with the fish. Everyone present ate his fill.

When they saw the miracle that Jesus had done, multiplying five loaves and two fish into enough to feed five thousand, everyone was amazed. They said to each other: "He must really be the Messiah, the Christ of whom the prophets spoke!"

However, the time had not yet arrived for Jesus to reveal himself for what he truly was. And so he left the crowd and went up the hill alone.

When evening fell the disciples went down to the sea, got into their boats, and began making their way back to Capernaum. All of a sudden a strong wind arose, and the boat was rocked by the waves; it was dark, and the disciples began to grow frightened.

But out of the darkness they saw Jesus approaching, walking on the water. They were amazed and could not believe their eyes, until Jesus spoke. He said: "Be brave, I am here: Do not be afraid." He got into the boat and the disciples threw themselves at his feet, saying: "You are truly the Son of God!"

Then they returned to Capernaum. The next day the crowd, which had eaten the bread made by the miracle, came to look for him again, and when they found him some of them asked him: "Master, when did you come here?"

Jesus answered them: "You are all looking for me because I gave you the bread, and you are hoping that I will give you more to eat. But I tell you that you should not be looking for material food, but the food which is not consumed and gives you the strength to gain eternal life."

Then they asked him: "How can we get the food of which you speak?" "You have to believe that I was sent by God," Jesus replied.

But someone objected: "To our ancestors in the desert, God gave manna, bread which came from the sky, to eat." Jesus answered: "Manna was food to nourish the body. I am the true bread de-scended from the sky: Whoever be-lieves that I have come down from heaven, nourishes his soul. Your an-cestors ate the manna, but they later died. Whoever has faith in me will never die!"

At these words they mumbled to each other, saying: "He is a man, he eats and sleeps like we do, we know that he comes from Nazareth . . . How can he say that he is de-scended from heaven?"

Jesus continued: "Do not mum-ble to each other. The bread that I give you to eat is myself, my body. Whoever eats my flesh and drinks my blood shall have eternal life. Whoever eats my flesh and drinks my blood remains in me, and I in him. For this reason his life will never end, and he will live forever together with me."

The people present did not un-derstand that Jesus was talking about faith: Whoever believes that he is the Son of God is united with him as if he were taking nourish-ment from him. And Jesus spoke of the Eucharist, where the commu-nion in the faith signifies the eating of his flesh through the bread.

Jesus said all these important things while speaking in the syn-agogue in Capernaum. All those who heard his words were surprised. When they heard that they had to eat his flesh, many of them did not want to try and understand, and they went away.

Even some of the disciples, who until then had followed him with love, went away and no longer fol-lowed him when they heard this speech.

Then Jesus turned to his twelve most faithful disciples, the Apostles, and asked them: "Do you wish to leave as well?"

Peter answered in the name of all of them: "And to whom shall we turn, Lord? Only you speak of eter-nal life. We believe you, and we know that you are the Christ, the Son of the living God."

John 6

1 The Coin in the Fish's Mouth

Matthew 17

At the time of Jesus it was the law that every Israelite should pay a tax for the upkeep of the temple in Jerusalem. The temple was dedicated to God: Therefore, the Son of God, Jesus, should not have had to pay this tax. But the time had not yet come for him to reveal himself to everyone.

One day the man who had to collect the tax asked the disciples: "Does your master pay the tax for the temple?" Peter answered "Yes, he pays it."

When Jesus arrived he asked Peter: "According to you, Simon, who should pay the taxes to the kings of this world, strangers or their own sons?" "Strangers," Peter replied.

And Jesus said: "Of course the sons are not obliged to pay the taxes. But just the same I will pay this tribute to the temple of my Father. Go down to the sea, cast your hook and take the first fish that bites. Open up its mouth and you will find a coin. Take it and use it to pay the tax for us both."

Peter faithfully did what Jesus had bid: He went and cast his hook, and the first fish that he caught had a silver coin in its mouth. Peter took it to the tax collectors.

2 The Parable of the Steward

Matthew 24

One day Jesus told this parable: "A man had to go away on a journey and leave his house, so he entrusted his steward to look after it and watch over the other servants. Then one day he returned, and he thought to himself: 'I am certain that my steward has been faithful to my orders. As a reward I will entrust him with the running of all my affairs.'

"Instead, when he entered the house, the master found the steward busy eating and drinking with the drunkards and layabouts, because he had thought: 'My master will re-turn late, and in the meantime I can do what I want.' So the lord of the house sacked the steward and forbade him ever to set foot inside his house again."

The meaning of this parable is clear. The owner of the house is the Lord. The steward is every man, to whom the Lord entrusts something to administer: his capabilities, his wealth, the authority he wields over others, and so on.

The master calls us to account when we pass from this life to the next. This often happens very unexpectedly. With this parable Jesus was telling everyone always to be ready to answer to God.

3 The Good Samaritan

Mark 12; Luke 10

One day a man asked Jesus: "Master, what must I do to enter into eternal life?"

Jesus replied: "Observe what is written in the law of Moses. The first commandment is: 'Love the Lord your God with all your heart, with all your soul, with all your mind and your strength.' The second is: 'Love thy neighbor like thyself.'"

But the man asked: "And who is my neighbor?" To make him understand Jesus told this parable.

"A man was traveling from Jerusalem to Jericho, when he was attacked by brigands who robbed him of everything and beat him, leaving him for dead. Then a priest came along; he saw the man but carried right on without stopping. Then a Levite from the temple did the same thing. Then a Samaritan came by and pitied the poor man. He treated his wounds, then lifted him onto his mule and took him to an inn to be looked after. The next day he had to continue his journey, and so he gave the innkeeper some money, saying: 'Take care of him, and if you spend more than I have given you, then I shall repay you when I return.'"

Jesus added: "According to you, which of the three behaved as a neighbor toward the man who had met with the brigands?"

"The one who took pity on him," replied the man who had asked Jesus the question.

And Jesus concluded: "Go, and conduct yourself in the same way."

With the parable of the Good Samaritan, Jesus wanted to teach us that we must always be ready to help anybody who has need of us, regardless of whether he is a stranger, or even an enemy. Because this is what Jesus did, when out of love for mankind he gave his own life.

4 Jesus and the Little Children

Matthew 19

One day a group of mothers with their children made their way through the crowd around Jesus. They wanted the Master to bless their children. But the disciples lost patience. Jesus was speaking and was not to be disturbed!

Jesus, on the other hand, turned and said: "Let the children come to me, because the Kingdom of Heaven belongs to the children and to those who are like them."

Then Jesus took the children to him, embraced them, and blessed them.

131

5 The Parable of the Two Sons

Matthew 21

One day Jesus said: "A man had two sons. He called the older and said: 'My son, go and work in the vineyard.' The son replied: 'I will go,' but did not. The father then called the younger and sent him. This one answered: 'I will not go,' but then went."

Then Jesus asked: "Which of the two sons carried out his father's wishes?" The people listening answered: "The second." And this was right. It is not enough to say that you love your Father, the Lord. Actions speak louder than words.

6 Jesus Meets a Rich Young Man

Matthew 19

A young man came up to Jesus and asked him: "Master, what must I do to gain eternal life?" "Obey the commandments," Jesus answered him. The young man insisted: "What commandments?" And Jesus replied: "Do not kill, do not steal, do not tell lies, honor your father and your mother . . . ."

"This I have always done," interrupted the young man. "What do I still lack?" So Jesus said to him: "If you want to be perfect, sell everything you own and give the proceeds to the poor. You will be assured a treasure in heaven. Then follow me."

But, after hearing these words, the young man went away with a sad face, because he had a great many riches and he was incapable of giving them up.

Then Jesus said to the disciples: "It is difficult for a rich man to enter into the Kingdom of Heaven! It is easier for a camel to pass through the eye of a needle than for a rich man to enter the Kingdom of God!"

The disciples were surprised at these words and they said: "So who will be saved?" And Jesus answered: "For men it is impossible, but for God everything is possible!"

7 Our Father who Art in Heaven

Matthew 6; Luke 11

One day a disciple said to Jesus: "Lord, teach us how to pray to the Father as well." And Jesus replied:
"When you pray, say:
Our father who art in heaven
Hallowed be thy name:
Thy kingdom come;
Thy will be done,
On earth as it is in heaven.
Give us this day our daily bread,
And forgive us our sins
As we forgive those who sin against us,
And lead us not into temptation,
But deliver us from evil.

8 The Parable of the Talents

Matthew 25

Jesus told the following parable: "A rich man who had to go away on a long journey, entrusted his servants with his wealth. To the first he gave five talents, to the second, two, and to the third, one.

"While the master was away, the servant who had received five talents went to invest them, and in the end he earned five more. The same thing was done by the one who had received two; in the end he made two more. The third servant, on the other hand, went and dug a hole in the ground, and in it he hid the talent he had received.

"When the master returned, he called the three servants to account. The first one gave him back ten talents, and the master said to him: 'Well done! You have been good and faithful. Feast with me.' The master said the same thing to the second servant who gave him back four talents.

"Then came the third servant with the talent he had gone to dig up, and he returned it. But to him the master said: 'You have been a bad and lazy administrator. You are not worthy to remain in my house!' "

This means that what we have was given by the Lord, but we must make it grow with good deeds.

9 The Reward for Whoever Follows Jesus

Matthew 19

"If you want to be perfect, go and sell everything that you own and give the proceeds to the poor, then come and follow me," Jesus had said to the rich young man.

Then Peter turned to Jesus and said: "Look, we disciples have abandoned everything to follow you. What reward will we have?"

It was true; to be with Jesus and follow him about from one city to another, the apostles had left their homes, their work, and their loved ones. Often, together with the Master, they had nowhere to sleep.

Jesus knew this. When a man had asked him where he lived, he had replied: "Foxes have their dens and birds have their nests. I do not even have a stone on which to rest."

But it was not always to be like this! That day Jesus revealed to Peter: "When I shall be seated on my glorious throne, you twelve will be seated on twelve thrones beside me, to reign forever along with me."

He then added: "Whoever leaves his home, his work or his family out of love for me will receive a hundredfold more and will inherit eternal life. Many who are now the first will become the last, and many who for now are last shall be the first."

10 God Listens to our Prayers

Matthew 7

One day Jesus taught prayer with faith: God is a good Father.

Jesus said: "Ask and your wish will be granted. Seek and you shall find. Knock and the door will be opened. Who out of all of you would give a rock to his son when he had been asked for a piece of bread? Who would give him a serpent if he asked for a fish? Everybody, even bad people, give good things to their own sons. All the more reason for your Father to give good things to all those who ask him for them!"

11 The First Seats at the Table

Luke 14

One day Jesus, along with a lot of other people, was invited to dinner by a doctor of the law. He noticed that some of them sought to go and sit at the best places, as close as possible to the master of the house, to show the other guests that they were more important than the others.

Then Jesus recounted the following parable, to remind all those present of the need to be humble. In fact humility is very important in gaining a place in the Kingdom of Heaven.

Jesus said: "When you are invited to dinner by someone, do not go and sit at the best places. If a more important guest than you arrives, the master of the house will come to you and say: 'Give up your seat,' and filled with shame before everyone else, you will have to take the last place.

"Instead, when you are invited to dinner, go and sit at the last seat. It is possible that the master of the house will come to say to you: 'Come, friend! Take a better seat!' And this will be a great honor for you before all the other guests."

Jesus then concluded: "In fact, remember: Whoever exalts himself will be humbled. And the humble will be exalted."

12 Invite the Poor

Luke 14

Jesus had been invited to dinner, and all around him were seated rich guests. Jesus said to the master of the house: "When you offer a lunch or a dinner, do not invite your friends, or your relatives or your rich neighbors, in the hope that they will later repay you.

"On the contrary, when you give a banquet, invite the poor, the lame, the blind, and the crippled. They do not have the means to repay your invitation. But you must take heart from this, because you will be repaid by God with eternal life."

13 Two Men in the Temple

Luke 18

Two men went into the temple to pray. The first man, standing up, said: "Oh God, I thank you because I am not a sinner like that other fellow. I fast, and I obey even the smallest rules of your law." But the second man had stopped a distance away. He didn't dare to raise his eyes up to heaven, but beat his breast saying: "Oh God, have pity on me, a sinner."

God pardoned the second only because whoever exalts himself will be humbled, and whoever humbles himself will be exalted.

14 The Parable of the Prodigal Son

Luke 15

Jesus told the following parable: "A man had two sons. The youngest asked, 'Give me the part of your riches that is mine.' His father gave it to him and the son set off for a distant land where he squandered all his money on evil.

"He was now reduced to poverty and was forced to become a keeper of pigs, but still he went hungry. Then he thought: Many of the servants in my father's home eat their fill! I will go back to my father and say, I have sinned against God; I am not worthy to be your son. Treat me as one of your servants.' And then he set off toward home.

"He was still a long way away when his father saw him coming and he took pity on him. He ran out to meet him, he hugged him and he kissed him. The son began the speech he had prepared, but the father didn't even let him finish. He called his servants and said to them: 'Hurry, bring him the finest clothes and dress him. Prepare a great banquet, and we will celebrate!'

"The elder son was out working in the fields. On his way home he heard the sounds of the feast from afar; he called a servant and asked him what was happening. When he found out he grew angry and he did not want to enter the house.

"Therefore his father came out to get him to come and join the joyous celebration. But the elder son said to him: 'I have worked every day for many years and no feast has ever been given in my honor. And now this brainless son of yours, who has wasted everything, comes home and you prepare a banquet for him!'

"The father replied: 'Son, you are always with me and everything that is mine is yours. But we have to feast and celebrate, because your brother was like a dead man, and now he has come back to life. He was lost and now is found!'"

15 The House Built on Rock

Matthew 7

One day Jesus said: "Whoever listens to what I say and puts it into practice is similar to a wise man who has built his house on a foundation of rock. When the rains fall, the rivers overflow and the wind blows against this house, it will still not fall, because its foundations are solid.

"Whoever, on the other hand, listens to what I say and does not put it into practice, is similar to a stupid man who has built his house on a foundation of sand: rain, rivers, and wind will hurl themselves against that house, and it will fall down."

16 Jesus Cures Ten Lepers

Luke 17

Jesus was making his way to Jerusalem when, before entering a village, he was met by ten lepers.

Leprosy was a terrible and contagious disease. Lepers could not live among other people and had to remain outside the villages, keeping well away from those not suffering from the illness.

For this reason the ten lepers kept their distance, and they addressed Jesus, shouting from afar: "Jesus, Master, have pity on us!"

Jesus replied: "Go and present yourselves to the priests." In fact the law stated that lepers who were healed had to present themselves to the priests, who would verify that they were cured. By replying in this way to the lepers, Jesus led them to believe that he would heal them. And in fact this is what happened: While they were on their way, they were all healed.

Then one of them, a foreigner from Samaria, went back to thank Jesus. Jesus then observed: "Weren't all ten cured? Well, where are the other nine? Only this foreigner has returned to give glory to God!" Then Jesus said to the Samaritan: "Get up and go! Your faith has saved you."

17 The Offering of the Widow

Luke 21

One day Jesus was in the temple of Jerusalem with his disciples, and he was teaching not far from where the coins left in offering were kept.

Raising his eyes, Jesus saw a group of rich men who were leaving abundant offerings. Then there came a poor widow who left two copper coins.

And Jesus said: "In the eyes of God, that poor widow has left more than anyone. In fact, the others only left a bit of what they don't need. She, on the other hand, gave everything she had to live with."

18 Jesus at the Feast of the Tabernacles

John 7

It was about the time of the feast of the Tabernacles, celebrated in memory of the forty years spent by the people of God in the desert. Jesus went to visit Jerusalem. In the city everyone was talking about him. Some admired his teachings. Some were amazed by his miracles. Others wondered: "How does he know the Holy Scriptures, without studying them?" Jesus answered: "I teach things that are not mine, but God's." Some people even spread the word that he was tricking everybody. In order to put a stop to all these rumors, the leaders of the people had Jesus arrested. But the guards returned empty-handed. The leaders asked them: "Why didn't you arrest him?" And the guards replied: "No man has ever spoken like he does!"

On the last day of the feast, before the crowd, Jesus stood up in the temple and said: "Whoever is thirsty, come to me and drink!"

With these words Jesus announced a promise: Whoever believed in him would receive the gift of the Holy Spirit. He satisfies every thirst for what is most important to every man: to be a friend of God.

19 The Parable of Lazarus and the Wicked Rich Man

Luke 16

Jesus said to his disciples: "There was a rich man who wore fine clothes and held splendid banquets. Outside his door sat a beggar, by the name of Lazarus, who was covered with sores and hungry.

"One day Lazarus died, and he was taken up to heaven, beside Abraham. The rich man also died, and he went to hell. When he raised his eyes and saw Lazarus beside Abraham, the rich man cried out: 'Father, have pity on me! Send Lazarus to stick his finger in the water and wet my tongue. This fire is tormenting me!'

"Abraham replied: 'My son, during your life on earth you received a lot of good things, while Lazarus suffered greatly. Between us there is an uncrossable abyss!' Then the rich man said: 'At least send him to my house, to tell my five brothers to change their way of life before they too end up in hell.' But Abraham replied: 'Let them obey!'

"The rich man insisted: 'But if someone from the dead goes to them, then they will surely change their lives.' Abraham replied: 'If they do not listen to the word of God, then they will not be convinced, even by Lazarus!' "

20 Jesus is a Good Shepherd

John 10

Jesus tried in various ways to explain to those who listened to him who he was and why he had come down to earth. He took examples from things the people knew well.

One day Jesus spoke of sheep and shepherds, and the difference between the shepherd who owns his sheep and the shepherd who looks after other people's sheep.

Jesus said: "I am the good shepherd. A good shepherd would give his life for his sheep. The paid guardian, on the other hand, abandons the sheep and flees when he sees the wolf coming, because the sheep are not his. Then the wolf goes among them, scatters them, and creates havoc."

"These wild beasts are like thieves," Jesus continued. "They only come to steal, kill, and destroy. But I have come to make sure that my sheep are safe and enjoy an abundant life."

"I am the good shepherd" Jesus said. The people who listened to his parable remembered the psalm: "The Lord is my Shepherd." Therefore Jesus was the Lord God! This was why his sheep, his friends, would enjoy an abundant, everlasting life.

21 The Hunchbacked Woman in the Synagogue

Luke 13

One Sabbath Jesus was teaching in the synagogue, when he saw a poor, hunchbacked woman. She had been this way for eighteen years and could not straighten up. Jesus called to the woman, touched her, and said: "Woman, you are free from your infirmity." At once she stood up straight, and she praised God.

The leader of the synagogue, however, instead of congratulating the woman, grew angry: He considered what Jesus had done as work, and all work was forbidden on the Sabbath. For this reason he turned to those present and said: "There are six days for working; come and be cured on one of those days, and not on the Sabbath!"

Then Jesus said: "You untie your oxen or your donkey and lead them down to drink even on the Sabbath, do you not? And this poor woman who has been chained to her illness for eighteen years, should she not be freed from her chains on the Sabbath?"

When they heard this, the enemies of Jesus were ashamed. The crowd, on the other hand, was delighted at the wonders that Jesus continually worked, and the teachings that accompanied them.

22 The Parable of the Lost Coin

Luke 15

Jesus told the following parable: "A woman owned ten coins. She had counted them lots of times. One day she counted them again, and found only nine. So she lit the lights and looked in every corner, took her broom and swept everywhere, and found the missing coin. She then called her friends and neighbors and said: 'Come and share my joy, for I have found my lost coin!' In the same way, there is great joy in heaven for every sinner who changes his way of life."

23 If a Donkey Should Fall on the Sabbath

Luke 14

A rich man had invited Jesus to dinner, along with a group of masters of the law who were experts in saying what was and was not permitted according to the law handed down by Moses. It was the Sabbath.

Among those present, Jesus saw a man who looked ill. So he turned to the masters of the law and asked them: "According to you, does the law allow the curing of the sick on the Sabbath?"

But the masters remained silent: They were afraid that if they said it was forbidden, they would appear heartless. Then, by example, Jesus invoked the law of Moses. He took the sick man by the hand, healed him, and sent him home.

He then explained: "Who among you, if one of your oxen or donkeys falls down a well, even on the Sabbath, wouldn't rush to pull it out?"

The masters of the law remained silent. They had understood very well: Helping a man or a woman in need is more important than any other duty.

Christians observe the day of rest ordered by God on a Sunday instead of a Saturday. But this commandment does not stop people from doing good deeds on this day.

24 The Light of the World

John 8, 10

One day Jesus said: "I am the light of the world and of life. Whoever follows me will not walk in the dark." Jesus was talking about the life without end that he grants to his believers.

Another day, the leaders of the people said to him: "If you are the Christ, then say so openly." And Jesus replied: "I have told you, and you do not believe me! But it is confirmed by the works that I do. The Father and I are a single being. He sent me to earth to give eternal life to whoever believes in me."

25 The Tree and the Fruit

Matthew 12

One day Jesus said: "Whoever is not with me is against me. And whoever does not gather in the harvest with me, throws away the crops.

"If you take a good tree, then its fruits will also be good. If you take a bad tree, then its fruits will be bad as well. Because a tree can be judged by its fruits. But people can say good things, because what comes out of the mouth does not necessarily come from the heart. Anybody who says wicked things is like a tree bearing bad fruits, and one day he will be brought to account by God."

26 Whoever is Without Sin

John 8

Jesus was in the temple when the masters of the law brought in a woman accused of having committed the sin of adultery. "Master," they said, "for this sin the law states the guilty must be stoned to death. What do you say?"

In reality these men were hoping to lay a trap for Jesus so that they could accuse him. In fact, if Jesus said that they should pardon the woman, they could accuse him of violating the law of Moses; and if he said that she should be condemned, they would say that he was cruel.

Jesus did not reply to his enemies' question. However, they persisted, and raising his head, Jesus said: "Whoever of you is without sin, let him throw the first stone against her."

When they heard these words, those present began to drift away one by one. Jesus was left alone with the woman, and he asked her: "Where are those who accused you? Did no one condemn you?"

"No one," the woman replied.

And Jesus concluded: "Neither do I condemn you. Go and sin no more." In this way Jesus wanted to show that only God can judge the hearts of men.

27 The Parable of the Rich Fool

Luke 12

One day Jesus told this parable: "A rich man had some land that yielded excellent harvests. The man thought: 'My stores are already full. Where will I put the new harvest? I must knock them down and build bigger ones, so that it will all fit. Then, without working, I will enjoy myself for many years.'

"But God said to him: 'Fool! This very night you will die. And then what will become of your riches?'

"And this is what happens to people who do not try to grow rich in the eyes of God!'"

28 The Salvation of Zacchaeus

Luke 19

At the time of Jesus, the tax collectors were known as publicans. These officials worked on behalf of the emperor of Rome, who also ruled over Palestine. The Hebrews considered them traitors.

One day Jesus was walking in Jericho, surrounded by a vast crowd. The leader of the city's publicans, a man called Zacchaeus, was very curious to see this famous Jesus. When he heard that Jesus was in the city, he climbed up a tree, because, as he was small, this was the only way for him to see. When Jesus reached the tree, he raised his eyes and said: "Zacchaeus, quick, come down, because today I will stay at your house." The crowd was amazed that the Master would speak to a publican, and was even going to stay at his house.

However, Zacchaeus was beside himself with joy, and when Jesus entered his house, he said: "Look, Lord. I will give half of my belongings to the poor, and if I have stolen from someone, then I will repay him fourfold!"

Jesus then pointed out: "Today salvation has entered this house. The Son of man came to seek out and save those who were lost."

29 Jesus Heals a Man Blind from Birth

John 9

As Jesus was passing with his disciples, he met a beggar who had been blind from birth. Jesus took pity on him: He spat on the ground and made a little lump of clay which he rubbed on the blind man's eyes, saying: "Go and wash in the pool of Siloam." The man did as Jesus bid, and he could see.

All this took place on the Sabbath day and it caused heated discussion among the leaders of the people. They insisted that the man who was born blind should repeat several times how he had regained his sight.

Some of them said: "This man does not come from God, because he does not respect the Sabbath day and rest as God ordered." Others, however, replied: "But how could a sinner perform such miracles?"

Later, Jesus met the man who had been healed and asked him: "Do you believe in the Son of man?" Jesus called himself by this name, just as the prophet Daniel had foretold, to show that he was both man and God. The man who had been blind replied: "Tell me who he is, for I believe in him." And Jesus said to him: "You are looking at him." The man knelt down and said: "Lord, I believe!"

30 The Chiefs in the Kingdom of Heaven
Mark 10

One day, the brothers James and John went to Jesus and asked him: "Master, when you have established your kingdom, allow us to be second only to you in importance."

Jesus said to them: "You do not know what you are asking." And once again he explained to them that before rising up in glory, he would be captured by his enemies, made to suffer and slain. Jesus tried to make his disciples understand that, like him, they had to be ready to give their lives.

The disciples, however, did not understand this. On the contrary, when the others heard what James and John had asked, they grew angry with them, believing themselves to be no less deserving. They all wanted to be important, to be chiefs in the Kingdom of God.

Jesus then explained to them: "In my kingdom things will not be as they are in this world. Here, kings and other rulers command with force, and impose their will on their subjects. In the Kingdom of God, however, everything is different: Whoever wishes to be important shall serve the others; whoever wishes to be first, shall be the servant of all."

31 The Parable of the Wise and Foolish Virgins
Matthew 25

To explain what the Kingdom of God would be like, Jesus one day told this parable: "The Kingdom of Heaven is like ten virgins who were called to be maids of honor to a bridegroom. They took their oil lamps and went out to meet the groom. Five were foolish and forgot to take a spare container of oil. The other five were wise and took spare containers.

"The groom was late in arriving, and the virgins all eventually fell asleep. At midnight they were awakened by a shout: 'The bridegroom is coming! Go out and meet him!'

"The ten virgins awoke and found that all their lamps had gone out. The wise five relit their lamps with their spare oil, while the others were at a loss and had to go buy more oil.

"Meanwhile, however, the groom arrived and the five virgins who were waiting with their lamps lit went with him to the wedding feast. When the other five came back, they knocked on the door, shouting: 'Lord, Lord let us in!' But the groom replied: 'Truly, I do not know you!'

"Therefore," Jesus said, "Always be ready because you do not know when the Lord will come."

BIBLE STORY OF THE MONTH

Story of Lazarus

When he was in Jerusalem, Jesus often went to the nearby village of Bethany, to stay with three friends of his: Lazarus and his sisters, Martha and Mary.

They all dearly loved Jesus, and they welcomed him with great joy, each extending his best effort to please him.

Jesus said to Mary: It is good to take care of material things, but it should not be forgotten that listening to the voice of the Lord, and joining him in prayer, is of much greater importance.

It then happened that Lazarus grew sick with a very serious illness. Martha and Mary thought they should inform Jesus, who was a long way away, and they sent messengers to inform him: "Lord, your friend is ill."

When he heard this, Jesus said to his disciples: "This illness will serve to show the glory of God and the glory of the Son of God." Jesus remained for another two days in the place where he was, but he sorrowed greatly. Then he said: "Let us go to Jerusalem. Our friend Lazarus has gone to sleep, but I am going to wake him up."

"If he has gone to sleep, that means he is beginning to get better and soon he will be well," said the disciples. But they had not understood the words of Jesus; so he spoke to them more openly: "Lazarus is dead," he said, "and I am glad that none of you was there, because in this way you will believe. Let us go to him!"

When he reached Bethany, Jesus found that Lazarus had already been buried four days earlier. Since Bethany was only three kilometers from Jerusalem, lots of friends and relatives had come to console Martha and Mary over the death of their brother.

When Martha heard that Jesus was coming, she went out to meet him, while Mary stayed in the house crying. Martha said to Jesus: "Lord, if you had been here, my brother would not have died! But I also know that whatever you ask of God, God will grant you."

Jesus answered her: "Your brother will rise up."

"I know that he will rise up," exclaimed Martha, "like everyone else, at the end of the world."

Jesus then pointed out a very important thing to her. He said: "I am the resurrection and the life. Whoever believes in me, even if he dies, shall have eternal life: whoever lives and believes in me, will not die for all eternity." And he added: "Do

you believe this?"

Martha replied: "Yes, Lord. I believe that you are the Christ, the Son of God, who has come to earth." Then she hurried back into the house and said to her sister: "The Master is here, and he is calling for you."

Then Mary arose and went out. Those who were in the house with her got up and followed her, thinking: "Now she is going to cry at the tomb."

When Mary reached Jesus, she fell at his feet, saying: "Lord, if you had been here my brother would not be dead!" When he saw Mary, and all the others who were with

her, crying, Jesus was deeply moved and he asked: "Where have they laid him to rest?" "Come and see," they answered him. At that point Jesus burst into tears. Those present then said: "Look how much he loved his friend." But others objected: "He who gave sight to a man blind from birth, could he do nothing to stop Lazarus from dying?"

Still deeply moved, Jesus came to the tomb, which was a cave with a huge rock blocking the entrance. "Take away the rock," Jesus ordered. But Mary objected: "Lord, there is already a bad smell, for it has been four days since he was buried!" "As I have said to you, if

you have faith you will see the glory of God," replied Jesus.

Then they took away the rock. Jesus raised his eyes to the heavens and said in a loud voice: "Father, I thank you for having listened to me." Then he shouted out: "Lazarus come out!"

And Lazarus came out of the tomb alive. When they saw this, many of the people who had arrived from Jerusalem to console Martha and Mary came to believe in Jesus, and when they returned to the city they told everyone what they had seen.

Then the chiefs of the people met to decide what to do about Jesus. They said: "He works a lot of miracles. Many people believe in him and no longer obey our commands." On that very day, however, they decided to have him put to death.

Six days before the Passover, Jesus went back to Bethany to see his friends. They made a meal for him. Martha served, Lazarus sat with him, and Mary demonstrated all her love for Jesus by pouring a jar of rare perfume over his head. "What a waste," someone said, but Jesus defended her: "No," he said. "She did it because she loves me. I assure you that the whole world will talk about what she has done."

Luke 10; John 11–12

145

1 Jesus Enters Jerusalem in Triumph

Matthew 21; Luke 19

Jesus was journeying toward Jerusalem. When he was near the village of Bethphage, between Bethany and the Mount of Olives, he called two disciples and said to them: "Go to the village before you. As soon as you enter you will find that a donkey and its colt, that no one has ever ridden, have been tied up. Untie them and bring them here. And if someone should ask you why you untie them, answer that the Lord needs them."

The two disciples went and found everything as Jesus had said. They brought the donkey to him, covered it with their cloaks, and bade the Master ride it into the city. Then someone remembered that the prophet Zechariah, speaking of the Messiah who was to come, had announced: "Behold, your king will come to you, humble and riding on a donkey."

Along the way into the city, a huge crowd gathered around him. Some of them laid their cloaks on the ground where he was passing, others waved palm and olive branches, while they all exclaimed: "Blessed is he who comes in the name of the Lord! Glory to God in the heavens."

2 A Trap for Jesus

Luke 20

The enemies of Jesus laid traps for him, to have something to accuse him of. One day they presented him with a coin and asked: "Is it right to pay taxes to the emperor?"

This was a difficult question. Whatever the reply they would have a reason for accusing Jesus. In fact, if he said it was right, they would have accused him of being a traitor to his people, a friend of the emperor in Rome and his hated soldiers who commanded in Palestine.

If, on the other hand, he had said that it was not right to pay the taxes to the emperor, they would have gone to the governor, who ruled for the emperor of Rome, and accused him of treason, to have him arrested and condemned.

Jesus knew the tricks of his accusers. Therefore he said: "Show me a coin. Whose image is shown on it? And whose name is written around it?" "The emperor's," they said. And Jesus concluded: "Then give back to the emperor that which belongs to the emperor, and to God that which belongs to God." Amazed at this reply, the enemies of Jesus remained silent, and this time, too, they were forced to go away without being able to accuse him.

3 Jesus Promises That he Will Return

Matthew 25

After his triumphant entrance into Jerusalem, Jesus was to be found in the temple every day, teaching his disciples and anyone else who wanted to listen to him, while the chiefs of the people looked for a way to have him put to death.

Jesus promised that he would return, and he announced that he, Jesus, would judge the world on the instructions of God the Father. "I will call before me all men, and I will divide them into two groups, just as the shepherd separates the sheep from the goats," said Jesus.

4 Jesus Announces the Day of Judgment

Matthew 25

On the Day of Judgment Jesus will return to judge all men. He will gather them before him and separate them into two groups.

Jesus said: "To the first group, that of the just, I will say: 'Come and enjoy the reward prepared for you, because I was hungry and you fed me, I was thirsty and you gave me drink, I was homeless and you gave me shelter, I was naked and you gave me clothes, I was ill and you came to look after me. . . .'

"And they will answer me: 'But when did we shelter you? When, O Lord, did we give you all this?'

"And I shall explain: 'Every time you helped someone in difficulty, I considered it a gift for me.'

"To the wicked people, on the other hand, I will say: 'Get away from me forever, because I was hungry and you did not feed me, I was thirsty and you did not give me drink, I was a stranger and you did not give me shelter. . . .'

"They will answer me: 'But when, Lord, did we see you in need like this and not come to your aid?'

"And I shall explain: 'Every time that you refused to help someone who was in need, it was as if you were refusing to help me.'"

5 The Parable of the Fig Tree

Matthew 24

When Jesus spoke of his return, he said that on that day this world would end and a new world would begin. But when will that day be?

"Nobody knows," said Jesus, "except for God." This is why it is always necessary to be ready to be brought to account for our actions.

"Learn this parable from the fig tree and the other plants," Jesus said. "When its branches become tender and the first leaves appear, summer is at hand. This is what you must do: be ready and prepared for the Kingdom of God."

6 The Death of Jesus Is Decided Upon

John 11

The chiefs of the people of Israel held a meeting to decide on the matter of Jesus finally. They said: "He works numerous miracles and the people follow him. If we do not do something soon they will proclaim him king. But the emperor does not allow us to have our own king; he will send his soldiers to destroy the temple and maybe even kill us all."

For this reason, they decided to have Jesus put to death, and they made an agreement with one of the apostles, Judas Iscariot. In exchange for thirty coins, he promised to lead them to where they could capture Jesus.

Jesus knew that they wanted to capture him and put him to death. He knew it; and it was for this reason that he, the Son of God, had made himself into a man! However he wanted his death to take place when he decided the time was right, after the Passover feast. With this April feast, the Jews celebrated the alliance God made with his chosen people, through Moses. Through Jesus, dead and risen again, God was going to declare a new alliance, not only with the Jews but with all men.

7 Jesus' Last Supper

Mark 14; John 6, 13

Before allowing himself to be captured, Jesus wanted to join the apostles for the Passover meal. This was a meeting full of strange events.

In those days, before sitting down at the table, the lord of the house would order the servants to wash the guests' feet. But that evening Jesus himself filled a basin with water and washed the feet of the apostles. Then he explained the meaning of what he had done. "You all call me Lord and Master. Therefore, if I, your Lord and Master, have made this gesture out of love for you, then you must all act lovingly."

Then he made an announcement to the apostles: "One of you will betray me."

They were all stunned and could hardly believe their ears. But it was true: Judas Iscariot, for thirty coins, had promised to help the chiefs of the people capture Jesus. When he realized that he had been found out, Judas crept out into the night.

The meal continued according to the rules of the Passover supper, with the roast lamb, unleavened bread, and bitter herbs. But, at a certain point, Jesus suddenly took the bread, broke it, and gave it to the apostles, saying: "Take it and eat it. This is my body which I give to you in sacrifice."

In the same way he took the chalice of wine and passed it around saying: "Take this and drink it. This wine is my blood, which flows for you and for all men. It is the blood with which God establishes a new alliance with mankind, and forgives their sins."

This command is respected every time we follow Jesus' commands. In this way Jesus brought about the promise he had made in the synagogue in Capernaum: "Whoever eats my flesh and drinks my blood shall have eternal life."

8 The Olive Grove

Mark 14

When Jesus and the eleven remaining apostles had finished the Passover meal, they left the house where they were gathered and went up to the Mount of the Olives. At its foot was an olive grove called Gethsemane that belonged to friends of Jesus, who often allowed him to spend the night there.

On this night as well, Jesus went there. When they arrived he told the apostles to sit down while he went off to pray, accompanied by Peter, James, and John.

Jesus was the Son of God, and therefore he knew how much suffering he was about to undergo. But he was also a man, and like all men he was afraid of suffering. For this reason he sought strength, asking for it in prayer to God his Father.

Jesus said: "Father, if it is possible, take this pain away from me. But your will must be done."

So great was Jesus' suffering that he sweated blood.

After he had finished praying, Jesus went back to the three apostles, and found that they had fallen asleep. He woke them up and said: "Could you not even stay awake for one hour with me? He who will betray me is close at hand."

9 Jesus is Arrested

Matthew 26

Judas Iscariot, the traitor, knew that Jesus was going to spend the night in the olive grove of Gethsemane. He was approaching at the head of a group of guards, armed with swords and clubs. He had arranged a sign with the guards, so that in the dark they would not confuse Jesus with the other apostles, and would be sure of arresting the right man.

He had said: "He is the one I shall kiss." Judas entered Gethsemane with the guards and went up to Jesus and kissed him, saying: "Greetings, Master."

Jesus answered him: "My friend, with a kiss you betray me?"

The guards rushed to arrest Jesus. Peter wanted to stop them: He took out his sword and struck a guard, cutting off one of his ears. But Jesus said to him: "Put away your sword." And he told them: "He who draws the sword, dies by the sword." Then he touched the guard's ear and healed it.

Then he said to Peter: "Do you think that if I were to appeal to my Father, he would not send an army of angels to save me? But what the prophets foretold must be fulfilled."

While the guards were leading Jesus away, the apostles fled.

10 Peter Denies Jesus

Luke 22

When Jesus was arrested and dragged off by the guards, the apostles all fled. But Peter followed behind at a distance to see where they were taking him. In fact, during the Last Supper, Peter had promised Jesus: "Even if everyone else abandoned you, I would not!"

"Really?" Jesus had answered. "Before this night is out, you will declare three times that you do not know me!"

Now Peter wanted to show that he was brave and faithful to his word. For this reason, he followed along behind Jesus, and came to the courtyard of the house of Caiaphas. But when he discovered that Jesus was being beaten and had been condemned to death, he began to grow afraid.

Peter went up to a group of people who had lit a fire in a courtyard and were gathered around it to keep warm: the night was very cold. One of Caiaphas' maidservants looked at him for a moment, and then said: "You were with that man from Nazareth, weren't you?"

Peter was afraid of meeting the same fate as Jesus, and he answered: "I do not even know who he is."

He moved away from the group, but a guard recognized him and said: "Weren't you with him in the garden of the olives?" "No" answered Peter. "It's not true."

Then other people gathered around him and they said: "Yes, you are one of his followers! Even your accent shows that you come from the same area as he." And Peter repeated: "It's not true. I tell you that I do not know him."

And at once Peter remembered what Jesus had said to him: "This very night you will declare three times that you do not know me." Then Peter went out and wept.

11 Jesus is Tried by Caiaphas

Mark 14

Jesus was taken to the house of the high priest Caiaphas to be tried. All the other chiefs of the people were there as well, and they had paid people to slander Jesus. Caiaphas asked Jesus: "If you are the Son of God, then say so!"

And Jesus replied: "Yes, I am!"

On these words Caiaphas exclaimed: "He has blasphemed. We have no further need of witnesses. He deserves to be put to death!"

And then a lot of people began to insult Jesus, and they beat him and slapped him. Some even spat.

12 Jesus is Taken before Pontius Pilate

Luke 23

The chiefs of the people could not have Jesus put to death without the permission of Pontius Pilate, who ruled over Palestine in the name of the emperor in Rome. To convince Pilate Jesus should be convicted the chiefs told him Jesus had proclaimed himself king and was therefore a rival to the Roman emperor. Pilate understood that the chiefs wanted to condemn Jesus for other reasons, so he asked him: "Are you a king?"

"Yes, I am," Jesus replied. "But my kingdom is not of this world."

13 Jesus Is Tortured

Luke 23

In order to be rid of Jesus, Pilate sent him to Herod Antipas, the king of Galilee, who was then in Jerusalem. Herod interrogated him, but Jesus did not answer and so was returned to Pilate.

The chiefs of the people had gathered a huge crowd before the house of Pilate, and they had been paid to shout that Jesus should be condemned to death. Pilate tried to calm the crowd. He ordered his soldiers to whip Jesus. And they amused themselves by torturing him and pretending that he was a king:

They draped a red cloth over his shoulders and then placed a crown of thorns on his head.

Jesus was bleeding when Pilate presented him to the crowd saying: "Here is the man." But the crowd again yelled: "Put him to death! Crucify him! Crucify him!"

Pilate made a last attempt. He said: "At Passover it is the custom that I free a prisoner. Do you want me to free Barabbas, or this Jesus?"

Barabbas was a murderer.

"But what wrong has this man done?" insisted Pilate. "I find no fault in this Jesus!"

But the crowd repeated: "Crucify him! Crucify him!"

14 Jesus Is Condemned to Death

John 19

Pontius Pilate knew that Jesus was innocent, but he was afraid that the chiefs of the Jews would tell the emperor: "Your governor is really your enemy; he freed a man who proclaimed himself king."

For this reason, he handed Jesus over to the soldiers to be crucified, and he himself wrote the tablet to be stuck onto the cross, where the reason for the punishment was written: "Jesus of Nazareth, King of the Jews." The tablet was written in the three languages spoken in Palestine: Hebrew, Latin, and Greek.

April

15 The Road to Calvary

Mark 15

The soldiers made Jesus bear the heavy weight of the cross and led him through the streets of Jerusalem to the place of crucifixion. It was a rocky hill called Calvary, just outside the walls of the city.

There were many people who followed Jesus on the road that led to Calvary. Some laughed at him; others were simply curious. A group of women watched what was happening and wept. Jesus suffered a great deal, and every now and then he fell to the ground under the weight of the cross.

16 Mary and John

Luke 23; John 19

Jesus was very weak from the whipping he had received and from the crown of thorns which made his head bleed. When Jesus fell to the ground under the weight of the cross, the soldiers stopped a passerby, Simon the Cyrenian, and forced him to help Jesus.

When they reached Calvary, the soldiers stripped Jesus, laid him on the cross, and nailed his hands and feet to it. Then they raised up the cross and waited for Jesus to die. While they were crucifying him, Jesus said: "Father, forgive them,

for they know not what they do."

It was the custom for the soldiers to divide the clothes of a man condemned to death among themselves. Jesus had been wearing a single tunic, so, to avoid cutting it up, the soldiers decided to draw lots for the garment.

Mary, the mother of Jesus, and the apostle John stood together at the foot of the cross. Jesus turned to John to ask him to take care of his mother, and he told Mary to look upon John as her son from then on. "Woman, behold thy son," he said to Mary. And to John: "Son, behold thy mother." A large crowd had gathered as though it were a show.

17 The Good Thief

Luke 23

Two thieves had been found guilty of serious crimes and condemned to death alongside Jesus on Calvary. The soldiers had crucified them on either side of Jesus. One said to Jesus: "If you really are the Christ, then save yourself and us!" But the other thief spoke up: "Have you no fear of God? We are being justly punished, but he has done nothing wrong!" He then addressed Jesus, saying: "Lord, remember me when you come into your kingdom." And Jesus replied: "You will be with me in paradise!"

18 Jesus Dies

Luke 23; Matthew 27; John 19

Jesus had already been on the cross for some hours when an extraordinary thing happened. It was around midday when the earth was suddenly covered in a darkness which lasted for three hours. Jesus cried: "Father, into your hands I commend my spirit." And he died. At this there was an earthquake. When he saw this, the centurian in charge of the soldiers said: "This man truly was the Son of God!"

Even those who had only come to watch the crucifixion returned home beating their breasts after they had witnessed these events.

While this happened, the friends and disciples of Jesus and the women who had followed him from Galilee all stood together a little way off and watched in silence.

Since it was the day before the holy Sabbath, it was decided that the bodies be removed from the crosses. To make certain that the condemned men were dead, the soldiers broke the legs of the thieves who had been crucified with Jesus. Then they approached Jesus and saw that he was already dead. The soldiers did not break his legs, but one of them pierced his side with a spear.

19 Jesus Is Buried

Matthew 27; John 19

Out of fear of the authorities, Joseph of Arimathea had remained a secret follower of Jesus. When Jesus died, Joseph went to Pilate and asked for the body of Jesus. Pilate agreed.

The body was taken down from the cross, wrapped in a sheet and carried away at once to a nearby tomb which belonged to Joseph.

This was all done hurriedly, because the next day was the Sabbath and no work was permitted on that day. The body of Jesus, therefore, was not washed in oils and perfumed according to the custom.

Mary Magdalene and the other women who loved Jesus intended to return to the tomb the day after the Sabbath to attend to his body.

The chief priests and the elders of the people then went to Pilate and said to him: "We remember that when this impostor was alive he claimed he would rise from the dead after three days. Order a guard to be put at the tomb so that the disciples do not come and steal the body in order to tell the people that he has come back to life." And Pilate replied: "Do as you wish." Thus, they went away and sealed the stone at the entrance to the tomb and left several men to guard it.

20 The Third Day

Mark 16; John 20

Jesus had died on the cross and been buried on the day before the Sabbath. On the day after the Sabbath, several women went to buy ointments and spices for the body of Jesus and then went to the tomb.

Along the way, they asked among themselves: "Who is going to roll away for us the great stone that seals the tomb?" However, when they arrived they found that the stone had already been rolled away and the tomb was open. In amazement, they entered the tomb and saw a young man, an angel, clothed in a long white garment and they were afraid. But he said to them: "Do not fear! You are looking for Jesus of Nazareth, who was crucified: He has risen and he is here no longer. Now go and tell this to his disciples."

The women were astonished, and fled from the tomb, saying nothing to anybody of what they had seen and heard.

When Mary Magdalene returned to the tomb and found it empty, she believed that the body of the Lord had been stolen, and she began to weep. Suddenly, she heard someone call to her: "Woman, why are you weeping?" Through her tears she asked: "If you have taken the body, tell me where it is so that I can go and get it!" But the voice only called her name: "Mary!" At this, she recognized Jesus. He told her: "I will ascend to my Father. Go and give this news to my brothers!" Mary was filled with joy and ran to speak to the apostles: "I have seen the Lord!" she told them.

They did not want to believe her words. So Peter and John also returned to the tomb. When they saw that it was empty, they too began to understand that Jesus would indeed rise from the dead.

21 The Chief Priests' Deception

Matthew 28

After the resurrection of Jesus, the guards who had been watching over the tomb went to the chief priests to tell them what had happened. When they heard, the priests gave the guards a lot of money so that they would tell people that while they slept the disciples of Jesus had come by night and stolen the body. The chief priests also said to the guards: "If Pilate learns of this, we will take all responsibility and will guarantee your safety." The guards took the money and followed the chiefs' instructions.

22 The Two Disciples on the Road to Emmaus

Luke 24

On the same day that Jesus rose from the dead, two of his disciples set out on foot for the village of Emmaus. They knew nothing of what had happened that day and were still sad about the death of Jesus. As they walked, a traveler joined them and asked: "Why are you so sad?"

"You must be the only person who does not know what has happened in Jerusalem," they replied. "We had hoped that Jesus would free us from Roman rule and restore the kingdom of Israel. . . ."

The traveler was Jesus himself, but the two disciples did not recognize him. He then explained that the Messiah had not come to restore Israel, but to allow all men to enter the Kingdom of God.

When they reached Emmaus, the two disciples invited the traveler to dine with them. At the table, Jesus took the bread and broke it . . . just as he had done at the Last Supper. As he did this, the disciples recognized him, and Jesus vanished.

Filled with hope and joy, the two disciples decided to return at once to Jerusalem. There, they told the apostles what had happened on the road to Emmaus, and of how they had recognized Jesus.

23 Jesus Appears to the Apostles

Luke 24

Gathered together for supper, the two disciples who had been to Emmaus were telling the apostles that Jesus had risen from the dead and had accompanied them on their walk.

Suddenly Jesus himself appeared among them and said: "Peace be with you!"

They were all amazed and frightened. They could see that it was Jesus and yet he was not the same as before. But Jesus said: "Why are you surprised and troubled? Look at my hands and my feet. Do you not recognize me? A spirit does not have flesh and bones as you see that I have."

The apostles were overcome with joy at seeing that the Lord was alive, and they were so moved to see him that they did not know what to do. To give them further proof, Jesus asked: "Do you have anything to eat?" The apostles immediately offered him a portion of roast fish. Jesus took the fish and ate it in front of them to show that he was a real person.

"Everything has taken place as I told you it would," Jesus reminded them. "It was written that the Christ should suffer and rise from the dead on the third day."

 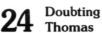

24 Doubting Thomas

John 20

On the same day that he rose from the dead, Jesus appeared to all the apostles and said to them: "Just as the Father sent me, so I send you." He then breathed on them and added: "Receive the Holy Spirit. Whoever's sins you now forgive, shall be forgiven in heaven. Whoever's sins you do not forgive, shall not be forgiven."

The apostle Thomas was not present at this meeting. Later, the others told him: "We have seen the Lord!" But he replied: "If I do not see the marks of the nails in his hands and put my finger into them, and put my hand into the wound on his side, I will not believe you." Eight days later, the apostles were once again together with Thomas. The doors were locked, yet Jesus appeared and said, just as before, "Peace be with you!"

He then turned to Thomas and went on: "Put your finger here and look at my hands. Stretch out your hand and put it into my side. Doubt no more, but now believe!"

And Thomas answered: "My Lord and my God!" Jesus then said to him: "You have believed because you have seen. Blessed are they who have not seen and believe!"

25 Breakfast by the Side of the Lake

John 21

A short while later a group of the apostles went fishing on the Sea of Galilee. As they were returning to the shore, a stranger on the beach asked them: "Have you caught nothing?" "Nothing at all!" they replied. The stranger then said: "Throw your nets into the water on the right-hand side of the boat." They did this and the net came up full of fish. John then understood that the stranger was Jesus himself! Jesus awaited them on the shore. "Bring your fish," he said, "and we shall have breakfast."

26 Feed My Sheep . . .

John 21

By the side of the Sea of Galilee, Jesus had made a breakfast of bread and fish for himself and a group of the apostles.

After they had finished eating, Jesus said to Simon-Peter: "Simon, son of John, do you love me more than the others?" "Of course, Lord. You know that I love you," replied Peter. And Jesus said: "Feed my lambs!"

A second time Jesus asked; "Simon, son of John, do you love me?" and again Peter replied: "Of course, Lord. You know that I love you." And Jesus said: "Feed my sheep."

Then, for the third time, Jesus said: "Simon, son of John, do you truly love me?" Peter replied: "Lord, you know everything. You know that I love you."

And Jesus said to him: "Feed my sheep."

At the house of Caiaphas, Peter had denied knowing Jesus three times. Now, on the shore of the Sea of Galilee, Jesus gave him three chances to show his love.

When Jesus said: "Feed my sheep," to Peter, he was telling him to take care of and nourish the faith of those who believed in him.

27 Jesus Returns to the Father

Matthew 28; Acts 1

In the forty days which followed Jesus' resurrection from the dead, he explained many things to the apostles concerning the Kingdom of Heaven, and told them what they had to do in his name.

He gave them the power to forgive sins so that everybody could, if they so wished, come to love God and one day enter his kingdom.

Jesus also said to them: "Every power in heaven and on earth has been given to me. Go, therefore, and teach all nations what I have taught you. You must baptize whoever believes in me, and I shall always be with you!"

Jesus then said that soon he would send the Holy Spirit among them and that, therefore, they were not to go away from Jerusalem.

Exactly forty days after his resurrection from the dead, Jesus led the apostles to the Mount of Olives and there, before their very eyes, he was raised up into heaven. The apostles continued to stare at the sky until two angels clothed in light appeared to them and said: "Why are you standing here, gazing up to heaven? This same Jesus, who has left you and gone up to heaven, will one day return in the same manner."

28 The Disciple Matthias

Matthew 27; Acts 1

After the ascension of Jesus into heaven, the apostles returned to the city and prayed with Mary, the mother of Jesus, and a group of disciples. They then decided to resolve a problem. Judas Iscariot, had betrayed Jesus, had realized he had done a great evil. He had taken the thirty coins he had received as payment for the betrayal and he had given them back to the high priests. Then he had hanged himself.

There now remained, therefore, only eleven apostles. For this reason Peter spoke: "We must find another man to take the place of Judas. He must be one of those disciples who has followed Jesus from the day he was baptized by John the Baptist. He must have heard all the teachings of Jesus and be able to bear witness that he rose from the dead and ascended into heaven."

Two disciples were chosen from those who fulfilled these requirements. They then all offered the following prayer: "Lord, you who know the hearts of men, show us which of these two you have chosen." They then drew lots and a disciple by the name of Matthias was chosen and thus joined the other eleven apostles.

157

29 Fire from the Sky

Acts 2

The feast of Pentecost fell ten days after Jesus had ascended into heaven. Jews from all around and from many distant countries had gathered in Jerusalem. Pentecost was, in fact, one of the most important Jewish feasts and was observed in celebration of the harvest.

It was nine o'clock in the morning. The apostles, Mary the mother of Jesus, and other disciples were gathered together to pray. Suddenly, a great noise like a rushing wind was heard and tongues of fire appeared over each of them.

They were all filled with the Holy Spirit, the gift promised them by Jesus. The Holy Spirit filled the apostles with courage and they all went out and began to speak of Jesus.

Drawn by the great noise, many people had gathered around the house. Every one of them, even the foreigners, realized to their great surprise that they were hearing the apostles speak in their own language. "How is it," they said, "that we hear these men speak in our own languages? Among us there are Parthians, Medes, and Elamites. Some come from Mesopotamia, some from Cappadocia, from Pontus, from Asia, from Phrygia, from Egypt, from Libya, from Crete, and some of us from Arabia. There are even some of us from Rome. How can we all, at the same time, hear these men speaking to us of the marvels of God?"

Others, however, laughed and said: "Those men who are speaking are drunk!" But Peter said to them: "No. We are not drunk! It is only nine o'clock in the morning! Rather, you should know this: The Jesus who was crucified was the Christ, the long-awaited Messiah. He was the Son of God! He has risen from the dead and sent the Holy Spirit among us!"

30 Three Thousand New Christians

Acts 2

Peter explained to the crowd that Jesus was the Messiah foretold by the prophets. "Our chief priests had him crucified," Peter said. "But God has raised him from the dead!"

Struck by his words, many people asked: "What must we do?" And Peter replied: "Repent and every one of you will be baptized in the name of Jesus Christ. Your sins will be forgiven and you will receive the gift of the Holy Spirit." When they heard this, many people asked to be baptized. Three thousand believers were added that day.

BIBLE STORY OF THE MONTH

Peter and Cornelius

Every day the number of those who believed in the Lord Jesus grew. They listened carefully to the teachings of the apostles and prayed together often. They took part in the celebration of the various rites, especially the one then called the "breaking of bread."

All the new believers shared their personal possessions. They were of one heart and one soul, and they openly declared their faith: Jesus, who had been crucified, had now risen from the dead and was standing at the right hand of the Father in heaven.

All the believers belonged to the people of Israel and they thought that Jesus had come to bring salvation to their people only. Very soon, however, another problem arose: an ever greater number of non-Jewish people, Greeks and Romans, for example, had heard talk of Jesus and were asking to become his followers. In the church, the family of the followers of Jesus, there was much discussion as to whether or not to admit those who did not belong to the people of Israel.

And there was yet another problem to resolve. The Jews observed many special rules, some of which concerned the food they ate. They did not eat certain animals like pigs, certain birds, any shellfish, and no animal that had died by suffocation. They considered all these foods to be "impure" and even when they became Christians they continued to believe that it was a sin to eat them. Those who were not Jewish, on the other hand, did not follow these rules. If they were to be admitted into this new church, if they were to become Christians, were they to be obliged to observe the laws of the Jews? Did they have to stop eating these "impure" foods?

The Lord himself intervened to solve these problems. It happened in the following way.

An officer in the Roman army, by the name of Cornelius, lived with his family in the city of Caesarea. He was a good man who loved God and sought to do his will: He prayed regularly and gave generously to the poor. One afternoon, around three o'clock, Cornelius had a vision. He clearly saw and heard an angel who said to him: "Cornelius, God has heard your prayers and looked upon your kindness to the poor. You must send some men at once to Joppa to bring back here a certain Simon, also known as Peter. They will find him living as a guest in the house of a tanner, also called Simon. The house is by the sea."

Cornelius immediately called two servants and a soldier whom he

trusted. He explained to them everything that had taken place and sent them to Joppa.

The next day, while the three messengers from Cornelius were still making their way toward the city, Peter went up onto the terrace of the house where he was a guest, to pray. It was around midday. Not having eaten, Peter, naturally, was hungry. During his prayers he suddenly had a vision: He saw a great tablecloth descend from the sky and on it were all the animals that he had always considered impure. A voice said to him: "Rise, Peter, and eat!" "No Lord, I cannot," replied Peter, "for I have never eaten any-thing that is impure." But the Lord said to him: "Nothing of what I have created is impure."

This scene repeated itself three times, and Peter could have no doubts as to what he had seen and heard. He understood what the Lord had said: Rules about food depended on the different customs of different peoples; nobody should expect other people to follow their rules about eating. He also understood that all peoples are equal before God; we are all equally dear to his heart.

In the meantime, the three messengers from Cornelius had reached Joppa and had arrived outside the house of the tanner. The Holy Spirit spoke to Peter: "Three men are seeking you. Go with them for they are sent by God."

The next day Peter, accompanied by a group of Christians, went with them to Caesarea. He entered the house of Cornelius and said: "You know that Jews like myself do not enter the homes of men from other peoples because they consider them impure. But God has shown me that nothing and nobody is impure. In fact, I realize now that he has no preference for any type of person: Whoever lives in a way that is pleasing to God is loved by God."

Peter then went on to tell them all about Jesus, and he was still speaking when the Holy Spirit came down upon everyone who was listening.

The Christians who had accompanied Peter were astonished that the Holy Spirit had also come down on those who were not Jewish. But, having seen what had happened, Peter said: "We cannot refuse to baptize these people who have received the Holy Spirit in the same way as ourselves."

Cornelius and the other members of his household were all baptized at once. They were the first non-Jewish people to become followers of Christ and enter the Christian family: the first of a long line that continues to this day.

Acts 2, 10

1 The Lame Man at the Beautiful Gate

Acts 3

One afternoon, about three o'clock, the apostles Peter and John went up to the temple in Jerusalem to pray.

When they reached the temple, they entered by a gate known as the "Beautiful Gate." There they saw a cripple who had been carried every day to the gate in order to beg.

The lame man asked Peter and John for alms, but Peter looked at him and said: "Look at us." The cripple obeyed, hoping to receive a few coins. Instead, Peter said to him: "I have neither gold nor silver, but what I have I will give you. In the name of Jesus Christ, get up and walk!"

As he said these words, Peter took the man by the right hand and lifted him up. And immediately the feet and ankles of the lame man grew strong. He leapt to his feet and began to walk around and then to jump for joy, before following the apostles into the temple to give thanks to God.

There were many people coming and going by the "Beautiful Gate" and they all knew the lame man who sat there to beg for alms: Every one of them was amazed when they saw him walking and jumping for joy.

2 Barnabas, a Generous Apostle

Acts 4

The first Christians shared all their possessions, so that everybody had what he needed. If one of them owned fields or houses, he sold them and brought the proceeds to the apostles, who then distributed the money to the neediest.

One of the men who did this was Joses, a Jew from Cyprus, whom the apostles called Barnabas. This name means "Son of Encouragement" and Barnabas, in fact, began to work closely with the apostles and was very active, speaking to everyone about Jesus.

3 Peter and John are Brought before the Council

Acts 4

Peter had healed the lame man at the Beautiful Gate of the temple. He explained to the crowd that he had acted in the name of Jesus.

Suddenly, however, the guards arrived and arrested Peter and John and put them in prison. The next day, the chiefs of the people questioned the two apostles: "Who has given you the power to do such a thing?" they asked.

Peter was filled with the Holy Spirit and he replied with great courage: "Jesus of Nazareth! The same Jesus that you put to death and God has resurrected, for Jesus alone can free us from evil!"

The chiefs of the people feared that the news of Peter's miracle might lead more people to become Christians, so they ordered the apostles not to speak about Jesus anymore. Peter and John, however, answered them: "You can judge for yourselves whether it is right to obey God or to obey you. We cannot help speaking about great things!"

Once again the chiefs of the people threatened Peter and John and then they released them, in fear of all the people who praised them for the miracle they had just performed.

4 Touched by his Shadow

Acts 5

Every day the apostles went to the temple and sat under Solomon's porch. There they taught the doctrines of Jesus, and performed many miracles among the people. They were respected by everyone and every day the number of those who believed in the Lord grew.

From all over Jerusalem and the nearby villages, people carried the sick on stretchers and laid them in the streets, so that when Peter passed by, at least his shadow might touch them. And every one of them was healed.

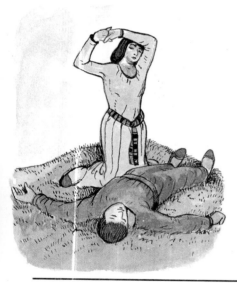

5 The Story of Two Liars

Acts 5

A certain man named Ananias and his wife Sapphira sold a field in order to distribute the proceeds among the poor. But, secretly, they kept some of the money apart.

Peter found out about this and said to Ananias: "As you well know, nobody forced you to sell your field. And even after you had sold it you could have done as you wished with the money. But you should not have said that you had given it all away! You did not lie to us, you lied to God!"

Ananias was so dismayed at what he had done that he fell to the ground, dead. A group of young men wrapped his body in a sheet and carried it off for burial. Sapphira, who did not know what had happened, arrived three hours later.

Peter asked her at once: "Sapphira, did you really sell the field for this amount of money?" Her reply was "yes," and Peter then went on: "You and your husband agreed to cheat the Lord! Look, the men who buried your husband are just returning. Now they shall also bury you!"

And, in fact, at that moment Sapphira too fell down dead and everyone understood that it was a great sin to lie to the Lord.

6 Seven Helpers for the Apostles

Acts 6

The numbers of the disciples of Jesus continued to grow and the twelve apostles could no longer carry out their work with all of them. Thus, they called a meeting and said: "It is not right that we should set aside the Word of God and concern ourselves with feeding people. Brothers, you must choose seven men of faith and wisdom from among you to be our helpers." This proposal pleased everyone, and seven men, including Stephen and Philip, were chosen to help the apostles distribute food.

7 Stephen, the First Martyr

Acts 6–7

Stephen was one of the seven helpers of the apostles and he was full of faith and love for the Lord Jesus. He argued very ably with the Jews in order to show them that Jesus was the Messiah sent by God.

Because they could not defeat him in argument, several of the Jews began to accuse him falsely. They said that Stephen had blasphemed against Moses, against the law of God, and against the temple. They repeated these false charges until Stephen was brought to trial before the high priest.

The high priest asked Stephen if the accusations made against him were true. Stephen then made a long speech: He reminded them that the people of Israel had often behaved badly toward God; they had not listened to the prophets and even ignored Moses; they had received the law from God, but had often failed to obey it.

Stephen then added that God had decided to make himself known to man and had therefore sent Jesus, his Son. Just as the Jews had killed the prophets sent by God in the past, so had they killed Jesus.

The chief priest and all those with him were enraged at Stephen's words. Stephen, however, said: "Behold, I look unto the heavens and see Jesus, standing at the right hand of the Father."

In this way, Stephen was proclaiming that Jesus, too, was God. The chief priest and the judges were shocked and angry and they condemned Stephen to be stoned to death. They dragged him outside of the city at once and began to throw rocks at him. Stephen began to pray and, like Jesus on the cross, he said: "Lord, accept my life." Then, knowing that he was close to death, Stephen fell to his knees and added: "Lord, forgive them for what they are doing."

8 Saul Against the Christians

Acts 6–7

Stephen was the first Christian martyr, the first of many men and women to give their lives for love of Jesus. The people who stoned him to death had given their cloaks to a young man named Saul to hold.

In those days, there was a great deal of persecution against the Christians in Jerusalem. Saul would go into houses and arrest men and women and have them thrown into prison. Many fled to other cities where they could speak of Jesus and spread his teachings throughout the land.

9 Philip and the Magician Simon

Acts 8

Philip, one of the seven helpers of the apostles, went to a city in Samaria. There, he began to speak of the Lord and he accompanied the Word with many miracles.

In this way, many of the inhabitants of the city came to believe and were baptized. Among them, Simon the magician, who had enchanted many people with his spells for a great many years. Even Simon spent all his time at Philip's side and came to marvel at the many miracles and wonders that he saw Philip perform.

10 Peter and the Magician Simon

Acts 8

The apostles Peter and John went to Samaria to visit those who had received the Word of God. They prayed for the Samaritans and laid their hands on them and, in this way, the Samaritans received the Holy Spirit.

When Simon saw that the Holy Spirit was bestowed through the laying of hands, he went to the apostles and offered them a great deal of money, saying: "Give me this power, so that those on whom I lay my hands will receive the Holy Spirit!"

At once, however, Peter grew angry and replied: "Leave, and take your money with you! You believe that a gift from God can be bought for money: You must cease to believe such things. Pray to the Lord to forgive your wickedness! I see now that you are full of bitterness and a slave to evil!" Peter, of course, had remembered what Jesus told the apostles when he spoke to them of God's gift to us: "What you have freely received, that you must freely give!"

When he heard the words of Peter, Simon at once repented and said: "Pray to the Lord for me, that I might be forgiven."

11 The Minister of the Queen of Ethiopia

Acts 8

An angel of the Lord said to Philip: "Get up and go toward the south, on the road from Jerusalem to Gaza."

Philip set off, and while he was traveling he came across a chariot, inside of which a man was reading. He was an Ethiopian, the superintendent of the treasury of Candace, the queen of Ethiopia. He was a believer in God, and he was returning from Jerusalem where he had gone to pray in the temple.

Along the way, the superintendent had been reading the book of the prophet Isaiah, and when he met up with Philip he was reading the passage which says: "Like a sheep that is led to the slaughterhouse, and like a lamb that is dumb, he does not complain. . . ."

The Ethiopian asked Philip: "Tell me, please, who is the prophet speaking about?"

Philip explained that Isaiah announced the death of the Messiah, Jesus. He spoke so well, that when they reached a spring, the man said to Philip: "Look, what is to stop me from being baptized?" The superintendent stopped the chariot and they both got into the water, and Philip baptized him.

12 Saul on the Road to Damascus

Acts 9

Saul had decided to destroy the disciples of Jesus. For this reason, he asked the chiefs' permission to go to Damascus and arrest the Christians. He obtained their permission and an armed escort.

He was traveling toward Damascus when, suddenly, a light came down from the sky and wrapped itself around him. He fell to the ground and heard a voice that said: "Saul, Saul, why do you persecute me?" Who are you?" replied Saul. And the voice continued: "I am Jesus, whom you persecute."

13 Saul and Ananias

Acts 9

There, on the road to Damascus, Jesus revealed himself to Saul, the persecutor of the Christians. Jesus also said to him: "Get up and enter the city: Someone there will tell you what you have to do."

Saul got up from the ground and realized that he was blind. His guards led him into the city.

In Damascus there lived a Christian named Ananias. In a vision the Lord spoke to him in the following way: "Go to Straight Street, and look for a man from Tarsus called Saul. At this moment he is praying, and in a vision he has seen you arrive and place your hands on his eyes to give him back his sight."

Ananias replied: "Lord, I know of all the evils that he has done to the faithful in Jerusalem." But the Lord said: "Go and put your hands on his eyes. For me, he is a tool that I have chosen in order to make myself known among all peoples."

Ananias went, he placed his hands over Saul's eyes and said: "Saul, my brother, the Lord has sent me to you." And Saul regained his sight and was baptized. And to show everyone that he was a different man, Saul changed his name to Paul.

14 Paul Lowered in a Basket

Acts 9–13

Saul had received baptism and had become Paul, a new man who believed in the Lord Jesus. He immediately began going around announcing his faith in the synagogues of Damascus. The Hebrews were astonished and said: "But isn't he the one who threw the Jews into prison in Jerusalem? How is it that now he has become a Christian?"

Some of the Hebrews decided to put him to death. But Paul found out about their plans, and at night he had himself lowered from the walls of Damascus in a basket.

15 Peter at Lydda

Acts 9

The Church was enjoying a period of peace, and it was growing continually.

Peter, the leader of the Church, decided to go and visit the different Christian communities. When he reached the city of Lydda, he found a man named Aeneas, who had been lying paralyzed on his bed for eight years. Peter said to him: "Aeneas, Jesus Christ heals you. Get up and make your bed." At once the paralyzed man arose. The inhabitants of Lydda saw him and were converted to the Lord.

16 Peter Raises up Tabitha

Acts 9

Peter was visiting the community of Lydda, when, in the nearby city of Jaffa, a Christian woman grew ill and died. Her name was Tabitha, which means "gazelle," and she was much loved by everyone because she never tired of doing good and giving charity to the poor.

The Christians were very sad over the death of Tabitha, and when they heard that the apostle Peter was in Lydda they sent two men to call him, and they said to him: "Come with us at once."

Peter went, and as soon as he arrived they took him into the room where the woman's body had been laid out. There were a group of widows present and, in tears, they showed Peter the clothes that Tabitha had made for them.

Then Peter told everyone to leave, and he knelt down to pray. Then, turning to the body, he said: "Tabitha, get up!" She opened her eyes, saw the apostle and sat up; he took her by the hand and raised her up, then he presented her to the widows and the other Christians.

All of Jaffa heard of the resurrection of Tabitha, and because of this, many people came to believe in the Lord Jesus, becoming Christians.

17 Herod Has Peter Imprisoned

Acts 12

In Jerusalem King Herod began to persecute the Christians, and had the apostle James put to death. Seeing that this pleased the Hebrew leaders, he had Peter arrested as well and placed him under heavy guard: four squads of four soldiers each.

It was a few days before the Passover feast, and the king planned to try the leader of the Church in public after the feast.

While Peter was in prison, an incessant prayer went up from the Church to God for his safety.

18 Peter Is Freed from Prison

Acts 12

The day was approaching on which Herod planned to try Peter before the people. The night before the trial Peter slept in prison, bound in chains and watched over by the soldiers. And then a bright light filled the cell, and an angel of the Lord came down. The angel woke Peter and said: "Get up, hurry!"

At these words the chains dropped from his hands. The angel continued: "Put on your belt and your cloak and tie your sandals." Peter did so. Then the angel said: "Follow me."

Peter could not believe that what was happening was real. He was convinced that he was having a vision. He followed the angel, and with him he passed the first guard and then the second, until they were before the iron gate which gave access to the road from the prison. The door opened by itself before them.

They went out and walked a little way along the road; then Peter realized that the angel had disappeared. Only then did he truly realize what had happened, and he thought to himself: "The Lord has sent an angel to free me. He has delivered me from the hands of Herod, who sought my ruin."

19 A Girl Named Rhoda

Acts 12

The prayers of the Church had been answered: The Lord had sent his angel to free Peter from prison. Now in the streets of Jerusalem, Peter thought that as soon as the guards noticed he was gone from his cell they would come to look for him.

He had to find somewhere to hide himself. After thinking about it, he decided that the best place was the house of some friends of his: the house of Mary, the mother of John, also called Mark, who was later to write one of the Gospels.

In that house there were a fair number of Christians, gathered together in prayer. As soon as they heard a knock on the door, they sent a girl named Rhoda to find out who it was.

She went up to the door. But when she recognized the voice, she was so overcome with joy that she forgot to open the door and instead rushed to announce to the others that Peter was outside.

"You don't know what you're saying!" was the reply. And meanwhile Peter continued to knock. When they finally got around to opening the door and saw him, they were speechless. And he told them what had happened.

20 The Community of Antioch

Acts 11

Those who had fled from Jerusalem, when the persecutions began at the time of Stephen, had been scattered far and wide. Some had gone to the great city of Antioch, in Syria.

There, they began to announce the Lord Jesus again, to both the Hebrews and the non-Hebrews, the pagans. The hand of the Lord was with them, and so a great many believed and were converted to the Lord.

In Antioch, for the first time, the disciples of Jesus were called Christians.

21 Paul and Barnabas are Sent by the Holy Spirit

Acts 4–13

One day the community of Antioch was gathered in prayer and there were many Christians present who were known for their faith and for their good works. As they were worshiping the Lord, the Holy Spirit came to them and said: "Tell Barnabas and Paul that I have chosen them especially to do difficult work for me." This work meant spreading the word of Jesus in places where it had never been heard before.

After they had fasted and prayed together, the Christians of Antioch laid their hands on Paul and Barnabas and said good-bye to them. Thus Paul and Barnabas departed on their long journey to the island of Cyprus.

Paul and Barnabas at once began to preach the word of the Lord in the various cities on the island. They decided that it was right to give the good news first to the Jews, and so every Sabbath day they went into the synagogues and spoke of the Lord Jesus.

On many occasions their words were heard with interest by the Jews; and some of them were converted to Christianity. But often they chose not to listen to the words of the apostles.

22 Paul and Elymas the Sorcerer

Acts 13

In the city of Paphos on the island of Cyprus, the Roman governor Sergius Paulus had called for Paul and Barnabas because he wished to hear the word of God. Among the servants of the governor was a sorcerer called Elymas the Jew, who did everything in his power to prevent his master from believing the apostles.

At this, Paul turned to Elymas and said: "When will you cease to work against the will of the Lord? Behold, for one whole season you shall be blind as a warning from the Lord!" And that was what happened.

May

23 Paul Is Persecuted

Acts 13–14

After they left the island of Cyprus, Paul and Barnabas continued on their voyage and they disembarked in Asia Minor, which today is Turkey. Here, they proclaimed the Word of God, first to the Jews, and then to the Gentiles.

Often the Jews opposed them in every way imaginable. At Lystra it was a group of Jews who persuaded the crowd to stone Paul so badly that they thought they had killed him. They dragged his body out of the city and dumped it. Fortunately, a number of disciples found Paul.

24 Paul and Barnabas Are Mistaken for Gods

Acts 14

On their long journey as missionaries, Paul and Barnabas had arrived in the city of Lystra.

There, Paul began to preach, and while he was speaking he noticed a man listening to him whose legs had been paralyzed from birth. Paul looked straight at him and said in a loud voice: "Get up and stand on your feet!" And, with a leap, the cripple got up and began to walk.

When they saw this miracle, the pagans immediately said to each other: "The Gods have come down among us in human form!" For they believed that Barnabas was the god Jupiter, and Paul was the god Mercury.

It was the custom of the pagans to offer animals to their gods in sacrifice. Thus, the priest of Jupiter then arrived, followed by a large crowd, with a bull that he intended to offer in sacrifice to Barnabas. However, when Paul and Barnabas saw this, they raced into the crowd shouting: "Citizens, do not do this! We are men like you! We came here especially to tell you not to worship these false gods and to turn instead to the Father, the one true God!" Finally, Paul and Barnabas convinced the crowd not to offer them a sacrifice.

25 Paul Is Sent to Europe

Acts 16

After he had returned to Antioch, Paul once again departed, this time with a disciple named Silas, to spread the Word of God. At Lystra, Paul met a young Christian by the name of Timotheus whom he took with him on his journey. When they reached Troas, a doctor, Luke, joined the group. One night Paul had a vision. He saw a man from Macedonia who begged him: "Come and save us!" The vision was given to him by the Lord, and Paul set sail at once for Europe.

May

26 Lydia, the Seller of Purple Dye
Acts 16

On his second journey as a missionary, the apostle Paul was accompanied by Timotheus and other disciples. One of these disciples was Luke, a young physician.

After the vision had told Paul to move from Asia into Europe, the little group boarded a ship which took them to Neapolis in Macedonia. From there they proceeded on foot to the important city of Philippi.

That Sabbath day they decided, as usual, to spread the good news first among the Jews. They went where the Jews met, outside the city, on the banks of a river.

When the apostles arrived, they came across a group of women. They immediately sat down and began to speak with them. Among those was Lydia, a seller of purple dye. The Lord opened her heart and she became a convert at once and was baptized along with all her family. She then invited Paul and the other disciples to her home: "If you are convinced that I have really heard the word of the Lord, then you can come to my house." And Paul and the others accepted.

27 Paul Is Imprisoned in Philippi
Acts 16

In the city of Philippi Paul succeeded in forming a small group of Christians. Many citizens, however, were opposed to him. One day, some of them grabbed Paul and his disciple Silas and dragged them both before the judges.

Here, they accused them in the following way: "These two men are spreading disorder by preaching practices different from ours." The crowd that was gathered grew angry at Paul and Silas when they heard these words and the judges ordered them to be thrown into prison.

28 An Earthquake at Philippi
Acts 16

Paul and Silas had been thrown into prison at Philippi. During the night, while they prayed and sang hymns of praise to the Lord, a great earthquake shook the foundations of the prison, opened all the doors and broke the chains of the prisoners.

When the warden saw all the doors lying open, he thought that the prisoners had escaped. He knew that he would be held responsible and drew out his sword in order to kill himself. When Paul saw this, he shouted loudly: "Do yourself no harm, we are all here!"

The warden could not believe it. He took a lamp and rushed into the cell of Paul and Silas. When he saw that they really were still there, he was very glad. He led them outside and said to them: "I see that you are better men than others. I have faith, therefore, in the words you speak. What must I do?"

"Believe in the Lord Jesus and you will be saved," replied Paul and he then explained who Jesus was.

The prison warden at Philippi heard Paul's words and believed in them and was baptized at once. He then took care of Paul and Silas, washing their wounds and inviting them to his own house to eat.

171

29 The Arms of the Christian

Ephesians 6

When he was in prison, Paul watched the soldiers who were guarding him closely. The arms that they carried led him to think of every Christian as a type of soldier, armed by God to conquer evil. This is what Paul said:

"Brothers, the truth is your belt. Good works are your armor. The sandals on your feet should be the readiness to spread the good news. Your faith is your shield and the salvation brought by Jesus is your helmet. Your sword is the Word of God!"

30 Paul, the Citizen of Rome

Acts 16

At Philippi the judges had ordered Paul and Silas to be beaten and thrown into prison. The next day they gave orders that they should be freed. Paul, however, said to the guards: "First they beat us with sticks and imprison us without a trial though we are citizens of Rome! And now they wish to release us in secret? No, the judges must come and release us themselves, thereby recognizing before all the people that we have done nothing wrong."

The guards repeated these words to the judges, who became very frightened when they heard that Paul and Silas were citizens of Rome. The laws of Rome were very severe; it was forbidden for anybody to beat one of its citizens.

The judges, therefore, went straight to the prison to apologize to Paul and Silas for what had happened the previous day and to set them free.

The apostle and Silas left the prison and went to the house of Lydia, the seller of purple dye, and remained as her guests. Here they had many meetings with the Christians of Philippi and they filled them with faith and courage before departing.

31 Like Runners in a Race . . .

1 Corinthians, 9

When he spoke, Paul often used examples that his listeners could understand, like the following sporting example.

"Brothers, you know that many runners take part in a race, but only one will win the prize. In a way, all of you are running in a race to win a prize that is offered by the Lord.

"You also know that runners train and suffer for long periods in order to win a crown of glory that soon disappears. We, on the other hand, are running for a prize that lasts forever, the glory of the Lord!"

BIBLE STORY OF THE MONTH

Paul Preaches In Greece

Paul, who had persecuted the Christians, had had a dramatic encounter with the risen Christ on the road to Damascus. From that moment on, he dedicated himself tirelessly to spreading the Word of God. Either alone or in the company of other disciples, he went on long and difficult journeys through Europe and Asia, and he succeeded in converting many people. Paul journeyed by ship or on foot, usually in the company of other Christians. Of these Mark and Luke each wrote one of the Gospels.

When Paul arrived in a city, he would await the Sabbath and then go into a synagogue to talk about Jesus with the Jews. A few of these would follow, but the majority would always oppose him and Paul would then preach to the pagans.

When he reached Athens, the most important Greek city, Paul had a strange adventure. The city was full of magnificent temples dedicated to gods. Paul trembled within himself when he saw all of these false gods and idols. He went at once to the main square and began to talk to the people that he met. Paul even argued with the philosophers, many of whom were highly respected in Athens. Some of them said: "What has this charlatan come to teach us?" Others, however, said: "He has come to talk of strange gods."

And since the most popular pastime in Athens was listening to and talking about the latest news and gossip, Paul was invited to speak before the council of the city, which was called the Areopagus.

In front of the most important people of the city, Paul began to speak: "Citizens of Athens, I see that you are very religious people. I have walked through your city and I have noticed that you build temples to many gods. As I walked through one part I even came across an altar dedicated to "The Unknown God." Good! For I have come to show you the God whom you worship and do not yet know."

The citizens of Athens were astounded at these words, but Paul went on: "This God created the world and everything in it. He is the Lord of heaven and earth and, truly, he does not live in the temples built by men. He does not need men to serve him, for he lacks nothing. On the contrary, it is he who gives life and everything else to all things. He created the first man and gave him as his descendants other men and all the peoples who live on the earth. And since he has made us in his image, we must not believe that he is made of gold or silver or marble. We must not believe that statues built by men for their own gods

are images of the true god.''

Paul now had to explain the most delicate aspect of his message to the Athenians and he did it using these words: ''God has decided to forgive us for the past, when men lived in ignorance. He has sent his only son, Jesus, among men. He will judge all men righteously at a time decided by God, when all men rise from the dead, just as Jesus himself died and rose again. . . .''

When they heard this explanation from Paul, some of the Athenians began to laugh and others mocked him. Those who did not believe Paul joked: ''We will have to go over this point again, later!'' and

many of them walked away. A few of the Athenians, however, believed the words of Paul and became Christians.

The life Paul led really was extraordinary. After he had completed his third journey he was arrested and held prisoner for a long time in Palestine, before being transferred to Rome. He then was freed and went on other journeys, always taking care to spread the Word of the Lord wherever he went. In a letter to the Christians of the city of Corinth, he told the following story: ''I have received five times the Jewish penalty of thirty-nine lashes. Three times I have suffered the Roman

penalty of being beaten with rods. And once I was stoned.''

''I have been shipwrecked three times,'' Paul went on, ''And I have spent a day and a night on the open sea. I have traveled a great deal and I have faced every kind of danger: danger on rivers, danger in cities, danger in the desert and at sea. I have been attacked by brigands and by those who were not Christians, and I have been attacked by those who only pretend to follow Christ. I have borne great burdens and have spent entire nights without sleep. I have endured famine and thirst. Often, when I have not eaten, I have remained out in the cold because I had nothing with which to cover myself.

''Over and above all this, I have concerned myself every day with the well-being of the whole Christian community. If someone is in difficulty, I too am worried. If someone is weak in his faith, I suffer.''

But where did Paul find the strength to confront all these problems? He himself told us: ''Fourteen years ago I was taken up into heaven. There I heard words which were so marvelous that it is impossible for a man to repeat them.'' God, therefore, had granted to Paul a taste of the great joy that he would certainly be given when he had completed his work.

Acts 17: 2 Corinthians 11–12

1 Paul at Corinth

Acts 18

After Paul had been to Athens, he went on to Corinth. In this city, he met a Jew, Aquila, who had fled to Corinth from Rome with his wife Priscilla, after the emperor had ordered all Jews to depart.

Paul was welcomed under their roof, and since he was an expert in the work they did, the sewing of tents, he began to help in their business. Paul, in fact, always tried not to impose on other people, but to pay his way by working. And then, every Sabbath day, he would go to the synagogue.

2 Paul's Dream

Acts 18

In Corinth, Paul went to the synagogue on every Sabbath day to preach to everyone, Jews and Greeks, in order to convert them. To all of them he explained that Jesus was the Messiah sent by God. The Jews, however, did not want to believe him and they refused to listen and insulted him.

When this happened, Paul showed his anger. "I am doing everything I can to save you. If you will not be saved, it is your own fault! I will now go out and seek to save those who are not Jews!" Thus

Paul left and went to the home of a Greek. One night the Lord appeared to Paul in a dream and said to him: "Do not be afraid! Continue to spread the Word and do not fall silent, for I am with you!"

Paul stayed for a year and a half in Corinth and preached the Word of God. As the Lord had promised, many Jews were converted. Among these was the chief of the synagogue, Crispus.

A group of pagans also became converts and together all these people formed a large Christian community. Paul taught them in the faith with the help of his disciples Silas and Timotheus.

3 Gallio's Reply

Acts 18

One day several of the Jews of Corinth carried Paul before the Roman Governor Gallio. "This man," they said to him, "tries to persuade people to worship God in a way which is against the law."

Paul did not even have time to defend himself, before Gallio said: "If you are talking about a crime, an attack, or an evil deed, I will listen to you, O Jews! But since you are arguing over the subtleties of your own laws, you must decide for yourselves. I do not wish to judge such matters!"

4 Apollos Preaches in Ephesus

Acts 18

In the city of Ephesus a Christian by the name of Apollos spoke with great love of Jesus to both the Jews and the pagans. Aquila and Priscilla, the married friends of Paul, heard him speaking and realized that Apollos said many things that were not true, because he had never been instructed in his faith in Jesus. Therefore, they took him aside and carefully taught him everything he did not yet know. In this way, Aquila and Priscilla helped Apollos to spread the work of the Lord.

5 Paul in Ephesus

Acts 19

Paul left Corinth and the country of Greece in order to return to Asia Minor. He crossed the mountainous regions and arrived in the large and important city of Ephesus. There were already a number of believers in the city and Paul asked them: "Did you receive the Holy Spirit when you became Christians?" And these believers replied: "We do not even know what the Holy Spirit is. We were baptized in the way of John the Baptist."

Paul then explained to them that the baptism of John was for those who agreed to change their way of life and to believe in the one who was to come, namely Jesus; only by receiving the Holy Spirit could they now become Christ's followers.

When they heard this the disciples of Ephesus all asked to receive the Holy Spirit. Paul laid his hands on each and they were filled with the Holy Spirit. At once they began to speak in strange tongues and to prophesy and to bear witness for the Lord Jesus. Through Paul, God performed great miracles. People would take handkerchiefs and clothes that had been in contact with Paul and lay them on the sick, who would suddenly be healed.

6 The Magicians of Ephesus

Acts 19

When people saw the miracles performed through Paul, many tried to profit from them. One day, seven Jewish brothers went to a man possessed by a demon and said: "In the name of the Jesus whom Paul worships, be gone from this man."

The evil spirit, however, replied: "I know Jesus, and I know who Paul is, but who are you?" And immediately the possessed man threw himself upon them, overcame them, and beat them until they fled. After this, many magicians and sorcerers confessed and became Christians

7 A Young Man Named Eutychus

Acts 20

During one of his journeys Paul performed another great miracle. It was the anniversary of the resurrection of Jesus, and Paul was celebrating a meal in the name of the Lord. A young man named Eutychus was sitting on the window ledge until overcome with fatigue, he fell asleep, and fell from the third floor. They found him dead.

Paul went down to the young man and, taking the body in his arms, said: "Do not be sad. The boy is alive!" Eutychus was carried back into the house safe and sound!

8 The Silversmiths of Ephesus

Acts 19

At the time when the apostle Paul was working in Ephesus, a revolt broke out because of him.

A silversmith by the name of Demetrius earned his living making silver shrines for the goddess Diana, whereby he reaped profits.

One day, Demetrius called together all those who did the same work as he and said to them: "Have you not heard what the foreigner called Paul is saying? He says that the things we make with our hands, and which bring us such wealth, are not true gods. He has persuaded many people to stop worshiping the goddess Diana, and there is the risk that our trade will be ruined."

All the silversmiths then began to shout together: "How great is Diana, the goddess of the Ephesians!" They then went around the city, rousing the people. The crowd ran to the great open-air theater and began to shout and protest against Paul and his helpers.

After a while, two of Paul's companions, Aristarchus and Gaius were dragged into the theater. Paul feared for their safety and wanted to go into the theater in order to speak to the crowd, but the other Christians of the city stopped him, fearing it was too dangerous.

Meanwhile, there was great confusion in the theater. Some people said one thing and some another. For two hours many kept up a chorus of "Diana is great, the goddess of the Ephesians!"

The city chancellor then arrived, and with great difficulty succeeded in getting the crowd to listen to him. He told them: "You have dragged these men here, but they have not offended our goddess Diana. If Demetrius and the others believe they have been harmed, let them appeal to the court. The rest of you go home." The crowd obeyed and Gaius and Aristarchus were freed.

9 Farewell at the Port of Miletus

Acts 20

While traveling by ship, Paul arrived at the port of Miletus. There, he gathered the Christian community around him and said to them: "Now I intend to return to Jerusalem and I foresee that we shall not meet again. The Holy Spirit has warned me that I will have to face many difficulties. But the most important thing of all is that I continue to carry out my task: to tell everyone of God's love!"

Everyone burst into tears at the thought of not seeing Paul again, and when he left, they accompanied him to his ship.

10 By Sea toward Jerusalem

Acts 21

Paul was returning from one of his long, tiring, and dangerous missionary journeys. He was heading for Jerusalem, where he planned to celebrate the feast of Pentecost with his fellow believers.

He knew, and had told several of his companions, that many difficult times awaited him. The chiefs of the Jews were still opposed to his work as an apostle of Jesus, and in Jerusalem they would seek some new means of preventing him from carrying out his mission.

When the ship that Paul was traveling on reached Tyre, he took advantage of the long delay to meet the Christians who lived in that city. They, too, understood that it was very dangerous for Paul to return to Jerusalem and they urged him not to go.

Paul, however, was resolute: He considered it his duty to go, even if this meant he had to give up his life as Jesus had done. Thus, when the hour of his departure arrived, the Christians of Tyre, along with their wives and children, accompanied Paul to his ship. They knelt on the beach and prayed together before saying an affectionate farewell. Then Paul boarded his ship and set sail.

11 Some of Jesus' Words

Acts 20

The Gospels, which recount the life and works of Jesus, do not tell us everything about him, but only the parts that each evangelist considered most important.

One day, in one of his speeches, the apostle Paul told of a phrase spoken by Jesus which is not written in the Gospels. Jesus was telling his listeners to be full of love for their neighbors, and to particularly help those most in need. Paul then told them to remember what Jesus had said: "There is more joy in giving, than in receiving."

12 The Prophecy of Agabus

Acts 21

The ship in which Paul was traveling to Jerusalem stopped at the port of Caesarea. There Paul and his companions went to visit Philip, who was one of the seven who first helped the apostles.

They had been at Philip's house for several days when a prophet by the name of Agabus arrived from the region around Jerusalem. When Agabus came into Philip's house, he picked up Paul's belt and tied it around his own hands and feet. He then said: "This is what the Holy Spirit foretells: The man who owns this belt will be bound with it by the Jews of Jerusalem and handed over to the Gentiles."

When they saw and heard these things, Paul's traveling companions, Philip, and his other friends, all wept and begged him to change his plans and not travel to Jerusalem.

Paul, however, replied to them: "Why are you doing this? If you continue to cry in this way, you will break my heart. I am ready not only to be tied and bound, but to die in Jerusalem for my love of Jesus."

Just as he said he would, after he had completed his preparations several days later, Paul set out to finish his journey to Jerusalem.

13 Paul is Arrested in Jerusalem

Acts 21

After all his travels, Paul returned to Jerusalem where the other Christians greeted him joyfully. Paul first greeted James, who, after Peter had departed, had become the head of the Christian community.

Then, like every good Jew, Paul went to pray in the temple. Once there, however, he was seen by a group of non-Christian Jews from Asia Minor, who leaped on him and began to shout out: "Help us, men of Israel! This is the man who teaches all men everywhere to go against our faith!"

The people dragged Paul out of the temple, and were about to kill him when the Roman soldiers arrived.

When they saw the soldiers, the Jews stopped beating Paul. The captain of the soldiers arrested Paul and then asked the people around what crime he had committed. Everyone began to shout at the same time and they all said different things. At this, the captain decided to transfer the prisoner to the fortress to question him calmly. In order to save Paul from the violence of the crowd, the soldiers had to carry him on their shoulders. Many Jews shouted: "Put him to death!"

14 Paul's Defense

Acts 22

As Paul was being carried into the fortress, he asked the Roman captain if he could be allowed to address the crowd. "How is it that you can speak Greek?" the captain asked him, and then gave him permission to speak to the crowd.

Paul spoke to them in Hebrew, saying: "Brothers, listen to my defense. I am a Jew and I used to persecute the followers of Jesus, but then he himself spoke to me on the road to Damascus." Paul told them what Jesus had said, but the crowd shouted: "Put him to death!"

15 Paul Is Comforted by Jesus

Acts 22–23

Paul's defense before his own people in Jerusalem had proved useless. The crowd shouted that he was a traitor and should be put to death. The Roman soldiers led Paul into the fortress and tied him up in order to whip him. Just as he had once before pointed out to Philip, Paul now said: "Roman law forbids you to whip a Roman citizen, and I am a citizen of Rome!" When the captain of the guards heard these words, he was afraid, so he decided to send Paul to be tried before the highest court of the Jews.

When Paul appeared before the Jewish court, a great argument started at once over how to judge him. There were some who saw nothing wrong with what he had done, and there were some who wanted him put to death. The argument grew so heated that the captain feared for Paul's life and decided to take him to safety to a cell in the fortress where the Jews could not enter. That night, in his cell, Paul had a vision in which Jesus appeared to him and said: "Have courage! You have publicly declared yourself to be my disciple, here in Jerusalem. Now you must do exactly the same thing in Rome!"

16 Paul Escapes From a Plot

Acts 23

The apostle Paul had been imprisoned in the Roman fortress in Jerusalem. Several Jews who were his sworn enemies vowed they would kill him.

They decided on the following plan: They would convince the leaders of the people to try Paul before the court again. then attack and murder him. This plot, however, came to the attention of a young relative of Paul, who passed the information on at once to the Roman commander. Paul was immediately sent in secrecy to Caesarea.

17 A Letter to the Roman Governor

Acts 23

The Roman commander in Jerusalem wrote the following letter in which he entrusted the responsibility for Paul's life to the governor of Palestine. "I am sending you this man who has been arrested by the Jews. They were about to kill him when I intervened. Since he is a Roman citizen, I freed him and sent him before the Jewish court, to find out what the accusations against him were. The Jews have prepared a conspiracy against him and I am therefore sending him to you!"

18 Paul Appeals to the Roman Emperor

Acts 25

In order to save his prisoner from death at the hands of the Jews of Jerusalem, the commander of the Roman guards had taken Paul to Caesarea, where he could be tried in person by the Roman governor who ruled over Palestine.

The leaders of the Jewish people traveled from Jerusalem to Caesarea in order to accuse Paul of preaching a new faith. This was not a crime under Roman law. However, in order not to displease the Jewish chiefs, he ordered Paul kept in prison.

Two years later a new governor arrived in Caesarea. He retried Paul but could not condemn him. He therefore announced his intention of sending Paul, once again, back to Jerusalem.

Paul, however, knew that once he was in Jerusalem his enemies would find it very easy to put him to death. At this point there was only one course of action open to him. As was permitted by law to citizens of Rome, Paul announced his intention to appeal to the emperor, to be judged by the courts of Rome. "You have turned to the emperor, and so to the emperor you shall go!" the governor replied.

19 Paul Is Brought Before King Agrippa

Acts 25–26

A few days later, King Agrippa and his sister Bernice arrived in Caesarea as guests of the Roman governor. The governor told them the story of Paul, and King Agrippa said: "I want to hear what this man has to say."

The next day, Paul was brought before King Agrippa, who was a learned Jew. Paul explained to the king all the reasons that proved that Jesus was the Messiah. Paul also told his own story. Paul spoke so well that Agrippa said: "You have almost persuaded me to become a Christian!"

20 Storm and Shipwreck

Acts 27

Under the guard of several Roman soldiers commanded by the centurion Julius, Paul was sent from Caesarea to Rome to be judged by the emperor's court. Two of his companions were sent with him.

Their ship sailed very slowly, arriving at the island of Crete in winter, so they could sail no farther. However, the captain of the ship wanted to set off again at once in order at least to reach a more hospitable port. Unfortunately, a hurricane came up and the ship was caught in a whirlwind.

The ship drifted for fourteen days, driven and buffeted by the winds and the waves. The passengers had lost all hope of ever reaching safety, but Paul encouraged them saying: "Do not be afraid! Last night an angel of my God appeared to me and comforted me by telling me that I shall reach my destination, Rome, and that none of the people on the ship will perish. You should eat something now to give yourselves strength, and have faith in me."

Paul was the first to start eating and then all the others, with new hope, did the same. Meanwhile, the sailors had the impression that there was land nearby, so they cast out

the anchors and waited for dawn to find out where they were. When day came, they noticed a creek and tried to steer toward it. The ship, however, ran aground a long way from the shore and began to break up in the violent waves. The soldiers feared that the prisoners would escape by throwing themselves into the sea and so they decided to kill them. But the centurion Julius stopped them. He ordered those who could swim to throw themselves into the water, then everybody else, clutching onto planks of wood. Just as Paul had predicted, every one of the people on board safely reached the shore.

21 Bitten by a Viper

Acts 28

Paul and all who had escaped from the shipwreck had reached the shore of the island of Malta. The natives of the island greeted them with a huge fire.

Paul, too, gathered a bundle of twigs and branches to throw on the fire: but a viper that was awakened by the heat leaped out and fastened onto his hand. When they saw this, the people present thought: "This man must certainly be a murderer. He must pay for his crime!" But Paul simply shook his hand and the viper dropped into the fire.

183

22 Paul in Malta

Acts 28

Paul had been shipwrecked and had arrived on a beach on the island of Malta. He had gone to gather wood for the fire which the natives had lit. A viper had leaped from the wood and fastened itself to Paul's hand. The people who saw this expected to see Paul's hand swell up or even watch him fall down dead from the venom. But after seeing that nothing was wrong, they concluded he was a god. "This man must be a god!" they whispered.

A few days later they witnessed another miracle. The governor of the island was a man named Publius and he invited Paul and his companions to stay with him as his guests and he treated them with great courtesy. While they were staying there, the father of Publius fell ill with a high fever. Paul went to see him, prayed, laid his hands on the sick old man, and cured him.

When this became known, all the other people of the island who were sick came to Paul, and they too were cured by him. As a result of this, Paul was treated with great respect by everyone. Three months later he set out again, and the Maltese supplied all the provisions needed for the voyage.

23 On the Via Appia

Acts 28

It was impossible to sail during the winter and, so, in spring, Paul and his two companions, Luke and Aristarchus, set out once again on their journey to Rome. There, Paul was to be tried at the court of the emperor. Several Roman soldiers escorted him. The ship on which they set sail left Malta to the east, and sailed for Sicily. They crossed the Straits of Messina and arrived at Rhegium. The following day the south wind blew strongly and they quickly reached Puteoli.

At Puteoli, Paul was met by other Christians who invited him to stay with them for a week. He then set off once more, this time on foot, for the capital of the empire. The Christians of Rome were informed of his imminent arrival and went to meet Paul on the Via Appia.

When Paul saw them, he thanked the Lord and felt greatly heartened. And when they reached Rome, while he was awaiting trial, permission was immediately granted for Paul to live alone, with a single soldier as a guard.

Paul spent two years in his house in Rome. To every one of the many people who came to visit him he told the good news about Jesus.

24 Paul Teaches of Love

1 Corinthians 13

Paul was tireless in teaching everyone about Jesus Christ and what is pleasing to him. And what Jesus loves most of all is Love.
Though I might speak all the languages of men and of angels,
If I do not have love
I am like a clanging bell
Or a tinkling cymbal.
Even if I were a prophet
And I understood all of the mysteries
And I had a faith that could move mountains,
Without love it has no meaning.

Love is patient.
Love is thoughtful.
Love is not envious
And never boasts.
Love never swells with pride
And is always respectful.
Love forgives and has faith in everything.
Love hopes for everything and bears it all.
Love will have no end.
Now we do not see God clearly
But as if through an ancient mirror,
But, one day, we shall see him face to face.
Three things only have true value:
Faith, Hope, and Love.
And the greatest of these is Love.

25 Paul Helps a Runaway Slave

Letter to Philemon

The apostle Paul was a prisoner in Rome when he met a man named Onesimus. This man was a slave who had robbed his owner and fled. Paul spoke with Onesimus and persuaded him to become a Christian. He even convinced him to go back to his owner, taking a letter from Paul.

Paul already knew the owner of Onesimus. He was a man called Philemon, and he was a Christian who welcomed other Christians of the city to pray with him.

Thus, Paul wrote to Philemon: "I have sent Onesimus back to you: He has become like a son to me. If he has offended you, forgive him. If he still owes you something, I will pay his debt. Since I am still kept prisoner because of the love I have for the Lord Jesus, I would have been glad to keep Onesimus with me. You must not treat him like a slave, but rather as a brother. If you consider me your friend, then you will greet Onesimus."

Everything went just as Paul wished. Philemon received his fugitive servant and instead of punishing him, he treated him like a brother. This was just as Paul had asked and as Jesus had taught.

185

June

26 The Rich Man and the Pauper

James 1

Among the followers of Jesus there was a man named James who almost certainly later became the head of the Christian community in Jerusalem.

James wrote: "Brothers, if one of you is poor, let him rejoice because God has honored him. If one of you is rich, however, he should be glad for God to humble him. The rich man passes away like a flower in a field. The sun comes up and its warmth dries the land and the flower falls and its beauty vanishes forever."

27 A Life Offered in Sacrifice

2 Timothy 6

Paul's imprisonment in Rome lasted for two years. At the end of this period his innocence was acknowledged and he was set free. Paul at once began to travel again, to carry the Word of God to as many people as possible. He visited Christian communities that were already established and he founded many others. When Nero became emperor, however, Paul was once again arrested and brought to Rome.

In his twenty years of traveling and teaching, Paul had taken and spread the Gospel over the entire Roman empire. His life, however, was now drawing to a close, and he himself knew that his martyrdom was at hand. Knowing this, Paul wrote to his friend Timothy and said: "I am about to offer my life in sacrifice to God. The time has come for me to set out on my very last journey. I have fought the good fight. I have reached the end of my road and I have kept the faith. A winner's crown has been set aside for me as my reward. The most righteous judge of all, the Lord himself, shall give it to me. On the last day he will reward not only me but all men who await his return with love."

28 Actions Speak Louder than Words

James 2

The Word of God is full of the most marvelous lessons for us. One of the most important of these lessons is that words alone do not suffice; actions, too, are essential. James wrote: "Brothers, what does it mean if a man says he has faith and then does not show it in his actions? Suppose you meet a man with no clothes or with nothing to eat. If you say to him: 'Cover yourself' or 'Eat as much as you want!' they are words without sense if you do not give him clothing and food with which to satisfy his hunger!"

29 The True Christian Loves Peace

James 3

According to James, what is it that makes a true Christian? The true Christian is both good and mild, and his heart is full of the desire for peace. He is a man to whom God has given wisdom, and the wisdom that comes from God is pure, peaceable and gentle, expressed through good works. People who work for peace will enjoy the fruits of justice.

To be peaceful we must also know how to moderate what we say. James wrote: "The tongue is only a tiny part of our body and yet it is responsible for a great deal. The tongue is like the helm of a ship; if the helm steers properly then even a large and heavy vessel which is buffeted by great winds will go where the pilot directs it."

The true Christian is patient and awaits with faith the return of the Lord. He is like the farmer who waits for his crops to grow out of the earth, and awaits patiently the spring and autumn rains.

The true Christian is sincere and does not swear in the name of heaven or of earth. He simply says yes when he means yes and no when he means no! It was Jesus himself, remember, who told us this.

30 I Am the First and the Last

Revelation 1

John was a follower of Jesus who, because of his faith, was sent to live in exile on the island of Patmos in the Aegean Sea. Not only did he write the Fourth Gospel, the Gospel according to John, but he also wrote another book of the New Testament which is called The Revelation, which describes the many visions which John saw.

"One day," he wrote, "while I was in exile on the island of Patmos for having spread the Word of God, I heard a voice like a trumpet blast which said: 'Write all that you see in a book and send it to the seven churches.' "I turned and saw seven golden candlesticks and, a figure like the Son of Man, holding seven stars in his right hand.

"When I saw him I fell at his feet. But he placed his hand on me and said: 'Do not be afraid. I am the First and the Last. I am he who lives. I was dead and now I live forever. Write down what you have seen and what you will see and send it to the seven churches, which are symbolized by the seven candelabra and the seven stars.' "

It was Jesus himself, the Son of God, who commanded John to spread the Word of God.

Index

October

BIBLE STORY OF THE MONTH

Absalom, Son of David

1. The Lord Is My Shepherd
2. A Prophecy for David
3. The Gratitude of David
4. For Love of Jonathan
5. Solomon Is Crowned King
6. Solomon's Dream
7. The Judgment of Solomon
8. A House for the Lord
9. The Temple on Mount Zion
10. The Sanctuary of the Temple
11. The Holy of Holies
12. Offerings to the Lord
13. Priests and People in the Temple
14. The Lord Enters into his Temple
15. Pilgrims on the March
16. The Gratitude of the Pilgrims
17. The Pilgrims' Departure
18. The Feasts of Pentecost and the Day of Atonement
19. The Feast of the Tabernacles
20. The Ships of Solomon
21. The Greatness of Solomon
22. A Throne of Gold and Ivory
23. The Queen of Sheba's Caravan
24. Solomon and the Queen of Sheba
25. The Kingdom Divided
26. The Prophets of the Lord
27. The Lord Appears to the Prophet Isaiah
28. Amos the Prophet
29. Amos Speaks of Salvation
30. The Trials of Jeremiah
31. Jeremiah Goes to the Potter

November

BIBLE STORY OF THE MONTH

Jonah

1. King Ahab and the Prophet Elijah
2. Elijah Is Fed by the Ravens
3. The Widow's Flour
4. Elijah and the Widow's Son
5. The Faith of Obadiah
6. Elijah Challenges the Priests of Baal
7. The Return of the Rain
8. Elijah in Flight
9. Elijah Meets the Lord
10. The Vocation of Elisha
11. Naboth's Vineyard
12. The Prophet Elijah Confronts King Ahab
13. Into Heaven in a Chariot of Fire
14. The Spirit of Elijah Remains with Elisha
15. The Healing of the Waters
16. The Widow's Oil
17. The Breath of Life
18. Naaman's Leprosy
19. The Ax Head in the Water
20. Joash, the Little King
21. The Lesson of the Arrows
22. Josiah and the Rediscovered Book
23. The Temple Is Destroyed
24. Four Boys in the Court of Babylon
25. The Statue and the Little Stone
26. Nebuchadnezzar and the Statue of Gold
27. The Fiery Furnace
28. The Writing on the Wall
29. Daniel Prays
30. Daniel in the Lions' Den

December

BIBLE STORY OF THE MONTH

Esther the Queen

1. By the Waters of Babylon
2. The Visions of the Prophet Ezekiel
3. The Return from Exile
4. The Joy of the Returning Exiles
5. Nehemiah and King Cyrus
6. Nehemiah Rebuilds the Walls
7. The Renewal of the Covenant
8. Job Is Put to the Test
9. Job Is Struck Again
10. Job and his Three Friends
11. Job Questions God
12. Job Is Rewarded
13. Waiting for the Messiah
14. The Vision of the Son of Man
15. The Long-Awaited One Is Here
16. Zacharias and Elisabeth
17. Zacharias and the Angel
18. Zacharias Returns Home
19. A Young Woman Named Mary
20. Mary, the Mother of God
21. Mary Goes to See Elisabeth
22. His Name Is John
23. Joseph the Carpenter
24. The Journey from Nazareth to Bethlehem
25. Jesus Is Born
26. The Song of the Angels
27. The Good News Given to the Shepherds
28. Mary Praises the Lord
29. The Homage of the Shepherds
30. Zacharias Gives Thanks to the Lord
31. Unto us a Child Is Born

January

BIBLE STORY OF THE MONTH

Baby Jesus in the Temple

1. The Wise Men From the East
2. They Will Bring Gold and Incense
3. The Journey of the Magi
4. Herod, King of the Jews
5. King Herod and the Magi
6. The Adoration of the Magi
7. King Herod and the Children of Bethlehem
8. The Flight into Egypt
9. Jesus in Nazareth
10. John Preaches Repentance
11. John and Jesus: "Behold the Lamb of God"
12. The Baptism of Jesus
13. Jesus Defeats the Devil
14. Jesus Announces the Good News
15. The First Disciples
16. Jesus Calls Philip and Nathanael
17. The First Miracle at Cana
18. Jesus Drives the Merchants from the Temple
19. A Nocturnal Visit
20. The Parable of the Sower
21. The Kingdom of God and the Grain of Mustard Seed
22. The Son of the Nobleman
23. The Yeast and the Treasure
24. Jesus Heals a Leper
25. Jesus Calls Levi Matthew to Him
26. The Fishing Net
27. The Man Lowered from the Roof
28. The Man with the Withered Hand
29. Jesus Chooses the Twelve Apostles
30. A Group of Women Help Jesus
31. The Parable of the Weeds

February

BIBLE STORY OF THE MONTH

Jesus and His Disciples

1. Jesus in the Synagogue
2. Jesus and the Man Possessed by the Devil
3. Jesus Cures Peter's Mother-in-Law
4. Jesus Cures Many Sick People
5. Where Is Jesus?
6. Who Is the Greatest?
7. The Killing of John the Baptist
8. The Rich Man and the Sinner Woman
9. The Brothers of Jesus
10. The Son of the Widow
11. Anger and Reconciliation
12. The Lost Sheep
13. A Woman Touches the Garment of Jesus
14. The Precious Pearl
15. The Law of God
16. A Herd of Swine in the Lake
17. To Do Good in Secret
18. A Great Banquet
19. Love Your Enemies
20. Jesus Resurrects the Daughter of Jairus
21. Like Sheep Among the Wolves
22. The Parable of the Merciless Servant
23. Jesus Cures a Deaf and Dumb Man
24. You Are Peter
25. The Blind Man of Bethsaida
26. The Laborers in the Vineyard
27. Jesus Like Jonah
28. The Faith that Moves Mountains
29. The Transformation of Jesus

March

BIBLE STORY OF THE MONTH

The Bread of Life

1. The Coin in the Fish's Mouth
2. The Parable of the Steward
3. The Good Samaritan
4. Jesus and the Little Children
5. The Parable of the Two Sons
6. Jesus Meets a Rich Young Man
7. Our Father who Art in Heaven
8. The Parable of the Talents
9. The Reward for Whoever Follows Jesus
10. God Listens to our Prayers
11. The First Seats at the Table
12. Invite the Poor
13. The Men in the Temple
14. The Parable of the Prodigal Son
15. The House Built on Rock
16. Jesus Cures Ten Lepers
17. The Offering of the Widow
18. Jesus at the Feast of the Tabernacles
19. The Parable of Lazarus and the Wicked Rich Man
20. Jesus is a Good Shepherd
21. The Hunchbacked Woman of the Synagogue
22. The Parable of the Lost Coin
23. If a Donkey Should Fall Down a Well on the Sabbath. . . .
24. The Light of the World
25. The Tree and the Fruit
26. Whoever Is Without Sin
27. The Parable of the Rich Fool
28. The Salvation of Zacchaeus
29. Jesus Heals a Man Blind from Birth
30. The Chiefs in the Kingdom of Heaven
31. The Parable of the Wise and Foolish Virgins

April

BIBLE STORY OF THE MONTH

Story of Lazarus

1. Jesus Enters Jerusalem in Triumph
2. A Trap for Jesus
3. Jesus Promises that he Will Return
4. Jesus Announces the Day of Judgment
5. The Parable of the Fig Tree
6. The Death of Jesus Is Decided Upon
7. Jesus' Last Supper
8. The Olive Grove
9. Jesus Is Arrested
10. Peter Denies Jesus
11. Jesus Is Tried by Caiaphas
12. Jesus is Taken before Pontius Pilate
13. Jesus Is Tortured
14. Jesus Is Condemned to Death
15. The Road to Calvary
16. Mary and John
17. The Good Thief
18. Jesus Dies
19. Jesus Is Buried
20. The Third Day
21. The Chief Priests' Deception
22. The Two Disciples on the Road to Emmaus
23. Jesus Appears to the Apostles
24. Doubting Thomas
25. Breakfast by the Side of the Lake
26. Feed my Sheep
27. Jesus Returns to the Father
28. The Disciple Matthias
29. Fire from the Sky
30. Three Thousand New Christians

May

BIBLE STORY OF THE MONTH

Peter and Cornelius

1. The Lame Man at the Beautiful Gate
2. Barnabas, a Generous Apostle
3. Peter and John Are Brought before the Council
4. Touched by his Shadow
5. The Story of Two Liars
6. Seven Helpers for the Apostles
7. Stephen, the First Martyr
8. Saul Against the Christians
9. Philip and the Magician Simon
10. Peter and the Magician Simon
11. The Minister of the Queen of Ethiopia
12. Saul on the Road to Damascus
13. Saul and Ananias
14. Paul Lowered in a Basket
15. Peter at Lydda
16. Peter Raises up Tabitha
17. Herod Has Peter Imprisoned
18. Peter Is Freed from Prison
19. A Girl Named Rhoda
20. The Community of Antioch
21. Paul and Barnabas Are Sent by the Holy Spirit
22. Paul and Elymas the Sorcerer
23. Paul Is Persecuted
24. Paul and Barnabas Are Mistaken for Gods
25. Paul Is Sent to Europe
26. Lydia, the Seller of Purple Dye
27. Paul Is Imprisoned in Philippi
28. An Earthquake at Philippi
29. The Arms of the Christian
30. Paul, the Citizen of Rome
31. Like Runners in a Race

June

BIBLE STORY OF THE MONTH

Paul Preaches in Greece

1. Paul at Corinth
2. Paul's Dream
3. Gallio's Reply
4. Apollos Preaches in Ephesus
5. Paul in Ephesus
6. The Magicians of Ephesus
7. A Young Man Named Euthycus
8. The Silversmiths of Ephesus
9. Farewell at the Port of Miletus
10. By Sea toward Jerusalem
11. Some of Jesus' Words
12. The Prophecy of Agabus
13. Paul Is Arrested in Jerusalem
14. Paul's Defense
15. Paul Is Comforted by Jesus
16. Paul Escapes from a Plot
17. A Letter to the Roman Governor
18. Paul Appeals to the Roman Emperor
19. Paul Is Brought before King Agrippa
20. Storm and Shipwreck
21. Bitten by a Viper
22. Paul in Malta
23. On the Via Appia
24. Paul Teaches of Love
25. Paul Helps a Runaway Slave
26. The Rich Man and the Pauper
27. A Life Offered in Sacrifice
28. Actions Speak Louder than Words
29. The True Christian Loves Peace
30. I am the First and the Last

BEACHAM'S GUIDE TO LITERATURE FOR YOUNG ADULTS

volume 3

Kirk H. Beetz
Suzanne Niemeyer
editors

BEACHAM'S GUIDE TO LITERATURE FOR YOUNG ADULTS

◆

Editors
Kirk H. Beetz
Suzanne Niemeyer

Associate Editors
Mary Esselman
Jessica Dorman

Photo Editor
Catherine McCarthy

Production
Nancy Gillio
Patricia Price
Elizabeth C. Gilbert

Design
Patricia DeAngelis

Library of Congress
   Cataloging-in-Publication Data
Beacham's Guide to Literature for Young Adults
   Includes bibliographical references.
   Summary: A multi-volume compilation of
analytical essays on and study activities
for fictional and biographical works written
for young adults. Includes a short biography
for the author of each analyzed work.
   1. Young adults—Books and reading. 2.Young
adult literature—History and criticism. 3. Young
adult literature—Bio-bibliography. 4.Biography
(as a literary form) 5. Biography—Bio-bibliography.
[1. Literature—History and criticism. 2. Literature—Bio-bibliography]
   I. Beetz, Kirk H., 1952
   II. Niemeyer, Suzanne
Z1037.A1G85 1989   028.1'62   89-18048
ISBN 0-933833-11-3

Printed in the United States of America
First Printing, March 1990

PREFACE

Books are vital training grounds for the dynamic and complex social future that faces every young adult. The books discussed in *Beacham's Guide to Literature for Young Adults* will not only help young adults become comfortable with the challenges of language, but will help them become cosmopolitan—they will learn about the world at large as well as about themselves.

Selecting the titles to be covered in *Beacham's Guide to Literature for Young Adults* was a long and difficult process. Our original list of topics was over four thousand titles long, then pared to a thousand. In paring this second list even further, we had five main considerations: 1) was the title a popular one that young people were likely to be curious about? 2) did the work possess literary merits that warranted calling it to the attention of young readers and their parents and teachers? 3) was the work a classic that had over time won a permanent young adult audience? 4) was the title a critically acclaimed work that had won awards such as the Newbery Medal? 5) was the book appropriate for a junior high or high school audience? Scholars, teachers, and librarians advised us about what books were of particular interest to young adults. The resulting list is about four hundred fifty titles long and covers a cross section of the complex world of young adult literature. The series is published as two sets: the first three-volume set covers mainstream novels and short story collections, historical novels, classics, biographies, autobiographies, and nonfiction; the second three-volume set covers science fiction, fantasy, adventure novels, myths, mysteries, and gothic novels. Periodically, individual volumes will be added to the series to pick up new titles or cover older titles that could not be included here.

Beacham's Guide to Literature for Young Adults will likely have a large and disparate audience: young adults who just want to know more about their favorite books and authors, young adults who are researching term papers and book reports, teachers, librarians, parents, college students, and professors. An easy-to-follow format had to be devised that would provide the clarity that young readers require while providing detailed information and depth of thought to satisfy the interests of more experienced readers. In addition to carefully formatted title-by-title analyses, *Beacham's Guide to Literature for Young Adults* contains two appendices in the third volume of each set. One appendix groups titles by themes, the other lists Newbery Medal winners and Newbery Honor Books that are included in the set. Also, each volume contains a glossary of frequently used literary terms. When literary terms, such as *personification*, are used, they are explained briefly in the text, but the glossary provides a more detailed description.

The opening of each article gives the basic data for its subject: title of the work under discussion, date of first publication in English, and kind of work it is (e.g., novel, biography, short story). Following the opening data are:

◆ About the Author ◆

The basics of the author's life are laid out here, with particular attention to the events that shaped the writer's work or sensibilities. This section also discusses the author's critical and popular success.

◆ Overview ◆

This section emphasizes the appeal and contents of the book, while pointing out its value to readers. Teachers presenting the book in class may find this section particularly useful because it outlines some of the qualities that will interest young readers; this presentation is intended in part to encourage readers and capture their interest in the classroom.

◆ Setting ◆

Many books for young adults are intended to acquaint them with places they have never been and cultures they have never experienced. Novels about faraway lands, historical times, the inner city, and the farm, all serve to transport readers into the unfamiliar, helping them to broaden their outlook and to understand other cultures' similarities to and differences from their own culture. The "Setting" section explains the significance of place and time to the individual book, helping to acquaint readers with the special aspects of the setting (such as including additional historical background to explain the merits or weaknesses of a historical novel), as well as showing how the author uses place and time to develop themes and characterizations.

◆ Themes and Characters ◆

This section explains how the themes and characters are woven together to create a unified work of art. Some writings are more thematically complex than others, and the length of the "Themes and Characters" section varies accordingly. The object of this section is to give insight into a work's literary merits by taking a hard, in-depth look at how well rounded the characters are, how plausible they are, and how well they fit into the work's themes. This section is intended to provide serious critical treatment, thereby enriching a reader's appreciation of the literary work.

◆ Literary Qualities ◆

Writings for young adults vary widely in the depth of literary techniques that they present, but most of the titles discussed in *Beacham's Guide to Literature for Young Adults* feature well-developed characters and engrossing themes. The "Literary Qualities" section analyzes the techniques employed by authors to communicate with their readers. It explains the skill behind the artistry. By helping the reader better understand how an author communicates, this section shows the reader how he or she can write meaningfully and read more thoughtfully.

◆ Social Sensitivity ◆

Often books for young adults are controversial. For instance, some old classics for young readers contain racist undercurrents that were overlooked in less enlightened times. On the other hand, since the 1960s the subjects that books for young adults treat have broadened to include topics that were once thought to be strictly for adults, such as sex, drug addiction, and hatred toward one's parents. Some books are very violent, others are intensely frightening, and still others express doubts about the morals and ethics of religion, science, or society. The "Social Sensitivity" section alerts parents, teachers, and librarians to the possible pitfalls in a given title. Contributors to *Beacham's Guide to Literature for Young Adults* have been encouraged to ferret out even remote possibilities of potentially disturbing materials. The "Social Sensitivity" section not only points out potential pitfalls but analyzes the social context of a book and explains how the sensitive aspects of the book fit in with its setting, themes, characters, and plot. It should be noted that none of the contributors advocates censorship, and that, indeed, we oppose it. The "Social Sensitivity" section will alert adults to sensitive issues, but they should keep in mind that young adults crave books that talk to them honestly about their lives and the world around them—that they are deeply interested in the possibilities of nuclear war, their own sexual urges, broken homes, racism, the meanings of religious faith, and a host of other "real world" issues. The "Social Sensitivity" section indicates how honestly and fully a title deals with socially sensitive subjects. Does the book pander to the young reader's immaturity and prejudices; does it sensationalize sensitive topics without conveying an understanding of them; or does it do a notably outstanding job of investigating and explaining a difficult social issue? This section gives meaningful answers.

◆ Topics for Discussion ◆

This section provides a list of thoughtful, sometimes provocative, topics and questions that may inspire classroom discussions among students. Parents as well as teachers may find "Topics for Discussion" useful for stimulating discussion with young adult readers. The topics vary in difficulty, but they all suggest important aspects of the book.

◆ Ideas for Reports and Papers ◆

The analysis in *Beacham's Guide to Literature for Young Adults* is designed to lead readers toward ideas for additional reading assignments, writing assignments, and in-class presentations. A librarian may use "Ideas for Reports and Papers" to guide students who are searching for report topics. This section provides suggestions for simple reports as well as complex term papers. Its purpose is to get students thinking about their topics and to offer them some guidance as to what approaches to the work in question will be most effective.

◆ Related Titles/Adaptations ◆

This section discusses books by the same author that share similarities with the main title. Often these books form part of a series, such as the Narnia books by C. S. Lewis. In other cases, these may be books that have themes, settings, or characterizations in common. The object of this section is to give the reader some idea of what else is available that may help him or her gain a greater understanding of what the author is trying to say. In addition to related books, adaptations to stage, radio, television, and film are discussed, with an emphasis on how true to the original title the adaptations are.

◆ For Further Reference ◆

It is our hope that the articles in *Beacham's Guide to Literature for Young Adults* will be but beginnings in a reader's search to understand literature. This bibliography includes annotations for each reference. Whenever possible, the books, essays, and reviews discussed in this section are ones that are easily available. In some cases, there is a wealth of published material on a particular author or a particular title; in those cases, "For Further Reference" guides the reader to the most helpful sources. On the other hand, much of the information contained in the articles in *Beacham's Guide to Literature for Young Adults* is unique or nearly unique, limiting the scope of many of the bibliographies.

It is heartening that *Beacham's Guide to Literature for Young Adults* provides much new material that cannot be found elsewhere, but it also serves as an indication of how very much more work needs to be done in studying the many meritorious works in young adult literature.

Kirk H. Beetz, Ph.D.

ACKNOWLEDGMENTS

ATHENEUM PUBLISHERS. Jacket illustration by E. L. Konigsburg for *A Proud Taste for Scarlet and Miniver* by E. L. Konigsburg, © 1973. Reprinted by permission of E. L. Konigsburg. Illustration by Alvin Smith for *Shadow of a Bull* by Maia Wojciechowska, © 1972. Reprinted by permission of Atheneum Publishers. Jacket painting by James Shefcik for *A Solitary Blue* by Cynthia Voigt, © 1983. Reprinted by permission of Atheneum Publishers.

BANTAM BOOKS. Jacket painting by Bob McGuinness for *Wuthering Heights* by Emily Bronte, © 1983. Reprinted by permission of Bantam Books.

THOMAS Y. CROWELL CO. Jacket by Peter Burchard for *Rifles for Watie* by Harold Keith, © 1957. Reprinted by permission of Thomas Y. Crowell.

DELL PUBLISHING CO, INC. Jacket for *The Pigman* by Paul Zindel. Harper & Row edition, © 1971. Reprinted by permission of Dell Publishing Co. Jacket for *Slaughterhouse-Five* by Kurt Vonnegut, Jr, © 1969. Dell Publishing Co. reprinted by arrangement with Delacorte Press.

DOUBLEDAY PUBLISHING CO. Illustration by Gordon Grant for *Penrod* by Booth Tarkington, © 1931. Reprinted by permission of Doubleday. Jacket for *The Story of My Life* by Helen Keller, © 1954. Reprinted by permission of Doubleday.

E. P. DUTTON. Photographs of Mildred Taylor, Bette Greene and Julius Lester courtesy of E. P. Dutton.

HARPER & ROW, PUBLISHERS, INC. Jacket by Marcia Sewall and Harper & Row for *Sarah, Plain and Tall* by Patricia MacLachlan, © 1985. Reprinted by permission of Harper & Row. Illustration by James Barkley for *Sounder* by William H. Armstrong, © 1969. Reprinted by permission of Harper & Row. Illustration by C. Walter Hodges for *The Silver Sword* by Ian Serraillier, © 1959. Reprinted by permission of Criterion Books/Harper & Row.

HOLT, RINEHART, & WINSTON. Illustration by Elizabeth Enright for *Thimble Summer* by Elizabeth Enright, © 1966. Reprinted by permission of Holt, Rinehart, & Winston. Illustration by Kurt Wiese for *Young Fu of the Upper Yangtze* by Elizabeth Forman Lewis, © 1973. Reprinted by permission of Holt, Rinehart & Winston.

HOUGHTON MIFFLIN CO. Jacket illustration by Robert Andrew Parker for *The Sign of the Beaver* by Elizabeth George Speare, © 1983. Reprinted by permission of Houghton Mifflin. Jacket for *Sing Down the Moon* by Scott O'Dell, © 1970.

CONTRIBUTORS

Lucien L. Agosta
California State University,
  Sacramento

Cara Akerley
U.S. Naval Academy

Emily J. Alward
University of Kentucky

David J. Amante
University of North Carolina at
  Charlotte

Kwaku Amoabeng
State University of New York at
  Stony Brook

Andrew J. Angyal
Elon College

Mary H. Appleberry
Stephen F. Austin State University

Stanley Archer
Texas A&M University, College Station

Karl Avery

Margaret Ann Baker
Iowa State University

Rebecca Barnhouse
University of North Carolina at
  Chapel Hill

Craig Barrow
University of Tennessee at
  Chattanooga

Diana Barrow
University of Tennessee at
  Chattanooga

Kirk H. Beetz
National University, Sacramento

Mary G. Bernath
Bloomsburg University

Catherine Blanton

Kathleen A. Boardman
University of Nevada-Reno

Mary K. Boyd
University of Missouri-Rolla

Harold Branam

Sidney Brown
University of Virginia

Carl Brucker
Arkansas Tech University

Glenn S. Burne
University of North Carolina at
  Charlotte

Edgar L. Chapman
Bradley University

William Condon
University of Michigan

John W. Conlee
College of William and Mary

John J. Conlon
University of Massachusetts-Boston

David L. Cowles
Brigham Young University

Gloria L. Cronin
Brigham Young University

Hazel K. Davis

J. Madison Davis
Pennsylvania State University,
  Behrend College

James E. Davis
Ohio University

Frank Day
Clemson University

Paul J. deGategno
North Carolina Wesleyan College

Rosanne F. Donahue
University of Massachusetts at Boston

William Ryland Drennan
University of Wisconsin Center-
  Baraboo/Sauk County

Mary Esselman

Paul Ettenson
State University of New York at
  Old Westbury

Ronald V. Evans
University of West Florida

Cynthia J. Faughnan

Lawrence B. Fuller
Bloomsburg University

Kathy Johnson Gale

Susan Garness

Greg Garrett
Baylor University

Joe Glaser
Western Kentucky University

Kenneth B. Grant
University of Wisconsin Center-
  Baraboo/Sauk County

Marlene San Miguel Groner
State University of New York at
  Farmingdale

Lenore J. Gussin

Lyman B. Hagen
Arkansas State University

Jay L. Halio
University of Delaware

Maryhelen C. Harmon
University of South Florida

Stephen M. Hart
Westfield College, University of
  London

William J. Heim
University of South Florida

Terry Heller
Coe College

Dixie Elise Hickman

Elbert R. Hill
Southeastern Oklahoma State
  University

Shula Hirsch
Five Towns College

Elvin Holt
Southwest Texas State University

Elizabeth A. Holtze
Metropolitan State College, Denver

Linda Howe

Caroline C. Hunt
College of Charleston

Veda Jones

William E. Judd
Ohio Wesleyan University

Richard S. Keating
U.S. Air Force Academy

Kara K. Keeling
Indiana University

Ann Kelly
U.S. Naval Academy

James M. Kempf
Frostburg State University

Meena Khorana
Coppin State College

Barbara King

Reyn Kinzey
Virginia Commonwealth University

Catherine E. Kirkland
University of Pennsylvania

Lynne Klyse
California State University,
    Sacramento

Carrol Lasker
State University of New York at
    Stony Brook

Leon Lewis
Appalachian State University

Henry J. Lindborg
Marian College of Fond du Lac

Mary Lowe-Evans
University of West Florida

George M. Luker
U.S. Air Force Academy

George E. McCelvey
Western Kentucky University

A. Abigail McCormick
Estill County (Kentucky)
    Public Library

Fred B. McEwen
Waynesburg College

David D. Mann
Miami University, Ohio

Susan Garland Mann
Indiana University Southeast

Jill P. May
Purdue University

Laurence W. Mazzeno
Mesa State College

Etta Miller
Texas Christian University

Joseph R. Millichap
Western Kentucky University

Robert E. Morsberger
California State Polytechnic
    University, Pomona

Gerald W. Morton
Auburn University at Montgomery

Charmaine Allmon Mosby
Western Kentucky University

Mattie J. Mosley
Louisiana State University-Shreveport

John Mulryan
St. Bonaventure University

Suzanne M. Munich

Harold Nelson
Minot State University

James M. O'Neil
The Citadel

Reba Pinney
Ohio University

Daniel R. Porterfield

David Powell
Western New Mexico University

Rhoda Preston

Catherine Price
Valdosta State College

Edward C. Reilly
Arkansas State University

Kathleen Rout
Michigan State University

Dale Salwak
Citrus College

Boria Sax
Pace University

Bernard S. Schlessinger
Texas Woman's University

June H. Schlessinger
University of North Texas

Ernst W. Schoen-René
California State University, Chico

Richard D. Seiter
Central Michigan University

Lynne P. Shackelford
Furman University

Jonathan C. Smith
Hanover College

H. R. Stoneback
State University of New York-
    New Paltz

Jane A. Stoneback

Elizabeth Q. Sullivan
State University of New York College
    of Technology at Farmingdale

Ruth Anne Thompson
Pace University

Elyse Trevers
Five Towns College

Laurie L. Walker
University of Michigan and Eastern
    Michigan University

Robbie Jean Walker
Auburn University at Montgomery

Alan T. Watters
California State University,
    Sacramento

Robert C. Wess
Southern College of Technology

CONTENTS

The Sign of the Beaver
Elizabeth George Speare

The Silver Sword
Ian Serraillier

Sing Down the Moon
Scott O'Dell

Slaughterhouse-Five
Kurt Vonnegut, Jr.

The Slave Dancer
Paula Fox

Smith
Leon Garfield

A Solitary Blue
Cynthia Voigt

The Soul Brothers and Sister Lou
Kristin Eggleston Hunter

Sounder
William H. Armstrong

Spunkwater, Spunkwater!:
  A Life of Mark Twain
James Playsted Wood

The Stone Book Quartet
Alan Garner

The Story of My Life
Helen Keller

Strawberry Girl
Lois Lenski

Summer of My German Soldier
Bette Greene

The Summer of the Swans
Betsy Byars

The Sun Also Rises
Ernest Hemingway

The Tale of Beatrix Potter
Margaret Lane

A Tale of Two Cities
Charles Dickens

That Was Then, This Is Now
S. E. Hinton

Thimble Summer
Elizabeth Enright

Thoreau of Walden Pond
Sterling North

The Three Musketeers
Alexandre Dumas

To Be a Slave
Julius Lester

To Kill a Mockingbird
Harper Lee

Tom Brown's Schooldays
Thomas Hughes

Tom Sawyer
Mark Twain

Traitor: The Case of Benedict Arnold
Jean Fritz

A Tree Grows in Brooklyn
Betty Smith

The Trumpeter of Krakow
Eric P. Kelly

Up a Road Slowly
Irene Hunt

Viva Chicano
Frank Bonham

Walden
Henry David Thoreau

The Walls of Windy Troy
Marjorie Braymer

Walt Whitman: Builder for America
Babette Deutsch

Waterless Mountain
Laura Adams Armer

The Wheel on the School
Meindert DeJong

Where the Lilies Bloom
Vera Cleaver and Bill Cleaver

Wild Animals I Have Known
Ernest Thompson Seton

William Blake
James Daugherty

William the Conquerer
Thomas B. Costain

Wind, Sand and Stars
Antoine de Saint-Exupéry

The Witch of Blackbird Pond
Elizabeth George Speare

Wuthering Heights
Emily Brontë

The Yearling
Marjorie Kinnan Rawlings

Young Fu of the Upper Yangtze
Elizabeth Foreman Lewis

BEACHAM'S GUIDE
TO LITERATURE
FOR YOUNG ADULTS

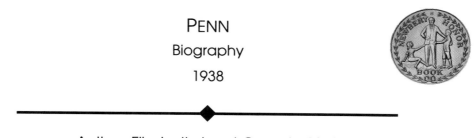

Author: Elizabeth Janet Gray, b. 1902

Major Books for Young Adults

Meredith's Ann, 1927
Tangle Garden, 1928
Tilly-Tod, 1929
Meggy MacIntosh, 1930
Jane Hope, 1933
Beppy Marlowe of Charles Town,
    1936
Young Walter Scott, 1937

Penn, 1938
The Fair Adventure, 1940
Adam of the Road, 1942
Sandy, 1945
The Cheerful Heart, 1959
I Will Adventure, 1962
The Taken Girl, 1972
Mr. Whittier, 1974

◆ About the Author ◆

The daughter of John Gordon Gray and Anne Iszard Gray, Elizabeth Janet Gray was born on October 6, 1902, in the old Germantown section of Philadelphia. She demonstrated an aptitude for literature early in life and began writing for school publications while in grade school in Germantown. She later attended Germantown Friends School and Bryn Mawr College; both institutions were associated with the Society of Friends religion, more commonly called Quakerism.

After receiving her bachelor of arts degree from Bryn Mawr in 1923, Gray started writing full-time but could not get her stories published. After a year of teaching, she enrolled in the library science program at Drexel Institute, now Drexel University. She earned her bachelor of science degree in 1926 and accepted a position at the University of North Carolina at Chapel Hill, where she published her first books and met Morgan Fisher Vining, a university administrator whom she married in 1929.

After sustaining serious injuries in a 1933 automobile accident that killed her husband, Gray moved to Washington, D.C. To help cope with the loss of her husband, she began attending Quaker meetings and began research for her book Young Walter Scott. In 1934 she returned to Philadelphia to live with her mother and older sister. She maintained her attachment to Quakerism, and her life and writings thereafter were profoundly influenced by her religion.

As a pacifist Quaker, Gray was horrified by World War II, but she contributed to the healing process after the conflict when, in 1946, she accepted an appointment as tutor to Crown Prince Akihito of Japan. She spent four years in Japan and described her experience in the best-selling autobiographical work *Windows for the Crown Prince* (1952), published under her married name, Elizabeth Gray Vining. Her other adult books, also published under her married name, include the nonfiction works *Contributions of the Quakers* (1939), *Friend of Life: The Biography of Rufus M. Jones* (1958), and *Flora: A Biography* (1966); the novels *The Virginia Exiles* (1955), *Take Heed of Loving Me* (1964), and *I, Roberta* (1967); and the autobiographical studies *Return to Japan* (1960), *Quiet Pilgrimage* (1970), and *Being Seventy: The Measure of a Year* (1978).

Gray also continued to write fiction and biographies for young adults. Gray has received numerous honorary degrees and other awards, including the 1943 Newbery Medal for *Adam of the Road*. From 1952 to 1971 she served on the Board of Trustees of Bryn Mawr College. In 1972 she retired to Kendal-at-Longwood, a Quaker retirement community near Kennett Square, Pennsylvania.

◆ Overview ◆

As a prominent Quaker leader and the founder of Pennsylvania, William Penn is an important figure in religious and political history. He worked to bring religious freedom and tolerance to his native Britain, and when Pennsylvania was established as the last of the restoration colonies, he sought to graft these principles to the American experience. The colony's constitution, which Penn helped to compose, served as a model for the U.S. Constitution. Pennsylvania's democratic heritage was strengthened further when Penn made a peace treaty with the Native Americans who lived in the colony. Voltaire, a French philosopher, noted that the document was the only treaty with Native Americans that was "never sworn to and never broken." Neither the Quakers nor the Native Americans saw any need to swear to their word. Penn's vision extended to the international realm. More than two hundred years ahead of his time, he advocated a league of nations to maintain world peace.

Penn's life makes an exciting story. Born into the British establishment, Penn alienated his father, a famous admiral, by joining the Quaker movement, whose members were persecuted in seventeenth-century England. Penn was imprisoned several times for his religious beliefs. He was also incarcerated for failing to pay off a debt that was incurred to finance his colony. Despite his notoriety as a spokesman for a persecuted minority, Penn remained on cordial terms with King Charles II, who granted him the charter to found Pennsylvania; with the Duke of York, later King James II; and with the diarist Samuel Pepys, who was openly critical of Quakerism. Penn headed several estates, married twice, and raised a family. Although he was expelled from college as a young man, he developed an intellectual nature. He wrote numerous books and pamphlets, and devised the city plan for Philadelphia.

Penn offers a history not merely of an individual, but of a movement. Historically, Quakers have exercised an influence far greater, proportionally, than their small numbers would suggest. They have worked for social reform, founding good schools, spreading humanitarian ideals, and teaching peace and tolerance by example. The Quaker belief that "there is that of God in everyone" implies that human life is sacred and that all people should be treated equally.

◆ Setting ◆

Beginning with Penn's birth in 1644 and ending with his death in 1718, Gray's book covers the periods in British history known as the Commonwealth, the Restoration, and the Glorious Revolution. The years of Penn's life are marked by religious conflict among Catholics, Anglicans, and Nonconformists. The Nonconformists are composed of many diverse sects such as the Quakers. To escape religious persecution, the Quakers move to Pennsylvania, where they hope to find peace and tolerance.

◆ Themes and Characters ◆

Part 1 of the biography focuses on Penn's struggle with his father, Admiral Sir William Penn, and with government and church officials. Admiral Penn loves his first-born son and hopes for him to become a diplomat or other high government official. Young Penn is educated for such high office, but his turn to Quakerism ruins his father's plans. Ironically, it is the religiously tolerant admiral who introduces his son to the Quakers by allowing the Quaker Thomas Loe to preach to the household. The event makes a strong impression on young Penn, and Thomas Loe is later influential in Penn's conversion.

Penn's struggle with his father develops the theme of freedom of conscience or religion, but it also develops a more personal family theme: children must and will go their own way. Penn, who dearly loves his father and is hurt by his father's rejection, is obedient in all particulars except those of religion. Ultimately Admiral Penn comes to respect his son's strength of character, and on his deathbed, he asks the king and the Duke of York to give young Penn their protection.

Early in the book, Gray portrays a bright, sophisticated, handsome, and athletic Penn. Before he becomes a Quaker, Penn fights and distinguishes himself in the Irish campaigns. He even harbors notions of becoming a soldier and following in his father's footsteps. Thus, although Gray chooses not to analyze this, Penn's conversion to Quakerism involves considerable readjustment of his thinking.

Other characters who play significant roles in part 1 include Penn's good friend, the diarist Samuel Pepys, noted for his pursuit of pleasure and amusement. Pepys serves as clerk of the Royal Navy, later secretary of the admiralty, and lives in the Navy Gardens next to Admiral Penn's family. The genial nature of Pepys and his wife, who are shown entertaining and socializing with the Penn family, helps introduce the themes of friendship and tolerance that the book develops.

In addition, Charles II and his brother the Duke of York, whose names are synonymous with the Restoration and its libertine life, also prove to be exemplars of friendship and tolerance. They rescue Penn more than once, and Charles II signs the charter deeding a colony to Penn, naming it Pennsylvania over Penn's objections. But Charles and his brother also have political reasons for practicing friendship and tolerance: both are Catholics in a strongly Protestant country.

Unfortunately the religious and judicial authorities in the book exemplify

Illustration by George Gillett Whitney for *Penn* by
Elizabeth Janet Gray. Viking Press: New York
(1938).

neither friendship nor tolerance. Offended by Penn's pamphlet "The Sandy
Foundation Shaken," the Bishop of London imprisons him in the Tower of London without a trial. Penn stays in the
tower for almost nine months, enduring
cold and heat and other privations, until
the king orders him released. Later arrested for a trumped-up charge of disturbing the peace, Penn receives a trial,
but the ten justices involved include
some of the most determined per-
secutors of Quakers in Britain. When
the jury declares Penn not guilty, the
judges imprison the jury.

Part 2 of the biography, titled "Onas"
for a Native American translation of
"Penn," focuses on Penn's mature

achievements. These carry the theme of
religious freedom and tolerance to a successful conclusion with the establishment of Pennsylvania, the "holy
experiment," and Philadelphia, the "City
of Brotherly Love." But colonization and
development involve Penn in boundary
disputes, political contentions, and
other mundane matters of government.
The trusting Penn proves a bad judge of
character in the governors and school-
masters he appoints, in his personal
accountant, and even in his own son.

◆ Literary Qualities ◆

Although Gray covers the important
events throughout Penn's life, she
devotes half the book to his childhood
and young adulthood. This proportion
reflects the author's focus on matters
with which young readers can easily
identify, such as Penn's relationship
with his father. Gray's straightforward
style suits young readers.

Also in an effort to make Penn's story
accessible to young readers, Gray emphasizes outer rather than inner conflict, showing Penn clashing with
authorities in the streets and in the
courts. The resulting high drama clearly
delineates the issues and themes, but
neglects an examination of Penn's motives and inner struggles. Admiral
Penn's inner conflicts, interestingly
enough, receive more attention than do
his son's. Gray's reluctance to speculate
about the characters' motivations perhaps reflects her desire to keep her book
firmly grounded in historical fact.

Historical background contributes to
the settings, which play important parts
in the story both literally and symbolically. England is portrayed as almost a
prison, whereas Pennsylvania is a wild
but free place, wooded and green.

England is stormy with religious conflict, but Pennsylvania is inhabited by friendly Native Americans who trade with and babysit for the colonists. Even the air, bright and clear, has a different quality in Pennsylvania.

◆ Social Sensitivity ◆

Although *Penn* portrays a considerable amount of conflict, the book does not contain much violence. Admiral Penn's wars occur at a distance, the sounds of cannon fire marking great victories, and Gray only summarizes young Penn's exploits in the Irish campaign. An offended Frenchman draws his sword on Penn in Paris's dark streets, but Penn merely disarms him in an almost Quakerly manner. Otherwise, the worst to occur is that violent hands are laid on Penn to arrest him or to enclose him in a courtroom cage. If anything, Gray can be faulted for making situations seem too rosy, since persecution of Quakers and other religious minorities often included brutal treatment. Gray does not hesitate, however, to show death and disease, including the horrendous London plague.

Gray's discussion of religion never becomes doctrinaire in *Penn*. The strongest principle asserted is religious freedom and tolerance. Despite various descriptions of religious contention and persecution, Gray depicts few people of any religion unfavorably. Negative portraits necessarily include the Anglican authorities who persecute Quakers and a Presbyterian minister who challenges Penn to a debate, but Gray attempts to inject humor into these portrayals rather than to vilify Penn's adversaries.

◆ Topics for Discussion ◆

1. Young Penn bitterly disappoints his father. In turn, Admiral Penn takes stern measures against his son, at one point disowning him and at another letting him cool off all winter in the Tower of London. Is young Penn a good son? Is Admiral Penn a good father?

2. Admiral Penn has ambitions for young Penn to become an important statesman. Is he wrong to try to determine his son's future? How much say should parents have about their children's ambitions?

3. Ironically, by becoming a Quaker and disappointing his father, Penn eventually fulfills his father's hopes. That is, he founds Pennsylvania, helps bring religious freedom to Britain, and influences the U.S. Constitution. Do you think his father would have been satisfied?

4. Would Penn have been a better father himself if he had spent less time fighting for religious freedom and founding Pennsylvania? What do you think of the way his son Billy turns out? Is Penn to blame? How is this question related to the treatment he received from his own father? Who is ultimately responsible for Billy's behavior?

5. Penn is expelled from Oxford and serves time in prison. Is he such a good person after all? What is the difference between being good and being respectable?

6. The Quakers refuse to take oaths, refuse to take off their hats to superiors, and address people with the familiar "thee" instead of the formal "you." Do they get pleasure out of being contrary

and impolite, or do they have important points to make? If so, what are those points?

♦ Ideas for Reports and Papers ♦

1. Trace and analyze the stages of Penn's relationship with his father. What are the reasons for the changes in the relationship at each particular stage?

2. Try to imagine Penn's thoughts as he decides to become a Quaker instead of a soldier. What are some of the choices he has to make? Why do you think he finally makes them?

3. Discuss and analyze Penn's character. What are some of the traits that help make him great? What are some of his failings? How are the former and the latter sometimes related?

4. Define and discuss Penn's concept of democracy. What are its origins? How is it reflected, and how well does it work in the "holy experiment" of Pennsylvania? How does it influence the U.S. Constitution? How is it still controversial?

5. Define and discuss Penn's ideas on peace. What are their origins? How are they reflected in his relations with Pennsylvania's Native Americans? In his proposal for a league of nations? How are his ideas relevant today? Are they workable?

6. Discuss the Quaker beliefs and practices. What do Quakers think of priests? Of religious dogma? Of preaching and silent worship? Of church government?

7. Define and discuss the Quaker concept of humankind and its implications.

What do you think of the idea that "there is that of God in everyone"? Is this idea sacrilegious?

♦ Related Titles ♦

Readers interested in the Quakers might want to read some of the author's books for adults published under the name Elizabeth Gray Vining: *The Contributions of the Quakers*; *Friend of Life: A Biography of Rufus M. Jones*, about a prominent Quaker who lived from 1863 to 1948; and *The Virginia Exiles*, a novel about Quakers exiled to the Virginia mountains for refusing to fight in the Revolutionary War. Gray's forte is books with a historical background. Other biographies for young adults are *Young Walter Scott*, about the Scottish author, and *Mr. Whittier*, about the American Quaker poet John Greenleaf Whittier. Her novels for young adults include the award-winning *Adam of the Road*, which surveys Chaucerian England through the eyes of a young boy, and *I Will Adventure*, which does the same for Shakespearian England. Shakespeare himself is a main character in the latter. Two historical romances with female points of view are *Meggy MacIntosh*, about a Highland girl who comes to America, and *Jane Hope*, about a Civil War heroine.

♦ For Further Reference ♦

Beatty, Edward C. O. *William Penn as Social Philosopher*. New York: Columbia University Press, 1939. This scholarly work is an in-depth study of Penn's social, political, and economic ideas.

Bronner, Edwin B. *William Penn's "Holy Experiment": The Founding of Pennsyl-*

vania, 1681-1701. New York: Temple University Publications, 1962. This scholarly history provides a detailed examination of Pennsylvania's early years.

De Hartog, Jan. *The Peaceable Kingdom: An American Saga.* New York: Atheneum, 1971. A long but absorbing novel about Quakerism's beginnings in Britain and spread to Pennsylvania and westward.

Dunn, Mary Maples. *William Penn: Politics and Conscience.* Princeton, NJ: Princeton University Press, 1967. Concentrates on Penn as a political thinker and practical politician.

Punshon, John. *Portrait in Grey: A Short History of the Quakers.* London: Quaker Home Services, 1984. An excellent and readable history of the Quakers written by a British Quaker scholar.

Tolles, Frederick B., and E. Gordon Alderfer, eds. *The Witness of William Penn.* New York: Macmillan, 1957. This careful selection of Penn's writings includes excellent introductions by the editors.

Vining, Elizabeth Gray. *Quiet Pilgrimage.* Philadelphia: Lippincott, 1970. This full autobiography includes background on Gray's association with Quakerism and on the writing of *Penn.*

Wildes, Harry Emerson. *William Penn.* New York: Macmillan, 1974. This scholarly, clearly written biography concentrates on Penn's later years.

Harold Branam

PENROD
Novel
1914

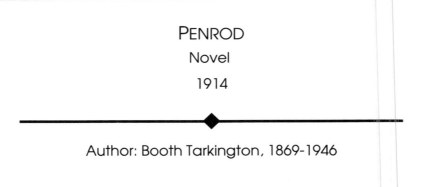

Author: Booth Tarkington, 1869-1946

Major Books for Young Adults

Penrod, 1914
Penrod and Sam, 1916
Penrod Jashber, 1929

◆ About the Author ◆

Newton Booth Tarkington was born in Indianapolis, Indiana, on July 29, 1869. He attended college at Purdue and Princeton before publishing his first novel, *The Gentlemen from Indiana*, in 1899. Tarkington is remembered for his realistic novels of the Midwest, including *The Magnificent Ambersons* (1918) and *Alice Adams* (1921), and for his young adult novels about Penrod Schofield.

Except for a two-year term in the Indiana state legislature, Tarkington spent most of his adult life writing, and his final output was prodigious, totaling more than sixty volumes. In addition to great popular success, Tarkington also achieved critical acclaim, winning two of the first four Pulitzer Prizes given for fiction, with *The Magnificent Ambersons* in 1919 and *Alice Adams* in 1921. Today's readers, though, are probably most familiar with his works for young adults: *Penrod* and its sequels, *Penrod and Sam* and *Penrod Jashber*. Tarkington continued writing until the end

of his life, and two of his novels were published after his death on May 19, 1946, in Indianapolis.

Tarkington, though a professed realist, was highly selective and decorous in his brand of realism. The American reading public appreciated his writing and made him possibly the wealthiest author of his era. In 1921 *Publishers Weekly* conducted a survey among writers and critics in order to find whom they considered "the most significant contemporary American authors." Tarkington headed the list, and in 1922 a *Literary Digest* poll named him "the greatest living American author." In a 1923 *New York Times* poll, he was the only writer named in a list of "the ten greatest Americans."

◆ Overview ◆

In the tradition of Mark Twain's *Tom Sawyer* or *Huckleberry Finn*, *Penrod* offers an engaging story about a young boy's daydreams, schemes, and desires. The experiences of twelve-year-old Penrod Schofield present true-to-life challenges that a young person of his time might conceivably face. While not full of the life-threatening adventure of Twain's books, *Penrod* is a humorous, thoughtful account of growing up in the Midwest early in the twentieth century. Tarkington has preserved the manners and morals, the talk and the popular pastimes, that made up life for a young person during a particular era of American history.

◆ Setting ◆

Although the setting is not specifically identified (except as a city with a population of 135,000), it seems likely that the story takes place in Tarkington's favorite location, Indiana, and may very well represent his hometown of Indianapolis. In presenting Penrod's environment, Tarkington describes many of the things that make up middle-class life in an early twentieth-century midwestern town, including Penrod's school, his playmates, a carnival, and a school play. *Penrod* is a period piece that describes the American Midwest during a time of innocence and prosperity for the nation. Though *Penrod* is intended as a piece of realistic writing, today the setting seems hopelessly idyllic, providing no glimpses toward the modern world.

◆ Themes and Characters ◆

While Tarkington addresses numerous social problems in his adult fiction, he deliberately avoids such issues in the Penrod series, believing that a book

intended to show boys as they really are cannot include adult concerns that boys normally ignore. Consequently, Tarkington does not concentrate on the development of themes in *Penrod*; his overriding purpose is to carefully document the microcosmic world of boys. Despite its narrow purpose, contrived before World War I shattered the innocence of America's youth, *Penrod* presents an interesting, challenging story.

Tarkington draws detailed portraits of Penrod and his companions; while the characters' psyches are not examined in any depth, their patterns of behavior are delightfully portrayed. The most important characters in the book are Penrod Schofield, a creative and somewhat mischievous boy, his dog, Duke, and his best friend, Sam Williams, who is described as being "congenial to Penrod in years, sex and disposition." Other children who appear in the book are Marjorie Jones, "amber curled and beautiful," the rich Maurice Levy, the brothers Herman and Verman, and Georgie Bassett, known as "the Little Gentleman." The book's humor derives from the characters' often unexpected responses to events. Within its limited scope, *Penrod* reflects on the nature of childhood.

Although many of Penrod's adventures are particular to the time and place Tarkington describes, young people of today may still identify with some of them—being persecuted by a bully, being caught daydreaming in class, presenting a backyard circus, or eating too much at a fair. Tarkington recreates the simple world of youth, and if the emotions and tragedies of childhood are not important in the eyes of adults, Tarkington realizes that they are serious to the young people undergoing them. This gives *Penrod* whatever lasting value

Illustration by Gordon Grant for *Penrod* by Booth Tarkington. Doubleday: New York (1931).

dismissed as light entertainment for younger readers.

Tarkington, whose literary mentor was Mark Twain, wrote *Penrod* and its sequels in order to accurately portray the development of boys between the ages of eight and fourteen. Tarkington's theory of childhood development was that a child, in the course of becoming an adult, repeats the history of the human race from savagery to civilization. At age twelve, for example, Penrod is essentially savage but gives indications that his savagery can someday be tamed. He presents a face to the adult world that is "carefully trained to be inscrutable," a necessity for a boy who is part con man, part showman. Childhood is amoral, Tarkington believes; only gradually are adult values accepted.

For readers of *Penrod*, it is useful to understand the evolution of thought from Twain to Tarkington. *Huckleberry Finn* (1884) and *Tom Sawyer* (1876) were written at the end of the romantic period in American literature, as romanticism was about to give way to movements called realism and naturalism. Romanticism does not refer to romance or to stories that have an optimistic view of life. Rather, literary romanticism means that the story's exterior suggests the turmoil hidden beneath the surface. Realism, on the other hand, attempts to show everything on the surface and depicts a world that is hostile to humankind. Twain wants the reader to interpret a story's events broadly; when, for example, Huck taunts the runaway slave Jim with the possibility of turning Jim over to the authorities, the reader knows that Huck is wrestling with the morality of slavery. Tarkington does not believe boys develop with such vision, and attempts to show boys as they act. Their thoughts are important only inasmuch as they suggest forthcoming ac-

it might have; it is a book that lets young people see others like them and that allows adults to reenter a world that they have lost.

◆ Literary Qualities ◆

Penrod is not a complicated novel and does not meet the criteria that critics set forth for a successful work of literature, although the novel continues to attract young adult readers. It lacks the symbolic and lyrical qualities of *Huckleberry Finn,* as well as the psychological urgency of J.D. Salinger's *The Catcher in the Rye.* But Penrod cannot be summarily tions. Realism is based on cause and effect, not on symbolic or poetic values. Naturalism embodies a refined and more scientific interpretation of realism. Simplified, naturalism contends that those who are strongest prevail. Nature kills or weakens everyone else. Boyhood is the time when survival tactics are developed, and the antics of Penrod and his friends are little tests of their ability to survive.

Penrod does suffer somewhat, however, from its author's decision to describe childhood from the perspective of an adult. Tarkington sometimes comments ironically on matters which, to a young person, might be important. When Tarkington makes Penrod and his friends figures of fun, he moves away from the strength of the book, which is its re-creation of the world of childhood.

Tarkington constructs *Penrod* and its two sequels with an episodic plot structure; that is, the various chapters are loosely connected by events, but the plot does not develop systematically. Tarkington believes that children live from day to day, from incident to incident, and that the long-term view of a careful plot does not fit a boy's psychology. Penrod concentrates on what the present moment offers. Critics accused Tarkington of writing episodic plots because the structure is tailor-made for magazine publication. *Penrod,* like most of Tarkington's works, provided a very lucrative income for the author when it appeared in serial form before it became a book.

◆ Social Sensitivity ◆

Penrod is socially insensitive, and modern readers should be duly offended by Tarkington's racist attitudes toward Jews and toward blacks, whom he describes as "beings in one of those lower stages of evolution." Two black brothers, Herman and Verman, are continuous targets of ridicule, and Tarkington repeatedly refers to them as "darkies." The treatment of these characters in the novel unfortunately reflects, to a large degree, their treatment in early twentieth-century American society, and may serve as a useful basis for discussion about the world of Penrod Schofield.

◆ Topics for Discussion ◆

1. What sort of literature does Penrod's "Harold Ramorez" represent? Do you read anything today that resembles Penrod's attempt at authorship?

2. Penrod, Sam, Herman, and Verman put together a show and charge admission for entry. Is creating a show still a popular pastime for young people? If not, what pastimes have replaced it?

3. Why does Penrod want to be like Rupe Collins?

4. Characters such as Penrod, Huckleberry Finn, Dennis the Menace, and Calvin from the comic strip "Calvin and Hobbes" seem to have a lasting popularity. Why do stories about "bad boys" make interesting reading?

5. How is Tarkington's portrayal of Herman and Verman different from his portrayal of the other characters?

6. What are some of the social attitudes that have changed since Tarkington wrote *Penrod?*

1. Mark Twain is one of many authors who have written "boys' books." How does *Penrod* compare to *Tom Sawyer* and *Huckleberry Finn*? Why are Twain's books more famous?

2. The nameless town where Penrod lives is described in enough detail that we have a good picture of life there. How is Penrod's world similar to the place you have grown up? How is it different?

3. We meet male and female characters of all ages in *Penrod*. Have the roles of men and women changed since Tarkington's day? If so, how?

4. Critics today agree that Tarkington's depiction of Herman, Verman, and their family is racist. Analyze Tarkington's depiction of blacks in *Penrod*.

5. Georgie Bassett seems to enjoy being called a gentleman, yet Penrod attacks anyone who dares to suggest that he is one. What does it really mean to be a "Little Gentleman" in Penrod's world? How would boys of today have to behave to earn such a title?

• Related Titles/Adaptations •

Tarkington began writing Penrod's story to please his wife, but the success of the first novel encouraged him to continued writing, and *Penrod* was followed closely by *Penrod and Sam*, the further adventures of the two friends and their circle. The third book in the series, *Penrod Jashber*, was written about the same time as the first two volumes but was published some years later. "Jashber" refers to Penrod's alter ego, "George P. Jashber," detective extraordinaire. The three books have been collected in *Penrod: His Complete Story*, and together provide a humorous and knowing look back at childhood.

George Tyler, a New York producer with whom Tarkington was long associated, urged him to adapt the Penrod stories into a play. The author was skeptical, insisting that "the detail—not plot—is what has made it a best seller." Despite Tarkington's objections, *Penrod* was dramatized and later adapted to film.

Of the three film versions involving characters from *Penrod*, none became an outstanding movie. *Penrod and Sam* (1937) was directed by William McGann and starred Billy Mauch and Frank Craven; *Penrod and His Twin Brother* (1938) was also directed by McGann and starred Billy Mauch, Bobby Mauch, and Frank Craven. *Penrod's Double Trouble* (1938) was directed by Lewis Seiler and starred Billy Mauch, Bobby Mauch, and Frank Purcell. *Penrod and His Twin Brother* especially irritated Tarkington. Since he had provided no real plots for any of the Penrod books, the studio had to invent plots; for *Penrod and His Twin Brother*, the studio simply borrowed the plot of Mark Twain's *The Prince and the Pauper*. Warner Brothers owned the rights to Tarkington's books, but this time even the good-natured Tarkington felt the studio had gone too far. He sued, but won only a token victory, with the company agreeing to let Tarkington read any future Penrod scripts before they were filmed. There were none.

• For Further Reference •

Fennimore, Keith J. *Booth Tarkington*. New York: Twayne, 1974. This book

provides an excellent general introduction to Tarkington's life and works.

Martine, James J., ed. *Dictionary of Literary Biography*. Vol 9, *American Novelists, 1910-1945*. Detroit: Gale Research, 1981. Article on Tarkington concludes that the Penrod stories represent one of his chief accomplishments.

Seelye, John D. "That Marvelous Boy—Penrod Once Again." *Virginia Quarterly Review* 37 (Autumn 1961): 591-604. Provides an excellent analysis suitable for older readers.

Woodress, James. *Booth Tarkington: Gentleman from Indiana*. Philadelphia: Lippincott, 1955. This biography is the best study of the life of Booth Tarkington.

Greg Garrett
Baylor University

Karl E. Avery

THE PIGMAN
Novel
1968

◆

Author: Paul Zindel, b. 1936

Major Books for Young Adults

The Pigman, 1968
My Darling, My Hamburger, 1969
I Never Loved Your Mind, 1970
Pardon Me, You're Stepping on My Eyeball, 1974
I Love My Mother, 1975
Confessions of a Teenage Baboon, 1977
The Undertaker's Gone Bananas!, 1979

A Star for the Latecomer, 1980 (with Bonnie Zindel)
The Pigman's Legacy, 1980
The Girl Who Wanted a Boy, 1981
Harry and Hortense at Hormone High, 1984
The Amazing & Death-Defying Diary of Eugene Dingman, 1987

◆ About the Author ◆

Paul Zindel was born on May 15, 1936, in Staten Island, New York. When Zindel was very young, his father abandoned him, his mother, and his sister, reducing his family to poverty. Frequent moves throughout the ethnic neighborhoods of Staten Island made Zindel and his family perpetual outsiders. Furthering the anguish caused by these dislocations, Zindel was diagnosed for tuberculosis at age fifteen and spent a year and a half in a sanatorium called Stony Wold. Despite these setbacks, Zindel managed to graduated from Port Richmond High School only one year late, and he went on to Wagner College in New York, where he graduated with a chemistry degree in 1958.

Zindel worked for a short time as a technical writer before he returned to Wagner, earning a master of science degree. He taught chemistry at a Staten Island high school from 1959 to 1969. Even before Zindel graduated from college, he began to write for the theater; his early work was promising enough to earn him a Ford Foundation grant to sharpen his talent at Houston's Alley Theatre.

Zindel's play *The Effect of Gamma Rays on Man-in-the-Moon Marigolds* won immense commercial and critical success—an Obie for best off-Broadway play (1970), a Pulitzer Prize for drama, a New York Drama Critics Circle Award for best American play (1969-1970), and a Drama Disk Award (1971). Although Zindel regards himself primarily as a playwright and screenwriter, he is a critically and commercially successful young adult writer as well. His marriage on October 25, 1973, and the birth of

"A 'now' book—thoroughly contemporary, sensitive . . ."
—*The Horn Book*

THE PIGMAN

A Novel by Paul Zindel

Jacket for *The Pigman* by Paul Zindel. Laurel Leaf Library/Dell (reprint of the Harper & Row edition): New York (1971).

defend themselves by cauterizing their wounds from rejection and seeking solace elsewhere. For twenty years, adolescents have responded favorably to Zindel's work.

◆ Overview ◆

Zindel's novels, with their mixture of humor, romance, and realism, frequently appeal to young readers. Many adolescents can empathize with John's struggle with his elderly parents and Lorraine's conflict with her twisted mother in *The Pigman*. The rich artistry of Zindel's best fiction helps train young readers for the complexities of authors such as Joseph Conrad and William Faulkner, and Zindel's self-generated symbol system prepares the way for the fiction of Nathaniel Hawthorne, Herman Melville, and other complex symbolic novels. *The Pigman* thus provides a great bridge to more demanding reading experiences.

two children have provided Zindel with a collaborator and fresh material for years to come.

Zindel's fiction seems to reflect his difficult childhood and adolescent experiences, particularly his father's abandonment. Parents and teachers in Zindel's novels generally appear hostile, although adult women are portrayed more sympathetically than adult men. Sympathetic adult male characters such as the Pigman are rare in Zindel's work. The author's novels usually feature adolescents recovering self-love by questioning those people—parents, peers, teachers—who make them doubt themselves. Ultimately the protagonists

◆ Setting ◆

The Pigman takes place in New York City, on Staten Island. John's father works for the Stock Exchange, and his family seems comfortably well off, but Lorraine and her mother live near the poverty level. Mr. Pignati, a retired electrician, can afford to take John and Lorraine on a buying spree, but his house is in disrepair. Little in the novel determines the exact time of the action, but it seems to take place during the early or mid-1960s. Franklin High School, the Baron Park Zoo, the Moravian Cemetery, Beekman's Department Store, and the homes of the major characters in the novel provide sites for the action.

◆ Themes and Characters ◆

John Conlan's father and mother, whom he has dubbed Bore and Hyper respectively, are more than forty years older than John. His mother is a compulsive cleaner, while his father, a former alcoholic with heart trouble, wants John to join him and John's older brother Ken at the Exchange. The Conlans appear worn out as parents and irritated by John's youthful imagination, and they wish he were grown up and out of the house. John, meanwhile, does his best to justify this irritation. John's ambition to become an actor does not meet with his parents' approval, and his flamboyance contrasts with his parents' conformity.

Lorraine Jensen's mother, a nurse who specializes in the care of dying cancer patients, steals from the families she helps and has a morbid fear of men, probably because her former husband abandoned her several years earlier. Lorraine's insecurities stem from Mrs. Jensen's constant nagging and devastating remarks about Lorraine's appearance. Lorraine's interest in writing and psychology arises from an attempt to understand her mother and her own situation.

Norton Kelly, another important character, is John and Lorraine's age. He enjoys thievery and inflicting cruelty on others, probably because he feels rejected himself. Norton and John are both outsiders, but they hate each other. Norton wants to steal from Mr. Pignati and hopes to use John as an informer against the old man. Norton's anger over not being invited to the party at Mr. Pignati's house and his envy of John and Lorraine result in the destruction of Mr. Pignati's pig collection. This act, more than the other destruction caused by the party, damages John and Lorraine's relationship with Mr. Pignati, for Norton destroys the symbol of Mr. Pignati's love for his deceased wife.

Angelo Pignati, a retired widower, is at once a parent and a child to Lorraine and John. He enjoys their company as if he were their child and is eager to roller skate, play games, and tell jokes. At the same time, he substitutes as a parent, opening his home to Lorraine and John and giving them treats their parents deny them. More important, Mr. Pignati trusts them, and he forgives them after the disastrous party.

Mr. Pignati's dual role as parent and child suggests the idea of alienation between adults and children that John voices in his closing narration at the zoo. John realizes that people must choose between the role of parent or child, because the middle ground is extremely precarious. Mr. Pignati trespasses on the role of child and pays with his life; John and Lorraine trespass as well, sidestepping adult responsibility with their careless, childish actions. Thus the child in them dies with Mr. Pignati; they realize that they must assume blame for Mr. Pignati's death, and that it is no longer possible for them to deny responsibility for their own actions. The grim implication of this reality is that Lorraine, John, and Mr. Pignati's best moments occur when all are lying. Eventually, truths start to emerge, despite the characters' efforts to avoid them, and the consequences are all the more painful because these truths have been suppressed for so long.

◆ Literary Qualities ◆

Characterized by fast-paced, melodramatic action and realistic dialogue that tends toward hyperbolic wit, *The Pigman* cleverly alternates between

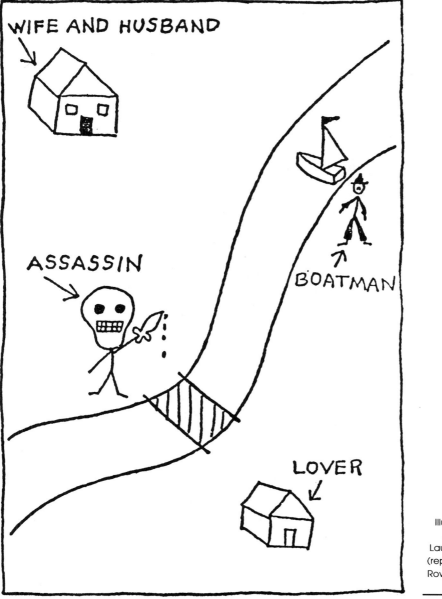

WIFE AND HUSBAND

ASSASSIN

BOATMAN

LOVER

Illustration for *The Pig-man* by Paul Zindel. Laurel Leaf Library/Dell (reprint of the Harper & Row edition): New York (1971).

John's and Lorraine's first-person points of view and develops a natural system of symbols. The narration recounts John and Lorraine's association with Mr. Pignati, who is already dead when their "memorial epic" begins. Four perspectives actually exist in the novel: those of John and Lorraine, the characters who participate in the novel's events and who do not know what is going to happen; and those of John and Lorraine, the narrators who know about Mr. Pignati's death and speculate on its significance. These varied perspectives allow for dramatic irony because the narrators, and to some extent the reader, know what is going to happen, while the characters do not. Since John and Lorraine the narrators have realized that Mr. Pignati's death is the direct result of their actions, their narration gives the novel's tragic outcome the sense of inevitability that is a hallmark of a strong plot. The contrasts between John's and Lorraine's personalities also enhance the narrative: John, dramatic and flashy, describes action well, and Lorraine, intuitive and analytical, ably assesses its significance. Roles are ultimately reversed, however, when in the final chapter John articulates the significance of the novel. His interpretation is all the more powerful because it reveals an inner self that his vivacity usually hides.

Other kids get elected G.O. President and class secretary and lab-squad captain, but I got elected the Bathroom Bomber.

Angelo Pignati serves as the symbolic core of the novel. His name suggests the duality of his personality. He is both pig and angel; his house is messy and cluttered, yet he provides security and warmth. He has chosen the unlikely symbol of a collection of pig figurines to express his love for his wife. The duality of his nature is also evident in his wavering between the roles of child and adult; in this sense, he represents adolescence. His death makes John and Lorraine realize that they cannot play both roles indefinitely, and that it is time for them to become adults.

◆ Social Sensitivity ◆

The Pigman exhibits Zindel's typical negative portrayals of adults. John's parents and Lorraine's mother are uncaring and critical of their sixteen-year-old children. Authority figures and others who might be expected to be helpful—teachers, police officers, nurses—only serve to aggravate John and Lorraine's problems. Adolescents enjoy Zindel's caricatures, and many consider them realistic. Perhaps this anti-establishment attitude reflects a 1960s cultural influence, which encourages antagonism between adolescents and adults.

Despite its caricatures of adults and its pessimistic, melodramatic ending, *The Pigman* credits the hero and heroine for their mature attempt to determine whom they have injured and how to cover the liability. Following the death of Mr. Pignati, Lorraine and John must become their own parents; they must become adults.

◆ Topics for Discussion ◆

1. What is unsatisfying about John's relationship with his parents and Lorraine's with her mother?

2. Lorraine seems more deeply attached to her mother than John does to his parents. What is the basis of Lorraine's relationship with her mother?

3. What do John and Lorraine find attractive about Mr. Pignati?

4. Norton Kelly and John hate each other even before Norton crashes John and Lorraine's party and destroys Mr. Pignati's pig figurines. Why? Why have they associated with each other previously?

5. Sometimes Mr. Pignati is described as a "baby," a "child," and a "kid," while at other times John and Lorraine describe themselves as the Pigman's children. Which, if either, is Mr. Pignati's true role, parent or child?

6. What causes Mr. Pignati's death? What is the significance of his life and death to Lorraine and John?

⧫ Ideas for Reports and Papers ⧫

1. Report on Zindel's use of symbols in *The Pigman.* Be sure to consider Mr. Pignati's pig collection and the animals at the zoo, particularly Bobo the baboon.

2. John and Lorraine sometimes narrate the same events. Determine what each tends to observe and judge, and the effect their judgments have on the reader.

3. Mrs. Jensen specializes in the care of the dying but steals from their families. She is abnormally afraid of sexual contact and her relationship to her deceased husband seems to reflect her entire character. Describe her character and explain the reasons for her behavior.

4. *The Pigman* features puzzles, quizzes, drawings, and newspaper clippings in its text. Determine their function in the novel.

5. Describe what John and Lorraine have learned from their friendship with the Pigman.

⧫ Related Titles/Adaptations ⧫

Zindel wrote a screenplay adapting *The Pigman* to film. Although Brighton Productions never released the movie, Zindel regarded his screenplay as a success. Zindel's sequel, *The Pigman's Legacy,* proved less effective than his screenplay. John and Lorraine find another old person to exploit, and the whole plot of *The Pigman* repeats itself, negating John and Lorraine's development in *The Pigman.* Closer in spirit to *The Pigman* are some of Zindel's other novels, such as *My Darling, My Hamburger,* which explores the complicated and painful relationships among four high school seniors and their parents.

⧫ For Further Reference ⧫

Clarke, Loretta. "*The Pigman*: A Novel of Adolescence." *English Journal* 61 (November 1972): 1163-1169, 1175. A well-balanced essay about the narrative point of view and Zindel's portrait of adolescent life.

Commire, Anne, ed. *Something about the Author.* Vol. 16. Detroit: Gale Research, 1979. Includes brief biographical information about Zindel.

Haley, Beverly. "*The Pigman*—Use It!" *Arizona English Bulletin* 14 (April 1972): 89-92. One of the best general essays on the novel, focusing on the novel's symbolic action.

Haley, Beverly, and Kenneth L. Donelson. "Pigs and Hamburgers, Cadavers and Gamma Rays: Paul Zindel's Adolescents." *Elementary English* 51 (October 1974): 941-945. A perceptive evaluation of Zindel's view of adolescence as revealed in his early novels and his award-winning play, *The Effect of Gamma Rays on Man-in-the-Moon Marigolds.*

Henke, James T. "Six Characters in Search of the Family: The Novels of Paul Zindel." *Children's Literature Annual* 5 (1976): 130-140. Henke examines adolescents who take over the parenting role in Zindel's first three novels.

Jakiel, S. James. "Paul Zindel: An Author For Today's Adolescents." *Arizona English Bulletin* 18 (April 1976): 220-224. Jakiel investigates Zindel's biases and their effect on his fiction.

Craig Barrow
University of Tennessee at Chattanooga

POLLYANNA: THE GLAD BOOK
Novel
1913

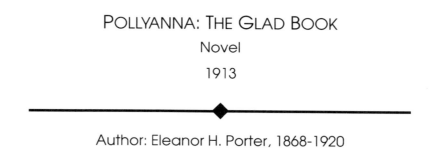

Author: Eleanor H. Porter, 1868-1920

Major Books for Young Adults

Cross Currents: The Story of Margaret, 1907
The Turn of the Tide, 1908
The Story of Marco, 1911
Miss Billy, 1911
Miss Billy Married, 1911

Miss Billy's Decision, 1912
Pollyanna: The Glad Book, 1913
The Sunbridge Girls at Six Star Ranch, 1913
Pollyanna Grows Up: The Second Glad Book, 1915
Just David, 1916

◆ About the Author ◆

Eleanor Hodgman Porter was born on December 19, 1868, in Littleton, New Hampshire. Porter's mother was an invalid, and Porter herself suffered from ill health as a child and never finished high school. Although she later recovered and led an active outdoor life, her childhood experiences provided material for the story of Pollyanna and for Porter's other works of fiction. As a young woman, Porter studied at the New England Conservatory of Music and embarked upon a career as a singer, but changed her profession to writing after her marriage in 1892. Porter submitted stories to magazines, at first with little success. But from the time she published her first novel, *Cross Currents,* in 1907, until her death in Cambridge, Massachusetts, on May 21, 1920, Porter was a remarkably prolific and successful writer of fiction for young adults. Her popularity continued well after her death, and many of her works were published posthumously.

Porter's greatest fame followed the publication of *Pollyanna.* An international best seller, the book appeared in scores of editions in the U.S. and was translated into the major languages of Europe and Asia. The famous actress Mary Pickford paid the then huge sum of $115,112 for the movie rights, and Pickford's silent film version of *Pollyanna* was a great success in 1920. There was even a "Mary Pickford Edition" of the book. Other stage and screen versions of *Pollyanna* continued to appear over the years, including the recent BBC serial production starring Elizabeth Archard. Enthusiastic readers everywhere played the Glad Game and founded Glad Clubs.

Pollyanna's fans include adults as well as children and young adults. Porter's basic theme, namely that even in the darkest situations people can find something to be glad about, seemed to appeal to everyone. Even prison inmates founded a branch of the Glad Club. Restaurants, resorts, apartment houses, commercial products, and babies were named after Pollyanna. One observer of the Pollyanna phenomenon commented that it was nearly as influential an event as the First World War. Eleanor Porter's *Pollyanna*, as both a literary creation and a cultural phenomenon, is one of the important and influential landmarks of the twentieth century.

◆ Overview ◆

In a fundamentally honest and straightforward way, Porter examines the trials of life—poverty, loneliness, and illness—and concludes that a cheerful child's presence can alleviate social and personal bitterness. Pollyanna makes people see the good in life rather than the sad and negative. The book is not, however, a sermon, nor is its tone preachy. It is a solid adventure-romance tale with many familiar but engaging elements. The poor orphan girl arrives in a strange place, lives in the "big house on the hill," and, through her liveliness and curiosity, explores and conquers a new environment. High-spirited and free of prejudice, Pollyanna is the only person in the small New England town willing to talk and associate with everyone. Nothing she does is cruel; when she breaks a rule, it usually results in some good for someone else.

One reason to read this book is to examine firsthand one of the most popular and influential books of the early twentieth century. The word "Pollyanna" has come to suggest a sentimental and simplistic outlook on life, but Pollyanna's vision of love and joy seems relevant in an age marked by cynicism and false sophistication. Pollyanna remains one of literature's irrepressible, effervescent characters, whose actions serve as an example for all those struggling to overcome difficulties.

◆ Setting ◆

The story takes place in a New England village in the early 1900s. Miss Polly Harrington has received word that her eleven-year-old niece has been orphaned, and the "Ladies Aid" wants Miss Polly to take Pollyanna into her home. Pollyanna is the daughter of Miss Polly's sister, who married a very poor young minister against the wishes of her wealthy family and was disowned. When the story begins, Miss Polly—the aristocratic Harrington family's only living descendant besides Pollyanna—is a rich, lonely spinster who feels obligated to care for her niece. Pollyanna arrives in Beldingsville, Vermont, and over the course of the novel not only has a dramatic effect on all those who live in the "big house on the hill," but also transforms the whole village from a rather stern, aloof town to a concerned, caring, and considerably more cheerful community.

◆ Themes and Characters ◆

Pollyanna features some credible and compelling characters as well as some characters who serve primarily as stereotypes. Although Pollyanna is the main character, Aunt Polly and John Pendleton are also significant and perhaps more engaging, since they experience a dramatic transformation of character.

Pollyanna's optimism dominates her personality, even though she has endured poverty, deprivation, initial rejection by Aunt Polly, and a tragic automobile accident that threatens to make her an invalid for life. Because Pollyanna is a naive eleven-year-old, she sometimes seems tactless in her conduct of the Glad Game, such as when she tells Old Tom the gardener, who is bent over with arthritis, that he should be glad he is so close to the ground and does not have to stoop down so far to do his weeding. The innocent literalism of her remark to the gardener is a fundamental trait of her character and is characteristic of the behavior of many eleven-year-olds. Although Pollyanna makes mistakes and misreads situations, her intentions are always good.

Pollyanna's Aunt Polly is a bitter, stern woman who looks much older than her years; she always frowns and is "severe-faced" and distant in her loneliness. Pollyanna's presence works a gradual change in her, and at the end of the tale, quite convincingly, Miss Polly has become a warm, loving person.

John Pendleton serves as the mystery man of the novel, walking the village streets in his long black coat and high silk hat, never speaking to anyone until Pollyanna initiates what will become a life-changing friendship for him. Wealthy and well-traveled, Pendleton has become a reclusive and rather cynical figure since Pollyanna's mother rejected him to marry the poor minister. Pollyanna's presence transforms Pendleton, and although she does not move in with him as he desires, she does ease his loneliness and restore his ability to care for others.

An important secondary character is Dr. Chilton, who like Pendleton has been disillusioned in love. At first lonely in his pride, he too becomes a strong and heroic character by the end of the story. Nancy, the hired girl, gets confused and does not always play the Glad Game in the right way, but she is devoted to making Pollyanna happy. The minor characters—Old Tom, Mrs. Snow, Mrs. Payson, the Reverend Ford, and Jimmy Bean—all find their lives much richer for Pollyanna's presence.

The story's sub-themes of duty, pride, loneliness, and invalidism are all linked to the overarching theme of the Glad Game that Pollyanna teaches the whole community to play. Pollyanna has perfected the game of "just being glad" no matter how disappointing, difficult, or hopeless a situation might seem; she welcomes the challenge of a tough situation, saying "the harder 'tis, the more fun 'tis." When Pollyanna arrives at Miss Polly's, for example, she hopes for a lovely room with nice furniture and mirrors and pictures on the wall. Instead, she gets a bare room in the attic. She decides she can be happy where there are no mirrors, because she will not have to look at herself and see her freckles, and she can be happy that there are no pictures on the walls, because she has the best picture—a view of the countryside—through her window. The implicit symbolic equation is that if she had mirrors and pictures on the walls, then she might be spoiled and self-centered instead of the outgoing child of nature that she is.

Pollyanna's greatest challenge occurs after the tragic automobile accident, when she almost yields to despair. But in a satisfying resolution of plot and thematic design, all of the villagers who have learned to play the Glad Game pull her out of despondence. Porter suggests that an individual's concern for others has the potential to generate communal reciprocation when it is most needed. At the end of the novel, Pollyanna writes a letter to Aunt Polly to tell her she can walk again, and she signs the letter, "with heaps of love to everybody." These are the last words of the book, and they reinforce its underlying themes.

◆ Literary Qualities ◆

Pollyanna successfully evokes the texture of life in small-town New England in the early 1900s. The use of country dialect and the rich regional flavor that marks the dialogue of such characters as Nancy and Old Tom typify the "local color" fiction popular early in the twentieth century.

Porter also skillfully employs imagery and symbolism. Miss Polly's "tight hair" represents her tight, aloof personality. The various images of prisms and rainbows define Pollyanna's character, while the images of the crutches and the missionary barrel foreshadow the near-tragic fate that awaits Pollyanna at the end of the book.

While some readers may tire of Pollyanna laughing "hysterically," breathing "tremulously" and "rapturously," smiling "eagerly," "bravely," and "cheerfully," the novel is generally satisfying, for it moves vivid characters along a tight plot line toward a satisfying resolution.

◆ Social Sensitivity ◆

It should be noted that Pollyanna is one of the very few characters in all literature to have given a word to the language. Dictionary definitions of a "Pollyanna" range from "a blindly

optimistic person" or "a foolishly optimistic person" to someone who is "fatuously or exasperatingly optimistic." People often use the term to suggest a person who is insensitive to the suffering and evil in the world, someone who persists in being optimistic despite evidence to the contrary. This appears to be the meaning of the term "Pollyanna" as our culture has come to define it, but this is definitely not the meaning of "Pollyanna" as found in Eleanor Porter's novel. The real Pollyanna is anything but complacent, inane, and self-deceiving.

The Pollyanna of Porter's book feels deeply the suffering of those around her; because she has had more than her share of random, inexplicable pain and tragedy, she wishes to live fully and to make the best of everything, no matter how bleak the circumstances. Even though Porter's *Pollyanna* may possess some of the marks of a sentimental romance, its fundamental vision of suffering and joyful redemption is shared by much of the world's great literature.

◆ Topics for Discussion ◆

1. Discuss the images of rainbows and prisms. What does Mr. Pendleton mean when he says that Pollyanna is the "finest prism of them all"?

2. Discuss the symbolism of the missionary barrel and the crutches.

3. Look up the word "Pollyanna" in several dictionaries. Do these definitions reflect or describe the character of Pollyanna in this novel?

4. Aunt Polly demands of Pollyanna, "Will you stop using that everlasting

word 'glad'! It's 'glad'—'glad'—'glad' from morning till night until I think I shall grow wild!" Do you get tired of hearing Pollyanna talking about being "glad"? Why or why not?

5. Would the world be a better place if there were more people like Pollyanna? Why or why not? List some of the world's best known altruists and activists. Are these people effective because they share or lack Pollyanna's "gladness"?

◆ Ideas for Reports and Papers ◆

1. Analyze several examples of the Glad Game. How many examples of the game seem silly or foolish? How many seem like a good way of dealing with life's difficulties?

2. Write about the difference between optimism and pessimism. Does Pollyanna's optimism deny the reality of suffering? Is she insensitive to the pain of others?

3. In most books about a young person growing up, important lessons are learned from the adults in the story. Does Pollyanna learn from the adults around her, or do the adults learn more from her? What do they learn?

4. Analyze the relationship between Aunt Polly and Pollyanna. What changes occur in their relationship? How does Aunt Polly change? Why does Pollyanna choose to stay with Aunt Polly when Mr. Pendleton asks her to come live with him?

5. Compare Pollyanna's character and maturity in *Pollyanna* and its sequel, *Pollyanna Grows Up*. Does the Glad Game change in the later book?

◆ Related Titles/Adaptations ◆

The only legitimate sequel to *Pollyanna* is Eleanor Porter's *Pollyanna Grows Up*, in which Pollyanna moves to Boston and tries to spread the Glad Game throughout that metropolis. Boston, she finds, is a much more difficult place to spread her brand of joy than was the small town of Beldingsville, Vermont. Many other Pollyanna tales have been published by other authors, such as Harriet Lummis Smith and Elizabeth Borton de Trevino, but these lack the freshness and force of Porter's original creation. Some of Porter's other works for young adults have certain similarities with the Pollyanna tales, but none of them place the same emphasis on optimism and gladness.

In 1960 Walt Disney released a motion picture version of *Pollyanna*, directed by David Swift and starring Hayley Mills and Jane Wyman. It received mixed reactions from young viewers; some enjoyed the eccentric characters, while others thought Pollyanna too goody-goody. In 1989 NBC-TV produced a made-for-TV movie adaptation of *Pollyanna* entitled *Polly*. The movie stars Phylicia Rashad, Brandon Adams, Dorian Harewood, and Keshia Knight.

◆ For Further Reference ◆

Allentuck, Marcia E. "Old Books: *Pollyanna* by Eleanor M. Porter." *Georgia Review* (1960): 447-449. Although Allentuck find *Pollyanna* "almost embarrassingly encumbered by the trappings of indiscriminate gladness," she places it "in the tradition of those works which find man's adjustment and growth more arresting than his disenchantment and fall."

Benet, William Rose. *Reader's Encyclopedia.* Vol. 20. New York: Thomas Y. Crowell, 1965. This brief passage finds Pollyanna a "synonym for the fatuous, irrepressible optimist."

Carpenter, Humphrey, and Mari Prichard. *The Oxford Companion to Children's Literature.* New York: Oxford University Press, 1984. A brief description notes Pollyanna's "sunny disposition" and "good influence."

Fisher, Margery. *Who's Who in Children's Books.* New York: Holt, Rinehart and Winston, 1975. This article finds Pollyanna "possibly the most exasperating heroine in fiction."

Kunitz, Stanley, and Howard Haycraft, eds. *Twentieth Century Authors.* New York: H. W. Wilson, 1942. This work contains a good brief summary of Porter's life and work.

Mainiero, Lina, and Langdon Lynne Faust, eds. *American Women Writers.* Vol. 3. New York: Frederick Ungar, 1981. This article presents a balanced survey of negative and positive views of *Pollyanna.*

Jane A. Stoneback

THE POWER AND THE GLORY
Novel

1940

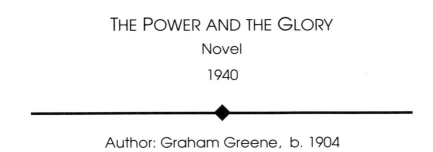

Author: Graham Greene, b. 1904

Major Books for Young Adults

The Power and the Glory, 1940
The Heart of the Matter, 1948
The Quiet American, 1955
Our Man in Havana, 1958
Monsignor Quixote, 1982

◆ About the Author ◆

Graham Greene was born October 2, 1904, at Berkhamsted, Hertfordshire, England, the fourth of six children. His exposure to books at an early age fueled his ambitions to travel and to write. After a troubled adolescence, during which he ran away from home and ended up in psychoanalysis, he enrolled at Oxford University, where he studied from 1922 to 1925 and wrote his only collection of poetry, *Babbling April* (1925). During that time, Vivien Dayrell-Browning, his future wife, wrote to him about an error concerning Catholic beliefs she had noticed in one of his film reviews; her letter triggered his examination of and eventual immersion in Catholic thought. Greene married Dayrell-Browning in 1927. He converted to Catholicism in 1926, and his religion greatly influenced his writing for the next twenty-five years. *The End of the Affair* (1951) marked his last novel written from a Catholic perspective.

After graduating from Oxford in 1925, Greene worked first In Nottingham as a reporter for the *Journal* and later as an editor for the London *Times*, a job he left in 1929 upon publication of his first novel, *The Man Within*. Intending to devote all of his time to writing, Greene soon realized that he could not support his wife and two children without a regular salary. He became a film critic but still managed to write a novel a year for the next six years. In 1938 he published *Brighton Rock*, his first novel with a strongly Catholic theme. He traveled to southern Mexico to learn about the repression of the Catholic church under the revolutionary government of General Lazaro Cardenas, a trip that spawned both *The Lawless Roads* (1939) and *The Power and the Glory*. Greene's World War II service with the British Secret Intelligence Service provided him with material for novels of intrigue and politics such as *The Ministry of Fear* (1943), *The Quiet American*, *Our Man in Havana*, *The Comedians* (1969) and *The Honorary Consul* (1973).

Greene has been a dedicated traveler all his life, consistently visiting parts of the world embroiled in turmoil and strife. Greene has documented his fascinating life in his travel books, his autobiographies—*A Sort of Life* (1971) and *Ways of Escape* (1980)—and his extensive diaries and correspondence. As one of the most prolific, widely read, and critically acclaimed authors of the twentieth century, Greene has been considered time and again for the Nobel Prize for literature, but the very themes that have made him so popular—violence and religion—have also made him controversial, and the committee has stated publicly that it will never award him the prize. Although he is elderly, Greene continues to travel and publish regularly. He lives on the French Riviera, in Antibes, when he is not traveling.

◆ Overview ◆

The Power and the Glory chronicles the plight of a Catholic priest who, for eight years, has continued to say Mass and administer the sacraments, even though Mexico's revolutionary government has outlawed these practices. Knowing that he will be executed if he is caught, the priest moves from village to village carrying on the work of the Church. He is relentlessly pursued by a nameless young lieutenant of police, a revolutionary who believes that the new government can help mitigate poverty; the lieutenant despises the Church for ministering to spiritual needs while ignoring poverty. The priest, however, believes that faith in the Church's teachings provides hope for the poor and oppressed. Because he considers himself a sinner, the priest empathizes with others who are weak, and feels compelled to fulfill his priestly duties despite the threat of execution. But the lieutenant sets traps for the priest by

killing hostages in the villages where the priest has held Mass and by luring him with liquor. The inevitable confrontation between these two men brings the novel to a dramatic climax.

◆ Setting ◆

The story takes place during the 1930s, a time of totalitarian reign in Mexico. It is set south of Mexico City in the province of Tabasco. In his introduction to the 1962 edition of the book, Greene explains that he traveled in Mexico from 1937 to 1938 for the express purpose of writing a novel. Greene relates that the towns he visited are depicted in the novel: El Frontera, where the story opens; Tabasco, a prohibitionist town; Villahermosa, where he developed the character of the priest and discovered the prototype for the lieutenant; and Las Casas, where churches still stood although no priest was allowed to enter them.

◆ Themes and Characters ◆

The conflict between the novel's two main characters, the "whisky priest" and the lieutenant, parallels the tension between the novel's two overlapping themes—the spiritual theme of religious faith and devotion, and the political theme of the Church's obligation to aid the poor. Although Greene seems to sympathize with the priest, and thus with the belief that the Church's primary obligation to the poor is spiritual rather than political or economic, his novel is more than a simple-minded tale of faith and devotion.

Greene never names the priest, referring to him only as the "whisky priest." In addition to being an alcoholic, the priest has fathered a child and thus has sinned in the eyes of the Church. He berates himself throughout the novel for being a "bad priest" and wonders if he is doing more harm than good by setting a bad example for his people. Yet he continues the work of the Church, even after all the other priests have gone into hiding or denied their faith and taken wives. Although he is an unlikely representative of God, the whisky priest says he stays in the region because if he were to leave "it would be as if God in all this space between the sea and the mountains ceased to exist."

Greene's choice of a whisky priest as hero underscores the novel's theme. The sacraments this priest administers are, according to Catholic teachings, as valid as those administered by the holiest of saints. When the priest is finally captured, he and the lieutenant discuss their differing beliefs, and the priest maintains:

> It's no good your working for your end unless you're a good man yourself. And there won't always be good men in your party. Then you'll have all the old starvation, beating, get-rich-anyhow. But it doesn't matter so much my being a coward—and all the rest. I can put God into a man's mouth just the same—and I can give him God's pardon. It wouldn't make any difference to that if every priest in the Church was like me.

Greene suggests that the priest's belief in God's pardon—and in his own power to grant God's pardon through the sacrament of penance—enables him to feel compassion for others even when they seem less than virtuous. During the sacrament, a person can envision the image of Christ in the priest even though he knows the priest to be an alcoholic and a fornicator. In the same way, the whisky priest learns to see the image of Christ in others:

> "When you visualized a man or woman carefully, you could always begin to feel pity—that was a quality God's image carried with it. When you saw the lines at the corners of the eyes, the shape of the mouth, how the hair grew, it was impossible to hate. Hate was just a failure of the imagination."

The priest considers the lieutenant a better man than himself, but the novel suggests that what matters is a certain kind of compassion sustained by understanding the holiness in everyone.

The lieutenant thinks of himself as a compassionate man driven by a desire to empower the poor and oppressed of his country. He views the Church as an instrument of oppression and feels physically repulsed when he recalls "the smell of incense in the churches of his boyhood" and "the immense demands made from the altar steps by men who didn't know the meaning of sacrifice." To the lieutenant, all priests are the same—fat, pampered men who squeeze money and mortification out of tired, suppliant peasants. The lieutenant, like the whisky priest, feels he has a vocation to save these peasants, but where the whisky priest offers spiritual salvation, the lieutenant demands social and economic redemption. The two characters seem to oppose each other in belief, method, and even appearance: where the whisky priest is round-faced, unkempt, and prone to nervous, drunken giggles, the lieutenant, in his polished uniform, is distinguished by his curt manner and "lean dancer's face." Yet the lieutenant, compared at times to a priest, a theologian, and a monk, ultimately discovers that he and the whisky priest share similar goals.

The novel is in many ways a parable about theological principles, a retelling of Christ's betrayal and crucifixion; most of the other characters seem motivated by the functional needs of the story. The poor mestizo who betrays the priest is a Judas figure, and the American bank robber and murderer is symbolically Barabbas for Greene's passion play. Like the whisky priest and the lieutenant, these characters remain nameless: the poor mestizo is referred to as "the half-caste," and the American is simply called "the Gringo." Although in his other novels Greene draws fully founded characters, here he creates characters who serve as symbols or mouthpieces for ideologies.

◆ Literary Qualities ◆

Greene uses several techniques that complement his religious themes. For example, the priest is detained three times when he is on the verge of escaping, called back each time to administer last rites to a dying person. This kind of repetition is common to all mythologies, and the particular plot motif of calling three times is deeply rooted in the Bible. Greene, a master of suspense, plays myth against plot line. The reader, as well as the priest, knows that the half-caste must betray the whisky priest so that the priest can attain martyrdom, but no one is sure when the betrayal will happen or how it will affect the symbolic crucifixion.

Greene also uses the conventions of the stories of the saints' lives. At the opening of the story, a woman is reading the story of a martyr to her children. Greene parodies the romantic nature of these stories: the martyr pardons his executioners and dies crying out, "Viva el Cristo Rey!" At the end of *The Power*

and the Glory, Greene echoes the stories of the saints by telling the more realistic story of the whisky priest's final night, which he spends drinking brandy and wishing he were somewhere else. The reader is prepared to accept the whisky priest as a saint without benefit of embellishments on the story of his life. Yet, as the same woman recounts the story of the priest's execution, she records him as shouting "Viva el Cristo Rey!" Although the woman's version seems hopelessly romanticized, it is consistent with Greene's theme: gaudy as the imagination may be, through it a human being finds some form of redemption.

A complex theological novel that defies simplistic analysis, *The Power and the Glory* has provoked dissension among both Catholic and secular critics. Greene's departure from conventional piety—his decision to make his priest a "sinful" man—has helped lead modern Catholic literature in a less sentimental direction. Four years after *The Power and the Glory* appeared, Evelyn Waugh published an unsentimental view of Catholicism in *Brideshead Revisited*, (1944) and American Catholic writers, such as Flannery O'Connor and Walker Percy, have furthered Greene's themes and opened the way for stories that would have been considered offensive before Greene's work.

◆ Social Sensitivity ◆

Greene has always been a provocative, controversial writer, often offending people either because of their political or religious beliefs. Although there is nothing offensive about the story itself in *The Power and the Glory*, the underlying views about Catholicism might cause concern. According to Greene, even the Vatican was divided. Pope Paul VI, on hearing that the book, which he had read, had been condemned by the Holy Office, replied: "Mr. Greene, some parts of your books are bound to offend some Catholics, but you should pay no attention to that."

The conflict between the priest and the lieutenant is the root of the theological controversy. Although the novel makes the reader sympathize with the priest, the lieutenant is also depicted as a good man who cares for the poor. He is himself from a peasant family, and when he encounters the priest in prison and mistakes him for a poor old man, he gives him money. His opposition to the Church is based on his belief that the Church has failed the people. As a secularist, he judges by a completely materialistic standard: if the people remain in poverty, the Church has failed. Although the priest maintains that the spiritual needs of the people must also be fulfilled, he recognizes some truth in the lieutenant's position and perhaps recognizes the compassion that lies beneath it.

• Topics for Discussion •

1. In what ways does the lieutenant believe the Church has failed the people? What evidence does the novel produce to support his view?

2. Why does the revolutionary government want to outlaw the Church?

3. In what ways does the whisky priest exhibit cowardly behavior? In what ways is he brave?

4. Is it possible that the whisky priest is both a "good man" and a "bad priest"? Explain this conflict.

5. What characteristics does the lieutenant exhibit that make him out to be a "good man"?

6. Why is it necessary to the conclusion of the story for the priest to be executed?

• Ideas for Reports and Papers •

1. Greene establishes loose parallels between his characters and some from the Bible. Explain how the whisky priest plays the role of Christ; the mestizo Judas, the lieutenant, Caesar; and Father Jose, the Apostle Peter. How does the story of the Good Samaritan serve as a foil? Are there other biblical allusions?

2. The title is taken from the Lord's Prayer. Analyze the importance of prayer (and the absence of it) in the novel. What does the title mean?

3. A principal theme is the power of corruption and the potential for redemption. Explain how the novel develops this theme.

4. Research and report the history of the repression of the Catholic Church in Mexico or in other countries.

5. How does Greene develop his objections to a totalitarian government? What does he suggest that the Church's role should be under such conditions?

• Related Titles/Adaptations •

The Power and the Glory was adapted for the screen by Dudley Nichols and directed and produced by John Ford as *The Fugitive* in 1947. Although Ford is considered a great filmmaker, the movie was not commercially successful, and it is considered by many critics to be Ford's weakest film. The film did receive some good reviews when it was first released, notably from the *New York Times*, which called it a "thundering modern parable on the indestructibility of faith." But the film tried to cater to conventional expectations of priestly conduct: Henry Fonda, as the priest, is a stronger person than Greene's character, and the lieutenant, who is portrayed as a complete fanatic, is made the father of the illegitimate child. These attempts to purify the priest rob Greene's vision of its power. On the other hand, in 1961 CBS produced a television version that was more faithful to the novel, and viewers were outraged at Sir Laurence Olivier's portrayal of the priest. The television adaptation cast George C. Scott as the lieutenant and Julie Harris as Maria, the woman with whom the whisky priest fathered a child.

Greene has written a number of other "Catholic" novels, of which *The Heart of the Matter* is generally considered the best. In this novel, Major Scobie, basically a good, honest man, is driven to suicide by pride, love, and perhaps a mistaken sense of duty. The religious question of the novel is whether Scobie, a Catholic, might have found salvation, despite the Church's position that suicide is an unforgivable sin. Greene's answer, given by a priest at the conclusion of the novel, is consistent with the ethics of compassion and forgiveness evident in *The Power and the Glory*: "The church knows all the rules, but it doesn't know what goes on in a single human heart."

The book that most closely parallels *The Power and the Glory* is *Monsignor Quixote*. The characters of *The Power and the Glory* reappear in this reworking of the Don Quixote story: the priest is Monsignor Quixote, and he is on the road again, this time hounded not by the revolutionaries but by his more modern Bishop. The priest is accompanied by the literary descendant of the Mexican lieutenant, the Communist ex-mayor of the town, whom Quixote insists on calling Sancho. The debate between religion and politics is rejoined, but this time in comic tones. There is even a suggestion that both Catholicism and Marxism are as outdated as Don Quixote's chivalry.

◆ For Further Reference ◆

Allain, Marie-Francoise. *The Other Man.* New York: Simon and Schuster, 1983. A series of interviews with Graham Greene.

Allott, Kenneth, and Miriam Farris. *The Art of Graham Greene.* London: Hamish Hamilton, 1951. This book on Greene remains one of the best, despite its essentially thematic approach. The chapter titles are chosen to illustrate Greene's "obsessive" subjects: the terror of life, the divided mind, the fallen world, and the universe of pity. Given their rather narrow focus, the readings are remarkably penetrating and cogent.

Consolo, Dominick P. "Graham Greene: Style and Stylistics in Five Novels." In *Graham Greene: Some Critical Considerations*, edited by Robert O. Evans. Lexington: University of Kentucky Press, 1963. Consolo's pioneering study of four "Catholic" novels and *The Quiet American* provides a detailed, rigorous analysis of Greene's recurring techniques of characterization, narrative viewpoint, structure, and syntax.

DeVitis, A. A. *Graham Greene.* New York: Twayne, 1964. DeVitis mounts a vigorous attack on critics who treat Greene's work as a species of theological argument.

Hoggart, Richard. *Speaking to Each Other.* London: Oxford University Press, 1970. Focusing on *The Power and the Glory* as representative of Greene's novels, Hoggart analyzes the "seedy" setting, the "allegorical" symbols, the "nervous, vivid, astringent" style, the puppet-like characters, and the melodramatic plot, finding them all to be powerful but unrealistic contrivances.

Lodge, David. *Graham Greene.* Columbia Essays on Modern Writers, no. 17. New York: Columbia University Press, 1966. A sympathetic and often perceptive survey of the novels.

Spurling, John. *Graham Greene.* Contemporary Writers, no. 14. London: Methuen, 1983. Concise overview of Greene's life and career, with due attention to the later works.

Stratford, Philip. *Faith and Fiction: Creative Process in Greene and Mauriac.* Notre Dame, IN: Notre Dame University Press, 1964. Stratford writes perceptively of Greene's adolescent crisis, and persuasively demonstrates how this experience shaped Greene's adult persona.

Reyn Kinzey
Virginia Commonwealth University

PRAIRIE-TOWN BOY
Autobiography
1955

◆

Author: Carl Sandburg, 1878-1967

Major Books for Young Adults

Abe Lincoln Grows Up, 1928
Early Moon, 1930
Storm Over the Land: A Profile of the Civil War, 1939
Prairie-Town Boy, 1955

◆ About the Author ◆

Carl August Sandburg was born on January 6, 1878, in Galesburg, Illinois. His parents, August and Clara Sandburg, were Swedish immigrants who never learned to write. Carl left school after the eighth grade and held numerous odd jobs, including those of newspaper carrier, custodian, milk delivery boy, pharmacist's assistant, and barbershop shoeshine boy. At age nineteen, he decided to be a hobo, riding on railroad boxcars to Iowa, Colorado, Nebraska, Kansas, and Missouri. The following year, he returned to Galesburg and worked as an apprentice house painter and then enlisted in the Illinois Volunteers, serving as a private in Puerto Rico during the Spanish-American War.

After returning from the war, Sandburg enrolled as a special student at Lombard College in Galesburg, where he served as editor-in-chief of the *Lombard Review* and reporter for the *Galesburg Evening Mail*. While a student, he also worked as a fireman and school janitor, and sold stereographs for Underwood and Underwood. He received an appointment to West Point, but failed the entrance examination in mathematics and grammar.

Sandburg dropped out of college only a few weeks before graduation and traveled as a salesman for Underwood and Underwood. His first three works, *In Reckless Ecstasy, The Plaint of a Rose,* and *Incidentals,* were published in 1904 and 1905 under the name Charles A. Sandburg. He gave lectures on Walt Whitman and other subjects, and he wrote and edited for numerous publications in Chicago and Milwaukee, occasionally using the pseudonyms Crimson, W. C. Coulson, and Sidney Arnold.

On June 15, 1908, Carl married Lillian (Paula) Steichen, a Latin teacher who became a champion breeder of dairy goats. They had three children, Margaret, Janet, and Helga. Both Paula and Carl supported and worked for the Social Democratic party: Paula translated

Illustration by Joe Krush
for *Prairie-Town Boy* by
Carl Sandburg. Harcourt,
Brace and World: New
York (1955).

German editorials into English, and Carl wrote a pamphlet entitled *You and Your Job.* In 1910, Carl became the private secretary to Emil Seidel, Socialist mayor of Milwaukee. He also wrote for the *Day Book,* a tabloid newspaper in Chicago that covered social issues.

Sandburg joined the staff of the *Chicago Daily News* in 1917 and continued to write for the paper until 1930. His articles on blacks in Chicago, originally written for the *Daily News,* were compiled in *The Chicago Race Riots* (1919). During World War II, the *Chicago Times* syndicated his weekly column on the war in Europe; some of these articles were collected in a book entitled *Home Front Memo* (1943).

In addition to his newspaper work, Sandburg also wrote poetry and won the 1914 Helen Haire Levinson Prize for best poems of the year with poems published in the March issue of *Poetry: A Magazine of Verse.* He shared the Poetry Society of America prize in 1919 for *Cornhuskers* and in 1921 for *Smoke and Steel* (1920),

and he was named a Phi Beta Kappa poet by Harvard University in 1928 and by William and Mary College in 1943. He was awarded the Pulitzer Prize for poetry in 1951 for his *Complete Poems* (1950), and he received the Poetry Society of America gold medal for poetry in 1953. He also won the Roanoke-Chowan Poetry Cup in 1960 for *Harvest Poems 1910-1960* (1960) and in 1961 for *Wind Song.* In 1963 he received the International United Poets Award as "Honorary Poet Laureate of the United States of America." His other books of poetry include *Chicago Poems* (1916), *Slabs of the Sunburnt West* (1922), *Early Moon* (1930), *The People, Yes* (1936), and *Honey and Salt* (1963). Collaborating with Norman Corwin, Sandburg adapted his poetry for the stage in a play entitled *The World of Carl Sandburg* in 1961.

Sandburg spent many years researching and writing about Abraham Lincoln. A two-volume biography, *Abraham Lincoln: The Prairie Years,* was published in

1926, and an adaption of the first twenty-six chapters of this book was published for young adults as *Abe Lincoln Grows Up.* Sandburg wrote *Mary Lincoln: Wife and Widow* (1932) with Paul M. Angle, and his four-volume *Abraham Lincoln: The War Years* (1939) received the Pulitzer Prize for history in 1940. Sandburg collaborated with Frederick Hill Meserve on *The Photographs of Abraham Lincoln* (1944). He also wrote the *Lincoln Collector: The Story of Oliver R. Barrett's Great Private Collection* (1949). Sandburg received numerous awards for his work on Lincoln, including the Friends of Literature Award (1934), the Theodore Roosevelt Distinguished Service Medal (1939), the American Academy of Arts and Letters gold medal for history (1952 and 1953), the New York Civil War Round Table silver medal (1954), the Presidential Medal of Freedom from Lyndon B. Johnson (1964), a National Association for the Advancement of Colored People award for being a "major prophet of civil rights in our time" (1965), and many honorary doctorates.

Sandburg wrote fairy tales for children, initially invented as stories for his daughters and later published as *Rootabaga Stories* (1922) and *Rootabaga Pigeons* (1923). He also loved music, particularly folk songs, and closed his lectures by singing and playing the guitar. He published two collections of American folk songs: *The American Songbag* (1927) and *New American Songbag* (1950).

Sandburg's autobiography, *Always the Young Strangers*, was published in 1952 and received the 1953 Taminent Institution Award. *Prairie-Town Boy* is an adaption of this autobiography for young adults. Sandburg also wrote a historical romance, *Remembrance Rock* (1948), and in 1960 served as a consult-

ant in Hollywood for the movie *The Greatest Story Ever Told.* Sandburg died on July 22, 1967, at his home, Connemara, in Flat Rock, North Carolina. He was eighty-nine years old.

◆ Overview ◆

Prairie-Town Boy is the autobiography of the poet and historian Carl Sandburg, written when he was in his seventies. Adapted for young readers from the longer *Always the Young Strangers*, which the *New York Times* called the greatest autobiography ever written by an American, the book tells of Sandburg's boyhood in Galesburg, Illinois, and continues through his entrance into college. In these memoirs, Sandburg recalls the people, places, and experiences that influenced his youth, including those that led to his deep respect for the common person and to his interest in the life of Abraham Lincoln. The book shows the role that immigrants—particularly Swedes—played in the settling of the Midwest, and in effect presents a social history of America in the 1880s and 1890s.

◆ Setting ◆

Sandburg is born in Galesburg, Illinois, in 1878, twenty years after one of Abraham Lincoln and Stephen A. Douglas's debates is staged in the town. At the time of Sandburg's birth, persons who knew and served with Lincoln still live in the area, and the country is still recovering from the Civil War. Galesburg is a young community, predominantly Republican and recently settled by immigrants, including many from Sweden. The Chicago, Burlington, and Quincy Railroads link the city to the rest of the nation. Although its population is only fifteen thousand, Galesburg boasts three colleges and is nicknamed "the Athens of the Midwest."

• Themes and Characters •

Numerous individuals appear in *Prairie-Town Boy*, but the one major character throughout the book is Carl Sandburg himself. The book centers on the many influences that shape the author's outlook on life, featuring a "scrapbook" of themes and memories rather than action and drama.

Family history and its effect on a person's life is one of the basic themes of the book. Sandburg's parents, August Sandburg and Clara Mathilda Anderson, and their relatives, John and Lena Krans and Magnus Holmes, come to America from Sweden, hoping for a better life and bringing with them a love for the land, a dedication to hard work, and a strong faith in God. Because they have a vision for themselves and their new country, they take financial risks and willingly change their names and their way of life, yet they always maintain a warmth and respect for their heritage.

Carl's immediate family significantly influences his life. Of the family's seven children, two die of diphtheria. Carl works before and after school from the time he is eleven to help support the family, and while he would prefer to go to high school, he quits school after the eighth grade in order to bring in money for the family. His father, a blacksmith for the Chicago, Burlington, and Quincy Railroads, is a hard-working, somber, and unsympathetic man with little appreciation for education. Unable to write his name, he refuses to learn to read English and becomes furious when his children spend his hard-earned money

on books. Carl's mother, however, smiles easily and encourages her family's interest in learning.

Sandburg illustrates the background of his love for books, history, and public speaking by describing his childhood hunger for learning. At the age of four, he longs for the ability to read. He lists his favorite books, which include histories and pocket biographies; acknowledges the encouragement of an excellent eighth-grade teacher; and recalls his first experience at public speaking in a Demorest Silver Medal Declamation Contest.

I decided in June of 1897 to head west and work in the Kansas wheat harvest. I would beat my way on the railroads; I would be a hobo and a "gaycat."

Prairie-Town Boy also develops a social history of America before the turn of the century, showing in characters such as George Brown, the mayor of Galesburg, and Newton Bateman, the president of Knox College, examples of the era's pioneer spirit. The lingering influence of Abraham Lincoln makes a deep impression on Carl. The political climate of the time comes to life as Sandburg describes his memories of a Republican rally for James G. Blaine, an unsuccessful presidential candidate; his attendance at a funeral parade for former president Ulysses S. Grant; his conversations with the Socialists; and his experiences in the military. The Sandburgs' financial difficulties mirror the hard times that many people face after the stock market panic of 1893, and Carl's experiences in a variety of jobs present a colorful picture of the types of work that are available. He gives a firsthand description of the life of a hobo and mentions details in midwestern life, ranging from visits to country fairs and the Barnum and Bailey Circus to descriptions of the different varieties of outhouses. The book gives an inside look at the leisure activities that people enjoy during the late nineteenth century, including baseball, minstrel shows, boxing, and listening to Thomas Edison's talking phonograph.

Prairie-Town Boy is a story of hope and responsibility. It challenges young people to look closely at life in order to learn what it has to offer, and to look closely at themselves to find ways to take advantage of the opportunities available to them.

◆ Literary Qualities ◆

Carl Sandburg's autobiography combines a collection of personal memories with the carefully researched history of a midwestern town. Each chapter of the book describes the people, places, and events that shaped an aspect of the writer's life. The biography is not fictionalized but gives authentic representations from Sandburg's own experiences. Sandburg devotes most of the narrative to descriptions and insights rather than action or conversation. Although the biography is not documented or footnoted, the events of the story have legitimate basis both in fact and feeling.

The tone of *Prairie-Town Boy* is warm but honest, poetic but unsentimental. Sandburg uses vivid details and natural impressions to show the vulnerability, awkwardness, and sensitivity of a boy. Written by a man in his seventies, the autobiography is a simple and thoughtful look at life that contains no moralizing or bragging. The book has unity of form and style, but each character and event stands alone; themes and characters, while important, may not be reintroduced. The end result resembles a scrapbook rather than a tightly woven collection of stories.

◆ Social Sensitivity ◆

Sandburg treats religion, particularly Swedish Lutheranism, with sensitivity and objectivity. He shows how his parents' faith shapes his upbringing, comments on how an immigrant landowner might view God as a farmer, and quotes the words of a zealous shoe repairman's witness. He does not, however, judge or preach. Instead he states personal beliefs vividly through his descriptions of meeting a man with no arms at the circus or through his realization that alcoholism can ruin a person's career.

Sandburg is openly sensitive to the needs and rights of blacks, and he tries to pass this sensitivity on to his readers. But readers may be offended by some of the language Sandburg uses, such as calling the upstairs of the new auditorium a "Nigger Heaven." In using such a term, however, Sandburg is not showing prejudice but reporting a commonly-used title, just as he means no offense by relating the nickname of one of his best friends, Frenchy Juneau.

Sandburg takes a candid view of immigrants. He does not stereotype or glamorize persons of any nationality. His feelings are hurt when a Swedish family in Kansas is the first to label him a bum. He does, however, admire the influence and spirit that immigrants bring to the Midwest. He shows this admiration in his unsuccessful attempt to swap for a pocket biography of nineteenth-century Swedish-American inventor John Ericsson.

Readers who are aware of Sandburg's interest in politics will recognize incidents and characters in *Prairie-Town Boy* that may have influenced his later political stances. For example, the behavior of Republicans during a presidential campaign rally for James G. Blaine cause six-year-old Carl to wonder about the difference between Republicans and Democrats, and Sandburg says that the Socialists Mr. Sjodin and his son John "got him to think" about Socialist issues. The autobiography, however, handles politics with a calm rationality: Sandburg remembers and even interprets political situations from his youth, but he does not propagandize or ridicule.

◆ Topics for Discussion ◆

1. Who were George Brown, Newton Bateman, and Justin Finley, and why do you think Sandburg chose to open his autobiography by discussing them?

2. Why is Sandburg disappointed with Robert Todd Lincoln and William Jennings Bryan?

3. Compare the personalities, backgrounds, and interests of Sandburg's father and mother.

4. What kind of relationship do Swedish immigrants, especially John Krans, Magnus Holmes, and August Sandburg, have to the land? What hopes and hardships did the land represent for them?

5. Why does Sandburg change his name from Carl to Charles? How does this compare to Holmes's name change?

6. What effect does Joe Elser have on Sandburg and Mart? In what ways does he serve as a father figure for them?

7. What role does the kitchen play in Sandburg's boyhood home? Why do you think that Sandburg goes into such a detailed description of this room?

8. What effect does Ulysses S. Grant's funeral parade have on Sandburg? What issues and questions does it raise for him?

9. Describe Sandburg's attitude towards baseball. Why is baseball such a popular sport at this time, and how does it get Sandburg and his friends into trouble? Why does he decide not to become a professional baseball player?

10. What impressions do the people in the circus side show have on Sandburg? Which of these people does he admire? Who does he feel sorry for and why? Who does he *not* feel sorry for and why?

11. In what ways is the Schulz Cigar Shop a significant location for Sandburg?

12. Who are the "Dirty Dozen" and how do they get their name? What is Sandburg's relationship to this group?

13. Describe Sandburg's attitude towards police officers and the law. What experiences does he have with jails, and what are the differences between these experiences?

14. Discuss young Sandburg's attitude towards work. What kind of jobs does he hold? Which jobs does he like

and which does he dislike? Why? Why do you think he changes jobs so often? How do you think the jobs make him feel about himself?

15. What is Sandburg's impression of Chicago on his first visit? What does it symbolize for him as a youth? How does this compare to his later feelings about the city?

16. What does Sandburg mean when he says, "I was not a hobo in Larned, Kansas"? What are some of the things you think Sandburg might have learned from being a hobo?

17. By the end of the book, how is Sandburg different from his father? How is he similar to him?

18. How does Sandburg's military experience differ from the typical military experience? How does it change his life?

• Ideas for Reports and Papers •

1. What does Sandburg mean when he says that there is "no regular pattern" of person living in Galesburg? How would you describe the town and its inhabitants? What is the significance of Sandburg calling himself a "Prairie-Town Boy"?

2. Why do you think Sandburg is so fascinated with Abraham Lincoln? Compile a list of people and places mentioned in connection to Lincoln in *Prairie-Town Boy*. What is the significance of each?

3. Compare Sandburg's autobiography with his biography of Lincoln, *Abe Lincoln Grows Up*. What similarities exist between the boyhoods of the two subjects?

4. Research the American economic situation in the 1880s and 1890s. What were the causes and results of the stock market panic of 1893? How did it affect the Sandburg family?

5. Research what it meant to be a hobo. Who were the hobos, what was their lifestyle, how did society relate to them, and what were some of their philosophies and traditions? How did a hobo differ from a bum?

6. Who are Sandburg's boyhood heroes and why does he admire them?

7. Compare the books Sandburg reads and admires as a youth with the books he eventually writes as an adult. How is he influenced by his early experiences with books?

8. Research the Lincoln-Douglas debates. Why, where, and when were they held? What topics were debated? Who was considered the winner? How did these debates compare to the political debates of today?

9. Trace how Sandburg develops an interest in each of the following during his youth: music, poetry, history, common people, newspaper reporting, and his making public appearances and lectures.

10. Sandburg describes the Sjodin family as "the first real radicals I knew." In what ways does Sandburg's later life reflect the Sjodin political viewpoint?

• Related Titles •

Prairie-Town Boy is an adaptation of *Always the Young Strangers*, a longer autobiography covering the same period of Sandburg's life. *Always the Young Strangers*, which the *New York Times* called the greatest autobiography ever written by an American, differs from *Prairie-Town Boy* in that it is written for adults and thus is more complicated, contains greater detail, and uses illustrations and explanations that might be inappropriate for young readers. It also contains an index, making it easier to locate facts about Sandburg's life.

and containing numerous color photographs, describes the Sandburg home at Connemara and presents a concise biography of Carl and Paula Sandburg. It includes an excellent chronology of Sandburg's life and a list of reference materials.

Rhoda Preston

◆ For Further Reference ◆

Detzer, Karl. *Carl Sandburg: A Study in Personality and Background.* New York: Harcourt, Brace, 1941. Written before *Always the Young Strangers* was published, this biography provides an overview of the earlier years of Sandburg's career.

Golden, Harry. *Carl Sandburg.* Cleveland: World Publishing, 1961. This biographical essay on Sandburg, written by a close friend, provides a personal portrait of a great American writer. The book gives an overview of Sandburg's life and work, shows the development of his ideas, and presents some unique material and insights. It is well indexed.

Steichen, Edward, ed. *Sandburg: Photographers View Carl Sandburg.* New York: Harcourt, Brace, 1966. A photographic essay of Sandburg, compiled by the award-winning photographer who was also Sandburg's brother-in-law.

Steichen, Paula. *Carl Sandburg's Home: Official National Park Handbook.* Washington, DC: U.S. Department of the Interior, 1982. This handbook, written by Sandburg's granddaughter

PRIDE AND PREJUDICE
Novel
1813

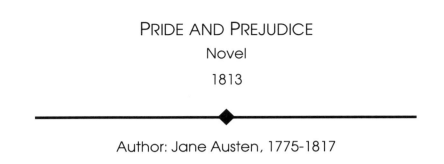

Author: Jane Austen, 1775-1817

Major Books for Young Adults

Sense and Sensibility, 1811
Pride and Prejudice, 1813
Mansfield Park, 1814

Emma, 1815
Northanger Abbey, 1818
Persuasion, 1818

◆ About the Author ◆

Jane Austen, one of England's most cherished and frequently read novelists, was born into the landed gentry in the town of Steventon on December 16, 1775. She was the sixth of seven children raised by strong parents: Cassandra, the daughter of an Oxford University scholar, and George, an Oxford-educated country clergyman. Never married, Austen lived comfortably with her family in Steventon until 1800, and thereafter in Bath, Southampton, and Chawton.

Many of her biographers have written that Austen's life lacked dramatic or noteworthy incidents. She and her older sister Cassandra were educated primarily at home by their father. As a youth she read literature avidly, wrote fragments of novels and histories, and took part in standard social activities such as formal dances and visiting. In adulthood her daily life included assisting her parents at home and looking after her many nieces and nephews. Two adult experiences do stand out: in 1801 a mysterious romantic interest of hers died, and in 1802 she accepted and then declined an offer of marriage from a man she did not love. Otherwise Austen seems to have lived happily and uneventfully. During her mature years, when she was an author of solid repute, she remained at home, preferring rural domesticity to the London literary scene. She died in Winchester of Addison's disease on July 18, 1817.

In her early twenties, Austen wrote in earnest, completing *Lady Susan, Elinor and Marianne,* and *First Impressions,* and drafting other works. Her father sent the novels to a publisher, but all were rejected, as was *Susan* in 1803. In 1804 she began *The Watsons* but abandoned it after her father's death. Perhaps because of these disappointments, Austen's interest in writing waned until 1809-1811, when she revised *Elinor and Marianne* and won it an anonymous printing as *Sense and Sensibility.* In 1812 she greatly revised *First Impressions* and saw it published, also anonymously, as *Pride and Prejudice*. Working intensely in a busy parlor in her Chawton home from 1813 to 1816, she composed *Mansfield Park, Emma,* and *Persuasion* and revised *Susan* into *Northanger Abbey,* a spoof of the popular romance and horror novels of the era. At the time of her death she was working on a manuscript entitled *Sanditon.*

All of these works deal with the lives of young, marriageable men and women in England's nineteenth-century rural landowning and aristocratic classes. Young readers have long admired Austen's endearing, if imperfect heroes and heroines, whose struggles to find the right partner are complex, moving, and often humorous. Austen's work is also known for its finely crafted plots, masterful language, and subtle irony, and for its vivid and sometimes satirical presentation of the only society in which Jane Austen lived.

◆ Overview ◆

Pride and Prejudice is a love story that is both humorous and deeply serious. It is primarily concerned with the Bennets, a family with five daughters ranging in age from twenty-two to fifteen. The family children live well but know that when their father dies they will lose their home and property to their cousin Mr. Collins, simply because the family has no male heir. Mrs. Bennet, a comically deluded woman, believes that her main business is to arrange for her children to marry rich or, at worst, reputable gentlemen. Her husband, a genial wit, refuses to support her schemes but rarely hinders them. As a result, when experiences with bachelors of varying worth lead to problems and new emotions, the daughters must struggle on their own, without parental guidance.

The novel portrays two remarkable characters with whom generations of readers have fallen in love: Elizabeth Bennet, the talented, independent second daughter, and Mr. Fitzwilliam Darcy, a haughty aristocrat who sees through Mrs. Bennet's manipulations and believes the Bennet family to be beneath him. In turn, Elizabeth develops a blinding prejudice against Darcy and puts him down as no one has dared before. Their relationship—a combination of attraction and contempt—is certainly one of the most exciting in all literature.

Through its vivid characters, *Pride and Prejudice* contrasts many human qualities: depth and superficiality; honesty and dishonesty; pride and humility; independence and servile compliance; selfishness and generosity. Most important, Austen contrasts weak, dense people with those who can recognize their own foibles and thus mature. It is the latter group that the writer sees as the moral leaders of her society.

◆ Setting ◆

The story begins in the autumn of 1811 when Charles Bingley, accompanied by his two sisters and Darcy, takes up residence at Netherfield, close to the Bennets' home at Longbourn. Both homes are located in a rural area of Hertfordshire, a county in southeast-central England. Other scenes take place in nearby Rosings in Kent county, where Mr. Collins occupies a clergyman's "seat," and in the central county Derbyshire, where Darcy lives. The novel also describes, but does not show, events that occur in London (located twenty-four miles from Longbourn) and in the popular seaside resort town of Brighton.

Pride and Prejudice

JANE AUSTEN

EDITED BY DONALD J. GRAY

Jacket for *Pride and Prejudice* by Jane Austen.
W. W. Norton: New York (1966).

Pride and Prejudice reveals distinctions of social class that may seem unusual to young American readers. Darcy and his aunt, Lady Catherine de Bourgh, are members of the aristocracy, England's hereditary ruling class. The Bennet family and the clergyman Mr. Collins—like Jane Austen herself—fall into the category of landed gentry, which means that they own property in the country, are well-bred, and hold a good social position. The Bennets are "poor" only in comparison with others of the gentry. Historically, the aristocracy and gentry mixed freely but tended not to cross lines for marriage. Both maintained business but not social dealings with people of "inferior" status, such as small merchants, tenant farmers, and servants.

The members of the Bingley family, from the north of England, are neither gentry nor aristocracy, but their wealth and cultivation earn them immediate prestige in Hertfordshire and make Charles an attractive bachelor. Finally, the officer corps of the militia contains men of diverse status, ranging from aristocrats such as Colonel Fitzwilliam to men of more ordinary background, such as Lieutenant George Wickham, whose father once managed the property of Darcy's father. Wickham's rank as an officer allows him to visit the Bennet family, but his lack of money or property renders him a poor choice for marriage, as Mrs. Gardiner reminds her niece Elizabeth.

Young readers should know that Austen considers rural communities like the Bennets' places of comfort and havens for traditional values. Families know each other well and care very much about how they appear to their neighbors. Unlike London, which values change, fashion, and commerce, Austen's country towns preserve pleasures considered more genteel: social graces, family living, and honorable courtship.

In this world marriage is a complex institution; teen-age women are considered "out" (or eligible for suitors) after they attend their first dance, and most of a young woman's life consists of preparing for marriage. For most women, the choice of a spouse is the most significant decision they will make. Because few women hold jobs, those who do not marry may live lonely, idle existences. Many couples—like Charlotte Lucas and Mr. Collins—wed not for love but to gain property or achieve a desired social rank. Austen's novels show such arrangements, but they do not approve of them; her heroes and heroines never marry coldly.

Jane Austen is a keen observer of human behavior. She shows that while men and women often think too highly of themselves, deceive or flatter others, and act stupidly, they are also capable of love, kindness, and moral growth. With this mingling of positive and negative traits, her heroes and heroines seem deeply human.

The novelist is reputed to have considered Elizabeth Bennet her favorite creation. Indeed, the twenty-year-old possesses brains, beauty, musical talent, confidence, and—for the era—rare independence. At every turn Elizabeth displays the latter trait: she walks several miles alone to visit her ailing sister Jane at Netherfield; she declines Mr. Collins's marriage offer despite her mother's outrage; she angrily rejects Darcy's condescending proposal in the novel's most stunning scene. But this independence—perhaps inherited from her mother—leads her to make mistakes: she judges Wickham, Darcy, and others too soon, and then clings stubbornly to her prejudices.

Fitzwilliam Darcy first appears as an exceedingly self-impressed figure. Early in the novel, as he rudely refrains from dancing at a ball, Elizabeth overhears him talking derogatorily about her and the other women. At the next dance, he "must" admit to himself, although he still considers himself superior, that Elizabeth's intelligent expression is "beautiful." He falls in love with her against his wishes—despite detesting her bumptious mother, despite erroneously distrusting her older sister Jane, despite disdaining her family's modest means, and despite detecting Elizabeth's thinly veiled hostility. Darcy's attempts to approach Elizabeth succeed only in offending her more, and to complicate matters, his arrogant Aunt Catherine expects him to marry within the aristocracy.

Pride and Prejudice develops other characters skillfully if less fully. Charles Bingley and Jane Bennet fall in love quickly and tastefully at the novel's outset. Both respect social form and refuse to write or visit the other improperly. Bingley's intrusive sisters and Darcy remove him to London in an attempt to break up their relationship. The sisters believe that their brother should marry someone of his wealth, while Darcy believes that Jane, like her mother, favors Charles only for his money. Jane, a thoughtful, self-denying woman—the opposite of Mrs. Bennet—tries to hide her heartbreak and humiliation from her family, particularly her mother, for whom their engagement had been a certainty.

Meanwhile, the youngest Bennet, Lydia, whose shallowness points to her parents' deficiencies, rushes into an ill-advised romance with Wickham, an officer who at first appears charming and trustworthy. Wickham recounts—to Elizabeth's satisfaction—how Darcy unjustly kept him from receiving the large inheritance Darcy's father had left for him. Later, after this lie is exposed by Darcy, Wickham fails in a ruthless attempt to marry a rich northern woman and impulsively elopes with the naive Lydia. The sixteen-year-old girl speaks recklessly, acts offensively, and must gratify her impulses instantly. Lydia fails to see that running off with Wickham scandalizes her family.

Pride and Prejudice depicts a leadership crisis in the Bennet family and in the community as a whole. Mrs.

Bennet's tactless meddling in Jane's affairs creates the appearance that her daughter is hunting Bingley's fortune. Mrs. Bennet also fails to anticipate the disastrous possibilities of her young daughter's flirting with militiamen. Her hunger for attention damages the family reputation at every public occasion. Meanwhile, as likeable as her husband may seem, he has no stomach for disciplining his children. He is not seriously engaged in their lives except when Lydia's flight jeopardizes the family. Then he reluctantly assumes his paternal duties and makes for London to reclaim his daughter, only to return in failure.

> *It is a truth universally acknowledged that a single man in possession of a good fortune must be in want of a wife.*

Several memorable minor characters also contribute to this leadership void. Lady Catherine de Bourgh, Darcy's aunt, is a rich, domineering woman who stifles others' spirits at every social gathering and considers Elizabeth a poor match for her nephew. Sir William Lucas, Charlotte's "empty-headed" father, lives inconsequentially, overly concerned with his own importance. Mr. Collins, the young clergyman, strives for no role of substance in his community, instead considering his only urgent duty to follow Lady Catherine's orders quickly and precisely.

Pride and Prejudice shows the Bennet family—and by inference the country life that Austen loved—to be in a state of crisis. With no strong adult influences, the best young people step forward. Darcy shows his true mettle by secretly helping Charles return to Jane, by ensuring that Wickham and Lydia return to Longbourn as a married couple with an income, and by proposing again to Elizabeth with new humility. Shamed, Elizabeth recognizes many of her misjudgments and accepts Darcy's proposal. Their personalities soften and blend beautifully.

Like any moralist, Austen shows that foolish or evil actions do have adverse consequences. Although Jane ends up happily married to Bingley, the scheming of her mother and Bingley's sisters causes her real pain. More severely, Lydia ends up living joylessly with her indifferent husband, always moving about and never financially secure. Darcy's intervention preserves her reputation, but her life amounts to little.

The novel ends on the hopeful note of two Christmas-time weddings for the eldest Bennet daughters. Elizabeth builds a friendship with Darcy's sister Georgiana, occasionally sends money to Lydia, and gradually moves her husband to reconcile with his aunt. By their actions and their shared sense of duty, Elizabeth and Darcy—a union of the gentry and the aristocracy—show themselves to have become leaders in their society.

◆ Literary Qualities ◆

Pride and Prejudice is an exciting, suspenseful story. The novel does not drag, for Austen writes succinctly and structures a tight plot. The story is based on a series of conflicts: the central one between Elizabeth and Darcy, and smaller ones concerning the other characters. Every chapter builds towards the novel's climax, Elizabeth's visit to Darcy's home in Derbyshire, and the resolution is both plausible and satisfying.

Pride and Prejudice is an excellent book to reread because of its foreshadowing—subtle hints of upcoming events. Darcy's first proposal to Elizabeth, Lydia's elopement, and Charlotte's marriage are among the novel's many foreshadowed occurrences.

Austen also uses language superbly, but not in flowery or flashy ways. Rather, she writes with great clarity and precision, and employs irony for a comic effect. Irony allows a writer to communicate more than the literal or expected meanings of his or her language. For instance, upon Darcy's entrance to a dance in chapter 3, Austen writes that "the report was in general circulation within five minutes...of his having ten thousand a year." Here Austen pokes fun at the gossipy nature of the people and shows why Darcy might be justified in feeling out of place. Austen also fills the novel's dialogue with irony, making people such as Mrs. Bennet and Mr. Collins reveal their foolishness to the reader through their ridiculous comments.

Many critics consider the novel a satire, which, in general terms, is a literary work that uses irony and humor to expose human or social faults. Thus, Lydia embodies vanity, Wickham dishonesty, Mr. Collins obsequiousness, and Mrs. Bennet a multitude of follies. Austen does not tear down country life or folk; rather, she directs the reader's gaze to some of the human imperfections that threaten the virtues of her culture.

Pride and Prejudice possesses other literary qualities. Austen renders splendid characters, showing how their errors result from their flaws. She uses symbolism sparingly but successfully; for example, the ordered, austere beauty of Darcy's grounds and home at Pemberly represents his real nature. Finally, Austen employs the omniscient point of view, which means that her all-knowing narrator has complete knowledge of the story and can reveal any character's thoughts and feelings to the reader. Most of the time, the narrator shows the world as Elizabeth sees it.

◆ Social Sensitivity ◆

Pride and Prejudice contains no violent or explicit scenes and adults should feel comfortable that it is appropriate for young readers. Nevertheless, the novel does present as "normal" certain attitudes that few readers share today. The class system imposes unwritten rules on who may marry or socialize with whom. Young readers may profit from learning about other manifestations of class discrimination: injustice, social unrest, and the levelling of aspirations.

Also, the novel does not question or challenge the inferior position allotted to women in early nineteenth-century country life. Mr. Bennet's daughters cannot inherit his property, and they receive less schooling than do males of the landed gentry. Twenty-seven-year-olds such as Charlotte Lucas marry lesser men for fear of wearing the label "spinster" at thirty. Women cannot work and thus are economically dependent upon men. For women, "success" is defined solely in terms of marriage and domestic affairs—in short, in terms of what they provide for men. But even in the home—Mr. Bennet's weakness notwithstanding—the father controls the money and holds ultimate authority. That Elizabeth is even considered "rebellious" is one measure of the restriction of women; her actions surely would not earn her that label today.

Teachers and other adults may find it helpful to discuss gender roles and sex discrimination with young readers. While Elizabeth has been called a pioneer for sexual equality (she tells Mrs. Gardiner that she will marry Wickham or whomever else she pleases), she does in fact take rather nicely to her appointed role in the end.

◆ Topics for Discussion ◆

1. Reread the first two sentences of chapter 1. Does the novel demonstrate those sentences to be true? Why do families vigorously compete for single men such as Charles Bingley?

2. Discuss Bingley's character. He is rich, friendly, and sociable, but he deserts Jane rather easily. How do you judge his treatment of her? Why doesn't he more vigorously resist his sisters' efforts to separate him from Jane?

3. Look back at the dance scenes in chapters 3 and 5. How do the townspeople change in their opinion of Darcy? What do these scenes show you about the way people make judgments?

4. Why do the Bingley sisters form lasting judgments of the Bennets based on the events following Jane's visit to Netherfield? What scheme does Mrs. Bennet devise? What prevents Jane from returning home? How do the Bingleys interpret her stay at their home? How do they view Elizabeth's walking from Longbourn to Netherfield?

5. What kind of person is Mary Bennet, the middle daughter? What makes her unique in the family? Can she be considered a satirical character? Why or why not?

6. What is Mr. Collins's main motive for getting married? Why does he decide to propose to one of the Bennet daughters? Why does Elizabeth turn him down, and why does this rejection anger her mother? Is Mrs. Bennet wrong?

7. When Charlotte accepts Mr. Collins's proposal, Elizabeth is shocked and angry. Why does Charlotte choose to marry the unimpressive clergyman? Is Elizabeth's harsh judgment of Charlotte correct?

8. When he first proposes to Elizabeth, Darcy admits that he loves her. Why, then, is she offended? What attitudes does he reveal through his marriage offer?

9. Besides disliking Darcy's general demeanor, Elizabeth resents him for two acts—wronging Wickham and influencing Bingley to reject her sister Jane. It turns out that Darcy actually treated Wickham better than he deserved. But what about his manipulation of Bingley? Why should Elizabeth forgive him for contributing to her sister's pain?

10. Why does Elizabeth feel it is inappropriate for Lydia to spend two months in Brighton with Colonel Forster's wife? Why does Lydia want to go? Mr. Bennet listens to Elizabeth's objections but allows Lydia to go. Why? Why does the elopement bring disgrace to the family?

11. What kind of woman is Lady Catherine de Bourgh? How would you

describe her relationships with others? Which of her traits surface in her nephew Darcy? In her daughter Anne? Clearly she seeks to control others' lives, but she ends up inadvertently promoting the marriage she is trying to prevent. How? Why do you think Elizabeth urges Darcy to make peace with her, even though she has insulted Elizabeth greatly?

12. Jane and Elizabeth marry happily, but Lydia's life seems dreary at best. Do you think the ending is cruel and vindictive? Does it appear that the narrator is almost gloating over Lydia's misfortune?

13. Does the world of the novel appeal to you? Would you want to live there? Why does Jane Austen value country life?

14. Considering Elizabeth's prodigious talents, what might she do with her life in the modern world?

◆ Ideas for Reports and Papers ◆

1. A moralist attempts to educate readers about the principles of right and wrong that he or she feels should govern human life. What principles does *Pride and Prejudice* espouse? Which specific incidents and characters bring out these principles?

2. Analyze Mr. and Mrs. Bennet as parents. What seem to be their strengths and weaknesses? How do their personalities and habits appear in their five children? What do you think the novel shows about parenthood?

3. Analyze the novel's title. Who else besides Darcy and Elizabeth displays prejudice and pride? In what incidents?

What makes the hero and heroine different from these other characters? What does the novel show the reader about pride and prejudice?

4. What distinguishes characters who are portrayed favorably from characters who are portrayed unfavorably? Elizabeth from Lydia? Darcy from Wickham and Collins? Jane from Mrs. Bennet and the Bingley sisters?

5. Etiquette—the distinction between good and bad manners—plays a major role in the world of the novel. Which characters are rude or tacky? In what specific ways? How does the behavior of polite characters differ? Why do you think social form and appearance are so important in this culture? In what ways does the modern world view manners similarly? Differently?

6. After you have completed *Pride and Prejudice,* view the film version. Does the movie successfully capture the characters and the world of the novel? What are the film's drawbacks? How does it differ from the book? Which did you enjoy more?

7. English history is more than a chronology of wars and rulers. Examine the condition of women in Jane Austen's era. Did urban women live differently than those in the country? What factors led to the expansion of opportunities for women?

◆ Related Titles/Adaptations ◆

Sense and Sensibility deals with the fortunes in romance of Elinor and Marianne Dashwood, daughters who could not inherit their father's property and thus are left in difficult circumstances.

The novel contains the unscrupulous Willoughby, a Wickham-like figure. *Mansfield Park* centers around Fanny Price, a timid girl given up at the age of nine by her weak, overwhelmed parents to her kind uncle Sir Thomas. While being raised in his troubled household, she suffers frequent abuses by empty, snobbish, or spiteful people but ends up growing into the strength of the family. *Emma,* often regarded as Austen's finest work, shows the smug title character's maturation as her failed efforts to control others and the wisdom of Mr. John Knightley gradually deflate her ego. *Northanger Abbey,* possibly the first of Austen's completed works, contrasts the melodrama of popular Gothic novels with reality. In it Catherine Moreland, a likeable girl who has read a few too many ghost stories, imagines on scant evidence that the father of the man she loves is engaged in criminal behavior. *Persuasion,* the writer's last completed work, is a tender, less satirical novel than its predecessors. The story concerns the quiet pain of Anne Eliot, unmarried at twenty-seven, who through circumstance becomes reacquainted with her now-prosperous ex-fiancé, a man she still loves—Frederick Wentworth. Years before she had broken their engagement on the advice of a trusted friend. Avid Austen readers will also enjoy Austen's letters, juvenile writings, and unfinished works, all of which can be found in the convenient volume *Minor Works,* published by Oxford University Press.

Readers may also be interested in the 1940 film version of *Pride and Prejudice.* The lavish production, which stars Sir Laurence Olivier as Darcy and Greer Garson as Elizabeth Bennet, also features Edmund Gwenn and Maureen O'Sullivan in supporting roles. Aldous Huxley co-authored the screenplay, which retains the wit and verve of Austen's novel.

◆ For Further Reference ◆

Cecil, Lord David. *A Portrait of Jane Austen.* London: Constable and Co. Ltd., 1978. Well-illustrated, this biography should be enjoyable to readers of all ages.

Hardwick, Michael. *A Guide to Jane Austen.* New York: Charles Scribner's Sons, 1973. Hardwick provides a character index, plot summaries, and other useful information for all of Austen's novels.

Honan, Park. *Jane Austen: Her Life.* New York: Ballantine Books, 1987. This is the most recent biography of Jane Austen.

Daniel R. Porterfield

A PROUD TASTE FOR SCARLET AND MINIVER

Novel

1973

◆

Author: E. L. Konigsburg, b. 1930

Major Books for Young Adults

Jennifer, Hecate, Macbeth, William McKinley, and Me, Elizabeth, 1967
From the Mixed-Up Files of Mrs. Basil E. Frankweiler, 1967
About the B'nai Bagels, 1969
(George), 1970
Altogether, One At a Time, 1971

A Proud Taste for Scarlet and Miniver, 1973
The Dragon in the Ghetto Caper, 1974
The Second Mrs. Giaconda, 1975
Father's Arcane Daughter, 1976
Throwing Shadows, 1979
Journey to an 800 Number, 1982
Up from Jericho Tel, 1986

◆ About the Author ◆

Born in New York City on February 10, 1930, and raised in small Pennsylvania towns, Elaine Lobl Konigsburg was a chemist and a teacher before becoming a writer. Her scientist's interest in how things work has influenced her psychological exploration of her characters. Married to psychologist David Konigsburg, she has three children whose lives often inspire her books. She enjoyed drawing in grade school and resumed this pursuit after her middle child was born.

Konigsburg writes at home, protecting her writing time by making it her first priority. She is a careful and thorough researcher, and many of her books have required some kind of preliminary investigation on topics ranging from medieval history and schizophrenia to physical handicaps and museum security. She enjoys gardening, eating chocolate, and walking on the beach.

Konigsburg has garnered an impressive array of awards for her writing. *Jennifer, Hecate, Macbeth, William McKinley, and Me, Elizabeth* was a Newbery Honor Book in 1968, the same year that *From the Mixed-Up Files of Mrs. Basil E. Frankweiler* won the Newbery Medal. *Father's Arcane Daughter* received an International Reading Association's Children's Book Award, and *Up from Jericho Tel* was also selected for this award. *Throwing Shadows* was an American Library Association Notable Children's Book and an American Book Award nominee. *A Proud Taste for Scarlet and Miniver* earned Konigsburg an American Library Association Notable Book Award and a nomination for a National Book Award.

◆ Overview ◆

Eleanor of Aquitaine was one of the most colorful and influential queens in history. Her forceful personality and strong sense of humor enabled her to accomplish great things and to endure misfortune. History happens because of people, although years later the people are often buried under the dates and facts. This book focuses on Eleanor's personality, illustrating why and how events are shaped by the people who live them. The history of Eleanor's part of the Middle Ages comes to life, from the Crusades and the Church's efforts to control government to the courtly love tradition and the foundations of English common law.

In *The Genesis of "A Proud Taste for Scarlet and Miniver"*, Konigsburg notes some of the ready-made connections between the Middle Ages and the middle-age (pre-adolescent) child, especially a tendency to literalness and a lack of perspective. Eleanor likewise lacks perspective and insight when she becomes a queen, but her experience helps her develop understanding. Thus, the book becomes a powerful metaphor for emerging maturity.

Jacket illustration by E. L. Konigsburg for *A Proud Taste for Scarlet and Miniver* by E. L. Konigsburg. Atheneum: New York (1973).

◆ Setting ◆

The story takes place in heaven ("Up") in the late twentieth century. Eleanor of Aquitaine, Empress Matilda, and William the Marshall are waiting for King Henry II to be admitted to heaven at last. The Abbot Suger stops to chat with Eleanor and stays to wait, too. To pass the time, the four recall Eleanor's time on Earth.

The flashbacks on earth are set during the Middle Ages in France and England, with a brief trip to the Holy Land. The flashbacks trace the highlights of Eleanor's life from 1137—when she is fifteen years old and about to wed Louis Capet, soon to be King Louis VII of France—to her death in 1204. Her life encompasses the rule of England by her husband Henry II and by her sons Richard and John.

◆ Themes and Characters ◆

Power, life's purpose, and a woman's place are among the themes of *A Proud Taste for Scarlet and Miniver*. Foremost, as illustrated by Eleanor's life, is the theme of choosing and developing the kind of person one wants to become. The ways government and the people it governs respond to each other intertwine throughout the book.

Four characters narrate different parts of the story. Abbot Suger has been Louis's teacher and Louis and Eleanor's confessor. Like Eleanor, he favors beautiful things. As a monk, he turns that taste toward decorating a new church. He recalls Eleanor's decisiveness at her wedding ceremonies, her growth in understanding a queen's role, and the disastrous Crusade to Constantinople, Antioch, Damascus, and Rome. While on earth, his understanding of Eleanor's nature helps hold the royal marriage together, but Louis divorces Eleanor, and she marries Henry of Anjou, who becomes King Henry II of England.

The Empress Matilda, daughter of King Henry I of England and mother of King Henry II, narrates the next segment. Matilda, a politically aware woman, has always recognized the value of Eleanor's experience, knowledge, beauty, and lands. With a mother's pride, she recounts Henry's accomplishments, duly acknowledging Eleanor's contributions and indicating that the fifteen years she observed seemed to be a perfect partnership of talents. An astute judge of character, Empress Matilda predicts the quarrel between Henry and his chancellor, Thomas Becket.

William the Marshall, a knight true and loyal to whichever Plantagenet currently rules England, narrates the third section, in which Eleanor, in revenge for Henry's infidelity, goes to Aquitaine to rear her sons Richard and John to rebellion against their father. In the Courtly Love game, which Eleanor and her daughter Marie set up to keep Richard

Illustration by E. L. Konigsburg for *A Proud Taste for Scarlet and Miniver* by E. L. Konigsburg. Atheneum: New York (1973).

and John occupied, William manages the tournaments. When Eleanor is imprisoned, William occupies the perfect position to note the growing dissatisfaction of Henry's sons, for Eleanor has trained her boys to rule while Henry refuses to allow them any real power.

Eleanor herself narrates the last portion of her life, beginning with her release from prison at age sixty-seven. Drawing on all she has learned about government, including how best to use her natural love for luxury and pageantry, Eleanor devotes herself to making Richard and John popular kings of England.

King Henry's vitality and self-assuredness match Eleanor's. Although he appears most often through the eyes of the four narrators, his greeting to Eleanor as he finally arrives in heaven demonstrates his forceful personality.

◆ Literary Qualities ◆

The device of placing characters in heaven allows Konigsburg to focus on Eleanor's personality and experiences without getting bogged down in all the details. This anachronistic approach—that is, taking the characters out of the time in which they lived—has been the focus of the critical response to *A Proud Taste for Scarlet and Miniver*; critics think it is either clever or too clever.

Beyond the narrative frame, Konigsburg's treatment of the four narrators deserves praise. Each speaks of a period in Eleanor's life unknown to the others, except Eleanor herself. Each narrator's unique style suits the personality revealed in the narration.

Konigsburg's illustrations are in medieval style. Most recall the illuminations, or ornamental designs and miniature drawings, of medieval manuscripts. One, showing Thomas Becket's envoy to the king of France, offers insight into the details of medieval life, much like the famous Bayeux tapestry from the eleventh century. The pen-and-ink drawings add flavor to the historical backdrop, depicting such specific activities and events as a tournament, a town receiving its charter, a royal wedding, and a crossing of the English Channel.

◆ Social Sensitivity ◆

The concept of an afterlife may cause some controversy, but Konigsburg uses it as a literary device, not as a means of advancing a particular point of view about religion. In the framework of *A Proud Taste for Scarlet and Miniver*, one is admitted to heaven ("Up") after spending time "Below" to remedy any character flaws remaining at one's death. Eleanor had not learned patience, and "she had done things on Earth for which there had been some Hell to pay."

Konigsburg jokes gently about admission to heaven and activities there. Lawyers and bank presidents are scarce; anyone in government will need some time in hell first. Heavenly inhabitants are requested not to race around or to drum their fingers on the clouds, because "Angels don't appreciate having to answer hundreds of requests for better television reception." This light-hearted approach characterizes the presentation of any theological assumptions.

◆ Topics for Discussion ◆

1. How much influence on the general populace does a ruler's style have? Eleanor believed that a ruler's duty included providing a touch of glamor in the lives of the common people. King Louis disagreed. Compare the styles of some U.S. presidents, such as the luxurious elegance of John Kennedy, the "plain folks" approach of Jimmy Carter, the Hollywood touch of Ronald Reagan.

2. Eleanor believed that festivals such as coronations, inaugurations, and world fairs are important for a sense of community: "There is nothing like a lavish display to give people pride in their country." Can we see this same principle working in smaller units, school homecomings or family celebrations, for instance?

3. Historically, the most important function of a queen was to produce an heir to the throne. What other functions does Eleanor find? Why can Henry gladly accept her help while Louis cannot?

4. One of King Henry's accomplishments was his effort to ensure that people would have equal legal treatment. The American judicial system is based on English common law. Despite the legal assurances of equality under the law, are there instances when justice does not seem to be applied equally?

5. Eleanor and Marie invent the Courtly Love games to occupy restless teen-agers and to teach them about acceptable manners and attitudes. What kinds of activities serve that purpose for teen-agers today?

6. For more information on some aspects of medieval life, contact your local chapter of the Society for Creative Anachronism. To find the chapter nearest you, contact the national headquarters: P.O. Box 360743, Milpitas, CA 95035.

♦ Ideas for Reports and Papers ♦

1. Who were the troubadours, and what did they do?

2. While Eleanor knew it would be difficult to make people take pride in King John, she could grant charters that would make towns take pride in their own government. The English forced King John to sign the Magna Carta. What did that document mean to English government?

3. Eleanor concedes that Blanche of Castile, wife of Louis VI of France, was a bad mother-in-law but a good queen. What happened during her reign?

4. Falconry was a favorite sport of King Henry II. Eleanor and Thomas Becket enjoyed it, too. How is the sport practiced today?

5. What were the benefits, both spiritual and materialistic, that men hoped to accrue from going on one of the Crusades to the Holy Land?

6. Many of Eleanor's interests—tapestries, rugs, pillows, incense—stemmed from a desire for comfort. What was it like to live in a castle in medieval England?

7. Eleanor promoted a consistent system of measurement for England. On what was that system based? How does the American system differ from the British?

8. The Vexin changed hands several times during Eleanor's life. Explain the importance of this triangle of land and trace its history.

9. Write a resume for Eleanor of Aquitaine.

♦ For Further Reference ♦

Commire, Anne, ed. *Something about the Author.* Vol. 4. Detroit: Gale Research, 1974. The article on Konigsburg includes her own account of the background of *Jennifer, Hecate, Macbeth, William McKinley, and Me, Elizabeth* and *From the Mixed-Up Files of Mrs. Basil E. Frankweiler.*

De Montreville, Doris, and Donna Hill, eds. *Third Book of Junior Authors.* New

York: H. W. Wilson, 1972. Includes Konigsburg's own account of her schooling and teaching and her move toward writing.

Konigsburg, E. L. *Forty Percent More Than Everything You Ever Wanted to Know about E. L. Konigsburg*. New York: Atheneum, 1984. A promotional pamphlet in which Konigsburg interviews herself, with emphasis on *From the Mixed-Up Files of Mrs. Basil E. Frankweiler*.

————. *The Genesis of "A Proud Taste for Scarlet and Miniver"*. New York: Atheneum, 1973. This promotional pamphlet, which tells how the book was written, can be obtained from the publisher.

Metzger, Linda, and Deborah A. Straub, eds. *Contemporary Authors*, New Revision Series. Vol. 17. Detroit: Gale Research, 1986. The article on Konigsburg summarizes the critical response to several books, including *A Proud Taste for Scarlet and Miniver*. Features a substantial interview with Konigsburg on being a writer.

Dixie Elise Hickman

QUEENIE PEAVY

Novel

1966

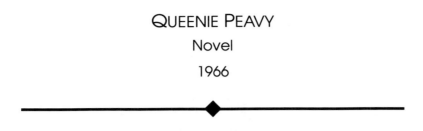

Author: Robert J. Burch, b. 1925

Major Books for Young Adults

Tyler, Wilkin, and Skee, 1963
D.J.'s Worst Enemy, 1965
Queenie Peavy, 1966
Skinny, 1969
Simon and the Game of Chance, 1970
Hut School and the Wartime Home-Front Heroes, 1974

Two That Were Tough, 1976
The Whitman Kick, 1977
Wilkin's Ghost, 1978
Ida Early Comes Over the Mountain, 1980
Christmas with Ida Early, 1983
King Kong and Other Poets, 1986

◆ About the Author ◆

Robert Joseph Burch was born on June 26, 1925, in Inman, Georgia. The seventh of eight children born to John Ambrose and Nell Graham Burch, he grew up on his mother's family farm in Fayetteville, Georgia, near Atlanta. Burch attended public schools and, following graduation from high school, joined the U.S. Army. During World War II, he served in New Guinea and Brisbane, Australia. After his discharge, he attended college at the University of Georgia, receiving a degree in agriculture with a specialization in horticulture. Unhappy as a horticulturist, he took a civil service job as a clerical worker. His duties involved a visit to Japan, from which point he began a trip around the world aboard a Danish freighter. When Burch returned to the United States, he took up residence in

New York City, where he studied writing under Dr. William Lipkind at Hunter College.

Burch began his writing career when he was thirty years old, and in 1960 he received a fellowship to the Bread Loaf Writer's Conference. His books have received many awards, and *Queenie Peavy* alone earned the Jane Addams Book Award, the Child Study Association of America's Children's Book Award in 1967, the Georgia Children's Book Award, and recognition as an American Library Association (ALA) Notable Book in 1971. *Queenie Peavy* was also selected for the George G. Stone Award in 1974 and the Children's Literature Association's Phoenix Award in 1986. *A Jungle in the Wheat Field* (1960) was an Honor Book in the *New York Herald Tribune*'s Spring Book Festival, and *Skinny* earned the Georgia Children's Book Award in 1964. The *Boston Globe-*

Horn Book Award was given to *Ida Early Comes Over the Mountain*, which was also an ALA Notable Book.

In 1962 Burch returned to the South. He now resides in Fayetteville, Georgia, in the home where five generations of his family have lived. He is best known for his stories of young people who live ordinary, yet eventful lives in historic rural Georgia. Writing is Burch's full-time profession, but he also enjoys traveling, fishing, gardening, and raising his saluki dogs.

◆ Overview ◆

Queenie Peavy depicts some of the pressures of growing up in a small town during the Great Depression: supplies are scarce, and both adults and children must work hard to keep themselves clothed and fed. The book's greatest value derives from its portrayal of one teen-ager's triumph over emotional conflict at school and an unfortunate domestic situation. Most people perceive Queenie Peavy as a problem child. She is troubled and troublesome. Eventually, by her own initiative, she works through her dilemmas and feels better about herself as a result. *Queenie Peavy* tells a universal story of the internal and external conflicts that most young people must resolve in order to leave childhood.

◆ Setting ◆

The story takes place during the 1930s in Cotton Junction, a small town in Georgia. The farmers lead a spare, hardworking life typical of rural communities during the Great Depression. Cotton Junction's business district consists of little more than the courthouse, post office, drugstore, cafe, and dry goods store. Because the town was one that "General Sherman somehow missed" on his destructive Civil War march through the South, Cotton Junction still boasts many handsome houses with large white columns and wide front porches. On the outskirts of town stand farmhouses and ramshackle homes. Queenie says "one good puff from an angry wolf" would splinter the two-room shack that she shares with her mother.

◆ Themes and Characters ◆

Queenie Peavy depicts one young woman's turbulent transition from childhood to young adulthood. Most of the townspeople of Cotton Junction view Queenie Peavy as a defiant tomboy, an eighth-grader who chews tobacco and throws rocks. Apathetic and impulsive, Queenie remains in constant trouble with school and town authorities. Queenie's father is imprisoned in the state penitentiary in Atlanta, and Queenie lives with her mother on the outskirts of town. Sadness over her father's imprisonment and anger over the frequent taunting of neighborhood children drive Queenie to frequent violent outbursts. Priding herself on her deadly aim, Queenie throws rocks at birds, squirrels, and buildings. She plays a prank on the bully Cravey Mason that results in his breaking his leg. Despite this tough exterior, however, Queenie is a bright and kind-hearted person. She excels in most of her classes when she is not being kicked out of them, and she delights in telling stories to or singing songs with the young children who live next door to her.

Martha Mullins, Queenie's best friend at school, is called Little Mother

Illustration by Jerry Lazare
for *Queenie Peavy* by
Robert Burch. Viking Press:
New York (1966).

because she is so "growny." She comes from a poor but proud family. Because Martha is so often responsible for the younger children in her family, she has developed many qualities traditionally associated with mothers. Sweet, polite, unselfish, and optimistic, she plays the role of peacemaker at home and at school, and is willing to sacrifice her own wants and needs for the sake of others. Too saintlike to be completely believable, Little Mother nonetheless teaches Queenie many lessons—including the difference between pride and foolish pride, and the value of restraint in the face of antagonism—which acquire an edge of realism when played out against Queenie's more fully developed character. Avis and Dover Corry, Queenie's playmates at home, live on the farm that neighbors the Peavy place. The Corrys own their land

and are one of the few successful black farm families in Cotton Junction. Avis is five years old and Dover is eight. Both are happy, curious children who idolize Queenie and vie for her attention. They especially enjoy the tall tales she tells about their dog, Matilda.

Queenie's classmate Cravey Mason is the leader of the children who tease Queenie about her father. His bullying causes her to retaliate in ways that later make her ashamed. Although Cravey is not a good student, he excels in sports and is admired by most of the children at school. Queenie hates him for his cruelty toward her but eventually realizes that her violent reactions merely encourage him and that, when others taunt her, she "must learn to consider it their own sadness," not hers.

Queenie idealizes her father, a convicted criminal who has been serving a prison sentence. Queenie envisions her dad as a loving father, misunderstood and wrongly accused. But upon his return home on parole, he disappoints her with his indifference. Queenie slowly comes to see that her father is cold, rude, self-centered, and vindictive.

♦ Literary Qualities ♦

Burch's descriptions of everyday life in a small town during the Great Depression are simple and well drawn. The narrative is credible, the dialogue natural, and the characters down-to-earth. The author also engages the reader with his subtle use of humor. The understated wit in Queenie's thoughts and conversations provides entertainment as well as insight into her character. When, for example, Little Mother makes a particularly angelic statement, Queenie decides that "Little Mother not only wanted her friends to get along with each other but was now promoting good will and understanding for the whole world." Queenie's interactions with Dover and Avis are also important for their revelations of the soft side of her personality.

For the most part, *Queenie Peavy* is a straightforward narrative featuring a simple, episodic plot. One literary device that Burch employs is the use of song lyrics to reveal Queenie's moods. Queenie often sings with the Corry children, and her choice of songs— "Foolish Questions" or "Work, for the Night is Coming"—often reflects her current state of mind. Music also serves as the vehicle through which Queenie first achieves public recognition of her talents. She overcomes her inhibitions and sings at a school assembly, and the audience enjoys her performance so much that it asks her to sing an encore.

Queenie looked over at her friend. "Maybe he'll die," she said, "wouldn't that be a good joke on me and you?"

Although the book is relatively free of symbolism, Burch does set up a symbolic contrast between the accuracy of Queenie's rock-throwing and the haphazard manner in which she approaches other aspects of her life. An intelligent girl, Queenie is, nonetheless, inconsistent; constantly in trouble at school, she seems unable to control her behavior or to direct her actions toward positive ends. But by the end of the book, Queenie has begun to focus her "deadly aim" on long-term goals, taking a part-time job in a doctor's office and expressing a desire to become a doctor herself some day. In one of the book's final chapters, Queenie decides against throwing a rock at a church: "Finally she unclenched her fist and looked at the rugged stone that had almost broken a church window." She drops the rock to the ground, where "it resembled any other rock in the world— except that its jagged edges reflected more sunlight."

♦ Social Sensitivity ♦

Although *Queenie Peavy* examines subjects such as juvenile delinquency, parental indifference, malnutrition, and the cruelty of children to one another, the book is, on the whole, uncontroversial. One troubling point is Burch's reference to the Corrys as "negroes" rather than as blacks; although this term was more common in 1966, when the book was published, readers should be aware that it is now considered offensive.

Despite the novel's somewhat bleak subject matter, Burch melds realism and optimism convincingly to yield a surprisingly upbeat portrayal of an adolescent struggling against great emotional odds. Queenie lives a solitary life; her mother works all day, and her father has never appreciated his daughter. To shield herself against possible hurt, Queenie assumes the persona of a self-sufficient, tough youngster who "doesn't care" about the results of her actions. Burch mixes scenes of Queenie as troublemaker with scenes of her entertaining the Corry children or helping her mother with chores. Burch suggests that Queenie is torn between the demands of bravado and those of decency, and thus he succeeds in painting an empathetic portrait of a juvenile delinquent.

Some readers may be disturbed by Queenie's callousness early in the novel; she hits a squirrel with a rock from the distance of some sixty feet and gleefully holds the dead creature by the tail for show. But this squirrel proves to be her only live target. Queenie refrains from killing birds at two later points in the novel and is exceedingly kind to the farm animals she tends at home. Burch does not make Queenie's transformation too abrupt; he notes in the final chapter that her "stone-throwing did not come to an altogether sudden end; she remained proud of her aim."

Although Queenie Peavy is the story of a juvenile delinquent, its protagonist in no way resembles the disaffected youth of many other young adult novels, and its ultimate theme affirms the value of the traditional social order. Burch sets his novel in a world governed by a strict moral code. Queenie's many trips to the school principal's office and her father's incarceration demonstrate the punishments meted out to those who fail to adhere to this code. Mr. Peavy's status as an outcast fuels Queenie's desire for revenge against the society that has rejected her father—but it also teaches her to fear the loneliness that accompanies societal disapproval. At first, Queenie is unable to acknowledge either this fear or its more positive corollary: the desire for respect and acceptance.

Although Mr. Peavy appears to be a shiftless and vaguely malevolent individual, Burch takes care to portray other adults in a more sympathetic light. Queenie's hardworking mother; her earnest school principal, Mr. Hanley; and the firm but thoughtful Judge Lewis all challenge Queenie—whether by spoken advice or unspoken example—to direct her talents and energies toward more productive ends. They teach her that a mature person is sensitive to both the needs and the faults of others. Thus, although Queenie Peavy is a novel of rebellion, all rebellion takes place within a closed system; Queenie's ultimate goal is not to be independent of but rather to be accepted by her society.

◆ Topics for Discussion ◆

1. The book is set in rural Georgia. What does the novel reveal about the customs, mores, and culture of the South during the Depression era? What does it tell you about the economy and social customs then?

2. What are Queenie's positive and negative qualities? Which of these qualities make her a sympathetic character? Why does she allow her negative qualities to override her positive ones so often?

3. Cravey Mason is characterized as the antagonist. How does he influence Queenie? Why do you think he taunts her? Who else in this novel might be called an antagonist? Why?

4. Reconstruct the history of Queenie's relationship with her father. What role does Mr. Peavy play in his daughter's upbringing? Why did he go to prison? How do the father and daughter relate to each other?

5. How is Queenie's mother characterized? How would you describe her relationship with Queenie as compared to Mr. Peavy's?

6. Why does the author include the Corry children in the story? What do Queenie's interactions with Avis and Dover reveal about her character?

7. Queenie has run-ins with several adults in authority positions. How do these adults react to her? How does she respond to them? Do their opinions of her change over time?

8. At what point do you sense a change in Queenie? Explain the change. What do you predict for her future? Why?

◆ Ideas for Reports and Papers ◆

1. How are the historical, social, and economic references in the book significant to its plot development?

2. Compare Queenie's perceptions of her father before and after his homecoming.

3. In the book, external conflicts are apparent. Describe the internal conflicts that might exist in Queenie Peavy, Little Mother, Cravey Mason, Persimmon Gibbs, Mrs. Peavy, Mr. Peavy, Mr. Hanley, and Judge Lewis.

4. After it is discovered that Little Mother suffers from malnutrition, the Mullinses accept government assistance to help feed the family. Research and report on national programs to assist the poor with food, supplies, or jobs during the Great Depression. You may find it helpful to focus your report on one specific program.

5. Queenie has a good singing voice and enjoys singing for Dover and Avis. List the songs that she sings during the course of the novel. See if you can find sheet music for any of these songs at a library or music store, and learn to play or sing the song yourself. You may wish to perform for some of your classmates, just as Queenie does. Whether or not you are able to find sheet music, research and report on popular songs of the Depression era. Do most of these songs teach certain lessons or stress certain themes? What are they?

◆ Related Titles ◆

Other "problem youth" books by Burch are *D.J.'s Worst Enemy*, the story of a twelve-year-old jealous bully; *Simon and the Game of Chance*, the story of a thirteen-year-old and his domestic troubles; and *The Whitman Kick*, the story of seventeen-year-old Alan and of Alex, a teen-aged thief.

◆ For Further Reference ◆

Evory, Ann, ed. *Contemporary Authors.* First Revision Series. Vol. 5-6. Detroit: Gale Research, 1981. Includes a short biographical sketch that highlights the author's personal life and career.

Estes, Glenn E., ed. *Dictionary of Literary Biography.* Vol. 52, *American Writers for Children Since 1960: Fiction.* Detroit: Gale Research, 1986. Gives background information on Burch's life and detailed descriptions of his better known books.

Smith, Charlotte Hale. "Bachelor Writes Children's Stories." *Atlanta Journal and Constitution Magazine* (November 29, 1964): 55, 57, 59. In this interview, the author talks candidly about his boyhood and its influence on his writing.

Catherine Price
Valdosta State College

RASCAL: A MEMOIR OF A BETTER ERA
Autobiographical Novel
1963

Author: Sterling North, 1906-1974

Major Books for Young Adults

Plowing on Sunday, 1933
Night Outlasts the Whippoorwill,
    1936
Seven Against the Years, 1939
So Dear to My Heart, 1947
Reunion on the Wabash, 1952
Abe Lincoln: Log Cabin to the White
    House, 1956
George Washington: Frontier
    Colonel, 1957
Young Thomas Edison, 1958
Thoreau of Walden Pond, 1959

Captured by the Mohawks, and
    Other Adventures of Radisson,
    1960
Mark Twain and the River, 1961
The First Steamboat on the Missis-
    sippi, 1962
Rascal: A Memoir of a Better Era,
    1963
Raccoons Are the Brightest People,
    1966
The Wolfling: A Documentary Novel
    of the Eighteen-Seventies, 1969

◆ About the Author ◆

Sterling North was born on a farm overlooking Lake Koshkonong in Edgerton, Wisconsin, on November 4, 1906, to David and Elizabeth Nelson North. His mother was a gifted linguist and biologist, and his father was an amateur naturalist and a specialist on Native American culture. In 1913 North's mother died; but his memory of her and his sense of loss at her death emerge as constant influences in his writing. On June 23, 1927, North married Gladys Dolores Buchanan while a student at the University of Chicago, where he developed his literary skill as editor of the campus literary magazine. In 1929 he graduated with a bachelor of arts degree.

Between 1929 and 1956, North was a reporter and literary editor for newspapers and periodicals. He joined Houghton Mifflin to edit the North Star Books, a series of history books for children and young adults. After completing this project, he devoted himself to his own writing. North died in Morristown, New Jersey, on December 22, 1974.

North's first significant publication was a volume of poetry published by the University of Chicago Press in 1925; he was nineteen years old. In 1929 his concern with values and with education surfaced in The Pedro Gorino, a sea story that initiated his career as a writer of fiction. Throughout his career, North received praise and awards for his works of poetry and prose, most of which were children's books. The public recognized him as a writer whose belief in basic moral principles shaped his craft. North won his most notable awards for *Rascal: A Memoir of a Better Era*, which received the 1963 Dutton Animal Book Award and a 1964 Newbery Honor Book citation.

◆ Overview ◆

The story line of *Rascal: A Memoir of a Better Era* stems from the basic idea that humans and nature should develop a mutual respect that would allow them to live together and to develop fulfilling bonds of love. North paints a believable picture in *Rascal* that avoids unreachable idealism, and the essential realism of his work is its primary merit. Living in a time of crisis in American life, young Sterling North, along with his constant friend Rascal, faces a personal crisis that accompanies his emergence into manhood. He confronts, with the easygoing encouragement of his father and the more disciplined shove of his sister, his need to grow when he is forced to cage his pet raccoon and to move his half-built canoe from the living room. Although minor incidents in comparison to the larger picture of life during World War I, these confrontations with responsibility shape North's response to his evolving maturity. Throughout these difficult times, he takes great comfort in his pet raccoon, whose tenacious and daring personality mirrors that of his master. Their ultimate separation highlights the significance of the time they have spent together and points to the greater theme of this work. Any reader of *Rascal* will understand the significance of the subtitle "A Memoir of a Better Era," which refers to both a better time in America and a better time of life, when longer summer nights and fresh breezes seem sufficient to engender hope.

◆ Setting ◆

The action of the novel takes place at the end of World War I, the point at which America was losing its innocence and developing a mature awareness of its international role. Set in a rural Wisconsin town, *Rascal* draws parallels between events in the world at large and the experiences of an eleven-year-old boy who shares his own loss of innocence and developing maturity with a devoted companion, his pet raccoon. North most directly signals the parallel between the American experience and that of his youthful self when the autobiographical narrator puts away his muskrat traps on Armistice Day:

> I burned my fur catalogues in the furnace and hung my traps in the loft of the barn, never to use them again. Men had stopped killing other men in France that day; and on that day I signed a permanent peace treaty with the animals and birds. It is perhaps the only peace treaty that was ever kept.

◆ Themes and Characters ◆

The parallels between emerging America and young Sterling North enhance the significance of the year that the boy and the raccoon spend together. Their conflicts with Sterling's sister Jessica and the townspeople, especially the Reverend Thurman and Slammy Stillman, precipitate a loss of innocence. Sterling tries to maintain his ties with Rascal during their several wilderness outings, but nature's call proves too strong and Rascal's desire for a mate outweighs his wish to remain with the companion of his first year. As they separate, the boy displays an ability to come to terms with change and to face the future: "And I paddled swiftly and desperately away from the place where we had parted."

Sterling and his pet raccoon Rascal are two of the most memorable figures in literature written for young people. Sterling, without the guidance of a mother and subject only to the lenient supervision of his distracted father, is an independent youth with a remarkably mature sense of responsibility. Yet he takes joy in youthful activities such as fishing, swimming, and tramping through the woods.

Sterling's resourcefulness is striking. The many tasks and the constant concern over money that fill his life bring out qualities that will serve him well as an adult. He does not fret about wanting a canoe; he builds one himself. He does not complain at having to cage Rascal; he finds ways to make the captivity more bearable.

Rascal proves as resourceful as his owner. Able to break time-honored instinct, he forgoes his food-washing ritual at one point so as not to lose a second sugar cube. Rascal's discoveries lend a sense of adventure to the book. Each new food, each new treasure that enchants the raccoon gives the narrator an opportunity to demonstrate the intelligence and fascination of young creatures.

The relationship between Rascal and Sterling provides the basis of the plot and sets the theme. The author's memories of their shared adventures—from catching fish side by side to standing up to the threats of the bully Slammy Stillman—convey a keen appreciation for the harmony that can be found in nature.

◆ Literary Qualities ◆

On one level, *Rascal* is a simple story about a boy and his pet. The story's primary appeal lies in its realistic depiction of the relationship between Sterling and Rascal, his pet raccoon. In the literary tradition of *Julie of the Wolves*, *The Yearling*, and *Incident at Hawk's Hill*, North's narrative presents a child and an animal who, because they both lack a conventional family structure, become family to one another. Rascal lives in relative isolation from raccoons and other wildlife, and Sterling is raised, without a mother, by an often preoccupied father. In the course of a year, these two characters share affection, adversity, and adventure, and North's description of their experiences together emphasizes Sterling's growing awareness of the world around him. Through his relationship with Rascal, Sterling learns to defend his beliefs and to accept inevitable change. North explores the classic theme of man versus nature as he depicts Sterling's coming of age; the boy emerges from his encounter with nature prepared to live as a courageous, resourceful adult.

The literal maturation of Sterling in *Rascal* can also be read, in a symbolic sense, as a type of allegory about the loss of innocence in post-World War I America. North's subtitle "Memoir of a Better Era" seems to encourage such an interpretation. In this reading, the harmonious relationship between Rascal and Sterling might represent the innocence of the pre-world war era in the United States.

◆ Social Sensitivity ◆

Rascal never concentrates on the experiences and feelings of young people at the expense of adults. Mr. North may be a distracted, possibly even an irresponsible, parent, but his primary appearance in the book occurs when he realizes the pain his son feels over caging Rascal, and he tries to relieve that pain with a two-week camping trip. Even the neighbors, whose insistence on Rascal's imprisonment makes them the villains in the work, find Sterling obedient despite his reluctance. In this regard, *Rascal* is especially responsible and sensitive to important matters of maturity in young people.

◆ Topics for Discussion ◆

1. At several points in *Rascal*, the narrator parallels his experiences with the larger events in America during World War I. How important are these parallels, and what do they add to the work?

2. Sterling has an unusual family life, largely because of his mother's death. How does this affect him? Does he appear to suffer as a result? How does he compensate for the lack of a tightly structured family?

3. Other than master and pet, how would you characterize the relationship between the narrator and Rascal?

4. *Rascal* introduces several animal characters. What do we learn about animals from the work? Do you feel that North is trying to educate his reader about animals in general and raccoons in particular?

5. We might look at the narrator's taking a baby raccoon from its mother as a cruel act. How do we reconcile this apparent cruelty with what we learn about the narrator in the story?

6. Explain the many meanings that the subtitle "Memoir of a Better Era" might have.

7. Think about other animal stories you have read. What do they have in common with *Rascal*?

◆ Ideas for Reports and Papers ◆

1. After conducting research on raccoons, discuss the accuracy of North's descriptions of Rascal's behavior.

2. Describe ways in which Rascal fills a void left in the narrator's life as a result of his family's fragmentation.

3. The narrator of *Rascal* has several animals. Discuss the community they form and how members of that community coexist.

4. How many episodes in the novel show the narrator and Rascal doing the same activities? How important are these parallels to the development of the theme?

5. Describe how the narrator views nature. Are these the thoughts of a boy or of a man remembering his boyhood?

6. Write a short paper describing an experience in your life with a pet that reading *Rascal* reminds you of.

◆ Related Titles/Adaptations ◆

In 1965 North adapted *Rascal* for young children and published it as *Little Rascal*. In *Raccoons Are the Brightest People*, he continues to pursue his interest in raccoons and his desire to educate young people about them. In a similar vein, *The Wolfling* reflects North's interest in young animals and their development.

In 1969 Disney Studios produced a film version of *Rascal: A Memoir of a Better Era*, starring Billy Mummy, and in 1979 Miller Brody produced a record/cassette entitled *Rascal.*

◆ For Further Reference ◆

Commire, Anne, ed. *Something about the Author.* Vol. 45. Detroit: Gale Research, 1986. The entry on North, expanded from that presented in volume 1 of this series, provides a complete and valuable review of his career with an emphasis on the extent of his literary production and the popularity of his work.

De Montreville, Doris, and Donna Hill, eds. *Third Book of Junior Authors.* New York: H. W. Wilson, 1972. Contains an autobiographical sketch by North.

Kirkpatrick, D. L., ed. *Twentieth-Century Children's Writers.* 2d ed. New York: St. Martin's Press, 1983. This source presents an excellent bibliographical review of North's career and a short but insightful analysis of his literary achievements.

Gerald W. Morton
Auburn University at Montgomery

REBECCA OF SUNNYBROOK FARM
Novel

1903

◆

Author: Kate Douglas Wiggin, 1856-1923

Major Books for Young Adults

The Birds' Christmas Carol, 1886
The Story of Patsy, 1889
A Summer in a Canyon, 1889
Timothy's Quest, 1890
A Cathedral Courtship, 1893
Penelope's English Experiences,
  1893
Polly Oliver's Problem, 1893
The Village Watch-Tower, 1895
Marm Lisa, 1896
Penelope's Progress, 1898
Penelope's Irish Experiences, 1901
The Diary of a Goose Girl, 1902
Rebecca of Sunnybrook Farm, 1903
Rose of the River, 1905
New Chronicles of Rebecca, 1907

Finding a Home, 1907
The Flag-Raising, 1907
The Old Peabody Pew, 1907
Susanna and Sue, 1909
Mother Carey's Chickens, 1911
A Child's Journey with Dickens,
  1912
The Story of Waitstill Baxter, 1913
Penelope's Postscripts, 1915
The Romance of a Christmas Card,
  1916
Golden Numbers, 1917
The Posy Ring, 1917
Ladies-in-Waiting, 1919
My Garden of Memory, 1923

◆ About the Author ◆

Kate Douglas Smith Wiggin, the daughter of Helen E. Dyer and Robert Noah Smith, was born on September 28, 1856, in Philadelphia. Robert Smith died when Kate was three years old, and Helen Dyer Smith took her two daughters to Portland, Maine. Kate's mother married Dr. Albion Bradbury in 1863, and the family moved to the nearby town of Hollis, Maine, where they lived until 1873, when they moved to Santa Barbara, California. Wiggin finished her studies at Abbott Academy in Andover, Massachusetts, before joining her family several months later.

During her childhood, Wiggin enjoyed a chance encounter with Charles Dickens on a train trip between Portland and Boston. She described this meeting in *A Child's Journey with Dickens* and again in her autobiography, *My Garden of Memory*. Her schooldays at Gorham Female Seminary inspired her first published story, "Half a Dozen Housekeepers," accepted by *St. Nicholas* magazine in 1876.

In 1877 Wiggin became acquainted with the German educator Friedrich

Froebel's concept of the kindergarten, and the next year she established the Silver Street Kindergarten in San Francisco, the first free kindergarten west of the Rocky Mountains. In 1880 she opened a training school for kindergarten teachers, including her younger sister Nora A. Smith, with whom she later wrote several books on educational theories and techniques. Wiggin's first two books, *The Birds' Christmas Carol* and *The Story of Patsy*, were privately published to raise money for the kindergarten project.

Wiggin continued her kindergarten work after she married Samuel Bradley Wiggin in 1881. Although they moved to New York in 1884, she returned to California each spring to supervise the kindergarten. In 1889, while Wiggin was in California, her husband died suddenly. Wiggin continued to live in New York until 1893, when she moved with her mother and her sister to Hollis, Maine.

After her husband's death, Wiggin made almost annual ocean voyages to Europe, and on one such voyage she met George C. Riggs, a New York businessman whom she married in 1895. Riggs's business interests required frequent trips to England, Scotland, Ireland, and Germany, and Wiggin traveled widely with him. She died on August 24, 1923, at Harrow-on-the-Hill, England.

◆ Overview ◆

The primary appeal of *Rebecca of Sunnybrook Farm* is its lively plot, which holds the attention of readers of all ages. Young readers can identify with Rebecca Rowena Randall because she is not the completely perfect, idealized child of many early twentieth-century young adult novels. Sometimes irresponsible, Rebecca does not always follow Aunt Miranda's rules, and her excuses sound familiar to anyone who has ever been scolded for childhood misdemeanors. Even when she tries to do the right thing, Rebecca makes mistakes, but her experiences demonstrate that most such errors can be corrected.

Further, Rebecca's example encourages readers to develop self-confidence. In both appearance and personality, Rebecca exemplifies the "ugly duckling." Initially the people of Riverboro consider her a strange-looking child whose imagination leads to distinctly odd behavior. Before the end of the novel, however, Rebecca's talents are recognized, and people begin to comment on how attractive she has become.

◆ Setting ◆

Rebecca of Sunnybrook Farm is set in Riverboro, Maine, a small town resembling Hollis, Maine, where Wiggin grew up. While Wiggin does not emphasize the time period, the novel appears to take place sometime around the 1870s, for one character's fiancé has been killed during the American Civil War.

◆ Themes and Characters ◆

In *Rebecca of Sunnybrook Farm*, Wiggin illustrates many of the principles she sets forth in her books on early childhood education. Foremost is encouragement of the imagination. From her father's family, Rebecca has inherited creativity, which eventually wins her the respect of her schoolmates, her teacher, the townspeople, and even Aunt Miranda. Likewise Rebecca's unusual interests for a young girl of her time emphasize the importance of individuality. Possessing the self-confidence to differ from her peers, she quickly becomes a leader at school. Above all, Rebecca demonstrates the winning force of good character. Despite her mistakes, Rebecca cares about others, and she tries to do the right thing. As a result, she not only wins honors at school but gains her mother's respect and Aunt Miranda's love.

The most completely developed character is the protagonist, Rebecca Rowena Randall. She first appears as Wiggin first imagined her, the lone passenger in a stagecoach headed for Riverboro. The author establishes both Rebecca's innocence and her individuality when she scandalizes her mother, Aurelia Sawyer Randall, by saying the word "nightgown" aloud in public. Perhaps intentionally, Wiggin leaves the description of Rebecca's physical appearance somewhat vague, mentioning that she is an unusual-looking child with long dark braids and fascinating eyes. Near the end of the novel, the grown-up Rebecca is described as strikingly attractive.

Rebecca's closest friend, Emma Jane Perkins, is Rebecca's complete opposite in personality and appearance. Idolizing Rebecca for her imagination and independence, Emma Jane remains her loyal follower, but this blonde, pretty, conventionally behaved friend seems to be overlooked whenever Rebecca is present.

Rebecca's aunts, Miranda and Jane Sawyer, have volunteered to raise one of their sister's daughters. Although Rebecca is not their first choice, Jane sympathizes with Rebecca immediately and, in defending her, finally finds the self-confidence to oppose Miranda's domination. Miranda considers Jane weak and softhearted, and takes pride in her own strength. The townspeople treat her with respect but secretly feel

Illustration by Lawrence Beall Smith for *Rebecca of Sunnybrook Farm* by Kate Douglas Wiggin. Macmillan: New York (1962).

sorry for any young person forced to live by her rules. Only her sisters have seen Miranda's kind gestures; Jane assures Rebecca that Miranda is proud of her accomplishments, and Aurelia tells how Miranda once helped her dress to attend a ball with Lorenzo de Medici Randall, although Miranda had assumed that she herself was the object of his interest.

Rebecca's foremost opponent turns out to be her cruel schoolmate Minnie Smellie. Unlike Rebecca, Minnie lacks any sort of sensitivity or sympathy toward those less fortunate than herself. While Rebecca befriends and tries to help out her needy neighbors, the

Simpsons, Minnie hurls taunts at the family.

Jeremiah and Sarah Cobb, the Sawyers' kindhearted neighbors, provide help, good advice, and a haven for Rebecca. In turn, she more or less replaces their only child, a girl who died in infancy. Jeremiah, a stagecoach driver, brings Rebecca to Riverboro and becomes her first friend in town. She turns to him when life with Aunt Miranda becomes unbearable. Sarah repairs clothes that Rebecca carelessly damages and generally mothers the lonely child. Later the Cobbs share proudly in her accomplishments.

Adam Ladd, a wealthy but unhappy young entrepreneur, becomes Rebecca's benefactor when he buys enough soap from Rebecca and Emma Jane for the girls to buy a lamp for the Simpsons. Attracted to Rebecca's personality, he guides her intellectual development, both by the books he gives her and by the direction he gives her teachers. Although he claims to fear young ladies, there are hints at the end of the novel that Adam will eventually court Rebecca.

◆ Literary Qualities ◆

Although Wiggin lacked formal training as a novelist, she was an excellent storyteller. *Rebecca of Sunnybrook Farm* is a series of entertaining stories about a young misfit who wants to live up to the expectations of her benefactors without sacrificing her individuality. The episodic plot is always amusing. Coincidence plays a role in the resolution of the plot but less so in this work than in most young adult novels of the same era.

The novel's greatest strength is Rebecca, a unique character among the many idealized young characters in early twentieth-century novels. Imaginative, unconventional, and sometimes irresponsible, Rebecca frequently makes mistakes, but her self-confidence and her individuality make her a leader among her peers and a favorite among young readers.

Wiggin shows more interest in developing her themes than in developing her characters, and with the exception of Rebecca, the characters tend to be stereotyped, and the motivations for their behavior at times seem unclear. Aunt Miranda's lack of development is the most disturbing. For most of the novel, she appears virtually unmoved by Rebecca's efforts to please her, and her deathbed change of heart seems rather sudden. Aunt Jane's explanation for Miranda's attitudes may be an attempt to provide the necessary motivation.

◆ Social Sensitivity ◆

Although the Sawyers are relatively affluent, they consistently demonstrate an egalitarian attitude. Unlike the Smellie family, for example, the Sawyers never flaunt their wealth, nor are they condescending toward neighbors who have less. Both Rebecca and her wealthy friend Emma Jane associate as equals with the impoverished Simpsons, and Rebecca becomes extremely angry when Minnie Smellie taunts the Simpson children because their father is in jail. Rebecca insists that the children should not be treated as thieves just because their father has been convicted of dealing in stolen property.

Furthermore, Rebecca demonstrates hospitality when she volunteers to entertain the foreign missionaries. Wiggin also notes that Rebecca hates gossip and refuses to listen to tales about others. In contrast, Minnie Smellie is condemned not only for her cruelty to those less fortunate, but also for her selfishness.

◆ Topics for Discussion ◆

1. Miranda Sawyer, Jane Sawyer, and Aurelia Randall are sisters, but they do not act very much alike. In what ways are their personality differences indicated? Why are they so different? Are there any similarities among them?

2. Rebecca and Emma Jane sell soap so that the Simpson family can have a new lamp for Christmas. Is their experience anything like selling Girl Scout cookies today? Do their prospective customers react in the same way?

3. In some ways, Jeremiah Cobb serves as the father Rebecca does not have. In what ways does he help Rebecca?

4. Adam Ladd is one of Rebecca's best friends. Some critics have suggested that when Rebecca grows up, she will marry him. Is their relationship really a romance?

5. Rebecca's foremost opponent is a schoolmate named Minnie Smellie. What impression of her personality does her name convey?

◆ Ideas for Reports and Papers ◆

1. Both Kate Douglas Wiggin and her character Rebecca attended small-town schools in mid-nineteenth-century Maine. Was Rebecca's school typical of most schools at that time? How did those schools differ from schools today?

2. Rebecca Rowena Randall was named for the two heroines of Sir Walter Scott's *Ivanhoe*. In what ways does she resemble each of these heroines?

3. The orphaned or fatherless young girl who wins the affection of a cold-hearted relative or guardian appears frequently in novels of the early 1900s. Compare Rebecca with another such heroine, perhaps Anne Shirley of Lucy Maud Montgomery's *Anne of Green Gables* (1908) or Elnora Comstock of Gene Stratton Porter's *A Girl of the Limberlost* (1909).

4. Rebecca's best friend is Emma Jane. How is Emma Jane different from her? Why does Wiggin make the two girls so different? Why are they friends?

5. Rebecca gradually wins the heart of Aunt Miranda. What are the steps in this process?

◆ Related Titles/Adaptations ◆

New Chronicles of Rebecca contains additional stories about Rebecca, set during the same period as *Rebecca of Sunnybrook Farm* and involving many of the same characters, but it never achieved the same popularity as Wiggin's first work about Rebecca.

Readers should note that the 1938 film *Rebecca of Sunnybrook Farm*, starring Shirley Temple, has no relationship to Wiggin's novel other than its title.

◆ For Further Reference ◆

Benet, Laura. "Kate Douglas Wiggin." In *Famous Storytellers for Young People*. New York: Dodd, Mead, 1968. A brief biographical sketch with little discussion of individual works.

Benner, Helen Frances. *Kate Douglas Wiggin's Country of Childhood*. Orono: University of Maine Press, 1956. A comprehensive biography, bibliography, and critical analysis of individual works. Published on the hundredth anniversary of Wiggin's birth, this work attempts "to record, from all available material, the story of Mrs. Wiggin's life, which had not previously been told to anyone outside her family circle; and to make some evaluation of her literary work and her role in the development of literature in Maine."

Cooper, Frederick Taber. "Kate Douglas Wiggin." In *Some American Story Tellers*. New York: Henry Holt, 1911. A complimentary description of Wiggin's romanticism in the "Rebecca" books and sophistication in the "Penelope" books.

Mason, Miriam E. *Kate Douglas Wiggin: The Little Schoolteacher*. Indianapolis: Bobbs-Merrill, 1962. An anecdotal biography covering the years 1863 to 1920, placing the events of Wiggin's life in historical context. Includes study aids, such as a glossary, study questions, and suggestions for projects.

————. *Yours with Love, Kate*. Boston: Houghton Mifflin, 1952. A lively biography written in a style resembling young adult fiction and ending as Kate Wiggin begins the composition of her autobiography.

Montgomery, Elizabeth Rider. "From a Dream to a Book." In *The Story behind Great Books*. New York: Dodd, Mead, 1946. The story of Wiggin's inspiration for *Rebecca of Sunnybrook Farm*.

Overton, Grant. "Kate Douglas Wiggin." In *The Women Who Make Our Novels*. Freeport, NY: Books for Libraries Press, 1967. A biographical sketch with comments about some of the specific books.

Seaton, Beverly. "Kate Douglas Smith Wiggin." In *American Women Writers: A Critical Guide from Colonial Times to the Present*. New York: Frederick Ungar, 1982. A brief biographical sketch with critical evaluation of major works.

Stebbins, Lucy Ward. "Kate Douglas Wiggin as a Child Knew Her." *Horn Book* (November-December 1950): 447-454. Childhood reminiscences of the Silver Street Kindergarten by one of the three people to whom *The Birds' Christmas Carol* was dedicated.

Wiggin, Kate Douglas. *My Garden of Memory: An Autobiography*. Boston: Houghton Mifflin, 1923. Nostalgic recollections of her career, emphasizing her personal reactions to people and events.

Charmaine Allmon Mosby
Western Kentucky University

The Red Badge of Courage

Novel

1895

◆

Author: Stephen Crane, 1871-1900

Major Books for Young Adults

Maggie: A Girl of the Streets, 1893
The Red Badge of Courage, 1895
The Little Regiment and Other Episodes of the American Civil War, 1896
The Open Boat and Other Tales of Adventure, 1898

◆ About the Author ◆

Stephen Crane was born on November 1, 1871, in Newark, New Jersey, the youngest child of the Reverend Dr. Jonathan Townley Crane and Mary Helen Peck Crane. The Cranes dated their roots in New Jersey back to 1665, when an ancestor also named Stephen Crane had settled in the area. The Reverend Crane died on February 16, 1880, after a brief illness. After her husband's death, Mrs. Crane moved her family to the nearby town of Roseville. In 1882 the Cranes moved to Asbury Park, a seaside town on the Jersey shore where Crane attended school for the next six years.

In 1888 Crane enrolled at Hudson River Institute (also called Claverack College), a semi-military academy. Crane entered Hudson with a less than stellar academic background, but although he failed to post an impressive academic record here, too, he did enjoy the cadet life at the academy. He stayed at Hudson for two years, working

summers at his brother's news service in Asbury Park, and it was during these years that he began his lifelong rebellion against religious dogmatism. In 1890 Crane entered Lafayette College, which, like Hudson, was a Methodist school. He rarely attended classes, failed his courses, and dropped out at the end of the semester. His next school was Syracuse University, where again he lasted for only one semester. While there, in 1891, Crane wrote the first draft of *Maggie: A Girl of the Streets*. After returning to New Jersey, he met Hamlin Garland, an established writer of realistic fiction who exerted a strong influence on Crane's writing.

In the fall of 1891 Crane moved to New York City, where he lived with art students in a boarding house and explored the slums of the city, particularly the Bowery. Following the advice of his mentor, Garland—who maintained that in order to depict slum life realistically, a writer must experience the pain endured by slum dwellers—Crane visited soup kitchens and other places where

Illustration by Herschel
Levit for *The Red Badge
of Courage* by Stephen
Crane. Macmillan/
Crowell-Collier: New York
(1962).

poor people congregated. Crane knew genuine deprivation during this period, and his health, never robust, was weakened. For the rest of his life he had a racking cough and a low resistance to disease. The Bowery became the fictional locale for *Maggie: A Girl of the Streets,* which was privately printed in 1893.

The novel won the praise of William Dean Howells, an important writer whom Crane met through Garland.

In 1894 an abridged version of *The Red Badge of Courage,* which Crane had started writing the previous year, was published by the Bacheller Syndicate in its newspapers. Crane traveled in the

West and Mexico from January to May 1895, and returned to see a book version of *The Red Badge of Courage* published by D. Appleton and Company in October. Before going West, Crane had become infatuated with a beautiful young society girl, Nellie Crouse. Some of his most revealing letters were written to her. Largely uninterested in social status, which was very important to Crouse, Crane knew his infatuation was hopeless. Their relationship was limited to the seven letters he sent her.

George's Mother, another novel set in the New York slums, and a revised version of *Maggie* were both published in June 1896. That December, *The Little Regiment and Other Episodes of the American Civil War* was published. These stories capitalized on the success of *The Red Badge of Courage*, and Crane was now obsessed with the wish to see a war firsthand. An attempt to reach revolution-torn Cuba failed when his ship sank off the coast of Florida on January 2, 1897. "The Open Boat," published in June, is a fictionalized account of Crane's experiences as he and three others rowed through high seas to shore.

Having failed to reach Cuba, Crane decided to go to Greece to cover the Greco-Turkish War. He was accompanied by Cora Taylor, whom he had met while waiting for passage to Cuba in Jacksonville, Florida, where she ran a bordello. Both Crane and Taylor worked as war correspondents in Greece. Twice divorced and five years older than Crane, Taylor was still legally married to an Englishman who refused to grant her a divorce. Nonetheless, Crane and Taylor were married on August 25, 1898. After covering the war in Greece, the couple settled in England, where Crane made friends with many leading writers of the time,

including Joseph Conrad, H. G. Wells, Ford Madox Ford, and Henry James. Always short of funds, the Cranes nonetheless entertained lavishly at their elegant house in Ravensbrook. Crane wrote constantly, but could not become solvent. When the United States and Spain went to war in Cuba in 1898, he sailed for New York, having borrowed money from Conrad and other friends. The U.S. Navy would not accept Crane as a seaman, but he was hired by Joseph Pulitzer's *New York World* as a war correspondent. In Cuba, fellow correspondents were impressed by his courage.

In 1897 Crane had been diagnosed with tuberculosis, but the disease seemed to be in remission. While in Cuba, however, he fell ill with malaria, an event that possibly reactivated his tuberculosis. His health deteriorating, Crane still managed to get out his dispatches, some of which rank among his best work as a reporter. Fired by Pulitzer as the result of a misunderstanding, he returned to New York and was hired by William Randolph Hearst's *New York Journal* as a war correspondent. In all, Crane covered the war from April to November 1898. Meanwhile, several of his better stories had been published, including "The Monster," "The Bride Comes to Yellow Sky," and "The Blue Hotel."

Crane returned home to England in 1898, and he and Taylor moved to Brede Manor, Sussex. As their extravagance continued, Crane, gravely ill, turned his hand to any kind of writing to pay his debts. He published a novel, *Active Service*, in 1899, its quality far below his usual standard. A volume of poems, *War Is Kind*, also appeared in 1899.

During a large Christmas week party at Brede, on December 29, 1899, Crane collapsed with a severe pulmonary hemorrhage. He died on June 5, 1900, at a sanatorium in Badenweiler, Germany. *The Whilomville Stories* and *Wounds in the Rain* were published posthumously the same year.

◆ Overview ◆

The Red Badge of Courage attempts to recreate the combat experiences of a young, frightened soldier in the American Civil War. Henry Fleming, the protagonist, has never seen a real battle and worries about how he will behave under pressure. Crane's novel has been praised ever since it first appeared in print as highly realistic in its presentation of the psychology of a young man facing injury and possible death. One of the best American short novels, Crane's work vividly presents some of the horrors, both physical and psychological, that soldiers encounter in battle.

◆ Setting ◆

The battle of Chancellorsville in northern Virginia, waged from May 1 to May 3, 1863, seems to have been Crane's model for the fictional battle in *The Red Badge of Courage*. The action of the novel follows that of the original conflict—a Confederate victory—quite closely. Chancellorsville is not mentioned in the novel, nor is General Joseph "Fighting Joe" Hooker, the leader of the Army of the Potomac at Chancellorsville. At one point in the novel, though, Crane does name the Rappahannock River, which separates the two armies. The real setting of *The Red Badge of Courage*, however, is the consciousness of Henry Fleming. The battle, his fellow Union soldiers, and the landscape are all seen through his eyes.

His attitudes, which change frequently, determine what he and the reader see.

◆ Themes and Characters ◆

War, for Crane, was a favorite metaphor for human life, equally applicable to coal miners ("In the Depths of Coal Mine," 1894) or to the people living in the slums of New York (*Maggie: A Girl of the Streets*). Courage and heroism come under Crane's scrutiny in his classic book about wartime, *The Red Badge of Courage*. Henry has read classical tales of heroism, and dreams of performing brave deeds on the battlefield, but he is deeply worried about what will happen when the regiment finally goes into action. He and his regiment have marched into northern Virginia, but since then have done nothing but wait. His concern is not "How will we men of the 304th New York Regiment do when we go into battle" but "How will I do?" In the course of his self-questioning, he has been "forced to admit that as far as war was concerned he knew nothing of himself." Of course, although Henry does not consider it, all the men around him are also worried about the coming battle and how they will behave under fire.

Henry, more often referred to as "the youth," has a small circle of friends that includes Jim Conklin, "the tall soldier," whom he has known all his life, and Wilson, "the loud soldier," who constantly struts and brags. Most characters in the novel remain unnamed except for epithets such as these. Henry's identification with his companions is not strong enough to give him a sense of community with them. The regiment is often pictured as a powerful organism breathing, snorting, and shooting flames like a dragon.

The Army of the
Potomac—Our Outlying
Picket in the Woods
sketch by Winslow Homer
for Harper's Weekly (1862)
reprinted in The Red
Badge of Courage by
Stephen Crane. Macmil-
lan/Crowell-Collier: New
York (1962).

The regiment goes into action after its long period of inactivity, and although Henry is relieved in a sense, his anxieties soon increase. When the enemy forces make their first charge, Henry's training helps him perform in the accepted manner; he and the regiment stand their ground, and the enemy is repelled. But all too soon a second charge is under way. The tired men of the 304th Regiment resume firing, but soon many of them throw down their rifles and run. Panic-stricken, Henry also heads for the rear, running "like a blindman" and crashing into trees.

As his panic subsides, Henry rationalizes his desertion: he has behaved in a highly reasonable fashion; he has saved the U.S. government a piece of valuable equipment, himself; and he has followed the dictate of nature, which bids every creature to protect itself. Guilt-ridden despite his rationalizations, Henry falls in with some wounded men who have been forced to seek shelter in the rear. He finds the company of the wounded preferable to that of his own regiment, which he hopes has been soundly defeated, for its defeat would vindicate him completely.

But Henry's conscience undergoes further assault when he notices a man referred to as a "spectral soldier," walking as if he were a dead man looking for a grave. Henry suddenly realizes that this mortally wounded soldier is Jim Conklin, his best friend. Henry, hysterical with grief, promises to take care of his friend, but Jim recognizes Henry only for a moment before he shakes off Henry's hand. In a fit of panic, Jim runs from the road into a field, where he convulses and dies as Henry looks on helplessly.

Henry later suffers a head wound when a frightened deserter unexpectedly hits him with the butt of his rifle. An unnamed friendly soldier leads Henry back to his regiment, where Wilson, previously known as the "loud soldier," is on sentinel duty. Henry finds that Wilson has matured from a swaggering braggart to a quietly confident soldier. Wilson and the corporal who examine Henry assume that he has been shot.

The wound is Henry's means of entry back into the military society, and he realizes that this is the only society available to him.

The youth, considering himself as separated from the others, was saddened by the blithe and merry speeches that went from rank to rank.

After Henry's cover story has been accepted, his remorse practically disappears. He still worries that his cowardice will be exposed, but his ego has been restored. No longer an isolated wanderer in the company of the wounded and dying, Henry learns to take pride in his regiment and in his own ability to contribute to the war effort. Going into battle he fights like a madman, firing so furiously that he wins the admiration of his fellow soldiers. Henry becomes less self-centered as he begins to identify with Wilson and the other soldiers, and he finds the strength of purpose to atone for his earlier cowardice.

Throughout Henry's transformation, Crane emphasizes that coming of age involves an awareness of and concern for others. Henry learns that he is a person of contradictory impulses and actions, at times brave, at times cowardly, and this knowledge allows him to identify with the society around him. He thinks of others as well as himself; his is no longer an egocentric universe.

But Crane is careful not to present war as a simple rite of passage; he emphasizes that war brings out the most horrible aspects of life. War indeed tests souls, but in the process it ruins more men than it converts to higher ideals. Although the survivors of war were sometimes stronger, more compassionate men, Crane could never reconcile this phenomenon with the horror and the suffering of innocent creatures everywhere. Henry is able to change, but Crane himself never came to terms with a God who could tolerate wars.

◆ Literary Qualities ◆

In preparation for writing *The Red Badge of Courage*, Crane studied the Civil War photographs of Matthew Brady and illustrations by painter Winslow Homer and drew on his own highly empathic imagination. The writers Joseph Conrad and Ford Madox Ford, Crane's good friends in England, claimed that Crane subscribed to the impressionistic literary movement and strictly observed the canon of impressionism: "render; never report." By means of his sharply etched and poetic images, Crane hoped to help his readers feel as if they were actually on a battlefield. For example, Crane describes the wounded enemy standard-bearer behaving as if he had "invisible ghouls fastened greedily upon his limbs" as he tries to escape with his flag; Crane also renders a vivid image of the dirt and smoke assaulting the regiment: "Wallowing in the fight, they were in an astonishingly short time besmudged ....Moving to and fro with strained exertion, jabbering the while they were, with

The Red Badge of Courage

their swaying bodies, black faces, and glowing eyes, like strange and ugly fiends jigging heavily in the smoke."

Ending *The Red Badge of Courage* was difficult for Crane. The professional writers among his friends marveled at how rapidly he produced his work, whether prose or poetry, and how rarely he revised what he had written. But three attempts to bring his second novel to a close were required, and even then he probably was not satisfied. Although he wrote the first draft of *The Red Badge of Courage* in nine days, he told Willa Cather that "he had been unconsciously working the detail of the story through most of his boyhood."

"It was essential that I should make my battle a type and name no names," Crane said when explaining the overall plan of his book. As several critics have noted, this choice makes *The Red Badge of Courage* resemble an allegory. What makes it different from typical allegories such as John Bunyan's *Pilgrim's Progress* (1678) or William Langland's *Piers Plowman* (c. 1395) is Crane's attitude toward conventional Christianity. Raised in a family of ministers and religious workers, he himself became an agnostic. Some of the imagery of the novel is drawn from religion, such as "the chapel," where Henry hopes to escape from the battle. But throughout the novel, everybody curses, nobody prays, and Crane uses imagery from his religious training to show that, for him, war is demonic; demons and devils abound in his poetic metaphors. Critic R. W. Stallman sees the death of Jim Conklin as a crucifixion and notes that the soldier's initials are the same as those of Jesus Christ. Critic Bettina L. Knapp sees the battle as an initiation similar to the one religious devotees experience before they receive illumination, the knowledge that God is with them and that they are one with him. The novel may well invite such interpretations because of its stark simplicity.

The best-drawn characters in Crane's books are usually those from low socio-economic backgrounds—inner-city residents, soldiers, coal miners, seamen, and farmers. Crane did not romanticize his characters because he recognized that poverty-stricken people are quite capable of making their have-not status a basis for conceit. Crane found this attitude quite prevalent in the Bowery, and he made it as much the target of his ironic barbs as he did the conceit of the rich.

◆ Social Sensitivity ◆

Crane's novels reflect his basic beliefs about humanity. The chronic misery of the poor aroused his sympathy, as did the plight of common soldiers in wars. Having rejected traditional theological explanations as a boy, Crane never found a philosophy that adequately explained the hardships inherent in the human condition.

Because Crane's theme in *The Red Badge of Courage* is the fear and isolation common to all war, he deliberately avoids all specific references to the Civil War itself. The battle is presumed to be Chancellorsville, but neither its name nor the names of commanding generals are mentioned. Few characters have names or identities, and even Henry is usually referred to simply as "the youth." Crane is not concerned with the causes of the war, the implications of slavery, the tactics of the armies, or even the outcome of his battle. For the purposes of the story, it makes no difference that this is the American Civil War, or that in the real battle of

Chancellorsville thirty thousand men were killed.

The novel vividly depicts the ravaging emotions that lead Henry to abandon his idealism, reevaluate his conception of bravery, recognize nature as a malevolent force, and repudiate the existence of God. The violence that he experiences holds no redemptive qualities. What he has learned in war— the indifference of death, the folly of valor and patriotism, and the illusion of God—becomes distorted and tangled in his memory by the novel's end, so that even the reality is lost and everything becomes a lie. There is no glory in war, not even for the heroes. There is only death for the victims and confusion for the survivors.

◆ Topics for Discussion ◆

1. Crane said that he learned from the German author Johann Wolfgang von Goethe that certain colors affect human feelings. What use does Crane make of colors in *The Red Badge of Courage*?

2. Many critics, including Crane himself, have been dissatisfied with the novel's resolution. Do you think that *The Red Badge of Courage* has a satisfactory ending?

3. How much real control over events do the officers exert in *The Red Badge of Courage*? Why does Crane choose a common soldier, rather than an officer, as his protagonist?

4. What is meant by the term anti-hero? Is Henry Fleming an anti-hero?

5. In his "Ode: Intimations of Immortality" (1807), the poet William Wordsworth portrays nature as a

"homely nurse of mankind." Read this poem. What do you think Wordsworth meant by the phrase "homely nurse"? Is nature portrayed in *The Red Badge of Courage* as a "homely nurse," or does it play some other role?

6. Can you find any examples of humor in *The Red Badge of Courage*? If so, what kinds, and where?

7. How does Henry Fleming measure up to the heroes of classical Greek antiquity whom he admires so much?

8. As the novel ends, Henry is still remembering with remorse the tattered soldier whom he twice abandoned. Explain that soldier's role.

9. In what sense might *The Red Badge of Courage* be a prose poem? How does Crane's use of imagery function more as a poetic than a prose technique?

10. What is an allegory? To what extent is the novel allegorical?

11. Is Wilson, as he is portrayed in the second half of the novel, as much of a hero as Henry? Can a novel have more than one hero?

◆ Ideas for Reports and Papers ◆

1. Compare the life of a private in the army as depicted by Crane in *The Red Badge of Courage* to that of a private in the war in Vietnam. You can find information about the Vietnam War in books such as Michael Herr's *Dispatches* (1977). Has the American soldier changed radically since the Civil War? Why?

2. Twentieth-century American author Ernest Hemingway said that he admired Crane's writings. Some critics have noted the influence of Crane in Hemingway's *A Farewell to Arms* (1929), a novel set during World War I. Compare the style and characterization in the two works.

3. Crane was reassured when he finally witnessed a battle and realized that his descriptions of war *The Red Badge of Courage* had been very accurate. Compare Crane's reports from Greece and Cuba to his Civil War fiction. You can find these reports, as well as Crane's other Civil War stories, in *Crane: Prose and Poetry*, a volume in the Library of America series.

4. Find a description of the battle of Chancellorsville. What use has Crane made of this battle in his novel?

5. Crane preferred his poetry to his novels. Read *The Black Riders and Other Lines* (1895), Crane's favorite book among his works. How do you think it compares to his fiction?

◆ Related Titles/Adaptations ◆

Crane's novel *Maggie: A Girl of the Streets* depicts the embattled lives of people surviving in the New York inner city and the brutalizing effects of poverty, ignorance, and drunkenness on their lives. The book has been labeled a work of naturalistic fiction; like Émile Zola, a nineteenth-century French naturalistic writer, Crane suggests that people are victims of their environments.

Following up on the success of *The Red Badge of Courage*, Crane wrote *The Little Regiment and Other Episodes of the American Civil War*. Possibly the most interesting story in this collection is "The Veteran," which shows Henry Fleming as an old man. When a barn catches fire, old Henry rescues a drunken hired man who set the fire; when Henry returns to the burning barn to save some colts, he becomes trapped and dies.

In "The Monster" (1898), a story similar to "The Veteran," Crane depicts a community's reaction to a disfigured man in its midst. In the story, a black man badly burns himself while saving a young white boy from a burning house; although the townspeople initially proclaim him a hero, they eventually brand him a monster. The renowned black American writer, Ralph Ellison, called "The Monster" the first story in American literature to feature a black man as a hero.

The Red Badge of Courage was made into a movie in 1951 by John Huston, who both directed the film and wrote the screenplay. It starred Audie Murphy, the most decorated American hero in World War II, as Henry Fleming, and also featured Bill Mauldin, Royal Dano, and John Dierkes. In 1974 Lee Philips directed an adequate television movie version of the novel starring Richard Thomas as Henry.

◆ For Further Reference ◆

Bergon, Frank. *Stephen Crane's Artistry*. New York: Columbia University Press, 1975. An analysis of Crane's stories and poems.

Berryman, John. *Stephen Crane*. New York: William Sloane, 1950. In this, the best literary biography of Crane, Berryman presents a Freudian analysis of *The Red Badge of Courage*.

Cady, Edwin H. *Stephen Crane*. 1962. Rev. ed. Boston: Twayne, 1980. Cady attempts the difficult task of determining what ideas and beliefs Crane held, and what books helped shape these ideas.

Colvert, James. *Stephen Crane*. New York: Harcourt Brace Jovanovich, 1984. A brief biography with good illustrations.

Conrad, Joseph. "His War Book." In *Last Essays*. New York: Doubleday, Page, 1926. Conrad, who became a close friend of Crane's, analyzes *The Red Badge of Courage*.

Knapp, Bettina L. *Stephen Crane*. New York: Frederick Ungar, 1987. This book has some good analyses but overworks the religious imagery in *The Red Badge of Courage*.

Stallman, Robert W. *Stephen Crane*. New York: George Braziller, 1968. The fullest biography of Crane yet written.

Karl E. Avery

THE RED PONY

Stories

1937, 1945

◆

Author: John Steinbeck, 1902-1968

Major Books for Young Adults

Tortilla Flat, 1935
In Dubious Battle, 1936
The Red Pony, 1937, 1945
Of Mice and Men, 1937
The Grapes of Wrath, 1939
The Moon Is Down, 1942
Cannery Row, 1945

The Wayward Bus, 1947
The Pearl, 1947
*Travels with Charley in Search of
    America*, 1962
*The Acts of King Arthur and His
    Noble Knights*, 1976

◆ About the Author ◆

John Ernst Steinbeck was born on February 27, 1902, in Salinas, California. His best books concern his idyllic youth and turbulent young adulthood in California.

Born just after the closing of the frontier, Steinbeck matured as an artist during the dark days of the Great Depression. Steinbeck often asserted, however, that he enjoyed a happy childhood. His father made enough money to indulge him in a small way, even to buy him a red pony, the germ of his most famous book for younger readers. His mother encouraged him to read and to write, providing him with the classics of English and American literature, such as the Arthurian tales of Sir Thomas Malory. A popular and successful student and athlete in high school, he was elected president of his senior class.

After graduation in 1919, Steinbeck enrolled at Stanford University. He soon suffered academic difficulties and dropped out of college several times to work on ranches in the Salinas Valley and to observe "real life." His interests were varied, but he settled on novel-writing as his ambition, despite his family's insistence that he prepare for a more ordinary career.

Leaving Stanford without a degree in 1925, Steinbeck moved to New York for several months, where he worked as a laborer, a newspaper reporter, and a free-lance writer. Disillusioned in each of these fruitless pursuits, Steinbeck returned to California, where he took a job as winter caretaker of a lodge at Lake Tahoe while finishing his first novel, *Cup of Gold* (1929). In 1930 he married Carol Henning and moved with her to Los Angeles and later to Pacific Grove, a seaside resort near Monterey, where they lived in his parents' summer house.

A friend, Edward F. Ricketts, a marine biologist trained at the University of

Chicago, encouraged Steinbeck to treat his material more objectively. Under Ricketts's influence, Steinbeck modified his earlier commitment to satire, allegory, and romanticism and turned to realistic accounts of the Salinas Valley. Steinbeck's next two novels were virtually ignored by the public and the critics. Steinbeck's short fiction, however, began to receive recognition; his story "The Murder" was selected as an O. Henry Prize story in 1934.

Tortilla Flat, a tale of Monterey's Mexican quarter, established Steinbeck as a popular and critical success in 1935. The novel's sales provided Steinbeck with money to pay his debts, to travel to Mexico, and to continue writing seriously. His next novel, *In Dubious Battle,* established him as a serious literary artist and began the period of his greatest success, both critical and popular. This harshly realistic novel about a Communist-led workers' strike in California was influenced by the realistic impulse of American literature in the 1930s. Succeeding publications quickly confirmed this development in his fiction.

Before 1940 Steinbeck had published two shorter novels, *The Red Pony* and *Of Mice and Men*; a story collection, *The Long Valley* (1938); and his epic of the "Okie" migration to California, *The Grapes of Wrath.* His own stage adaptation of *Of Mice and Men* won the New York Drama Critics Circle Award in 1938, and *The Grapes of Wrath* received the Pulitzer Prize in 1940. Steinbeck had become one of the most popular and respected writers in the country, a spokesman for an entire culture.

In 1941 the Japanese attack on Pearl Harbor changed the direction of American culture and of Steinbeck's literary development. Steinbeck's career stalled for many reasons. He abandoned the California subjects and realistic style of his finest novels, and despite serving for a few months as a front-line correspondent, he was unable to come to terms with a world at war. Personal upheavals paralleled literary ones. Steinbeck divorced his first wife and married a young Hollywood actress; she probably influenced his decision to move from California to New York, where Steinbeck began to write with an eye on Broadway and Hollywood.

He tried several times to write his way back to the artistic success of his earlier years, but commercial success kept getting in the way. With *East of Eden* (1952), Steinbeck's major postwar novel, the author attempted another California epic to match the grandeur of *The Grapes of Wrath.* Although the book became a blockbuster best seller, it was an artistic and critical failure. Steinbeck himself seemed to recognize his own decline, and in his last years he virtually abandoned fiction for journalism.

Despite the popularity of nonfiction works such as *Travels with Charley in Search of America* and the receipt of awards such as the Nobel Prize for literature and the Presidential Medal of Freedom, the older Steinbeck was only the shell of the great writer of the 1930s. He died in New York City on December 20, 1968.

◆ Overview ◆

Steinbeck began *The Red Pony* fairly early in his career; his letters indicate he was working on a pony story in 1933, and the first two sections of the story sequence, "The Gift" and "The Great Mountains," were published in the *North American Review* in November and December of that year. The third section, "The Promise," did not appear in *Harpers* until 1937, and these three parts were published in a slim volume in 1937. "The Leader of the People," the final section, was not added until the publication of his story collection *The Long Valley* in 1938. But manuscript and textual evidence suggests that the later sections were written some time before their publication, not very long after the first two stories. The four sections are connected by common characters, settings, and themes, forming a clearly unified story sequence, which was published separately as *The Red Pony* in 1945. A modestly successful movie version, for which Steinbeck wrote the screenplay, followed in 1949.

The Red Pony is among Steinbeck's finest works. This story sequence traces Jody's initiation into adult life with both realism and sensitivity, a balance that Steinbeck did not always achieve. The vision of characters caught up in the harsh world of nature is balanced by their deep human concerns and commitments.

◆ Setting ◆

The stories take place on the Tiflin ranch in the Salinas Valley, California. Steinbeck's evocation of the vital beauty of the ranch setting matches his work in *Of Mice and Men,* and his symbols grow naturally out of this setting. The setting stresses the end of the frontier and of the American dream; in a sense Jody's maturation matches that of modern America. In its depiction of an American variation of a universal experience, *The Red Pony* deserves comparison with the finest of American fiction, especially initiation tales such as William Faulkner's *The Bear* (1942) or Ernest Hemingway's Nick Adams stories.

◆ Themes and Characters ◆

All four stories involve the maturation of Jody Tiflin, a boy of about ten when the action opens. He lives on his family's ranch with his father, Carl, his mother, Ruth, and the hired hand, a middle-aged cowboy named Billy Buck. From time to time they are visited by Jody's grandfather, a venerable old man who led one of the first wagon trains to California.

"The Gift," the first story in the sequence, concerns Jody's red pony, which he names Gabilan after the nearby mountain range. The pony soon becomes a symbol of the boy's growing maturity and his developing knowledge of the natural world. Later he carelessly leaves the pony out in the rain, and it takes cold and dies despite Billy Buck's efforts to save it. Thus Jody learns of

Jacket design by Neil Stuart and jacket illustration by William Low for *The Red Pony* by John Steinbeck. Viking: New York (1959).

nature's cruel indifference to human wishes.

In the second section, "The Great Mountains," the Tiflin ranch is visited by a former resident, Gitano, an aged Mexican-American laborer raised in a hacienda that is no longer standing. Old Gitano has come home to die. Carl persuades Ruth that they cannot take Old Gitano in, but their dialogue proves pointless. Stealing a broken-down nag significantly named Easter, the old man rides off into the mountains to die in dignity. Again, Jody discovers some of the complex, harsh reality of adult life.

In "The Promise," the third story, Jody learns of the intricate connections between life and death, when, in order to get his son another colt, Carl breeds one of the mares. But the birth is complicated, and Billy Buck must kill the mare to save the colt.

The themes of death and life converge naturally in the first three stories, preparing readers for the final section of the sequence, "The Leader of the People." This story brings the sequence to an end with another vision of death and change. Jody's grandfather comes to visit, retelling his timeworn stories of the great wagon crossing. Carl Tiflin cruelly hurts the old man by revealing that nobody except Jody is really interested in these repetitive tales. The grandfather realizes that Carl is right, but later he tells Jody that the adventurous stories were not the point, that his message was "Westering" itself. For the grandfather, "Westering" is a force like the frontier, the source of American identity; now with the close of the frontier, "Westering" has ended. Westerners have degenerated to petty landholders such as Carl Tiflin and aging cowboys such as Billy Buck. In his grandfather's ramblings, Jody discovers a sense of mature purpose, and by the conclusion of the sequence he, too, can hope to be a leader of the people.

♦ Literary Qualities ♦

The literary qualities in *The Red Pony* typify the style that won Steinbeck immense popularity. Rising to prominence at the height of the Depression, Steinbeck seemed to reflect the mood of the era with his bare lines of simple prose.

Steinbeck derives his literary power from his use of symbolism for ironic effect. The symbolic images in the plot allow the reader to perceive the significance of an event on a much deeper level than do the characters. The pony in *The Red Pony,* for example, functions as a symbol of Jody's boyhood and innocence as well as a symbol of his future. When the pony dies, the reader experiences a sense of loss, because the pony's death represents Jody's loss of innocence. But while the reader understands that Jody's life has been dramatically altered by the death of the pony, Jody, ironically, grieves for his pony without the ability to fully see the death in a larger context.

During World War II, when people began to realize how complicated the world had become, Steinbeck's development as a novelist faltered, and he never recovered his artistic momentum. Even *East of Eden,* the work he thought his masterpiece, proved a critical failure although a popular success. Since his death, Steinbeck has remained widely read, both in America and abroad. His critical reputation has enjoyed a modest revival, and will most likely continue to develop, for few writers have better celebrated the American dream or traced the dark shape of the American nightmare.

A writer of great talent, sensitivity, and imagination, John Steinbeck entered into the mood of the country in the late 1930s with an extraordinary responsiveness. The Depression had elicited a reevaluation of American culture, a reassessment of the American dream; a harsh realism of observation was balanced by a warm emphasis on human dignity. Literature and the other arts joined social, economic, and political thought in contrasting traditional American ideals with the bleak reality of breadlines and shantytowns. Perhaps the major symbol of dislocation was the Dust Bowl. The American garden became a wasteland from which its dispossessed farmers fled. The arts in the 1930s focused on these harsh images and tried to find in them the human dimensions which promised a new beginning.

Incidents such as the killing of the mare in *The Red Pony* are powerful and may upset young readers. But few writers have better exposed the dark underside of the American dream, while simultaneously celebrating the great hope symbolized in that dream: the hope of human development. Steinbeck's best fiction depicts a paradise lost but also suggests a paradise to be regained in the future. Despite Steinbeck's faults and failures, his best literary works demonstrate a greatness of heart and mind rarely found in modern American literature.

◆ Topics for Discussion ◆

1. The name Jody gives his red pony, like many of the names in the book, proves important. Why does Jody choose Gabilan, a Spanish name?

2. The red pony was bought at the bankruptcy sale of a traveling carnival. Why is this important?

3. When the red pony dies, who does Jody blame? What is the significance of his childish anger?

4. The second story also concerns death, but this time focuses on the death of an old man. What does Gitano's dignified death demonstrate to Jody?

5. In the third story, why is it important that the birth of Jody's colt causes the death of the faithful mare?

◆ Ideas for Reports and Papers ◆

1. Steinbeck assembled the stories that make up *The Red Pony* over several years. Show how the succession of stories broadens and deepens the meaning of the entire book.

2. The natural setting is very important in the sequence. Discuss the complex relationships between nature and human nature in the work.

3. Jody is the central character of *The Red Pony*, but his relationship with other characters forms his personality. Trace the pattern of character relationships in the book and show how they operate in Jody's maturation.

4. Show how the final section of *The Red Pony* opens the story sequence up to a more universal interpretation as a fable of America's lost youth and innocence, the loss of the American dream nurtured on the frontier.

5. What impact does Jody's grandfather have on the formation of his developing character?

• Related Titles/Adaptations •

Steinbeck's fiction was intended primarily for adults, but young adults often read his books as high school assignments. Although its attitude toward Hispanic-Americans seems patronizing, Steinbeck's comic *Tortilla Flat* provides entertaining reading, as do its sequels, *Cannery Row* and *Sweet Thursday* (1954). Several stories in *The Long Valley* are often collected in anthologies, most notably "Flight," a harsh story of initiation. *Of Mice and Men* is also harsh and realistic, but its beautiful evocation of friendship and dreams makes it a timeless American classic. Another classic is Steinbeck's symbolic tale of a Mexican fisherman, *The Pearl*. Although Steinbeck's epic, *The Grapes of Wrath*, is somewhat long and complex, the mature young person will enjoy and profit from reading it. Steinbeck also wrote some fine works of nonfiction, such as *Log from the Sea of Cortez* (1941) and *Travels with Charley in Search of America*.

Steinbeck has fared better at the hands of Hollywood than have most classic American writers. *Of Mice and Men* has received two fine film treatments (1939, 1973). Director John Ford's film version of *The Grapes of Wrath* (1940) remains as much a part of Americana as the novel, and the film version of *The Pearl* (1947) is adequate. Steinbeck wrote the screenplay for the successful 1949 film treatment of *The Red Pony*, and Lewis Milestone produced and directed the film, which starred Robert Mitchum and Peter Miles. A 1973 production of *The Red Pony*, directed by Robert Totten and starring Henry Fonda and Maureen O'Hara, received favorable reviews. One of Steinbeck's best works of the postwar period was the script for the powerful film *Viva Zapata!* (1952), which was directed by Elia Kazan and starred Marlon Brando. Many of the films based on Steinbeck's work continue to appear on television.

• For Further Reference •

Benson, Jackson J. *The True Adventures of John Steinbeck, Writer*. New York: Viking Press, 1984. A work of formidable scholarship and lively style, Benson's biography traces the evolution of individual works and presents a complete picture of the novelist's literary development.

French, Warren. *John Steinbeck*. 1961. Rev. ed. Boston: Twayne, 1975. Accurately locates Steinbeck within the American traditions of idealism and pragmatism.

Hayashi, Tetsumaro. *A Study Guide to Steinbeck*. 2 vols. Metuchen, NJ: Scarecrow Press, 1974. Although the quality of these pieces proves somewhat uneven, overall they provide excellent introductions to many facets of Steinbeck's writing. The bibliographies will prove especially helpful for further study.

Levant, Howard. *The Novels of John Steinbeck: A Critical Study*. Columbia: University of Missouri Press, 1974. Levant's book provides a levelheaded but complicated reading of Steinbeck's novels. His approach is difficult, but it will repay the careful reader with excellent analyses of image and structure.

Lisca, Peter. *The Wide World of John Steinbeck*. New Brunswick, NJ: Rutgers University Press, 1958. Lisca's pioneering study was the first important book on Steinbeck, and it remains one of the best. The study combines careful consideration of Steinbeck's life with close critical readings of all the writer's works.

McCarthy, John. *John Steinbeck*. Modern Authors Series. New York: Frederick Ungar, 1980. Presents a short, competent introduction to Steinbeck and his works. Although there are some problems with biographical facts, McCarthy's overall reading of the writer's career is more than adequate.

Millichap, Joseph R. *Steinbeck and Film*. Ungar Film Series. New York: Frederick Ungar, 1983. This book considers a neglected aspect of Steinbeck's career. It analyzes not only the many film and television adaptations of Steinbeck's books, but also the influence of film on Steinbeck's writing. Steinbeck's later decline is explained here by his movement from the 1930s documentary to Hollywood melodrama.

Joseph R. Millichap
Western Kentucky University

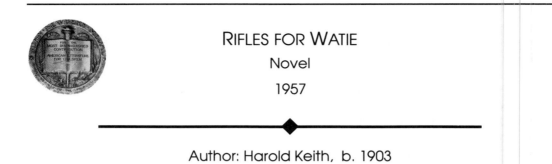

RIFLES FOR WATIE
Novel
1957

◆

Author: Harold Keith, b. 1903

Major Books for Young Adults

Boys' Life of Will Rogers, 1937
Sports and Games, 1941
Oklahoma Kickoff, 1948
Shotgun Shaw: A Baseball Story,
　1949
A Pair of Captains, 1951
Rifles for Watie, 1957
Komantcia, 1965

Brief Garland, 1971
The Runt of Rogers School, 1971
The Bluejay Boarders, 1972
Susy's Scoundrel, 1974
The Obstinate Land, 1977
*Forty-Seven Straight: The Wilkinson
　Era at Oklahoma*, 1984

◆ About the Author ◆

Harold Verne Keith, the son of Malcolm Arrowwood and Arlyn Kee Keith, was born on April 8, 1903, in Lambert, Oklahoma Territory, where his father was a grain buyer. From 1921 to 1924, Keith attended Northwestern State Teachers College. In addition to his studies, he wrote for daily and weekly newspapers in Watonga, Alva, Cherokee, and Enid, Oklahoma. After transferring to the University of Oklahoma, he became sports editor for the *Oklahoma Daily*, the student newspaper. Many of his columns dealt with the history of Sooner athletics, emphasizing the individuals as well as their accomplishments. Some of these columns were picked up by daily newspapers throughout the state.

Keith's experiences as a long-distance runner for the University of Oklahoma taught him the philosophy he later put in the mouth of the character Sergeant Pete Milholland: "You can always go farther than you think you can." In 1928 Keith placed first in the indoor mile and two-mile races at the Missouri Valley Conference championship meet. He also ran the anchor mile on the University of Oklahoma's All-American distance medley relay team.

After graduating with a bachelor's degree in history in 1929 and working briefly as an assistant to a grain buyer in Hutchinson, Kansas, Keith returned to the University of Oklahoma as sports publicity director, a job he held until his retirement in 1969.

On August 30, 1931, Keith married Virginia Livingston. After the birth of their two children, John Livingston and Kathleen Ann, Keith continued to study Oklahoma history, receiving his master's degree in 1938. Research for his thesis, "Clem Rogers and His Influence on Oklahoma History," provided some of the material for his first book, a biography of Clem's famous son, the humorist Will Rogers. In interviews with Civil War veterans, Keith also gathered much of the information he eventually used in *Rifles for Watie*. Published in 1957, the novel was awarded the Newbery Medal in 1958. Keith has also received the Western Writers of America Spur Award (1975) and two Western Heritage Awards (1975 and 1979).

Since his retirement, Keith has pursued his interest in long-distance running, University of Oklahoma athletics, and writing. In 1973 he set the U.S. Masters national records in the two- and three-mile runs, and in 1974 he set the record for 10,000 meters. His most recent book is *Forty-Seven Straight,* a history of the University of Oklahoma football program during the tenure of head coach Bud Wilkinson. Keith's manuscripts are housed at Northwestern State College library and the University of Oklahoma library.

◆ Overview ◆

Jeff Bussey, the main character of *Rifles for Watie,* learns about the cruelty, destructiveness, and waste that war creates. Few readers realize the intensity of the Civil War battles waged west of the Mississippi River, and this novel examines the issues, weapons, and strategies involved in the western campaigns. All the characters, whether admirable or evil, are believable, and Jeff Bussey's courage, perseverance, loyalty, and consideration for others make him an inspiring role model for readers of all ages.

◆ Setting ◆

Rifles for Watie begins at the Bussey family farm in Linn County, Kansas, during the spring of 1861. Once Jeff Bussey enlists in the Union Army, his company moves through Missouri, Arkansas, and Texas, but most of the action takes place in territory belonging to the Cherokee Nation, with brief forays into areas belonging to the Creek Nation and the Choctaw Nation. All of this land is now part of Oklahoma. The novel ends in June 1865, when Jeff returns to his family's farm after his discharge from the army, but Keith suggests that Jeff will soon return to the Cherokee Nation to marry Lucy Washbourne.

◆ Themes and Characters ◆

The primary theme of *Rifles for Watie* is Jefferson Davis Bussey's development from a naive sixteen-year-old into a mature gentleman and soldier. From the beginning of the novel, Jeff possesses the courage needed to challenge the bushwhackers who raid his family's farm, the initiative to travel to Fort Leavenworth and enlist in the Union Army, and the self-confidence to make his own decisions about the people he meets and the issues of the time. Jeff knows nothing about the army, however, and thus his experiences in the Civil War are, above all, enlightening. A foot soldier, an artillery man, a cavalryman, a scout, and accidentally a spy, he excels in each role. Through this experience, he learns that issues and people are much more complex than he has previously believed; not all the Union soldiers win his respect, and he is surprised to discover that he can feel loyalty for personal friends, even when they are officially his enemies. Though initially eager to fight the enemy, Jeff is quickly convinced that war is not a worthwhile endeavor, and each personal contact with a Confederate soldier or sympathizer teaches him that he and his supposed enemies are actually very much alike. At the end of the Civil War, Jeff returns to the family farm, having learned several important lessons about human nature and about himself.

The novel also explores the nature of noble behavior. Jeff wants to be a gentleman and is horrified to learn that the Confederate sympathizers think of Union soldiers much as he thinks of the bushwhackers. Consistently courteous, especially to the Confederate civilians he meets, Jeff wins the respect of others with his kindness. When Union soldiers stop to rest and eat at the plush home of a Confederate family, the Washbournes, Jeff learns that both Mr. Washbourne and his son, Lee, are enlisted in a rebel calvary unit commanded by the infamous General Stand Watie, who leads attacks on the homes of Union sympathizers. Despite this knowledge, Jeff uses his farm experience to help the Washbourne women, milking their cow and later showing them how to persuade the cow to accept her calf. Although he fights bravely and kills Confederate soldiers without reluctance in battle, Jeff refuses to be a member of the Union firing squad that later executes Lee Washbourne, and he demonstrates both compassion and a noble character when he arranges for Lee's body to be returned to his mother and sisters for burial.

Contrasting the hero's noble behavior, Captain Asa Clardy, who commands Jeff's unit, is vindictive, cowardly, cruel, greedy, and treacherous. He wrongly accuses Jeff of several transgressions and reports that Jeff is a troublemaker. Clardy avoids serving at the battlefront,

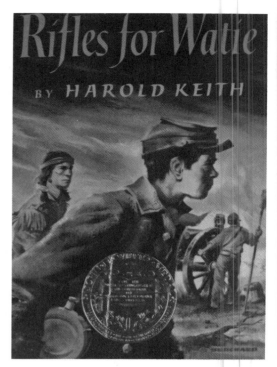

Jacket by Peter Burchard for *Rifles for Watie* by Harold Keith. Thomas Y. Crowell: New York (1957).

attempts to bully Lucy Washbourne, grinds his heel into the eye of a dying Confederate prisoner, and steals rifles from the Union Army to sell to Stand Watie. In addition, Clardy probably is responsible for the murder of Sparrow, a soldier who was the only witness to one of Clardy's earlier acts of robbery and murder. By revealing Jeff's identity to Watie's men, Clardy deliberately jeopardizes Jeff's life. According to Jeff's father, Emory, Clardy once "had the makings of a good officer," but became embittered by his failure to be elected colonel of the Mississippi Volunteer Rifles during the Mexican War.

A more sympathetic antagonist is the young, high-spirited Lucy Washbourne, who describes herself as "a rebel—to the backbone." A year younger than Jeff, she matches him in independence, courage, honor, loyalty, and even naiveté. From their first meeting, when his dog chases her cat, they clearly are on opposite sides of every issue; yet each comes to respect and admire the other. After Jeff becomes a reluctant recruit in Watie's army, Lucy urges him to change sides, but she does not betray him when he tells her he must return to Fort Gibson with the information about the stolen rifles.

◆ Literary Qualities ◆

The most striking literary quality in *Rifles for Watie* is its abundant historical detail. As Keith traces Jeff's development from a sixteen-year-old farm boy to a mature Union war veteran, he accurately recreates the routines and customs of the Civil War era. When Jeff is at home in Kansas, for example, he helps his father "thresh the wheat by hand, using two hickory clubs tied together with buckskin," and he and his family feast on " 'sweet toast,' home-baked wheat bread toasted in a pan over the fireplace coals." But when Jeff is in the field with his regiment, he learns about the grim realities of army life: when his friend Ford Ivey is wounded in the leg and has to have an amputation, Jeff watches the orderlies place him on a wooden table in a crowded, dirty tent, smells the "sweet odor of chloroform," and notices one of the attendants "cleaning bone fragments from a small saw." Jeff also meets a variety of people during his experience in the war—free blacks, slaves, Native Americans, Confederate sympathizers—and Keith uses these encounters as opportunities to relate historical information about the social and economic status of each group.

Much of Keith's historical detail is drawn from his extensive research on the Civil War. Keith interviewed twenty-two Confederate war veterans and studied veterans' diaries and letters in preparation for his novel. Although the plot of *Rifles for Watie* is completely fictional, several of the characters, such as General Stand Watie, are based on real-life figures.

In *Rifles for Watie*, Keith not only tells an exciting story, but also presents a realistic view of human nature—especially as revealed under the extreme stress of war. Keith has observed that a good plot spells constant trouble for the hero, who faces new complications as soon as he extricates himself from previous conflicts. The crisis, according to Keith, presents "the final knockdown punch" just as the protagonist thinks he or she is safe. In *Rifles for Watie*, Jeff finds himself in a continuing series of conflicts with Asa Clardy, Lucy Washbourne, Stand Watie's men, and his own divided loyalties. These conflicts, along with the actual battles, yield a fuller and more realistic picture of war than most war novels offer.

◆ Social Sensitivity ◆

Rifles for Watie shows great sensitivity in dealing with four significant social issues: war, sectional rivalry, racial hostility, and the role of the nonconformist. Jeff expects war to be exciting and noble, but finds that it is frightening and dirty. The initial training is so dehumanizing that one of his friends deserts, and only Jeff's sense of humor and his loyalty to the Union cause enable him to endure this experience. His individualistic attitude naturally resists military discipline, keeping him in constant conflict with his superior officers. The dark reality of war negates the glory of Jeff's heroic acts. Though a brave soldier, Jeff cries during his first battle, laments the deaths of his comrades, and is horrified by the amputations he observes. Forced to witness Lee Washbourne's execution, Jeff faces the constant threat of a similar fate while in the custody of Watie's men.

The book also demonstrates that human nature transcends regional and ideological boundaries. Jeff's Confederate enemies are as kind, honorable, and brave as his fellow Union soldiers. In fact, the Confederate officers generally show more concern for their men's welfare than most Union officers do. Though the Union opposes the system of slavery, an account of the Cherokee Trail of Tears brings the North's sense of justice under question. Clardy's cruelty toward the dying Confederate prisoner, the callousness of the confiscation orders, and Washbourne's execution offset the violence of the Confederate bushwhackers. As Jeff becomes better acquainted with his fellow soldiers and his Confederate enemies, he discovers that kindness and cruelty can be found in both armies and that the Union and the Confederate soldiers are actually very much alike.

Neither the Native American nor the black characters conform to conventional stereotypes, thus confounding Jeff's initial suppositions. The Jackmans and the Washbournes—both Native American families—surprise Jeff with their sophistication and their elegant homes. Even more astounding to Jeff is Stand Watie, the leader of the Confederate Cherokee. Jeff expects a large man with an air of command but finds that Watie is a short, nondescript man who sleeps beside a campfire, just as his followers do. Through Leemon Jones and the black regiment he joins,

Keith acknowledges the important role that blacks played in fighting the Civil War.

Jeff asserts the supreme value of individual conscience. Despite the orders of his superiors, he makes his own decisions concerning the issues he confronts. His individualism keeps him in perpetual conflict with army discipline, and he finds the casual attitude toward discipline one of the most appealing characteristics of Watie's army.

◆ Topics for Discussion ◆

1. Throughout the novel, Jeff demonstrates a knack for dealing with animals. He has easily trained Ring, and he quickly wins the friendship of Dixie, Sully, and even General Blunt's supposedly vicious bulldog. Likewise, he knows how to manage the various horses, oxen, and cows he encounters. What does this talent reveal about Jeff's character? How does Keith's description of this talent prepare the reader for the resolution of the novel's crisis?

2. What kind of man is Captain Asa Clardy? How does Keith reveal the extent of his evil character? What combination of events and background facts make Jeff his enemy? Is Jeff in any way responsible for the hostility that results?

3. When Jeff joins the Union Army, he is accompanied by two friends, John Chadwick and David Gardner. In the army, he meets a number of other young recruits, some of whom are killed or seriously wounded. These young men have enlisted for a variety of reasons, and they react differently to army life and war experiences. Why does Keith

include the contrasting attitudes, experiences, and reactions of Jeff's friends?

4. Jeff himself changes during the four years of the Civil War. When he enlists, what is his attitude toward war? How does it change after his first battle? What similar changes occur in his opinions about army officers, the Union and Confederate philosophies, and the people he initially considers his allies and enemies?

5. Wherever he goes, Jeff finds older, more experienced soldiers who befriend him, such as Mike Dempsey, Noah Babbitt, and Heifer Hobbs; young friends to share his adventures and complaints, including Bill Earle, Jim Bostwick, and Hooley Pogue; and suspicious enemies who are eager to catch him in a mistake, especially Sergeant Sam Fields and Captain Asa Clardy. What do their reactions reveal about Jeff's character and about human nature in general?

6. Although Jeff treats almost everyone with consideration, he shows special courtesy to the women he meets: Mrs. McComas, the women of the Jackman and Washbourne families, and Belle Lisenbee. What does Keith accomplish by making Jeff such a stereotypical, old-fashioned gentleman?

7. At the Jackmans' home, Jeff discovers that the family library consists of G. P. R. James's *History of Chivalry*, two Sir Walter Scott novels, William Gilmore Simms's *Guy Rivers* and *The Yemassee*, and an old copy of *Harper's Weekly*. What does this selection of reading material, fairly typical of ante-bellum Southern families, reveal about the values and attitudes of the Jackmans and their fellow Confederates?

8. Jeff Bussey finds his given name, Jefferson Davis, both an asset and a disadvantage. How does it work for and against him? Jeff explains why his father, a dedicated Union man, named him for the president of the Confederacy. How does Jeff's name influence his character development? How does it reveal one of Keith's basic themes?

9. Noah Babbitt, an actual historical figure, is one of the most carefully described minor characters in the novel. Jeff discovers that this itinerant printer hiked from Topeka, Kansas, to Galveston, Texas, just to see the magnolias in bloom. How does Noah influence Jeff's attitudes? Why does Keith describe him in such detail?

10. Generally, critics praise Keith for portraying war with unusual realism. What episodes develop this realism? Aside from Jeff's romance with Lucy Washbourne, are there any romantic elements in this novel? What are they?

◆ Ideas for Reports and Papers ◆

1. In the opening pages of the novel, Jeff and his family are attacked by bushwhackers from Missouri, and later one of Jeff's commanders is a former Jayhawker from Kansas. Using history books, investigate the guerrilla warfare between the slaveholders from Missouri and the abolitionists from Kansas. How did this struggle influence the allegiances of citizens in both states?

2. Jeff Bussey learns a little about the Cherokees' form of government through his contact with Stand Watie. Research and describe the Cherokee government in the 1860s. How accurate is Keith's account?

3. Joe Grayson, one of Jeff's friends in the Union army, says that much of the political conflict between the Watie and Ross factions can be traced to their different reactions to the enforced Cherokee removal to the West, the march called the Trail of Tears. Research and describe the events leading up to the march, the march itself, the justifications given for it, and its effect on later American history.

4. Most of the people Jeff meets in the Oklahoma Territory are at least part Native American. Many well-known Oklahomans, including the humorist Will Rogers, have Native American ancestry. Using biographies, histories, and other reference sources, describe the life of Will Rogers or some other famous Oklahoman of Native American descent.

5. Most accounts of the Civil War describe the warfare in the East, but in the West, the strategy, personnel, and weapons were somewhat different. Read an account of a campaign in the East, and compare it with the types of fighting Jeff experiences. Describe an important battle in the West.

6. Throughout the Civil War, Jeff fights with a single-shot Springfield rifle, but Keith says that some Union troops used Spencer repeating rifles late in the war. Using military histories, describe the kinds of weapons that were used by each side, the period in which each was used, and the effectiveness of each.

7. At the end of this novel, the Cherokee Nation is about to sign a treaty with the U.S. government. Using history books and other reference sources, describe what has happened in the governmental affairs of the Cherokee Nation since 1865.

8. One of the most famous Civil War diaries was kept by Mary Boykin Chesnutt. Read this diary and compare her experiences with those of the women in the Jackman and Washbourne families.

◆ Related Titles ◆

Harold Keith's favorite topics are Oklahoma history, Native Americans, and individual achievement that surpasses reasonable expectations. His first book, *Boys' Life of Will Rogers,* combines these interests, describing not only Rogers's success, but also the story of his family's role in Oklahoma history and tribal politics. *Komantcia,* like *Rifles for Watie,* is based on historical fact. A young Spanish man captured by the Comanche comes to respect them and adapts to their ways, much as Jeff respects Stand Watie's men and feels a kind of loyalty to them. *The Runt of Rogers School* is the story of a small athlete who, like Jeff Bussey, succeeds despite his physical size and the teasing it inspires.

◆ For Further Reference ◆

Commire, Anne, ed. *Something about the Author.* Vol. 2. Detroit: Gale Research, 1971. Contains a brief biographical sketch, list of works, autobiographical commentary, and bibliography.

Fuller, Muriel, ed. *More Junior Authors.* New York: H.W. Wilson, 1963. A brief biographical sketch.

Kingman, Lee, ed. *Newbery and Caldecott Medal Books: 1956-1965.* Boston: Horn Book, 1965. Section about *Rifles for Watie* includes a brief description of the novel, a biographical essay by Fayette Copeland, and the text of Keith's Newbery acceptance paper.

Kirkpatrick, D. L., ed. *Twentieth-Century Children's Writers*. 2d ed. New York: St. Martin's Press, 1983. Contains a brief biographical sketch and analytical comments about Keith's major works, along with a list of works.

Charmaine Allmon Mosby
Western Kentucky University

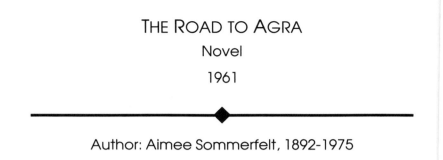

THE ROAD TO AGRA
Novel
1961

◆

Author: Aimee Sommerfelt, 1892-1975

Major Books for Young Adults

The Road to Agra, 1961
Miriam, 1963
The White Bungalow, 1964
My Name Is Pablo, 1965
No Easy Way, 1968
Dangerous Night, 1971

◆ About the Author ◆

Aimee Sommerfelt was born on April 2, 1892, in Oslo, Norway. As a child, she read a great deal, acted out Norwegian fairy tales, and invented romantic and suspenseful stories with her siblings and friends. To this creativity, Sommerfelt added the compassion and sensitivity toward others that she learned from her father, Henrik Arnold Thaulow, a respected psychiatrist.

She married Alf Sommerfelt, a professor of comparative linguistics at Oslo University, and had two daughters and a son. They settled in a rural area not far from her childhood home, and Sommerfelt started writing for young adults in Norwegian as early as 1933. Her philosophy, based on her happy childhood, was that books for young adults should be entertaining, not disturbing, but the Second World War and the German occupation of Norway turned her attention to serious topics. She responded to her changed environment by writing several historical novels to influence young readers. For example, the plot of *Miriam*, set during the German occupation of Norway, centers on a Jewish girl and a Christian girl whose friendship is tested and toughened by the Nazi cruelty toward minorities. Similarly, when her husband's assignment as one of the founders of the United Nations Educational, Scientific, and Cultural Organization (UNESCO) took the couple to India for four years, Sommerfelt began writing about the plight of young people in underdeveloped countries. *The Road to Agra*, her first book published in America, is an account of the way young adults live in overpopulated surroundings. *My Name Is Pablo*, the result of a similar visit to Mexico, tells of social pressures in an impoverished and crime-ridden community.

Sommerfelt's touching stories met with immediate success in Norway as well as in the United States, and her books have been published in twenty-five countries and translated into several languages. *The Road to Agra* won the Child Study Association of America Children's Book Award, the Boys' Clubs of America Junior Book Award, and the Jane Addams Children's Book Award, all in 1962.

Sommerfelt stated that in writing about characters from India and Mexico, she hoped to promote world peace and understanding. She believed that young people would be better able to understand the problems of developing countries and racial prejudice by becoming more open-minded in their formative years, because young readers identify with the characters they read about. While there can be no question of Sommerfelt's sincerity and genuine concern in writing these books, many Indian and Mexican readers, as well as American and European critics, are offended by the paternalism and racial bias implicit in her writings.

Sommerfelt continued to write and translate for children even after she became blind. She felt encouraged when two of her books written after she lost her vision won awards. Surrounded by the company of her children and grandchildren, she continued to live in her country home until her death in 1975.

◆ Overview ◆

The Road to Agra is a tender story of the love between thirteen-year-old Lalu and his younger sister, Maya, who is seven. Lalu protects his sister and takes care of her needs. His concern for Maya's failing eyesight, the result of a contagious disease called trachoma, prompts Lalu to take his sister on a perilous, three-hundred-mile journey on foot to seek medical help. Lalu's desire to better his situation in life and his unwavering commitment to his goal will inspire young readers.

◆ Setting ◆

Set in post-independence India in the 1950s, the story shifts locale from the village of Ratwa to the crowded, bustling city of Agra in northern India. As in centuries past, life in Ratwa still moves according to the rhythms of the seasons and the rising and setting of the sun and moon. The economy and well-being of the villagers is based on nature; if the monsoon rains fail to appear, loss of livestock and famine result. Only the local moneylender can capitalize on the vagaries of nature. Although educational opportunities are inadequate and medical facilities are nonexistent, Ratwa remains a peaceful place. Villagers are comforted and protected by Chaya, goddess of shade and mercy.

If village life represents traditional values, the city symbolizes Western technology. The city of Agra has a modern hospital with a famous eye doctor who performs medical "miracles." But the city also represents overcrowding, dirt, and constant activity; while the village exists in peaceful self-sufficiency, the city breeds exploitation of labor and lack of fellowship and humanity. Instead of the social cooperation characteristic of village life, urban life in India generates insurmountable economic and educational barriers among people.

Although the contrast between the city and the village is a theme of the novel, most of the action takes place on the road, as Lalu and Maya travel from Ratwa to Agra. The road becomes a microcosm of India, where the young travellers encounter wild animals and performing bears, as well as rich and poor, helpful and wicked people.

The adult characters, with the exception of the World Health Organization (WHO) and the United Nations International Children's Emergency Fund (UNICEF) crews, are insignificant to the central action; it is the teen-age Lalu who takes charge of his own life. Lalu's father, like the other villagers, is superstitious and old-fashioned in his thinking. He firmly believes that the stars determine fate; hence, he refuses to seek medical help for his daughter's blindness: "God will never allow Maya to go blind unless it is ordained that she *shall* go blind." The illiterate villagers are equally suspicious of school learning, believing that the truly wise do not need to read books and that schooling gives children a false sense of superiority. Of the older generation, only Nani, Lalu's grandmother, challenges this mode of thinking. She feels that the journey to Agra will make an adult of Lalu and help him acquire patience. Her speech is full of folk wisdom; when Lalu asks her if he is old enough to undertake the journey, she encourages him by saying, "the thin branch that bends is stronger than the thick one that cracks," and, "Each of us must fly according to the size of his wings." Nani is sensitive to Lalu's moods, and he is able to express his hopes to her. Sommerfelt successfully captures the loving, respectful relationship between grandparent and grandchild.

An independent young man, Lalu is determined to take control of his potentially bleak future. Yet Sommerfelt saves him from becoming an idealized character by attaching a selfish motive to his journey. Although his heroism is prompted by his love for Maya, he also has a personal stake: Maya has been given a coveted seat in the village school, and she must be able to see in order to continue her education and share her education with her brother. Lalu's vulnerability becomes apparent when he and his sister are imprisoned in the ox-shed and he weeps, fearing for his life and sensing that everything he has worked for has been destroyed.

Maya depends on Lalu for security; when she feels threatened, he reassures her with a story. He tells her, "If things are at their worst there is always something good, somewhere, even if it is nothing but a drop of honey." Despite her reliance on her older brother, Maya is not a stereotypical, passive female character. She complements her brother perfectly; when Lalu loses heart, she has the courage and strength to move on. In fact, it is Maya who thinks of a way to escape from the ox-shed when Lalu despairs. While riding to Allahabad, she thinks to let her scarf drag from the cart so that Lalu's pet dog, Kanga, can follow their scent.

Lalu and Maya's experiences express the tension between the opposing values of modernity and traditions. The city symbolizes progress through education, industrialization, and medicine. The village, on the other hand, represents traditional values. Lalu and Maya forsake traditional views, refusing to accept their condition passively; the outcome of the story implies that one's actions determine one's fate. But while Lalu's attempt to take control of his life contributes to the story's outcome, his future seems to be too much at the mercy of charitable Westerners.

The exploitation and the ill-treatment of the young and helpless that Lalu and Maya observe on their journey demonstrates the devastating effects of greed. Boys in villages do the work of adults, building contractors hire two workers for the price of one, and the weaving factory runs entirely on child labor. Though the young weavers are well-fed and kindly treated, Sommerfelt stresses that their jobs deprive them of the opportunity to learn to read and write. Even performing bears and monkeys are exploited by their owners for profit. Animals, Sommerfelt suggests, should be treated with love and dignity in the same way that Maya and Lalu treat Kanga.

Sommerfelt emphasizes that choosing selflessness over self-interest can lead to unexpected rewards. Jhandu, the camel driver, says that Lalu should go to Agra for Maya's sake and not for pragmatic reasons, because an honorable deed is a selfless act that is blessed by God: "There is no room for profit and honor on the same plate." In the end, Lalu's selflessness is rewarded, as a doctor in Agra offers him a job, a place to stay, and a seat at school.

The author's didacticism is unmistakable: the book calls for people to care for the unfortunate. People in Western countries, she feels, are selfish and should do more to help India, just as people living in Indian cities are urged to help their neighbors in the villages.

◆ Literary Qualities ◆

Sommerfelt employs the journey motif from epic literature to signify Lalu's transition from childhood to maturity. When he undertakes the long journey to Agra, he is young and unsure of himself. He feels "as if he were a branch pulled roughly away from the parent trunk, a branch which must certainly wither." Once he decides to take his journey, his elders treat him like an adult and give him advice on how to survive. As he traverses the dusty road to Agra, Lalu learns from both good and bad experiences. But although Lalu and his sister learn about human nature, they react to events instead of making them happen. Despite the emotional appeal of the children's situation, Sommerfelt is unable to portray well-rounded, multidimensional characters.

Lalu and Maya undergo a series of adventures on their way to Agra. The book's episodic plot follows an almost predictable pattern, in which one or two good experiences precede an unpleasant one. Another literary device Sommerfelt uses is foreshadowing. The village guru predicts that a gray elephant will bring good luck, and indeed good luck arrives in the form of a gray jeep driven by WHO workers. Similarly, the camel driver prepares the children for disappointment in Agra when he tells them that his little girl died because there was not enough room at the hospital.

In portraying a society and culture that is foreign to a Western audience, Sommerfelt relies on oversimplified and stereotyped characters and situations, providing little insight into the Indian customs and values that lend dignity to people. Thus, villagers are typically good-natured but ignorant and superstitious, while city people are impatient and unhelpful. Sommerfelt presents India as an "exotic" country, where holy cows with gilded horns sit in the middle of busy roads while traffic goes around them. Although Sommerfelt mentions the Indian caste system, she does not explain its function or make it an integral part of the story except to state that it results in discrimination against the lower castes. Unauthentic details further distort the picture. Nani fans the kitchen fire with a peacock feather fan, an item that in real life is sold mainly to tourists and is certainly not practical in front of a coal fire. Lalu and Maya meet a Maharajah's son who not only gives the two dirty, raggedy-looking children a ride on his elephant, but also buys their dog and feeds him all sorts of delicacies. The situation is improbable because of the differences in the characters' social and economic status. Furthermore, "Maharajah" is a Hindu title, and the author has him stop at a Hindu temple during a festival, but the prince's name, Nawab Khan, is Muslim.

◆ Social Sensitivity ◆

While *The Road to Agra* won international acclaim for Sommerfelt and touched readers with the central characters' plight, it is, nevertheless, a superficial look at the situation in India. Sommerfelt's central concern is to present India as a poor country that is ill-equipped to care for its subjects. She suggests that its only hope lies in the help it can get from Western countries. The protagonists' trek to Agra wrings sympathy from her Western audience, but it also gives the author the opportunity to make her story more dramatic. Sommerfelt also glorifies the West for its charitable efforts on India's behalf, such as when the children hear on the radio that WHO is giving another one million rupees for the treatment of lepers and that doctors and nurses will visit the villages with free milk and medicine.

Lalita Prasad, the Indian doctor in Agra, voices Sommerfelt's general attitude when she says, "India is the world's most unfortunate country if she cannot even help her own children." The author condescendingly states that it is not fair for other countries to have more; they should help India. In addition, the book makes statements that are insulting to Indian national pride. When Lalu and Maya express surprise at the free milk given to their dog, Sommerfelt adds, "Nurse Astrid...came from a country where there was plenty of food for dogs." Another passage states:

> Far, far away from here there is a country where everyone has plenty of food. Not like here in India, where there are lots of people and very little food. If some child or other in that far away country decided that he doesn't want an ice-cream cone and gives the money to UNICEF instead...then *you* will get a glass of buffalo milk. Do you understand?

The comparison is not only derogatory to India, but by ignoring the achievements and ancient traditions of India, it gives a biased and one-sided impression of life there.

◆ Topics for Discussion ◆

1. Discuss the relationships between parents and children in India. What value is placed on interpersonal relationships?

2. What techniques does Sommerfelt employ to elicit an emotional response to the plight of Lalu and Maya? Is the author playing on the reader's emotions, or is there justification for the action of the novel?

3. Many critics argue that Sommerfelt displays a condescending attitude toward India, implying that India's only hope is in the help it receives from other

countries. Do you think the author is condescending? If so, why? If not, discuss some ways in which she shows respect and admiration for India and its citizens.

4. In the journey motif, the young hero is usually assisted by older, wiser characters. Who are Lalu's mentor figures, and how do they aid him? Who are the villains? What are the conflicts that Lalu faces, and how do they affect him?

5. Some critics have seen Lalu's struggles as a metaphor for the challenges that faced the newly independent India. In what ways is his experience symbolic of India's growth and sense of identity?

6. WHO and UNICEF represent the Western world's efforts to assist less fortunate countries. What obligations, if any, do well-off people have to less fortunate peoples? Why should they help them? What reasons might they have not to help them?

◆ Ideas for Reports and Papers ◆

1. Does the dog Kanga play a symbolic role in the story? Does he embody the theme of the novel in any way?

2. What is the function of the episode in which Lalu is charged with thievery?

3. Research and describe life in India in the 1950s. Then discuss the accuracy of Sommerfelt's portrayal.

4. After a heroic journey in which Lalu has more or less been in charge of his own life, he is frustrated in Agra by the treatment of the callous gatekeeper. Is Lalu's defeatist attitude in keeping with his character when he resignedly turns back home? Would you change the ending to show Lalu in control rather than being indebted to the "do-gooder" Western characters?

5. Research and discuss U.S. efforts to help India or other underdeveloped countries. You might discuss the negative feeling these countries often develop toward America and the causes for this reaction.

◆ Related Titles ◆

Set three years after the events of *The Road to Agra*, *The White Bungalow* continues Lalu's story. After Maya's cure is complete, Dr. Prasad sends Lalu back to Ratwa with vague promises of a scholarship if he studies hard. Thus, the doctor's white bungalow in Agra becomes a symbol of hope and prosperity to Lalu. Lalu's stay in Agra has instilled a disdain for village life, and he wants to become a doctor like his benefactress. Lalu rejects farming, the profession of his ancestors, and thinks that medicine is the only worthwhile work in the "new" India. The story, thus, centers on the conflict between traditional and modern values. When the lack of rains and the ensuing famine lead to his father's illness, Lalu decides to stay home and assume family responsibilities. His friend Ram, who has no family ties because he has been rejected by his soldier father, is the one who leaves the village to study. In *The White Bungalow*, Sommerfelt expresses the dream of the new India, that one can serve by living in the villages and bringing science to farming.

◆ For Further Reference ◆

Commire, Anne, ed. *Something about the Author.* Vol. 5. Detroit: Gale Research, 1973. Includes a detailed list of books and awards won by Sommerfelt. The entry also has a brief biographical sketch with the author's account of her travels, family life, and aims as a writer.

DeMontreville, Doris, and Donna Hill, eds. *Third Book of Junior Authors.* New York: Wilson, 1972. Contains an autobiographical sketch in which Sommerfelt traces her writing talent to her childhood reading and inventions, and to her later travels to India and Mexico. As a writer, her aim was to sensitize young minds before adult prejudices could intrude.

Macbean, Margaret. "Long Trek." *New York Times Book Review* (October 1, 1961): 32. The author feels that Sommerfelt does not let her moralizing intrude and instead "allows the reader simply to share Lalu's adventures."

Moore, Opal, and Donnarae MacCann. "Paternalism and Assimilation in Books About Hispanics." *Children's Literature Association Quarterly* 12 (Summer 1987): 99-102. The authors briefly review Sommerfelt's novel *My Name Is Pablo,* which they assert implies that children are a special object of persecution in Mexico. They believe that Sommerfelt's work reflects a sense of European superiority, which she supports through "overgeneralizations and inappropriate cultural comparisons."

Nirodi, Vrinda. "Presenting Strange Lands." *Saturday Review* (November 11, 1961): 46, 48. Nirodi states that, in general, books on India lack "the perception and imagination it takes to make them more than a collection of facts," and contends that *The Road to Agra* fits the formula of emphasizing the sensational and bizarre aspects of Indian life.

"Review." *Commonweal* 75 (November 10, 1961): 186. Gives a brief plot summary and states that the story of the two children is "of such great poignancy that it would be quite unbearable if the tide did not turn at the last minute."

"Review." *Horn Book* 37 (December 1961): 553. After giving a brief plot summary, the reviewer praises the book's excitement and holding power, and states that Sommerfelt's understanding of India lends depth to the story.

"Review." *Kirkus Review* 29 (August 15, 1961): 732. The author feels that the book is an unsentimental portrait of India today, especially of the grim reality—softened only by old legends and religious beliefs—that faces most of the country's children.

Meena Khorana
Coppin State College

ROLLER SKATES

Novel

1936

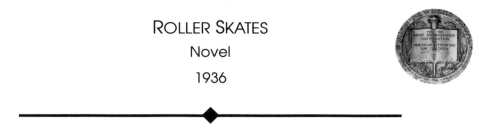

Author: Ruth Sawyer, 1880-1970

Major Books for Young Adults

This Way to Christmas, 1916
Tono Antonio, 1934
Picture Tales from Spain, 1936
Roller Skates, 1936
The Year of Jubilo, 1940
The Long Christmas, 1941
The Christmas Anna Angel, 1944
The Little Red Horse, 1950

Maggie Rose: Her Birthday
  Christmas, 1952
Journey Cake, Ho!, 1953
Daddles: The Story of a Plain Hound-
  Dog, 1964
Joy to the World: Christmas
  Legends, 1966

◆ About the Author ◆

Ruth Sawyer, the youngest of five children, was born on August 5, 1880, in Boston, Massachusetts. The only daughter of Timothy and Ethalinda Sawyer, she attended Miss Brackett's Private School in New York City and then, in 1888, went on to the Garland Kindergarten Normal School. Upon graduation she accepted a position in Cuba demonstrating the art of storytelling to teachers setting up a kindergarten for orphans. Her work in Cuba led to a scholarship to Columbia University, where she received a bachelor of science degree in education in 1904. While still a student, she worked for the *New York Sun* and spent two summers in Ireland writing feature stories for the newspaper and collecting Irish folktales for her own publications. She began her career as a professional storyteller and lecturer in 1908, setting up the first storytelling program for children in the New York libraries.

Almost all of Sawyer's thirty-five books are based on her own experiences or on folktales she collected in different countries. Her fascination with Christmas resulted in several publications about this holiday: *This Way to Christmas*; *The Long Christmas*; *The Christmas Anna Angel*; *This Is the Christmas: A Serbian Folktale* (1945); *Maggie Rose: Her Birthday Christmas*; *The Year of the Christmas Dragon* (1960); and *Joy to the World: Christmas Legends*.

The autobiographical *Roller Skates* and its sequel, *The Year of Jubilo*, reflect Sawyer's belief that unsuppressed children are the happiest. *Roller Skates* won the Newbery Medal in 1937. Two of Sawyer's books were Caldecott Honor selections: *The Christmas Anna Angel*, illustrated by Kate Seredy, and *Journey Cake, Ho!*, illustrated by Sawyer's son-in-law, Robert McCloskey.

In 1965 librarians in the United States honored Sawyer with the Laura Ingalls Wilder Medal for the diverse nature of her contributions to children's literature, including storytelling, retelling folk tales, and writing books for young people. That same year the Catholic Library Association awarded her the Regina Medal, commemorating a lifetime of valuable literary contributions. Sawyer died on June 3, 1970.

◆ Overview ◆

Roller Skates reflects Sawyer's strong belief that children should experience life and not be overprotected. The main character, ten-year-old Lucinda Wyman, is very independent and capable. A good role model for young people everywhere, Lucinda makes intelligent, sensitive decisions while escaping from the world of restrictions in which most children are compelled to live. Her moments of self-doubt and insecurity make her realistic and believable, enabling readers to relate to her today as they did during the first half of the century.

Lucinda also reflects Sawyer's great faith in young people and their capacity to understand and face the challenges of life. In her many positive encounters with adults, Lucinda finds them tolerant, interested, and supportive of children. Her guardian, Miss Peters, gives Lucinda the responsibility of deciding how to spend her afternoons, only requiring that the girl leave a note as to her whereabouts. Miss Peters and her sister, Miss Nettie, likewise leave notes for Lucinda when they go out, demonstrating their true regard for her importance as a valuable human being. While Sawyer has idealized her portrayal of adults, the exposure to such wonderful and sympathetic adults is refreshing.

Sawyer opposed depicting life as too soft or pleasant, even in books for young people, and her discussions of death in this book are forthright. Her attempt to let readers face the realities of life acknowledges their inner strength and affirms their ability to cope with truth.

◆ Setting ◆

Roller Skates is set in New York City in the 1890s, when hansom cabs travelled along macadam roads, when vendors arranged pyramids of fruit on sidewalk stands, when colorful "rags and bottles" men collected and sorted discards, and when children thought of books and stories as essential components of leisure time.

Lucinda becomes quite familiar with the city streets, skating along the avenues surrounding Central and Bryant Parks as regularly as possible. During the course of the story, she resides with the Peters sisters who care for her while her parents spend a year abroad. These guardians afford Lucinda freedom to explore parts of the city independently. Lucinda's world contains brownstone houses, Miss Brackett's Private School, the Gedney House Hotel, the Peterses' apartment, her friend Tony's cellar-home, Aunt Emily's "proper" home, and the various shops and restaurants within skating distance of these places. Lucinda's physical freedom parallels her spiritual freedom in this unrestricted but protective environment.

◆ Themes and Characters ◆

Distinctive characters represent a wide variety of ethnic, social, and age groups throughout *Roller Skates*. They include wealthy businessmen, shopkeepers, members of the gentry, cab drivers, police officers, and virtual paupers; they are of Italian, Irish, African, Polish, Asian, and Scottish descent; and they range from less than a year old to past retirement age. All these characters contribute to the development of the story's heroine, Lucinda Wyman.

Self-assured, confident, and capable, Lucinda Wyman has, at age ten, the compassion and sensitivity of a mature adult. She leaves a lasting impression on everyone she meets, garnering a treasure of supportive, genuine friends who delight in her free-spirited ways.

Three male characters who treat children respectfully develop a personal and protective interest in Lucinda's affairs. Mr. Gilligan, the hansom cab driver, provides a link between the affectionate but rather detached parents and Lucinda's temporary home with the Peterses. Patrolman M'Gonegal also befriends Lucinda and helps to provide her with a sense of security as she begins her year of skating the sidewalks of New York. He lives up to Lucinda's expectations of a police officer, personifying justice for her. Mr. "Night Owl," so named for his unconventional work schedule at the *New York Sun*, gives Lucinda a look at life through the eyes of a youthful adult. His lighthearted antics at the dinner table, his spontaneous invitation to the circus, and his willingness to share a ride on Jumbo provide an adult parallel to Lucinda's personality. Collectively these three men are substitute fathers for Lucinda, providing her love, acceptance, security, and a mature, but still carefree, look at life.

Lucinda's official guardians, the Misses Peters, are sweet, docile, and understanding—ideal adults for the curious and energetic Lucinda to live with. The elder Miss Peters is especially comfortable around children. A schoolteacher, she realizes the value of an inquisitive mind and tolerates Lucinda's need for freedom. Her sister, Miss Nettie, is more timid but also more loving. She needs Lucinda's affection as much as the child needs hers. A warm, genuinely loving relationship develops between the two.

Not all of the adults Lucinda encounters are pleasant. Aunt Emily, Mrs. Wyman's self-righteous older sister, has appointed herself overseer of Lucinda's training in "social graces." Aunt Emily's unwavering loyalty to "System, Duty, and Discipline" renders her incapable of sensitivity. Her own four daughters are "good little girls," perfectly molded; she cruelly considers Lucinda to be nearly hopeless, frequently reminding her that she is as "homely as two toads." Aunt Emily is an insecure, priggish, social snob whose one redeeming quality is that her kind husband occasionally influences her.

Lucinda's marvelous Uncle Earle, determined that Lucinda be allowed to maintain her individuality, shields her from Aunt Emily's severity. His practical good sense endears him to readers and makes him a dominant influence in the story. He is educated and wealthy, but not arrogant. When he cradles the panicked Lucinda on his lap and listens to her concerns about the Browdowskis' funeral plans, there is no doubt that he will act in a generous manner. His ability to talk about death with his niece demonstrates his great sensitivity. His devotion to her serves to firmly stabilize Lucinda, giving her strength and a sense of family security.

Lucinda's world is not filled entirely with adults. Tony Coppino, her primary playmate, is trustworthy and artistic.

Even though he lives in a very small cellar with his parents and several brothers and sisters, his cheerfulness is persistent. He becomes troubled only when a gang of bullies threatens him while he tends his father's fruit stand and when, at the end of the story, he begins to feel inferior and attacks Lucinda's social position. A talented artist, he proves his skill as a set designer during a production of William Shakespeare's play *The Tempest*.

Another playmate is Caroline Browdowski, nicknamed Trinket. The humble and destitute Browdowskis are among the most sympathetic characters in *Roller Skates*. An only child, the unassuming and quiet Trinket loves Lucinda, the only playmate she has ever had. She derives pleasure from simple things: decorated Christmas trees, visits to toy shops, listening to songs. Trinket's proud and determined parents try to hide their poverty, and their pride leads to the eventual death of their four-year-old daughter.

The fact that ten-year-old Lucinda easily survives her year in New York City without her parents attests to the enduring qualities of the Wymans' love. This theme of love and separation appears throughout *Roller Skates*, affecting permanent partings as well. After the deaths of Trinket and another friend, Princess Zayda, Lucinda realizes the lasting value of friendship and the possibility of keeping other people alive through memories. She comes to the understanding that love transcends all barriers, even death.

The conflict between Lucinda and Aunt Emily introduces the theme of individual freedom in *Roller Skates*. Lucinda refuses to stay with her aunt while her parents are gone because she realizes that Emily will end up owning her, molding her into something that she simply is not. Most of the other adults in *Roller Skates* value Lucinda's independent spirit, wistfully recognizing traits in her that remind them of their own carefree days of childhood. Miss Peters especially values a child not "run into a mold." Patrolman M'Gonegal instinctively knows that "young things shouldn't be tied up," and Mr. Gilligan confides to Lucinda's caretakers that he would not mind the freedom of being ten years old again. Lucinda's freedom is contrasted with the suggested constraint of Princess Zayda, whose jealous husband isolates her from the rest of the world. But eventually Zayda escapes, her freedom coming only in death.

◆ Literary Qualities ◆

Roller Skates is an endearing and entertaining story that relies heavily upon literary allusion for its effect. Sawyer's regular references to major works of literature not only entice readers to explore books on their own but also provide thematic connections throughout her novel. She draws from all of literature, alluding to the youthful freedom and discovery of "brave new worlds" in Lewis Carroll's *Alice's Adventure in Wonderland*; Frances Hodgson Burnett's *Little Lord Fauntleroy*; Howard Pyle's *Robin Hood*; Bernard Shaw's *Pygmalion*; the Bible; Alfred, Lord Tennyson's "The Lady of Shalott"; and many of Shakespeare's plays. Many pages are devoted to Shakespeare's *The Tempest*, allowing readers familiar with this play to recognize parallels between Prospero and Uncle Earle, Caliban and Aunt Emily, and both Miranda and Ariel and Lucinda. The enchanted New York City that Lucinda discovers during her unrestricted year mirrors Prospero's enchanted island.

Bird imagery reinforces the book's themes of freedom and independence. Lucinda's hair is "as fine and sleek as a raven's breast." With no governess around to object, she jumps off of chairs onto beds to practice "flying." After Trinket dies, the doctor shares a folktale about seagulls and their connection with people's souls. Allusions are also made to "Winged Victory" and Pegasus, the winged horse of Greek mythology.

Although *Roller Skates* is theoretically autobiographical, Sawyer writes it as fiction. The excerpts from a diary that Sawyer inserts into the narrative contribute to the story's credibility. The diary notes refer to historical events, such as the construction of General Grant's tomb, that add to the story's believability.

Sawyer also employs the literary technique of foreshadowing. An early reference to Bluebeard's beheaded wives foreshadows the subsequent murder of Princess Zayda, who is married to a man Lucinda nicknames Bluebeard. In a separate instance, when describing her friend Tony, Lucinda compares him to Michelangelo, hinting at the later discovery of Tony's artistic talents. Sawyer's control over every detail in *Roller Skates* makes the uncovering of such connections an adventure in itself.

♦ Social Sensitivity ♦

By the standards of the late 1930s, Sawyer's treatment of death in *Roller Skates* is unconventional. The story reflects her firm belief in honestly presenting the facts to children, and contrary to some negative reactions in the 1930s, most modern readers recognize the sensitivity with which she handles this subject. The facts about Princess Zayda's murder or Trinket's death are not kept from Lucinda, nor are they shared with her bluntly. The concerned hotel managers sooth Lucinda after she discovers the murdered princess. These sensitive people help the sobbing child, accepting her grief and confusion patiently, without question or condescension.

Sawyer also deals directly with the death of four-year-old Trinket. Lucinda participates fully in the care and treatment of Trinket, administering medication, persuading the small child to eat, and sleeping in the same room as her dying friend. Lucinda is encouraged to interact with Trinket's parents after their daughter's death and becomes instrumental in planning the child's funeral. The loss of these two friends leads Lucinda to think about how death divides people, with something going and something staying—a remarkably astute observation for a youngster.

It is important when reading *Roller Skates* to realize that many of the characters' attitudes accurately reflect life in the 1890s. While Sawyer's treatment of death is admirable, some readers might object to her treatment of women, ethnic groups, and the safety of children. Lucinda is a strong protofeminist, but many of the adult female characters are not, and they provide stereotypical nurturing while the male characters tackle difficult situations and solve perplexing problems. Other gender-related stereotypes appear when Lucinda acknowledges the need for a boy to handle certain parts of a theater production, when she feels awestruck by a woman daring to smoke, when she praises a boy who refrains from crying, and when she resigns herself to someday belonging to a husband and losing her own identity in the process. In all these instances, Sawyer presents a slice-of-life view of our country's historical attitudes. Most readers will be appeased when they realize Sawyer's novel reflects rather than advocates such practices.

Much of the charm in *Roller Skates* derives from Lucinda's frequent encounters with people of diverse ethnic origins. Occasionally, however, comments indicative of the times and reflective of a less sensitive culture surface. The Asian princess is thought to be a "heathen Chinee"; Aunt Ellen's resourcefulness is attributed to her Scottish heritage; Miss Lucy Wimple's cook is referred to as "faithful black Susan"; and suspicions about Tony's family are dismissed when it is found they are "simple, honest Italians, minding their own business." The attitudes of the heroine, however, do not reflect such insensitivity. Through Lucinda's childish innocence, the reader can see the beauty of regarding others as unique individuals. One of Lucinda's most appealing characteristics is her love of people. Despite the attitudes of the time, the novel clearly upholds the value of such unprejudiced love.

Since the late 1800s, the world has become an increasingly complicated place in which to live. The contrast between contemporary society and that of the 1890s is evident in the relaxed manner in which Lucinda's guardians respond to her propensity for striking up friendships with adult strangers whom she finds interesting. Today's children would be severely warned against going to the home of a cab driver for a "piece of griddle bread" or entering the apartment of a lady stranger who claimed to "like little children very much." Fortunately for Lucinda, most of her adventures are with decent, kind people. One, however, ends in terror, and Lucinda's discovery of the jeweled dagger embedded in Princess Zayda's back should suggest to modern audiences the dangers of being too trusting. This topic should be covered carefully by any educator using *Roller Skates* in the classroom.

◆ Topics for Discussion ◆

1. While on the way to the Misses Peters for the first time, Lucinda's cab driver realizes that no one has told him where to take her. What is the effect of depicting Lucinda, who is only ten years old, in this situation?

2. Aunt Emily is portrayed as a character addicted to "System, Duty, and Discipline," always doing everything "right." How does she compare with Uncle Earle? Does he, by contrast, do things that are "wrong"?

3. Lucinda befriends many strangers during her year in New York City. How does her behavior differ from the way many ten year olds today interact with strangers? Why?

4. Lucinda feels that a theater performance is "real the first time" and less so in subsequent performances. What does she mean by this statement? Do you agree?

5. After the production of *The Tempest*, many of the adults crowd around the tiny theater feeling "rather wistful." Why do you think they feel this way?

6. Some people might be critical of Mr. Spindler's method of handling the princess's death. Does he deal with the situation in the best way? Why does he choose to feign ignorance about the murder?

7. In the Schultzes' shop, Lucinda always walks about and unfastens all the jack-in-the-boxes. What is the function of this act to the book's development?

8. Uncle Earle has been described as one of the finest uncles in literature. Do you agree? Why or why not?

9. Lucinda is portrayed as a self-sufficient, confident girl, but in chapter 7 she decides to keep her diary key around her neck until her mother returns "to make it safe." Why does she do this? What insights does this give about her personality?

10. Lucinda is kind to old people, careful not to wear out her welcome, sensitive to the needs of others, and motivated to act against the injustices in the world. Why, then, does Aunt Emily consider her to be a bad influence on her own four daughters?

11. Why does Lucinda believe that after her parents return she will "never belong to herself again" and that eventually she will belong to her husband?

12. At the end of the novel, Lucinda returns to the carousel and sees other children on the horses that she and Tony always rode. Why does she want to stick her tongue out at them?

13. Why does Tony not want "stylish people" poking around in his cellar?

♦ Ideas for Reports and Papers ♦

1. *Roller Skates* is an autobiographical account of Ruth Sawyer's year in New York City without her parents. The author frequently mentions actual names and places from the 1890s. How do these allusions contribute to the success of the novel?

2. *Roller Skates* won the Newbery Medal in 1937. Its sequel, *The Year of Jubilo*, chronicles the Wyman family's life after the death of Lucinda's father. Compare the two books. Which book would you have given the award to? Why?

3. In her acceptance speech for the Newbery Medal, Sawyer said she believed a free child was a happy child. What evidence is there to suggest that Lucinda was a happier child during her year in New York City? Support or dispute the wisdom of Sawyer's assertion with evidence from the text and from your own experience.

4. Ruth Sawyer makes many allusions to the works of Shakespeare in *Roller Skates*. How do his plays relate to this novel?

5. In what ways is Lucinda an unconventional child?

♦ Related Titles ♦

Roller Skates describes ten-year-old Lucinda Wyman's year in New York City. Its sequel, *The Year of Jubilo*, begins after the family moves to Maine following Mr. Wyman's death. This novel chronicles Lucinda's maturation. Another book that, like *Roller Skates*, explores relationships between the young and the old is *Maggie Rose: Her Birthday Christmas. Daddles: The Story of a Plain Hound-Dog* treats themes of death in a manner similar to *Roller Skates*.

◆ For Further Reference ◆

Haviland, Virginia. *Ruth Sawyer*. New York: Henry Z. Walck, 1965. A short critical account of Sawyer's life and work. It includes biographical information and a discussion of several of her books.

McCloskey, Margaret Durand. "Our Fair Lady!" *Horn Book* 41 (October 1965): 481-486. This article, written by Sawyer's daughter, provides insights into the author's personal life.

Moore, Anne Carroll. "Ruth Sawyer, Storyteller." *Horn Book* 12 (January 1936): 34-38. Besides providing a short history of her storytelling career, this article describes the origins of a Christmas festival in the New York City libraries in which Sawyer participated.

Overton, Jacqueline. "This Way to Christmas with Ruth Sawyer." *Horn Book* 20 (November 1944): 447-460. The author calls upon Sawyer's ability to lift spirits during a wartime Christmas. The article also tells of Sawyer's experiences collecting folktales in Spain.

Sawyer, Ruth. *The Way of the Storyteller*. 1942. Reprint. New York: Viking, 1962. This is not a book devoted to the "hows" and "whats" of storytelling but rather to those special qualities that contribute to a storyteller's expertise. It includes eleven of Sawyer's stories and an extensive bibliography for other noteworthy sources of folktales.

Lynne Klyse
California State University, Sacramento

ROLL OF THUNDER, HEAR MY CRY
Novel
1976

Author: Mildred D. Taylor, b. 1943

Major Books for Young Adults

Song of the Trees, 1975
Roll of Thunder, Hear My Cry, 1976
Let the Circle Be Unbroken, 1981

◆ About the Author ◆

Mildred D. Taylor was born in Jackson, Mississippi, on November 13, 1943. Motivated by a racial incident, her father moved the family to Toledo, Ohio, when Taylor was only three weeks old. This migration did not diminish the family's devotion and attachment to the South, and Taylor grew up with a tremendous fascination for the region, eagerly anticipating annual visits there. She received her education in the Toledo schools, where she was an honor student, editor of the school newspaper, and a class officer.

While completing her college work at the University of Toledo, Taylor aspired to be a writer and a Peace Corps volunteer. Throughout her college years, she prepared herself by diligently researching the places she longed to visit. She volunteered with the Peace Corps in Ethiopia for two years and returned home to recruit new volunteers before beginning her journalistic training at the University of Colorado. At Colorado, Taylor was active in student government and participated in curriculum changes that emphasized black studies.

Taylor's novel *Song of the Trees*, set in Mississippi, introduces the Logan family. *Song of the Trees* won the Council on Interracial Books Award in the African-American category and was listed by the *New York Times* as an outstanding book of 1975. The following year, Taylor wrote another novel about the Logans: *Roll of Thunder, Hear My Cry*. This book, which emphasizes family love, determination, pride, and dignified rebellion against racial injustice, won the Newbery Medal in 1977.

Let the Circle Be Unbroken, which was nominated for the 1982 National Book Award, resumes the Logan family saga, dramatizing many of the themes and ideas dominant in Taylor's earlier works. The racial confrontations remain, but Taylor emphasizes the effects of family unity in the face of hostile social forces. Taylor continues to write full-time, and her own strong family bonds contribute significantly to her fiction.

◆ Overview ◆

Roll of Thunder, Hear My Cry's depiction of social interactions and relationships in the 1930s South remains relevant today. The novel dramatizes the consequences of historical realities, such as slavery, through the oral history recounted by the older characters. Despite its depiction of hardships and reversals, *Roll of Thunder, Hear My Cry* offers a comforting view of social continuity. Overall, the novel focuses on the uplifting aspects of life: challenge, family solidarity, love, courage, pride, and determination. Although the narrator and several of the principal characters are quite young, their needs are strikingly similar to those of young adults. They demonstrate a need and desire for acceptance, and they are curious and speculative about the world around them.

◆ Setting ◆

Roll of Thunder, Hear My Cry is set in Mississippi at the height of the Great Depression; most of the action occurs between 1933 and 1934. The Logan farm, comprising four hundred acres of land, is home to the narrator Cassie, her parents, her three brothers, and her paternal grandmother. Cassie's grandfather, Paul Logan, purchased this land in two separate transactions, acquiring two hundred acres in 1886 and two hundred more in 1918. The family still owes a mortgage on the latter purchase, and the first requires tax payments. Ever since the price of cotton fell in 1930, Cassie's father, David Logan, has had to take jobs in other cities during the off-season to fulfill his financial obligations. The Logans are the sole black property owners in this community, the only black family in the narrative to escape the sharecropping system. Their farm borders a dense forest, with an ancient oak tree serving as an official dividing mark. Although the Logans are not poverty-stricken, their financial resources are quite modest and require careful monitoring to ensure the family's continued independence and survival.

◆ Themes and Characters ◆

The pride with which the Logans work to keep their land demonstrates the value they place on independence. The white landowners—the Grangers, the Montiers, and the Harrisons—all work to maintain the white power structure, using various strategies to achieve this purpose. Another prominent family in the white community, the Wallaces, own the community store and cooperate with the landowners to keep the current social structure intact. In this environment, the Logans encounter many challenges, both subtle and overt, to their independence and self-esteem.

Cassie Logan, the nine-year-old narrator, embodies the spirit of independence, the trademark of the Logan family and one of the primary thematic emphases of the novel. Although not truly rebellious, Cassie questions and challenges practices that many of the other characters accept at face value. When she travels with her grandmother to the town of Strawberry to sell milk and eggs, Cassie unflinchingly questions and criticizes the accepted practices that force her grandmother to

Photograph of Mildred
Taylor courtesy of
E. P. Dutton.

display her goods behind the white sellers' wagons. She is equally assertive when she informs the store owner that she is next in line after he has waited on three white customers out of turn, and again when she refuses to accept the worn-out school books that have been issued eleven times to white students before being offered to students at the all-black school.

Cassie is consistently assertive and logical as she proves in her well-planned retaliation against Lillian Jean Simms, a twelve-year-old white girl who delights in humiliating Cassie. Lillian Jean directs Cassie to call her "Miss" and to carry her school books from the bus stop to her home. Even while following Lillian Jean's orders, Cassie methodi-

cally plots her revenge. She listens to Lillian Jean's secrets during this period of service, ultimately threatening to reveal them in order to keep Lillian Jean from reporting the beating Cassie gives her. Cassie's independence is symbolic of the family's emphasis on freedom from the prevailing sharecropper system, although, in her retaliation against Lillian Jean, she compromises family values somewhat by defending fairness at the expense of peace.

Mary Logan, Cassie's resourceful and strong mother, teaches seventh grade at Great Faith Secondary School, manages the family during her husband's frequent absences, and works cooperatively with Big Ma, her mother-in-law, to keep the family intact. She demands acceptable, courteous behavior from her children, supporting the school's punishment of Cassie and Little Man, her youngest son, for refusing to accept the worn-out schoolbooks. She is, however, sufficiently disturbed by the affront that prompted her children's action that she refuses to condemn them categorically for their behavior.

Politically committed to the cause of dignity for blacks, Mary helps to organize and implement the boycott of the Wallace store after the Wallaces participate in the lynching of black men. False reports of Mary's incompetence as a teacher, along with her determination to teach her students all the historical facts—even the ones excluded from the old textbooks—contribute to her dismissal from her job, a loss she accepts stoically. Her most painful task is attempting to make Cassie see that certain racial injustices have to be endured while at the same time assuring her daughter that blacks are as good as whites.

David Logan, Cassie's father, demonstrates intense pride in the family property and considers it his greatest obligation to maintain this land for his children's sake. He is gentle and kind to his wife and children, and displays respect and love for his mother. Particularly protective of his family, he attempts to ensure their safety by bringing an unemployed rail layer, Mr. Morrison, to live at the farm while he is away. He makes no effort to perpetuate racial strife but does caution his son against forming close relations with a white youngster, hoping to shield his son from potential hurt. Toward Cassie, he exhibits extreme patience, urging her to control her temper but also encouraging her to identify and fight for the values she cherishes. He is understanding of others' circumstances and does not condemn a sharecropping neighbor for withdrawing from the boycott of the Wallace store for fear of retribution.

David's mild temperament contrasts sharply with that of his brother Hammer, who lives in the North and exhibits an impatience with the status of race relations in the South that causes his family considerable anxiety when he visits them in Mississippi. Hammer, however, is equally devoted to the cause of land ownership and sells his fancy car when the banks, in an act designed to punish the Logans for their participation in the boycott, call in the mortgage. The brothers are emboldened by the strength and determination of Big Ma, who provides support for her sons and inspiration and information for Cassie. She ensures her sons' legal entitlement to the Logan land by carefully supervising the transfer of ownership.

Cassie's brothers, Stacey, Christopher-John, and Little Man, share a genuine commitment to the family. Stacey displays commendable responsibility in protecting the rest of the family while his father is away. Loyal to his friends, he remains supportive of his irritating friend T.J., even when he does not approve of T.J.'s actions. Christopher-John is less rigid and intense than either of his brothers or Cassie, exhibiting sensitivity for others and attempting to please as many people as possible. He refuses to dwell on unpleasant matters or controversies. Little Man has a penchant for cleanliness and neatness, and reacts vigorously to humiliation of any nature.

T. J. Avery, the son of a black sharecropper, is capricious and unreliable. Although he possesses some positive character traits, he is cunning and deceitful, thriving on the discomfiture of those around him. Angered by a second failing grade in Mary Logan's class, he reports to the white community that her teaching is ineffective and that she is responsible for the boycott of the Wallace store. At times he is repentant, but his character remains flawed. His ambiguous behavior during racial crises estranges him from both blacks and whites. T.J. demonstrates his weakness by participating with the Simmses in an attempted robbery. Overall, T.J. is the antithesis of the book's main themes, lacking integrity, pride, independence, and group loyalty.

Jeremy Simms and attorney Wade Jamison contrast sharply with the oppressive white characters in the novel. Jeremy, the older brother of Cassie's nemesis, Lillian Jean Simms, exhibits understanding toward the Logan youngsters, often opting to walk with them and awkwardly bringing Christmas gifts to their home. Essentially conciliatory, he often apprises the Logans of the prevailing views and attitudes of the whites. His refreshing sensitivity and kindness enhance the humanitarian aspect of the novel. Equally exemplary is Wade Jamison, an attorney from whose family the Logans obtained their land. He is supportive of the Logans' efforts to retain their property, offering legal advice and drawing up the papers that transfer the ownership from Big Ma to her two sons. He demonstrates tremendous support in the boycott of the Wallaces' store and volunteers to help obtain credit in Vicksburg for the boycotting sharecroppers. His fairness and honesty are consistent with the positive themes Taylor emphasizes.

◆ Literary Qualities ◆

Roll of Thunder, Hear My Cry features a straightforward and uncomplicated style. Taylor's controlled use of symbolism lends depth to the work's major themes. The old oak tree that borders the Logan land, for example, represents the Logans' strength and perseverance. The frequent allusions to slavery afford a backdrop for the Logans' struggle and provide revealing, instructive historical background. The characterizations are, for the most part, effective and believable, although Cassie sometimes seems unbelievably perceptive for her age. Despite limited physical descriptions, the interactions among characters reveal much about their personalities and motivations.

Taylor deftly manipulates diction, shifting appropriately between the relaxed idiom of the children and the rather stilted, impersonal language of teachers addressing their classes. The rhythmic dialect in the informal conversations lends itself well to reading aloud. The pace of the narrative is somewhat slow, rendering the book less exciting than many other novels for young adults, yet the progression of the plot is masterfully controlled and free from confusing subplots. The few flashbacks fit naturally into the context of those scenes in which they appear.

The point of view from which the story is told, that of an eight- or nine-year-old girl, permits a naiveté that illuminates an illogical social system. It also offers a view of reality from a character who is still too young to be embittered by the injustices that are a part of her life. Cassie's inquisitiveness forces the adults to see the hypocrisy in accepted behaviors and value systems. An older narrator more thoroughly indoctrinated and inhibited by the social climate could not have raised the same provocative questions that serve to highlight the failures and inconsistencies of the immediate environment.

In this novel, oral history provides valuable information about the influence of past events on the characters. Cassie's grandmother recounts past events so often that Cassie can almost recite the stories simultaneously. Much of the story that Mr. Morrison tells about the death of his parents when he was only six years old may have been engraved in his memory in a similar manner.

Strong verbs add vitality to the book's descriptive passages, allowing the reader to visualize the scenes and characters. Taylor's use of language and her manipulation of scenes establish a generally nonconfrontational tone. In many instances in the novel, the adversaries do not face one another, and consequently many negative reactions are portrayed indirectly. This authorial strategy reduces the emotional intensity and harshness that could well have resulted from a different presentation.

of the novel offsets the acts of violence. The events of the novel need not be distorted or minimized since most younger readers are emotionally capable of confronting the difficult issues raised.

Violence is not a major theme of the work, but the nature of the conflict necessitates some solutions and strategies that contradict the values that families such as the Logans would usually uphold. On occasion, characters in the novel include guns in their preparation for a potential confrontation, but the conflicts are resolved without the use of firearms.

The racial conflict among the school children in the community is not particularly intense and in some instances differs little from normal tension among young people in any community. This dimension of the work should pose few, if any problems.

◆ Social Sensitivity ◆

Throughout the work, Taylor addresses the dynamics of racial tension, and although the dramatization of this sensitive issue is carefully controlled, some students might benefit from background information concerning the era in which the novel is set. The attitudes and tolerance of the older blacks toward social injustices could prove problematic. Some students may find it difficult to accept the older characters' assertions that some situations simply must be endured. Careful preparation should precede discussion of the scenes depicting burnings or referring to lynchings and hangings. Ultimately, the sense of community demonstrated by both blacks and whites toward the end

◆ Topics for Discussion ◆

1. The Logan family exhibits pride and independence. Which family member seems to exhibit these traits most consistently?

2. The Christmas celebration at the Logans' motivates the recounting of a considerable amount of oral history. What information gleaned from these conversations enables the reader to better understand some facts or some attitudes presented in the novel?

3. How do you rate Mary Logan's strength and leadership ability?

4. Stacey is forced to grow up quickly because of his father's frequent absences. Of the several actions that he

takes to protect and maintain the family's interests, which do you consider the most admirable or impressive? Why?

5. Cassie is perplexed by Big Ma's instructions to apologize to Lillian Jean Simms, who has openly humiliated Cassie for accidentally bumping into her on the street. Are you disappointed with Big Ma's actions in this case? Are there other actions by the characters in this novel that disappoint you? Consider some possible explanations for these actions.

6. Cassie and Little Man refuse to accept the worn-out textbooks issued by the school they attend. How do you view their actions? Would some other reaction on their part have been more appropriate?

7. David Logan and his brother Hammer share a determination to keep the Logan land, yet their attitudes toward dealing with the power structure in the community are quite different. Which character, in your opinion, has the more effective strategy for dealing with those who oppose the family's independence and determination?

8. More than once, Wade Jamison actively supports the blacks in the community. How do you account for his courage in view of the certain criticism and condemnation he will receive from the white community?

9. Discuss the attitude of Jeremy Simms toward the Logan children and describe how his attitude differs from the attitudes of the other white children in the community.

10. Some literary classics are listed among the books the Logan children receive for Christmas, including *The Count of Monte Cristo* and *Aesop's Fables*. What other books might provide good reading for children of these ages? Explain your choices.

♦ Ideas for Reports and Papers ♦

1. All societies in one way or another establish roles and expectations for people of different genders and cultural groups. Research the roles and expectations of the early 1930s, the time period covered by this novel. Analyze the extent to which the characters in this work uphold traditional roles.

2. Review the descriptions of slavery in this work and compare them with descriptions in other works for young adults such as *Amos Fortune, Free Man* by Elizabeth Yates or *Harriet Tubman: Conductor on the Underground Railroad* by Ann Petry. Identify the major differences in the descriptions and give as many reasons as you can that account for these differences.

3. Mary Logan is fired from her job as a secondary school teacher because of negative testimony from one of her son's friends and school board members' dissatisfaction with her teaching philosophy. Assume the character of Mary Logan and write a journal entry at the end of the day on which you were dismissed.

4. Oral history, the sharing through conversation of memorable incidents from the past, seems to be a cherished tradition of the Logan family. Write about an event that is shared time after time by older members of your family

and describe the importance of this event to you.

5. T. J. Avery is the source of many conflicts in the narrative, and his motivations are not always clear. Select any event in which you think T.J. behaves inappropriately. Imagine that you are T.J. and write a letter to another character, rationalizing the action taken.

6. Write a short character analysis of Cassie's teacher, Miss Crocker, based on your impressions of her behavior on the day she issued the old textbooks to the students at Great Faith Elementary School.

7. The reactions of Cassie and Little Man to the worn-out textbooks are open to different interpretations. Write two paragraphs, one defending their right to reject the books under the circumstances and the other discussing the possible negative results of such actions by students.

◆ Related Titles ◆

Roll of Thunder, Hear My Cry is the second of three books about the Logan family. Taylor's first work, *Song of the Trees,* addresses similar themes: the complex nature of racial conflict, the strength of family love, and the Logans' determination to keep their land. She continues the saga of the Logan family—which in many respects resembles her own family—in *Roll of Thunder, Hear My Cry.* In *Let the Circle Be Unbroken,* the same characters continue to grow, their interactions further clarifying Taylor's themes of family pride and determination in the midst of racial strife.

◆ For Further Reference ◆

Dussell, Sharon L. "Profile: Mildred D. Taylor." *Language Arts* 58 (May 1981): 599-604. Presents interesting biographical details and relates them to Taylor's writing and world view. Dussell discusses *Song of the Trees* at some length.

Estes, Glenn E., ed. *Dictionary of Literary Biography.* Vol. 52. Detroit: Gale Research, 1986. An excellent biographical and literary source that chronicles Taylor's early life as well as her literary career. Also summarizes and provides critical comments on Taylor's works.

Fagelman, Phyllis J. "Mildred Taylor." *Horn Book* 53 (August 1977): 410-414. A biographical sketch that includes an analysis of Taylor's effectiveness as a writer and a chronological survey of Taylor's life.

Rees, David. "The Color of Skin: Mildred Taylor." In *The Marble in the Water: Essays on Contemporary Writers of Fiction for Children and Young Adults.* Boston: Horn Book, 1980. Discusses Taylor's work in the tradition of other works addressing racial prejudice. The issue of racism, rather than family pride and loyalty, is emphasized in this essay, which offers an essential and interesting perspective on the work.

Taylor, Mildred. "Newbery Award Acceptance." *Horn Book* 53 (August 1977): 401-409. An outstanding and intensely personal speech by Mildred Taylor before the American Library Association. The speech, mostly autobiographical, details quite effectively the influence of Taylor's family on her success. She pays an especially warm tribute to her father and relates several instructive observations concerning the writing and publication of *Roll of Thunder, Hear My Cry.*

Robbie Jean Walker
Auburn University at Montgomery

A ROOM MADE OF WINDOWS
Novel
1971

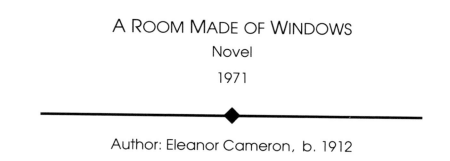

Author: Eleanor Cameron, b. 1912

Major Books for Young Adults

The Wonderful Flight to the
  Mushroom Planet, 1954
Stowaway to the Mushroom Planet,
  1956
Mr. Bass's Planetoid, 1958
The Terrible Churnadryne, 1959
A Mystery for Mr. Bass, 1960
The Mysterious Christmas Shell,
  1961
The Beast with the Magical Horn,
  1963

A Spell Is Cast, 1964
Time and Mr. Bass, 1967
A Room Made of Windows, 1971
The Court of the Stone Children,
  1973
To the Green Mountains, 1975
Julia and the Hand of God, 1977
That Julia Redfern, 1982
Beyond Silence, 1983
Julia's Magic, 1984
The Private Worlds of Julia Redfern,
  1988

◆ About the Author ◆

Eleanor Cameron was born on March 23, 1912, in Canada, to Henry and Florence Butler. Cameron attended the University of California and the Art Center School in Los Angeles, and worked in the Los Angeles Public Library and with several advertising agencies before launching a writing career. She married Jan Stuart Cameron in 1934. Their son David inspired her to write the science fiction novel *The Wonderful Flight to the Mushroom Planet* and its sequels. Her time fantasy, *The Court of the Stone Children*, won the National Book Award in 1974, and *A Room Made of Windows* garnered the *Boston Globe-Horn Book Award* in 1971. Several of the Julia Redfern novels have been recognized as American Library Association Notable Books. Cameron's *The Green and Burning Tree: On the Writing and Enjoyment of Children's Books* (1962) is considered a major critical work in its field. Cameron lives in Pebble Beach, California.

◆ Overview ◆

A Room Made of Windows plunges into the chaotic life of Julia Carolyn Redfern. Her life simmers with consistent intensity, whether she is searching for her lost cats, rescuing a trapped rabbit, slamming her brother's bike into a telephone pole, flirting with a boy visiting in her neighborhood, or rebelling at her mother's remarriage. Preoccupied with writing, she records her observations in her *Book of Strangenesses*. She aspires to become a professional writer, considering it the only worthwhile career for her, and she is critical of peers who view marriage and raising children as suitable life goals. As she becomes more tolerant and open-minded, Julia moves closer toward maturity.

◆ Setting ◆

Julia lives in Berkeley, California, during the 1920s in a neighborhood of stately older clapboard homes. The house in which twelve-year-old Julia lives with her mother and brother has been divided into three apartments. The apartment that Mr. and Mrs. de Rizzio, the landlords, live in has an aviary. Mrs. de Rizzio's father, whom Julia affectionately calls Daddy Chandler, lives in the small attic apartment, where he writes about his mother and her friend, a famous dancer in mid-nineteenth-century San Francisco. Julia loves her own small "room made of windows" because it is her first private space since her father's death in World War I. Although the room is quite small and really meant to function as a sewing room off her mother's bedroom, Julia basks in the atmosphere created by the windows on two sides, a glass door leading to a small balcony on the other side, and a skylight above her bed. The room is large enough to hold the desk her father made for her, and her memory of him is intensified in this space.

The neighborhood becomes important, too, since Julia explores the yards, homes, and lives of its occupants. On one side, in an elegant but neglected home, lives an older woman, Mrs. Rhiannon Moore, who becomes a special friend to Julia. Mrs. Moore's veranda, her eucalyptus trees, and the old windmill on the back property line offer alternative retreats for Julia and her imagination. Near Julia's home live Addie Kellerman and her troubled family in a stark and brooding structure that Julia avoids as much as possible. Other settings in *A Room Made of Windows* give Julia more aesthetic and cultural depth, and they add to the authenticity of the portrait of the early twentieth-century Berkeley-San Francisco area, but the neighborhood provides a sense of stability and permanence.

◆ Themes and Characters ◆

The central theme in *A Room Made of Windows* concerns recognizing and accepting change as an inevitable part of life. Julia resists change, especially her mother's plans for remarrying, because the marriage would displace Julia as the priority in the life of her mother, Celia Redfern; it would also displace her from her beloved room made of windows. Julia wants to be a writer and considers her room and the desk her father made for her essential in achieving this goal. Her father's dream was to be a published writer, and she has adopted his life goal. She holds an intense affection for his memory as a perfect man. His photograph as a handsome, robust man sits on her desk, reinforcing this view of him.

Her mother's fiancé, Phil Stanhope, seems pale and weak compared to the photograph and memory of her father. Julia criticizes Phil Stanhope's hesitancy and indecisiveness when Mrs. Redfern reminds Julia that her father was a difficult man to live with and that she was frequently unhappy, especially when moodiness and volatility would overtake him.

Recognizing and understanding the fallibility of her father is crucial to Julia's emotional maturation. No longer can she use her father, "the perfect man," as an objection to her mother's future plans. Julia must confront her own stubbornness, selfishness, and possessiveness in her relationship with her mother. Being willing to share her mother by giving her approval to the marriage indicates Julia's recognition of her own imperfections. Despite her tantrums, Julia is an intense, fascinating character—a likable girl on the verge of becoming a caring young adult who understands the needs of those she loves.

Julia's maturation is reflected in the development of relationships with several significant characters in the novel. She gains a new appreciation of her brother, Greg, a fourteen-year-old intellectual devoted to the study of Egyptology. Greg's insight and sensitivity help Julia to understand and accept change.

Julia's friendship with Mrs. Rhiannon Moore, a seventy-year-old reclusive pianist, inspires her interest in poetry and contributes to her growing awareness of serious adult concerns—such as loneliness and aging. Mrs. Moore, whose husband left her years ago because she placed her music career before him, encourages Julia's writing aspirations but advises her to become more considerate of others' feelings and needs.

Daddy Chandler, the eighty-four-year-old father of Julia's landlady, Mrs. de Rizzio, provides Julia with a source of grandfatherly love and artistic support. Daddy diligently works on his novel every day, and Julia loves to visit him in the attic where the two share peppermint candies, jokes, and conversation about writing.

Jacket illustration by Trina Schart Hyman for A Room Made of Windows by Eleanor Cameron. Atlantic Monthly Press/Little, Brown: Boston (1971).

Julia's best friend, Addie Kellerman, lives with her stubborn grandmother, her brother Kenny, and her abusive, alcoholic father. Despite her tense domestic life, good-natured Addie remains a loyal friend to Julia. Addie's brother, however, annoys, offends, and sometimes frightens Julia. The frequent victim of his father's drunken beatings, Kenny is a nervous, manipulative, angry boy. Addie and Kenny's cousin Paul, whom Julia comes to admire romantically, effectively tries to control Kenny's aggressiveness.

Julia also finds a new friend in Leslie Vaughan Carlson, a fourteen-year-old who publishes her poems in *St. Nicholas* magazine. Julia admires Leslie's talent and dedication, and Leslie encourages Julia to pursue her writing. Leslie also shows a romantic interest in Greg, which Greg seems to reciprocate.

> *Felony Franklinburg she'd named her doll, years and years ago when her father was alive, the most beautiful name she could think of and wished it might be her own.*

Finally, Mrs. Kathryn Penhallow, the editor of the Young Writer's Page in the local newspaper, takes time from her busy schedule to invite Julia to her home for tea. Like Leslie, Daddy Chandler, and Mrs. Moore, Mrs. Penhallow serves as a literary mentor for Julia. Julia develops renewed enthusiasm and self-confidence as a result of her visit with Mrs. Penhallow.

◆ Literary Qualities ◆

The character of Julia reflects Cameron's memories of herself as an aspiring young writer. In the foreword to *The Green and Burning Tree*, Cameron states that she has been "preoccupied with the craft of writing since the age of eleven," and she has alluded to the books in the Julia Redfern series as "autobiographical in spirit." At the core of Julia's intense character is her love of words, exemplified in her *Book of Strangenesses*. She records lists of words she detests or considers beautiful. She bases her opinion on how the words sound. "Okra," "mucus," and "intestines" sound repulsive to Julia, while "undulating," "melifluous," and "Mediterranean" sound graceful.

Julia begins to appreciate the meanings of words, in addition to their sounds, when she wants the name of a medical doctor to be "Mendenheal" as in "mend-and-heal" instead of his actual name, Mendenhall. Cameron as a writer shows a similar awareness in naming the children's page editor Mrs. Penhallow, a name that symbolically indicates the character's importance to Julia as a developing writer; Mrs. Penhallow teaches Julia that writing is a serious and sacred activity. Julia is most impressed with the advice Mrs. Penhallow gives about "the gift of seeing" that writers need: "You must always see clearly the objects you're describing and find exactly the right words to explain what you feel about the object, and how it looks."

Cameron follows this advice throughout *A Room Made of Windows*, especially in creating a sense of place and atmosphere. In the basement of the music store where her mother works, Julia finds a blend of solace and tension by playing an abandoned pump organ that "looks like a wedding cake." She listens to the "scutterings" of the rats in the darkness as she sweeps dust and the sprinkles of rat pellets off the organ keys. Striking the chords, she makes "a mournful tune creep out, a tune like the voice of some mad Ophelia, for she could no more play the organ than she could play the piano...."

The place Cameron evokes most lovingly is Julia's special room, a room that could "glow like the inside of a shell" as late afternoon, "honey-colored" sunlight filters through the skylight and windows. Julia can lie on her army cot, and view through her skylight directly above "clouds bowling along in stormy seasons, the tops of trees bending, and birds being swept about in the air," or at night she can "watch the cold, patterned stars in warm comfort."

Cameron also uses symbolism to emphasize themes and characterization. Kenny, for example, is compared to a frightened rabbit; Greg describes Kenny as acting "like that rabbit up in the hill that was caught by the legs and then screamed when we all closed in on it." And Julia's short story, "The Mask," comes to represent her coming to terms with her father's legacy as a writer; after discussing the meaning of her story with Mrs. Moore, Julia writes, "...maybe the mask was not only [her father's] desire to write but his whole difficult complex self that he's handed on to me..."

◆ Social Sensitivity ◆

Although *A Room Made of Windows* is set in the 1920s, it effectively portrays a common conflict of today—the tension between child and parent on the issue of remarriage. Cameron juxtaposes failed marriages among other characters with Mrs. Redfern's struggle to gain her daughter's approval to marry Phil Stanhope. Julia is forced to think about Mrs. Moore, their neighbor and Julia's friend, who has been separated for years from her husband because she was preoccupied with her career as a pianist. Another neighborhood couple, the Kellermans, fail in their marriage because Mr. Kellerman drinks to excess and abuses his children and wife. Julia is also aware of the tension that exists

between her Uncle Hugh and Aunt Alex; Alex dominates the marriage through her purse strings because Hugh works for her firm. These marriages—filled with abuse and neglect, career preoccupation and failure—help Julia to understand that she cannot let her selfishness and resistance to change interfere with her mother's chance for a happy marriage.

◆ Topics for Discussion ◆

1. Describe Julia's friendships with Addie and Leslie. Does Julia nurture one relationship at the expense of the other?

2. Is Mrs. Moore influential in Julia's life? Does her advice about being responsive to the needs of others make an impression on Julia?

3. Describe Julia's relationship with Daddy Chandler. Why does she feel guilty at his death?

4. Is Mr. Kellerman a threatening character? Describe how others help Julia understand more about his shame and unhappiness.

5. What does Julia discover about herself, her father, and their respective careers as writers when she composes the short story "The Mask"?

◆ Ideas for Reports and Papers ◆

1. List the points of advice about writing that Julia receives from various characters. Then write a short story of your own, attempting to incorporate the advice that Julia receives.

A Room Made of Windows

2. Trace the steps of Julia's gradual acceptance of her mother's marriage to Phil Stanhope. What events in Julia's life help her to accept Uncle Phil? How does her mother help? How does Uncle Phil help?

3. Read Ivan Southall's *Josh*, a novel about an adolescent boy who wants to become a writer. Compare Josh's and Julia's reasons for wanting to write, how they work to improve their writing, and how their experiences affect their writing.

4. Julia's friend Leslie publishes her poetry in *St. Nicholas*, an influential magazine of writing for and by young people in the late nineteenth and early twentieth centuries. Research and report on the history and significance of *St. Nicholas*. Discuss some of the famous writers who published their early work in this magazine.

5. Julia holds an idealized view of her deceased father in the beginning of the novel and only gradually comes to terms with the reality that he was an imperfect man. In Cynthia Voigt's *Solitary Blue*, Jeff clings to a similarly idealized view of his living, but absent mother. Read Voigt's book and compare how Jeff and Julia learn to accept that the parents they have idolized are flawed human beings. How does idealizing an absent parent affect each character's relationship with his or her other parent?

6. Read the sequel to *A Room Made of Windows* entitled *The Private Worlds of Julia Redfern*. Explore how Julia is beginning to understand more about adult relationships, and how failed or compromised marriages are significant in these last two books in the Julia Redfern series.

♦ Related Titles ♦

A Room Made of Windows is the earliest published novel in a series of five about Julia Redfern. *Julia and the Hand of God, That Julia Redfern,* and *Julia's Magic* explore her character at a younger age, while *The Private Worlds of Julia Redfern* portrays her at age fifteen.

Julia is a preschooler in *Julia's Magic,* and her father is still living. Less mature and constantly in trouble, she suffers the effects of poison oak after she undertakes a forbidden adventure to a canyon, and she also breaks a perfume bottle in her Aunt Alex's boudoir. Her father's strong sense of honesty encourages Julia to admit her unintentional act of destruction. Although Julia is slightly older in *That Julia Redfern,* she continues to be mischievous, taking her brother's bike and nearly running down her haughty, generously-proportioned Aunt Alex and gorging herself on berries, that make her sick. Julia's misadventures as an eleven-year-old are the focus of *Julia and the Hand of God.* In these prequels, Julia learns about adult relationships, especially concerning the marriage between Uncle Hugh and Aunt Alex. This marriage dissolves in *The Private Worlds of Julia Redfern* when Julia unintentionally discovers Uncle Hugh's involvement with a woman he loved before his marriage to Alex. Julia grows to accept people as they are and to recognize that others have private lives just as she has a private, complex existence.

♦ For Further Reference ♦

Block, Ann, and Carolyn Riley, eds. *Children's Literature Review.* Vol. 1. Detroit: Gale, 1976. Contains a collection of excerpts from reviews of

Cameron's books published before 1976.

Cameron, Eleanor. *The Green and Burning Tree: On the Writing and Enjoyment of Children's Books*. Boston: Little, Brown, 1962. A collection of articles that originally appeared in *Horn Book* magazine. Cameron establishes challenging literary standards and praises writers such as Wanda Gag, Lucy Boston, and Rumer Godden for their contributions to the field. She also reflects at length on the composition of the Mushroom Planet series.

Commire, Anne, ed. *Something about the Author*. Vol. 1. Detroit: Gale, 1971. Contains a longer biographical entry on Cameron with emphasis on her son as an inspiration for her creation of the Mushroom Planet series.

Ethridge, James, and Barbara Kipala, eds. *Contemporary Authors*. Vols. 1-4. Detroit: Gale, 1962. Includes a brief biographical entry with emphasis on *The Wonderful Flight of the Mushroom Planet*.

Weiss, Jaqueline Shachter. *Prizewinning Books for Children*. Lexington, MA: D.C. Heath, 1983. Contains a brief thematic reference to *The Court of the Stone Children* and *A Room Made of Windows*.

Richard D. Seiter
Central Michigan University

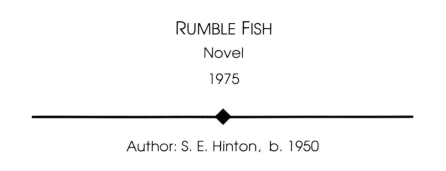

RUMBLE FISH
Novel
1975

Author: S. E. Hinton, b. 1950

Major Books for Young Adults

The Outsiders, 1967
That Was Then, This Is Now, 1971
Rumble Fish, 1975
Tex, 1979
Taming the Star Runner, 1988

◆ About the Author ◆

A publicity-shy novelist (she will not give out her date of birth), Susan Eloise Hinton completed her first book, *The Outsiders*, while she was still a high school student. The author has stated that she wrote *The Outsiders* in order to change the negative stereotype of teen-agers who were labeled "greasers." This ground-breaking novel achieved great success and set the precedent for the uncompromising, realistic fiction for young adults—sometimes called the "New Realism"—that soon followed it. Long after publication, Hinton's novels remain both popular and controversial, and four of them have been converted into commercially successful films.

Born in 1950 in Tulsa, Oklahoma, Hinton was a loner in school and shunned the kind of teen-age groups she has written about. Her ambition was to write, and after her initial success, she sharpened her skills while studying at the University of Tulsa.

People with whom Hinton grew up, particularly the cliques of teen-agers she knew in high school, appear in all of her work. She strives to portray the lives of adolescents growing up in hostile environments. As a result, many adults have been alarmed by the attention Hinton gives to violence, drinking, drugs, sex, and gang behavior. Some critics have accused Hinton of being little more than a rebellious post-adolescent eager to record her antisocial attitudes, a sensationalistic writer motivated to profit from trends, and a vehement social critic bent on tearing down society and glorifying outlaws. Nevertheless, Hinton has received a great deal of acclaim for her innovative use of symbolism, her literary allusion, and her diverse narrative techniques.

Hinton's emphasis on male characters and her use of initials rather than her first name have lead many readers to believe that she is a man. Hinton has said that she initially disguised her gender in order to prevent potential male readers from assuming that they could not relate to her work. Apparently she has not scared off readers of either sex, for her books are immensely popular and have garnered several awards. *The Outsiders* received the Media and Methods Maxi Award in 1975 and was chosen by the *New York Herald-Tribune*, as one of the best teen-age books of 1967. It was also an honor book in the 1967 *Chicago Tribune* Children's Spring Book Festival as was *That Was Then, This Is Now* in 1971. Both books were on the American Library Association's Best of the Best book list in 1975, and *Rumble Fish* was named one of the American Library Association's Best Books for 1975.

* Overview *

Hinton's fiction marks a radical departure from the adolescent novels that preceded it. Whereas these earlier novels generally revolved around romantic crises or adolescent-parent conflicts, Hinton examines the divisive character of adolescent society, the complicated relationships between individuals and groups, and in the case of *Rumble Fish*, the tragic consequences of the ways in which some young people approach life.

A short novel, *Rumble Fish* demonstrates a skilled writer's ability to compress explosive power into a limited amount of space and to create language and imagery that convey great emotional force. Hinton's sophisticated use of symbolism and literary allusion lends great depth and complexity to *Rumble Fish*. The author superimposes her plot on the broad background of classical and traditional literature, particularly Greek tragedy and medieval legend, while simultaneously placing her char-

acters within the philosophical climate of contemporary fiction. Her unflinching sketches of Rusty-James and his brother, the Motorcycle Boy, evoke their helplessness, disenchantment, and confusion. Although decidedly depressing, Hinton's powerful characterizations may alert young readers to the hazards of giving up on decision-making or letting limited experience skew one's entire perspective on life.

* Setting *

Set during the late 1960s or early 1970s, *Rumble Fish*—like all of Hinton's novels—takes place in a southwestern city that the author never explicitly names in the text but has identified as her native Tulsa, Oklahoma. The characters in *Rumble Fish* are oppressed by their environment. They live on the "wrong side" of the river and seldom if ever escape city limits. Hinton sets up parallels between the bleakness of her characters' psychological landscape and the darkness of their physical surroundings. Most of the novel is set at night, and the few daytime scenes take place largely indoors, in pool halls or darkened rooms.

The river that bisects the city separates the characters in *Rumble Fish* from "bright lights" and bustling crowds. When the Motorcycle Boy leads Rusty-James and his friend Steve Hays on an excursion across the river, Hinton contrasts the dizzying whirl of activity that confronts the boys with the menacing, dark world that they leave behind. But Hinton suggests that although Rusty-James has a degree of physical mobility, he will never be able to cross certain boundaries. Essentially alienated from his physical environment, Rusty-James resembles his brother, who, when asked about a trip to California, replies sarcastically, "It was one laugh after another. Even better than here, as amusing as this place is." And although the book opens and closes with Rusty-James sitting on a beach, far from the inner city, it is clear that he has become oblivious to his surroundings and thus remains profoundly alone.

◆ Themes and Characters ◆

Rumble Fish records the experiences, friendships, and conflicts of a group of Oklahoma teen-agers. Hinton's most ambitious work, it focuses on the character of Rusty-James, through whom the reader confronts a disillusioning vision of life as an empty, pointless experience wholly controlled by destiny.

Hinton traces the evolution of Rusty-James's personality by comparing him to the book's two other central characters: his brother, the Motorcycle Boy, whom he emulates, and Steve, an emotional, shy, and awkward teen-ager whom he nevertheless considers his best friend. As Rusty-James steps further away from his troubled but self-regulated life, he achieves a greater understanding of his world, and the full meaning of Hinton's dark image of adolescent despair emerges.

Rusty-James assumes a tough exterior to mask his vulnerability and loneliness. He admits that he is afraid to be alone, obsessed with appearance, and dependent on the company of others. Rejected by the school authorities and his girlfriend, he gradually "burns out" and succumbs to the disturbing family traditions that have helped shape his negative outlook on life. Unable to identify with the gang that once boosted his sense of self-importance, he gravitates toward the "cool" but self-destructive model of the Motorcycle Boy.

Rusty-James's mother abandoned the family when he was two years old, leaving his father to sink into alcoholism and the Motorcycle Boy to grow estranged from virtually all of humanity. Rusty-James himself is unable to overcome his family's legacy; his fate echoes Greek tragedy, which asserts that humanity behaves primarily according to biological necessity and destiny. The fighting "rumble fish" for whom the book is named, as well as mythological figures such as Prometheus who dare to resist this determinism, are inevitably destroyed.

Rusty-James's father and the Motorcycle Boy seem well aware of this tragic reality from the beginning of the book, and Rusty-James gains a similar awareness as he evolves. Maturity, Hinton suggests, is more a matter of awareness than of physical change. As Rusty-James learns more about himself and sees into the soul of the brother he idolizes, his confusion increases, his confidence crumbles, and his childish view of reality gives way to an undeniable glimpse of his own stagnation and helplessness. He soon discovers that he has no more freedom than the fighting fish, confined to solitary fishbowls and prevented from swimming free. When Steve calls Rusty-James a ball in a pinball machine, he correctly assesses his friend's disorientation.

Although Rusty-James ultimately gains a measure of independence from the Motorcycle Boy's violent world, he has nonetheless retreated from society and has become the same sort of cynical drifter his brother was. Rusty-James's alienation leads to his spiritual collapse. He has achieved physical survival, but seems destined over time to repeat the fate of the Motorcycle Boy.

The Motorcycle Boy is the mirror in which Rusty-James sees himself. He floats through the murky world of *Rumble Fish*, becoming active only in the concluding chapters, but his image inspires and guides Rusty-James throughout the course of the book. The product of violence, the Motorcycle Boy has passed into a grey world without illusions or hope. He seems to have peered into the very heart of things and seen the darkest of truths.

Interestingly enough, the Motorcycle Boy appears to be bright, articulate, and well-read; but so too does his father, a law school graduate. The fate of father and son, both of whom have retreated into a vacant existence, underscores the imprisoning nature of family tradition and despair. Like Rusty-James, the Motorcycle Boy accepts "the way things are," and his dramatic attempt to liberate the fighting fish from the pet store—an act which leads to his death—can be seen only as a self-destructive, arbitrary attempt doomed to failure.

Described as a heroic figure born at the wrong time or as "royalty in exile," the Motorcycle Boy resembles an Arthurian knight blessed with vision and committed to his sense of reality, however bleak. But he is entirely amoral, lacks direction and purpose, and cannot win the admiration of a society that considers him a misfit. Inevitably, he becomes an object of hatred for the local police, who await the opportunity to destroy him.

Rusty-James wishfully considers himself an heir to his brother's image, but people continually emphasize the differences in their natures. The chief irony of the novel is that Rusty-James inevitably becomes like his brother and, in the book's epilogue, turns up far from home but devoid of ambition, resolve, or purpose. Rather than viewing her characters as "losers" who have spoiled their lives, Hinton seems to pity those who have never had and never will have control over their futures.

◆ Literary Qualities ◆

While Hinton's other novels are straightforward narratives of adolescent life, constructed around conflict and confrontation, *Rumble Fish* presents a concentrated structure of images, offering a penetrating examination of its central character by creating a dream-like atmosphere that reflects his confusion and despair. As Rusty-James slips away from reality, his memory becomes the elusive point of view from which the reader must determine what really happened; his increasingly selective recollection means that this point of view is not completely trustworthy. But despite his forgetfulness and skewed perceptions, Rusty-James attempts to be honest. His naive narration creates dramatic irony: readers understand what it happening to him more than Rusty-James does himself.

This sense of impending doom contributes a great deal to the tone and color of the novel. The characters' failure to escape their fates reflects a strong element of Greek tragedy. The classical tragedy revolves around a heroic figure who attempts to avoid destiny but, because of a "flaw" in his or her character, has no control over the future. Echoes of this literary tradition resound in *Rumble Fish*, elevating it well beyond the typical young adult novel. The Motorcycle Boy's color blindness brings to mind the tragic figure of the ancient Greek playwright Sophocles' King Oedipus, who blinds himself after unwittingly fulfilling a prophecy that predicted he would kill his father and marry his mother. The Motorcycle Boy's attempt to defy nature and free the fighting fish suggests the myth of Prometheus, who risked destruction by defying the gods and passing the secret of fire on to humanity. Cassandra, the Motorcycle Boy's drug-addicted girlfriend, shares with her mythological namesake the ability to see the future and the inability to make anyone believe her.

Hinton's symbolism is complex and intense. Because her theme stresses biological necessity, she equates physical characteristics with spiritual characteristics. Hinton uses color blindness to represent disenchantment and bleak reality, and blurred vision to emphasize Rusty-James's confused perception and motives. In the early sections, Rusty-James seems to enjoy colors. Later, when the Motorcycle Boy is killed by the police, Rusty-James temporarily loses his ability to see color, symbolizing the loss of his childish illusions.

Equally important to the novel's symbolic structure are the references to animals, which constitute another aspect of Hinton's biological determinism. Each of the major characters is associated with a specific animal appropriate to his nature. The Motorcycle Boy is termed a panther, dangerous, aloof, and easily camouflaged in its habitat; Steve, who Hinton often contrasts with Rusty-James, is called a rabbit, sensitive to his environment and easy prey; Rusty-James is a dog, affectionate, trusting, and obedient, but he is also associated with the fighting fish that attack blindly.

Finally, because environment plays a vital role in human destiny, Hinton uses the river and the ocean to show how Rusty-James and his brother are bound to their environment. The river separates their territory from the rest of the city, cutting them off from the majority of society. The Motorcycle Boy visits California but never sees the ocean, and by the time Rusty-James sees the ocean, he is only a shell of his former self.

◆ Social Sensitivity ◆

Hinton's novels have continuously drawn the objections of critics who feel that books like *Rumble Fish* romanticize lawless behavior and glamorize rebellion. Others condemn the emphasis on persistent violence. There is no denying that Rusty-James's life is organized around antisocial behavior. Drinking bouts, drug use, sexual encounters, truancy, and casual violence are all a part of this novel; a teacher in the story even offers to pay Rusty-James to beat up another student. Hinton intends for the novel to document Rusty-James's disintegration, and it is abundantly clear that his way of life is self-defeating in the end. Nevertheless, Hinton does not withhold details, the most disturbing of which may be the intoxication Rusty-James feels from his violent acts.

◆ Topics for Discussion ◆

1. Critics have noted Hinton's extremely negative portrayal of parents in *Rumble Fish.* What does she reveal about Rusty-James's parents? Does Hinton have a purpose for drawing such characterizations?

2. In what ways do the fighting "rumble fish" for which the book is named

parallel the natures of Rusty-James and the Motorcycle Boy?

3. In many ways, Steve is a comic character, yet his fate is far more desirable than Rusty-James's. What factors account for his survival?

4. What does Rusty-James admire about his brother? Why does it seem unlikely, for much of the novel, that he will grow up to be like him?

5. The Motorcycle Boy is a mass of contradictions. Explain his opposing traits.

6. Rusty-James's father believes that the Motorcycle Boy is exactly like his mother. What traits do they share?

7. An observer in the pool hall calls the Motorcycle Boy "royalty in exile." What does he mean?

8. Police Officer Patterson is described as having a vendetta against the Motorcycle Boy. What might be the policeman's motives for wanting to destroy the Motorcycle Boy?

9. Some readers (as well as Steve) think that the Motorcycle Boy is mentally ill. Give some reasons for this opinion.

10. The Motorcycle Boy claims that his expulsion from school resulted from his perfect scores on tests and his perfect behavior. Is it possible that a student could be thrown out for such reasons? Why or why not?

11. The Motorcycle Boy condemns gang fights as "cowboy and Indian crap." He also rejects drug use. Explain his attitude in light of his otherwise asocial behavior.

12. Cassandra, an aspiring teacher, is a drug addict. Is the Motorcycle Boy responsible for this, or do other forces affect her?

13. Cassandra sends Rusty-James a message: "Life goes on ... if you let it." What does she mean, and why is this advice appropriate for Rusty-James?

◆ Ideas for Reports and Papers ◆

1. The film version of *Rumble Fish* attempts to convey the emotions and mood of the novel. View the film and discuss the ways in which director Francis Ford Coppola attempts to translate these qualities to the screen.

2. Research and report on the "New Realism" that some critics credit Hinton with introducing to young adult fiction. Compare her work, particularly *Rumble Fish*, to young adult fiction before and after.

3. Some critics view *Rumble Fish* as the successor to J. D. Salinger's *The Catcher in the Rye* (1951). Compare Rusty-James and Holden Caulfield. Pay special attention to their attitudes toward society and their acts of rebellion. Does Rusty-James continue a tradition or break from it?

4. Research incidences of teen-age violence, both in gangs and among individuals. Show how Rusty-James's attitudes and actions support or contradict the views held by psychologists and sociologists.

5. Compare *Rumble Fish* to a Greek tragedy such as Sophocles' *Oedipus*

Rex. Explain the similarities in theme, philosophy, and literary technique.

6. Compare *Rumble Fish* to another realistic young adult work such as Robert Cormier's *Chocolate War* (1974). Do the two writers share any common points of view?

◆ Related Titles/Adaptations ◆

The Outsiders, published when Hinton was still in high school, begins a series of novels dealing with the conflicts teenagers have with one another and with society. *That Was Then, This Is Now, Rumble Fish,* and *Tex* are the other books in this series. Although *Rumble Fish,* which concentrates on a single character, marks a change in style and focus, Hinton's fiction is limited to one time and place: Oklahoma in the 1960s or early 1970s.

The film versions of *Tex, The Outsiders,* and *Rumble Fish* all starred the popular young actor Matt Dillon and were praised by critics. Directed by Tim Hunter, *Tex* (1982) was the first of Hinton's works to be adapted to screen. The celebrated director Francis Ford Coppola directed both *The Outsiders* and *Rumble Fish* in 1983, filming the latter in black and white to stress the theme of color blindness. The film version of *Rumble Fish* starred Mickey Rourke, Diane Lane, and Dennis Hopper in addition to Dillon. The three movies have served as showcases for an impressive array of young talent; other performers featured in the various Hinton films include Emilio Estevez, Nicolas Cage, Rob Lowe, Ralph Macchio, Vincent Spano, Patrick Swayze, and Tom Cruise. *That Was Then, This Is Now* was adapted to the screen in 1985.

◆ For Further Reference ◆

Daly, Jay. *Presenting S. E. Hinton.* New York: Twayne, 1987. A comprehensive study of Hinton and her work. Daly finds her to be a ground-breaking figure in what he terms the "New Realism."

DeMarr, Jean, and Jane S. Bakerman. *The Adolescent in the American Novel Since 1960.* New York: Ungar, 1986. Brief comments on Hinton's protagonists as they reflect the era.

Donelson, Kenneth, and Aileen P. Nilsen. *Literature for Today's Young Adults.* Glenview, IL: Scott, Foresman, 1980. Contains an evaluation of Hinton as a "new" writer of adolescent fiction.

Egoff, Sheila. *Thursday's Child.* Chicago: American Library Association, 1981. Contains brief comments on Hinton's contribution to young adult fiction.

Lenz, Millicent, and Ramona M. Mahood. *Young Adult Literature.* Chicago: American Library Association, 1980. Classifies Hinton with the new voices in young adult literature.

Senick, Gerard. *Children's Literature Review.* Vol. 3. Detroit: Gale Research, 1978. Brief remarks on Hinton's interest in social classes.

Stanek, Lou W. *A Teacher's Guide to Paperback Editions of the Novels of S. E. Hinton.* New York: Dell, 1980. A guide to help teachers pose questions and evaluate the literary style of the novels.

Sutherland, Zena. *The Best in Children's Books*. Chicago: University of Chicago Press, 1973. Contains a short commentary on Hinton's career.

"Teens Are For Real." *New York Times Book Review* (August 27, 1967): 29. A discussion of the realistic approach to young adult novels as typified by Hinton.

Varlejs, Jana. *Young Adult Literature in the 1970s*. Metuchen, NJ: Scarecrow Press, 1978. An interesting evaluation of Hinton's styles and themes.

Paul Ettenson
SUNY, Old Westbury

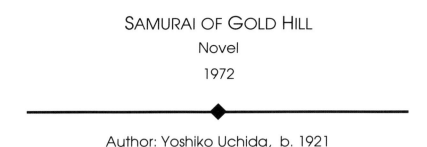

SAMURAI OF GOLD HILL
Novel

1972

Author: Yoshiko Uchida, b. 1921

Major Books for Young Adults

*The Dancing Kettle and Other
    Japanese Folk Tales*, 1949
*The Magic Listening Cap: More Folk
    Tales from Japan*, 1955
The Promised Year, 1959

*The Sea of Gold and Other Tales
    from Japan*, 1965
In-Between Miya, 1967
Journey to Topaz, 1971
Samurai of Gold Hill, 1972
Journey Home, 1978

◆ About the Author ◆

Yoshiko Uchida was born on November 24, 1921, in Alameda, California, and grew up in Berkeley. Her father, Dwight Takashi Uchida, was a businessman who worked in San Francisco; he and his wife, Iku, enjoyed entertaining and often played host to young Japanese visiting the area. Yoshiko was a creative child who liked to draw and, by age ten, had begun writing short stories. She often traveled during the summers, and visited Japan when she was about twelve years old.

In 1942 Uchida graduated from the University of California, Berkeley, with a bachelor's degree in English, philosophy, and history. She received her diploma through the mail in a cardboard roll because she and others of Japanese ancestry who lived on America's West Coast were taken from their homes and sent to inland camps

after war with Japan broke out. Uchida was evacuated first to the Tanforan Race Track, and from Tanforan to the Topaz, Utah, internment camp. Most Japanese-Americans lost their homes and businesses; much of what they could not carry, they had to sell or give away. They experienced humiliation and were deeply marked by their miserable internment. Although she found useful work teaching second grade at Topaz, Uchida says that her memories of the time center on the awful living conditions—snakes and scorpions infested the camp—and the abiding sense of unjust treatment.

In 1943 Uchida left Topaz for Northampton, Massachusetts, where she studied at Smith College on a fellowship. She received a master's degree in education from Smith the following year and taught at Frankford Friends' School in Philadelphia from 1944 to 1945. She was a secretary for the Institute of

Photograph of Yoshiko Uchida.

Pacific Relations from 1946 to 1947, and it was during this period that she decided that she wanted to write. While working as a secretary for the United Student Christian Council in New York, she published her first and second books—*The Dancing Kettle and Other Japanese Folk Tales* and *New Friends for Susan*. The latter, published in 1951, differs from most of Uchida's later books in that it does not specifically address Japanese or Japanese-American topics.

Uchida spent 1952 in Japan on a Ford Foundation Foreign Study and Research Fellowship, researching materials for her second collection of folktales, *The Magic Listening Cap*. She remained in Japan until 1954, all the while writing articles for the *Nippon Times* of Tokyo. During the years 1955 to 1964 she served as the West Coast correspondent for *Craft Horizons* of New York, and wrote a column, "Letters from San Francisco," for the magazine. From 1957 to 1962 she also worked as a secretary for the Lawrence Radiation Laboratory at Berkeley.

Published in 1971, *Journey to Topaz* was named an American Library Association (ALA) Notable Book for 1972, and *Samurai of Gold Hill* received the Commonwealth Club of California Medal for best juvenile book by a California author that same year. In 1981 Uchida received the Distinguished Service Award from the University of Oregon for her work in helping Americans better understand Japan and the heritage of Americans of Japanese descent. Her book for younger children, *A Jar of Dreams* (1981), received the 1982 Commonwealth Club of California Medal for best juvenile book. *The Best Bad Thing* (1983), the first sequel to *A Jar of Dreams*, was named an ALA Notable Book for 1983. In 1985 Uchida was given the Young Authors' Hall of Fame Award by the San Mateo and San Francisco Reading Associations.

Uchida speaks Japanese and French as well as English, and has been active in improving understanding between American ethnic groups. One of her books for adults, *Desert Exile: The Uprooting of a Japanese American Family* (1982), is an important resource for those interested in learning about the internment of Japanese-Americans during World War II.

◆ Overview ◆

Samurai of Gold Hill recounts the adventures of Koichi, the son of a samurai warrior, who leaves Japan at the end of a civil war and joins other Japanese immigrants in building a colony in California. Much of the novel's fascination stems from its authentic portrait of feudal Japan and its depiction of the conflict between this culture and that of the American frontiersmen during the gold rush era. *Samurai of Gold Hill* is based on real historical events, and Uchida's careful research provides a solid base of information about the experiences of Asian immigrants in the 1800s. But the novel is primarily a story of extraordinary adventure—from the farms, shops, and cities of Japan to the constant dangers of life in nineteenth-century frontier California—that will captivate its readers.

◆ Setting ◆

Samurai of Gold Hill begins in the Year of the Serpent, 1869, in Wakamatsu, a town in northern Japan's Bandai-Azuma mountains. The castle of Lord Matsudaira has been gutted by fire but still looms over Wakamatsu. Many samurai warriors have perished in the battle to defend Wakamatsu, and Lord Matsudaira himself has been imprisoned. Entrusted with a secret mission on behalf of Lord Matsudaira, Koichi's father—Matsuzaka, Gentai (the surname goes first in Japanese names)—gathers together the companions he will need for a great adventure. Koichi, trained to be a samurai and to obey his leader without asking any questions, journeys with his father to the bustling port city of Yokohama; he is filled with curiosity about his father's mission but waits until his father chooses to reveal the secret plan.

Eventually Koichi learns that his father plans to establish a colony in California to serve as Lord Matsudaira's home in exile after his release from prison. Koichi, his father, and the others sail to San Francisco and from there take another ship upriver to Sacramento. The land seems dry compared to Japan, which is in its rainy season; Koichi feels like he has "come from a land of soft gray mist to a land of eternal harsh sun." The travelers ride wagons to Placerville, a boisterous frontier town where they face the hostility of many of the white settlers. From Placerville, they ride to Gold Hill, the site of their future colony.

Some of the immigrants' neighbors, both Native Americans and white farmers, are friendly and helpful, but others—especially the gold prospectors—are suspicious of the Japanese's efforts to establish a new home. California's climate differs from that of Japan, and it, too, often seems hostile toward their crops and farm.

◆ Themes and Characters ◆

The principal theme of *Samurai of Gold Hill* is that of "strangers in a strange land." This theme emphasizes the problems people have when they feel that they are different from those around them, as well as the excitement people experience when they explore a new and different world. The other themes—racial discrimination, cowardice, and sexism—give the main theme its focus and help to clarify the relationships between the novel's characters.

At the start of the novel, Koichi already finds himself alienated, even though he is in his own town. His side in the civil war has lost, and his country now belongs to the enemies of his father and Lord Matsudaira. Too young to fight and die honorably as has his brother, Koichi finds himself surrounded by uncertainties; the samurai code of honor does not prepare him for defeat, and his life—which had seemed well planned, with the certainty that he would become a samurai warrior like his brother and father—is adrift, its future unpredictable. Thus, at the beginning of *Samurai of Gold Hill*, Koichi and the other followers of Lord Matsudaira are already strangers in a strange land—they are alienated from their own country. Their decision to leave for California to create a colony-in-exile seems a logical and natural development.

In California, Koichi and his companions find themselves the objects of intense curiosity and sometimes intense dislike. Some Californians, such as the farmers Thomas and Kate Whitlow, offer them help and friendship. Other Californians are openly hostile, picking fights with the Japanese immigrants and trying to make life on Gold Hill difficult for them. Much of the immigrants' life in California is a struggle for acceptance, and the racist hostility of some of their neighbors—along with the inhospitable weather—eventually overwhelms the colony.

Sexism is an ever-present factor in the lives of Koichi and the other followers of Matsudaira. In the opening chapters, the social differences between men and women loom large. Men make the important decisions; women merely obey the commands of the men. Even Koichi's beloved grandmother is not allowed to make important decisions about the life of her family. During the voyage to California, the alienation of the Japanese women finds its focus in Toyoko Schnell. She bears a double burden, for not only is she a woman in an almost totally male-oriented society, but she is only one-half Japanese. Toyoko's father is J. Henry Schnell, a German, and Toyoko "looked neither Japanese nor Prussian, but was a strange mixture of the two. The people in Wakamatsu had said she would never find a proper husband because she was half barbarian." In addition, Toyoko is only eight years old and has no playmates. Koichi, twelve years old at the start of the novel and well on his way to becoming a samurai warrior, is the nearest person to her in age, and he would much prefer to have a boy for a companion. In this, Koichi has no choice; he and Toyoko, the youngest of the colonists, are given joint tasks. Toyoko wins Koichi's respect with her efforts to preserve the silkworms, and she slowly develops self-respect by proving that she can be a productive member of the colony even though no one expects her to be very helpful. Toyoko's is an individual battle for respect; the colonists' views toward women in general change little.

The Japanese are always struggling to understand their new world. The climate is different from that of their homeland, so they need to abandon some of their customary ways of farming and learn new ones, such as how to irrigate their land with only one stream as a source of water. In their attempt to cope with an alien society, the Japanese come to know and appreciate the local Native American community. Like the Japanese, the Native Americans live lives rich in rituals, and their closeness to the land echoes the Japanese farmers' closeness to their old land at Wakamatsu.

The racists in *Samurai of Gold Hill* tend to be cowardly people. The worst is "One-eye," a nasty bully who hates the Japanese colonists primarily because they are different from white Californians. He picks a fight with Rintaro, Lord Matsudaira's chief carpenter, and loses, further embittering him toward the Japanese. The problems caused by racism are present throughout the novel. The Japanese themselves regard white people as barbarians, and they claim that white people wear heels in their shoes because they have cloven hooves instead of feet. Even Toyoko, who should know better, fears that a diet of milk and beef will cause her to lose her toes and to develop hooves.

When they reach Placerville, the Japanese find themselves to be every bit as much the subject of foolish fears as Herr Schnell and Toyoko were in Japan. When they try to find wagons to take them to Gold Hill, they find that most people refuse to help them. One-eye's treachery and cruelty represent the blind hatred of all those who are hostile to the colonists simply because they are Japanese. When One-eye finally succeeds in destroying the Gold Hill colony by cutting off the water supply, he finishes the work of many other racists. Most of the colonists find work on local farms owned by people such as the Whitlows, who are concerned more with the value of the Japanese's work than with their race, while some—such as the Schnell family—return to Japan.

The colonists are attractive because of their courage and pluck. Koichi, in particular, matures into a thoughtful and courageous young man. Well into his teens at the novel's end, he becomes more open-minded than he would have been had he stayed in Japan. He comes to appreciate Toyoko's strength of character and to admire the Japanese farmers, all of whom would be beneath his social station in Japan. However, history must disappoint those readers who hope for the success of the colonists. Bad weather and hostile miners doomed the colony, and the ending is therefore a sad one, with some of the characters—such as the Schnell family—returning to Japan, and with others scattering across northern California in search of work.

◆ Literary Qualities ◆

Samurai of Gold Hill is based on the history of a real Japanese settlement, the Wakamatsu Colony. Its site was made a California Historical Landmark in 1969, one hundred years after its founding. The Japanese civil war, the village of Wakamatsu, Lord Matsudaira, Herr Schnell, and the servant Okei are all genuine historical figures. Out of the historical facts, Uchida has tried to depict what life would have been like for the Japanese colonists. Her Japanese characters cling to their customs, finding in them a sense of community that helps them fend off the hostility of their new land. Although Toyoko becomes more independent in her new home, she does not stray beyond historically believable limits; she remains subject to the wishes of the men.

Although Toyoko and Koichi function as realistic and complex characters in the novel, they also serve as symbols of a new Japanese generation. Toyoko, considered a "half barbarian" even in her own country, must learn to strike a balance between Japanese and American female roles. Koichi, likewise, no longer has a clearly defined Japanese identity; he has little use for his samurai training in the remote hills of California. Unseated in Japan and unwelcome in America, both children find themselves growing up as Japanese-Americans. Koichi comes of age at a time when his culture is also undergoing a radical change.

Gold Hill, an actual gold-rush town settled by the Japanese colonists, represents the fantasy of a prosperous and shining future in a new land. The name takes on ironic significance by the end of the novel, however, when the Japanese lose their long, upward struggle against racial prejudice and are forced to give up their "golden" dream.

Uchida uses symbolism in her characterization of One-eye, the prospector whose bigotry tarnishes the Japanese's hopes for a Gold Hill colony. As his name suggests, One-eye has limited vision, both literally and figuratively. His narrow perspective blinds him to the needs of others; he sees only his needs and is unable to envision Gold Hill as an integrated, harmonious community.

♦ Social Sensitivity ♦

The sad ending is likely to disappoint some readers, but its truthfulness enhances the credibility of Uchida's account of the Gold Hill colony. In the unflinching ending, the legal authorities refuse to help the colonists, and the hostility of racism overcomes the best intentions of the Japanese and their farmer neighbors. That racism can overcome good work and good intentions is not an uplifting message, and will likely disturb some readers. Yet anger is a valid emotional response to cruel racial prejudice. In the classroom in particular, the book's ending can be useful for generating discussion about how racism sometimes overwhelms more honorable points of view, and about how a tragic conclusion may be more memorable and meaningful than a happy one.

Although Uchida is generally evenhanded in her portrait of racism, she presents the Japanese more sympathetically than she does One-eye and other anti-Japanese racists. By depicting the silly myths the Japanese have about "barbarians," Uchida shows the foolishness of racist views. The fact that the colonists have superstitions about their white neighbors enhances the development of Uchida's themes, and reminds readers that racism is not restricted to one ethnic group. The loneliness and frustration of being a stranger in a strange land become broad statements of universal truth in *Samurai of Gold Hill.*

♦ Topics for Discussion ♦

1. Why does Koichi wish to go off to battle, probably to die, as his brother has?

2. Why does Koichi refrain from asking his father about the secret plan?

3. What is the most significant adjustment the Japanese colonists make when they come to California?

4. Why do the Native Americans help the colonists?

5. In the seventh chapter, "The Silent Cellar," Koichi gives Toyoko an order, and Uchida notes: "Toyoko nodded obediently. Just as her mother did whatever her father asked, she knew that it was her place to listen to Koichi. He was older, and besides that he was a boy. That put him at least two notches above her in their small world, and she knew it." How do Toyoko's views about gender roles change during the novel? Why do they change? How liberated is she at the novel's end? Do you think she will get along well when she is back in Japan?

6. Do Koichi's views toward women in general change during the novel, or is

the change only in his view of Toyoko, alone?

7. Why do Lord Matsudaira's followers want to establish a colony in California, rather than somewhere else? Why do they choose to go into exile at all?

8. How do the colonists deal with the differences between the climates of Wakamatsu and Gold Hill? Do they do the right things to make their farm a success?

9. Why does Koichi's father, a proud samurai warrior, agree to run a farming colony?

10. Why are the Japanese children not allowed to go to school in California?

11. Why do some of the non-Japanese people harbor racial myths about the Japanese? Are any of these myths still prevalent today? Why do some of the Japanese characters believe that white people are "barbarians"?

12. Are the themes of *Samurai of Gold Hill* unified and clear at the novel's end? Does the ending provide a satisfying conclusion to the adventures of the Japanese immigrants?

◆ Ideas for Reports and Papers ◆

1. The towns and cities mentioned in *Samurai of Gold Hill* are all real places. Research one of these Japanese or California towns or cities and explain what it was like from 1869 to 1873, the approximate years during which the novel takes place.

2. What were farms around Placerville like during the time of the novel?

3. How accurate are Uchida's depictions of the Japanese customs of the 1860s? What were the lives of Japanese women like at this time?

4. The Japanese civil war that opens *Samurai of Gold Hill* actually happened. Why was it fought? What happened to the winners? What happened to the losers?

5. What were the duties and responsibilities of samurai warriors?

6. How were samurai warriors trained? What training would Koichi have received by the time he was twelve years old?

7. What special laws did California have regarding Asian immigrants during the second half of the nineteenth century? Why did such laws exist? How long did they last? Does the United States still have such laws?

8. What happened to the real-life settlers of the Wakamatsu Colony? What happened to Lord Matsudaira? Were there any other efforts by Japanese immigrants to establish colonies in America?

9. Trace the development of the theme of racism in *Samurai of Gold Hill.* Are all the racist views alike? Are all the people who harbor racist views alike?

10. Yoshiko Uchida has written extensively about Japanese experiences in the United States. Read *Journey to Topaz, Journey Home,* or *Desert Exile: The Uprooting of a Japanese American Family* and compare the views of the Japanese-American experience found in the book you choose with those in *Samurai of Gold Hill.* What seem to be

Uchida's overall views about life for Japanese-Americans? Is she inconsistent in some of her views? Why might this be?

• Related Titles •

Most of Uchida's writings deal with Japan or Japanese-Americans. Her autobiographical novel *Journey to Topaz* tells about a family uprooted from its Berkeley, California, home during World War II and sent to a detention camp. The novel's sequel, *Journey Home*, depicts the aftermath of the family's exile to Topaz. Both are well-written books that vividly depict life in the 1940s.

• For Further Reference •

Commire, Anne, ed. *Something about the Author.* Vol. 1. Detroit: Gale Research, 1971. Article on Uchida summarizes her life and work.

Sutherland, Zena, and May Hill Arbuthnot. *Children and Books.* 7th ed. Glenview, IL: Scott, Foresman, 1986. Contains a brief evaluation of Uchida's books, focusing on those for younger children.

Uchida, Yoshiko. "Yoshiko Uchida." New York: Margaret K. McElderry Books/Macmillan, 1986. An autobiographical pamphlet that provides an account of Uchida's life and includes some of her views about her own work.

Kirk H. Beetz
National University, Sacramento

SARAH, PLAIN AND TALL

Novella

1985

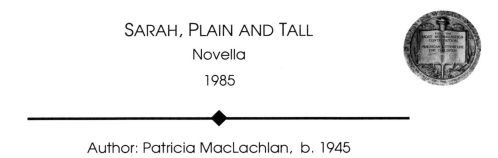

Author: Patricia MacLachlan, b. 1945

Major Books for Young Adults

Arthur, for the Very First Time, 1980
Cassie Binegar, 1982
Tomorrow's Wizard, 1982
Unclaimed Treasures, 1984
Sarah, Plain and Tall, 1985

◆ About the Author ◆

Born in 1945 in Cheyenne, Wyoming, Patricia MacLachlan grew up as an only child whose parents encouraged her interest in reading and writing. MacLachlan graduated from the University of Connecticut and in 1962 married Robert MacLachlan, with whom she has two sons and a daughter. The family lives in Leeds, Massachusetts.

During the 1980s, MacLachlan has enjoyed much success as a writer. Her first novel, *Arthur, for the Very First Time*, won the Golden Kite Award from the Society of Children's Book Writers in 1980. *Unclaimed Treasures* was a 1984 *Boston Globe-Horn Book* Award honor book, and in 1986 *Sarah, Plain and Tall* won the Newbery Medal. The latter book was inspired by a trip to the North Dakota farm where MacLachlan's father was born and by a true story told to MacLachlan by her mother.

◆ Overview ◆

Sarah, Plain and Tall is a simple story of a family that needs a mother and of the woman who gradually fills this need. It is not a tale of wild action or frightful events. Instead, it emphasizes the humanity of characters who yearn to be loved but fear they may be unworthy of love. The novella focuses on honest emotion and portrays characters attempting to cope with complex feelings. *Sarah, Plain and Tall* is popular with young readers, who enjoy its vivid re-creation of a different era and appreciate MacLachlan's understanding of the universal emotional needs of young people.

◆ Setting ◆

Because MacLachlan does not refer to specific locations or historical events, both the geographic and temporal settings of *Sarah, Plain and Tall* are difficult to pinpoint. The story is set somewhere on the great American prairie at a time when horses still served as the major mode of transportation, probably in the late nineteenth or early twentieth century. MacLachlan, born in Wyoming on the high plains, finds great joy and inspiration in this open country. In *Sarah, Plain and Tall*, the prairie is a living presence whose weather and seasons constantly shape the lives of its inhabitants. An unseen but important additional setting is Sarah's beloved Atlantic Ocean, which she misses intensely after her relocation to the prairie. Its colors—green, blue, and gray—are essential elements of her world. When, at the end of the book, she drives to town and brings back green, blue, and gray colored pencils, Sarah fills a gap in both her life and the lives of the children. By bringing the colors of the sea to the prairie, Sarah serves as a personal bridge between the two environments, completing the family's household just as she has succeeded in completing the spectrum.

◆ Themes and Characters ◆

Anna, the narrator of this story, misses her deceased mother and must cope with an unruly younger brother. Caleb is a chatterbox who also misses his mother, even though he never knew her. His constant questions make him a pest to Anna, and he realizes that his desire for attention sometimes makes him a problem for others. When Sarah comes, he is afraid that he might drive her away.

Papa, Jacob Witting, is a lonely and hard-working man. Like his children, he misses his wife, but he realizes that eventually he must move on with his life. Therefore, he places a newspaper advertisement "for help." "You mean a housekeeper?" Anna asks. "No," her father says. "Not a housekeeper. A wife." Papa receives a reply from Sarah Wheaton, who lives in Maine. Although she loves living by the ocean, Sarah accepts Papa's offer to move inland and try living with him and his children.

The story focuses on Sarah and her new family getting to know one another. Sarah is under no obligation to marry Papa and is free to leave if she so desires; much of the story's suspense depends on whether or not she will decide to stay. Sarah describes herself in a letter to Papa as "plain and tall." Upon arriving at the farm, she proves to have good sense, an interest in helping with even the most physically demanding chores, and a quiet, warm personality.

Sharing is one of the important themes of the book. It is through sharing that Sarah slowly makes herself part of the family, and it is through sharing that the children come to know and love her. The children are at first unsure of whether they should share part of themselves with Sarah. Caleb thinks his unruly behavior might drive Sarah away; thus, he keeps his distance from her. Anna is afraid that Sarah will miss the ocean too much and will leave the farm to return to New England; thus, she is slow to commit her love to Sarah. Only the farm animals are able to offer unconditional love, for they are not afraid of being hurt; MacLachlan notes that "the dogs loved Sarah first."

Sarah's efforts to share in all of the farm's labors, including the repairing of a roof, are tempered by her need for independence. When she learns to drive the wagon by herself and then leaves for town, the children and their father worry that she will not return. When she does return, she has not only established her freedom to stay or leave, but she has won the confidence of her new family. She has shown that she stays not out of necessity but out of choice. MacLachlan presents the growth of the sharing relationship between Sarah and her new family deftly, making Anna's fears of rejection suspenseful while showing a gradual and believable development of bonds among the characters. This treatment makes *Sarah, Plain and Tall* a moving account of people developing a sense of belonging and a belief in their own self-worth.

◆ Literary Qualities ◆

In her Newbery Medal acceptance speech, MacLachlan asserts that complex levels of meaning exist "behind each word or between words" and that the unspoken words often create the most powerful aspects of a book. Indeed, the title character of *Sarah, Plain and Tall* is a quiet woman. She shares her time, her interests, and her love, but she keeps her thoughts to herself. Throughout the novel Anna must guess at Sarah's real intentions. When Sarah learns to repair the roof, she appears to want to stay. On the other hand, when she learns to drive a horse and buggy by herself, it seems that she might leave.

Sarah loved living near the great, wide-open sea, and she learns to love the similarly wide-open spaces of the prairie. The images of windswept fields and a prairie that "reached out and touched the places where the sky came down" complement Sarah's own character. Like the land of her new home, she has the capacity to speak with her silence and to make her actions more meaningful than words.

Jacket © 1985 by Marcia Sewall and Harper & Row for *Sarah, Plain and Tall* by Patricia MacLachlan, Harper & Row: New York (1985).

MacLachlan narrates the story from the point of view of Anna, a sensitive young girl who is mature enough to grasp some of the undercurrents of her family situation. Anna realizes that her father no longer sings because he is unhappy, and she notices from the start that Sarah misses her old home in Maine. By telling the story through the watchful eyes of Anna, MacLachlan stresses the importance of emotional ties among family members; Anna reacts to events ever mindful of how happy or unhappy Sarah seems, her concern a manifestation of her love for Sarah. The dialogue in the book is sparse, and thus plot advances are signaled primarily by a gradation of emotions. Hopeful yet slightly reserved at first, the children eventually open their hearts completely to Sarah. At the end of the story MacLachlan reports that "suddenly Caleb smiled," and this spontaneous show of emotion more accurately reflects the happiness that has come to the family than could any words Caleb might speak.

♦ Social Sensitivity ♦

MacLachlan, in her Newbery Medal acceptance speech, tells of her parents' influence on her and of their "belief that it is the daily grace and dignity with which we survive that children most need and wish to know about in books." Perhaps the most outstanding quality of *Sarah, Plain and Tall* is its ability to speak movingly and honestly about what it means to belong to a family and to survive from day to day as a family. Anna, Caleb, Papa, and Sarah all must work to make their lives together successful and meaningful. They make up their own games, tell their own stories, sing songs, and share in the work of the farm. The theme of sharing makes the book a positive reading experience. Its emphasis on ordinary people finding strength in ordinary relationships can only be encouraging to young readers, especially when the everyday difficulties of life often seem overwhelming. Although the family members in the book all fill traditional roles, the book is unlikely to strike anyone as sexist. Sarah's character refutes any such negative reading because in addition to her traditional role she insists on sharing in all the farm work, including those jobs usually assigned to men. Furthermore, Papa performs duties stereotypically associated with women without a hint of embarrassment or resentment. Anna, the narrator, is impressed by Sarah's insistence on helping with all the tasks necessary to make a farm succeed. By sharing the responsibilities for the farm and family, Sarah and Papa forge a successful relationship.

♦ Topics for Discussion ♦

1. Why is Anna uncomfortable around Caleb? Why does she associate him with her mother's death? Is it fair that she thinks of her mother's death when she thinks of Caleb?

2. Sarah is lonely, but she has turned down marriage proposals before answering Papa's advertisement. Why would she come to live with strangers on the prairie if there are men in Maine who want to marry her?

3. Why is it important that Sarah sings "Sumer Is Icumen In"?

4. Why is it such a shock to Sarah to find the dead sheep?

5. Sarah teaches Anna and Caleb how to swim. How does this affect their growing relationship?

6. Maggie, a neighbor's wife, teaches Sarah that "there are always things to miss, no matter where you are." Maggie, Sarah, and Anna all miss something. What does each miss? What does this tell the readers about each character?

7. Sarah insists on helping Papa repair the roof and on learning to drive a horse and wagon. Why doesn't she let Papa repair the roof himself, considering that the task is difficult and there is a squall coming on? Why does she insist on

driving the wagon by herself when Papa can take her where she likes?

8. Sarah runs out into a nasty squall to tend her chickens. Why? What do you think of the description of the squall itself?

9. Caleb says that Sarah's drawing lacks the colors of the sea. Why is this important?

◆ Ideas for Reports and Papers ◆

1. The prairie and its changing seasons and weather play an important role in the novel. Discuss how the weather and seasons affect events and how they reflect the characters' actions and emotions.

2. What did farm children do for fun in the late nineteenth and early twentieth centuries? What were some of their favorite games? What were their toys? How did children on remote midwestern farms get their schooling?

3. Research the everyday life of a farm woman during the late nineteenth and early twentieth centuries. What were the most difficult aspects of this life? In what ways was prairie life rewarding or un-rewarding?

4. It is very important to Anna, Caleb, and Papa that they form a traditional family unit that includes a mother. How important was the family unit to people living on prairie farms in Sarah's day? Is the basic family unit of father, mother, and children still important on mid-western farms?

5. The children like to sing and value Sarah's singing to them. How important

was singing for pleasure in the days before radios, television, and the movies? What sort of songs would people sing in their own homes? Be sure to cite some examples; they do not have to be famous songs. Quote a few lines to give your reader a good idea of what you are talking about. If you make this an oral report, try singing or playing a few bars on a musical instrument.

◆ Related Titles ◆

Arthur, for the Very First Time describes the adventures of a shy ten-year-old who spends a summer in the country. It features the same fine char-acterization one finds in *Sarah, Plain and Tall.* The illustrations by Lloyd Bloom are sensitive and evocative of character and place. In *Cassie Binegar,* a girl learns to cope with her eccentric family. *Unclaimed Treasures* delves into the longings and dreams of girlhood.

◆ For Further Reference ◆

Babbitt, Natalie. "Patricia MacLachlan: The Biography." *Horn Book* 62 (July/August 1986): 414-416. Babbitt analyzes MacLachlan's character and outlook.

Commire, Anne, ed. *Something about the Author.* Vol. 42. Detroit: Gale Reesearch, 1986. Contains a two-paragraph summary of MacLachlan's career, with a few comments about the novels.

MacLachlan, Patricia. "Newbery Medal Acceptance." *Horn Book* 62 (July/August 1986): 407-413. This is MacLachlan's response to receiving the Newbery Medal for *Sarah, Plain* and Tall. In an emotional and humorous discussion, she talks about the influences on her writing, her hopes for how young readers will respond to her books, and her views about language and literature.

MacLachlan, Robert. "A Hypothetical Dilemma." *Horn Book* 62 (July/August 1986): 416-419. Robert MacLachlan provides significant details about his wife's life, family, and friends. The portrait he provides is of a loving, warm-hearted, and busy woman.

Kirk H. Beetz
National University, Sacramento

THE SCARLET LETTER

Novel

1850

◆

Author: Nathaniel Hawthorne, 1804-1864

Major Books for Young Adults

Twice-Told Tales, 1837
Mosses from an Old Manse, 1846
The Scarlet Letter, 1850
The House of the Seven Gables, 1851
The Blithedale Romance, 1852
The Marble Faun, 1860

◆ About the Author ◆

It was almost inevitable that Nathaniel Hawthorne would grow up to write fiction about the New England past. Born on July 4, 1804, in Salem, Massachusetts, Hawthorne could trace his family tree on both sides to the Puritans, whose unbending attitudes toward religious conformity were branded on the American, and especially the New England, consciousness. His great-great grandfather, John Hathorne, was one of the three judges at the famous Salem witch trials in 1692. (The family name was spelled "Hathorne" until the novelist himself added the "w".) Hawthorne's father, a sea captain, died in Surinam in 1808; the four-year-old Hawthorne and his family found themselves living on the charity of relatives. The family moved from Salem to Raymond, Maine, when Hawthorne was twelve; he remained there for three years, and became accustomed to a life of solitude. In 1821 he entered Bowdoin College in Brunswick, Maine, graduating in 1825 near the middle of a class that included future president Franklin Pierce (one of Hawthorne's best friends) and the poet Henry Wadsworth Longfellow.

For the next several years, Hawthorne secluded himself in his Salem home, reading prolifically and writing the ghostly stories that only slowly came to be recognized by his contemporaries as works of artistic merit. Although his privately published romance *Fanshawe* (1828) did little to help his career as a writer, Hawthorne continued to compose his tales. In 1832 his story "The Gentle Boy" was accepted by the *Token*; others appeared in succeeding years, and by 1837 he was able to bring out a collection, *Twice-Told Tales*. The work drew praise from Longfellow and others.

In 1839 he took a job as measurer in the Boston Custom House, and at about the same time, fell in love with Sophia Peabody. Hawthorne resigned from the

Custom House job in 1840 and in 1841 spent seven months at nearby Brook Farm, an experimental site dedicated to communal living and backed by many Transcendentalist thinkers of the time. The following summer, on July 9, Hawthorne and Peabody were married; the couple moved to The Old Manse in Concord, Massachusetts, where they became friends with neighbors such as the writers Ralph Waldo Emerson and Henry David Thoreau, and the feminist leader Margaret Fuller. The Hawthornes' first child, Una, was born in 1844; a son, Julian, and a second daughter, Rose, followed in the next seven years.

Despite the publication and moderate success of *Mosses from an Old Manse* in 1846, Hawthorne discovered that full-time writing did not provide sufficient income for the family. He worked as surveyor in the Boston Custom House from 1846 until 1849, when he turned once again to full-time writing. After working steadily for nine months on a "romance" set in Puritan New England, he published *The Scarlet Letter* in April 1850. The work sold modestly, but met with exceptional critical acclaim. Buoyed by the encouragement of his peers, Hawthorne embarked on two years of furious literary activity, publishing *The House of the Seven Gables* and *The Snow Image* in 1851 and *The Blithedale Romance* in 1852. That same year he wrote a campaign biography of his college friend, Franklin Pierce, who captured the presidency of the United States. In return for past favors, Pierce appointed Hawthorne U.S. Consul at Liverpool, a post he held for four years.

Hawthorne produced little fiction while in Liverpool, but upon resigning in 1857 he moved to Italy, where he wrote *The Marble Faun*. Hawthorne returned to the United States, and *Our Old Home*, his last novel, was published in 1863. Hawthorne's health began to fail in 1863, and he died on May 19, 1864, while undertaking a trip to Plymouth, New Hampshire, in an effort to improve his health.

Though he had not achieved monetary independence through his fiction, by the time of his death Hawthorne was regarded as one of America's few truly successful and original novelists. Unlike his Transcendentalist contemporaries Emerson and Thoreau, or his friend and fellow-novelist Herman Melville, Hawthorne established a reputation that never suffered a serious decline. His works, especially *The Scarlet Letter* and *The House of the Seven Gables*, remain staples of American fiction, and continue to be admired by modern critics.

◆ Overview ◆

The Scarlet Letter is one of the few American works of literature that has justifiably earned the accolade "classic." Primary among the novel's virtues are its tightly structured plot and sophisticated exploration of character and motivation. Through the tale of Hester Prynne's and Arthur Dimmesdale's transgressions of conventional morality, Hawthorne offers an assessment of the Puritan consciousness, a code of thought and action that helped form the American psyche. He uses historical materials to create a novel about universal, timeless human problems: the struggle of the individual to achieve freedom in a society that imposes considerable restraints, and the dilemma individuals face in balancing personal feelings against social or moral norms.

◆ Setting ◆

Set during the mid-seventeenth century, *The Scarlet Letter* takes place in Boston, Massachusetts, and the surrounding countryside. Any reader familiar with American history will no doubt be predisposed to view critically the high-handed and intolerant attitudes directed toward Hester Prynne by the people of Boston. The placement of the action in an intolerant Puritan community permits Hawthorne to introduce suggestions of other-worldly powers at work: witches, spirits, demons, and even the Devil. Nevertheless, the suggestion that supernatural powers may be responsible for events in the novel is always couched in less-than-definitive language; Hawthorne counters the fantastic explanations that he places in the mouths of his characters with more commonsensical explanations of his own.

◆ Themes and Characters ◆

In *The Scarlet Letter*, Hawthorne explores two important themes, the first of which has been described by critics as the conflict between "heart" and "mind." Hawthorne contrasts the feelings of the more sympathetic characters, such as Hester Prynne, with the harsh rules of conduct established by those, such as the Puritan magistrates, who seem incapable of any emotional response whatsoever to their fellow human beings. This conflict is dramatized within the context of the Puritan moral and social code: individuals who are predestined for salvation exhibit their election by living in strict accordance with "God's laws." These laws are interpreted by Puritan elders who have rigid attitudes toward dress, decorum, and

above all, sexual conduct. Men and women who commit acts of sexual misconduct are branded—literally, in Hester's case, with the decree that she wear the letter "A" over her heart. Hawthorne demonstrates that individuals who have sinned in the eyes of their fellow citizens are still capable of exceptional goodness, while those who relentlessly pursue the exposure and punishment of sinners are often the real villains.

On the breast of her gown, in fine red cloth, surrounded with an elaborate embroidery and fantastic flourishes of gold-thread, appeared the letter A.

Hawthorne's second major theme is the nature of sin itself. His examination is complex and heavily shaded with irony: although Hester and Arthur are guilty of committing adultery, it is clear that they turned to each other because they both found themselves in loveless, emotionally barren situations. Hester and Arthur feel guilty for having transgressed the moral order but gradually come to realize that Puritan society shares part of the blame.

Hawthorne concentrates on four characters in his dramatization of these themes. Hester Prynne, a woman of great courage and pride, suffers the disgrace of wearing the scarlet "A" as a sign of her sin. Although she is a devoted

Illustration by Felix Octavius Darley for *The Scarlet Letter* by Nathaniel Hawthorne. Dodd, Mead: New York (1948).

mother to her daughter Pearl and is genuinely repentant for her transgressions, Hester feels that she and Arthur are not totally culpable for their actions. She seems to take pride in being set apart from society, and is willing to make a life for herself and Pearl despite her ostracism.

On the other hand, Hester's lover, the minister Arthur Dimmesdale, suffers tremendously but silently. Unable to expiate his sin by making a public declaration of his guilt, he suffers inner torments until he finds the strength to confess to the community in Boston. Pearl, the offspring of Arthur and Hester's unlawful union, is depicted as a child of nature, more at home in the forest than the city and often unwilling to heed the strictures of society. Hawthorne develops Pearl more as a symbol than as a realistic, engaging child.

Roger Chillingsworth, Hester's husband who is living in Boston incognito, proves the most problematic character in the novel. Obsessed with discovering the father of Hester's child, Chillingsworth seems to associate himself with the forces of evil. Though his motives seem understandable—he wants the man who cuckolded him to pay for his sin—Chillingsworth never gains the reader's sympathy. Hence, the suggestion that characters such as Chillingsworth are less admirable than the sinners they pursue lurks beneath the surface of the work .

◆ Literary Qualities ◆

Hawthorne carefully structures his novel, using three climactic scenes that take place on the scaffold outside the Boston prison as centerpieces to highlight key revelations of character or changes of fortune for his hero and heroine. The first two scaffold scenes set the stage for the third, in which Dimmesdale publicly confesses that he is the father of Hester's daughter, Pearl.

Hawthorne also makes skillful use of imagery in *The Scarlet Letter*, infusing the natural world of Boston and the surrounding wilderness with symbolic qualities; in particular, Hawthorne makes symbolic associations between his characters and natural instances of light and darkness. Dimmesdale's name symbolizes his moral plight. The light of his spirituality is dimmed by his secular desires, and Hawthorne's physical descriptions of the minister frequently stress his pale complexion. At one point in the novel, after Hester and Dimmesdale meet in the forest and agree to begin a new life together, a ray of sunlight breaks through the gloom. This sunlight, referred to as "the sudden smile of heaven" upon the reunited couple, vanishes when it becomes apparent that the couple's plan is unrealistic. Hester herself is also subject to the fluctuations of light and darkness. Radiant and blushing when she temporarily casts off the scarlet letter, she pales when forced to pin it back upon her breast. "As if there were a withering spell in the sad letter," writes Hawthorne, "her beauty, the warmth and richness of her womanhood, departed, like fading sunshine; and a gray shadow seemed to fall across her."

The most elemental symbol of the novel is the letter A, introduced in the first scaffold scene as a punishment for Hester's adultery and associated with a multitude of meanings as the novel progresses. When arrayed in a crimson tunic, Pearl is described as "the scarlet letter in another form, the scarlet letter endowed with life." It is ironic that the scarlet A that appears in the sky during the second scaffold scene is interpreted to stand for "Angel." And in the final scaffold scene, Dimmesdale bares his chest, revealing the outlines of "a SCARLET LETTER—the very semblance of that worn by Hester Prynne—imprinted in the flesh." This wound suggests both Dimmesdale's adultery and his atonement.

♦ Social Sensitivity ♦

The subject of *The Scarlet Letter*, adultery, is a sensitive topic. Hawthorne focuses on the effect of adultery on individuals and on the community. Though no character discusses the actions of Hester and Arthur in explicit detail, the subject of adultery nevertheless is unavoidable if any meaningful examination of this novel is to be made. Hawthorne does not condemn his sinners; although they realize they must make amends for their sin, they are presented quite sympathetically. The villain of the novel, Roger Chillingsworth, is the one character intent on exposing the sinners. It may be easy for readers to misunderstand Hawthorne's point regarding sin and forgiveness: he does not really excuse sin, but he does criticize the heartless society that drives people such as Hester and Arthur to seek fulfillment for their emotional needs outside accepted social boundaries.

♦ Topics for Discussion ♦

1. Explain how Hawthorne uses nature and the natural world as a means of exposing the hypocrisy and oppressiveness of Puritan society.

2. Compare Hester's and Dimmesdale's characters. Does one character seem stronger or more sympathetic than the other? Does one suffer a greater punishment than the other? What does each character lose and gain as a result of the adultery?

3. In chapter 17, Dimmesdale tells Hester that they are not "the worst sinners in the world"; rather, Chillingsworth's campaign of revenge against them is worse because "he has violated, in cold blood, the sanctity of the human heart." Do you think Dimmesdale is right? Why or why not?

4. In chapter 19, Pearl refuses to join her mother and Dimmesdale because Hester has removed her cap and the scarlet letter from her dress. What does this incident reveal about Pearl's character? What does Hawthorne suggest by this scene?

5. Though the novel focuses on Hester, Dimmesdale, Pearl, and Chillingsworth, numerous other characters appear in *The Scarlet Letter*. How do they function in the novel? Does Hawthorne use them simply to further the plot, or do some of them serve larger thematic purposes?

◆ Ideas for Reports and Papers ◆

1. Writers often use patterns of imagery (repeated references to places, objects, activities) to highlight their themes. Choose a specific pattern of imagery—such as light and darkness—and show how Hawthorne uses it to illuminate a particular character or theme in the novel.

2. Read Hawthorne's short story "The Minister's Black Veil." Compare the protagonist of that story with Dimmesdale. In what ways are they similar? In what ways are they different? What do they reveal about Hawthorne's attitude toward the Puritan ministry?

3. Look up the definition of "Gothic fiction" in a handbook of literature or in an encyclopedia. How does Hawthorne use Gothic elements in this novel? Is *The Scarlet Letter* a Gothic novel? Why or why not?

4. Read a short history of the Puritan movement in New England. How accurate is Hawthorne's portrait of seventeenth-century Puritan society? What details does he highlight for artistic purposes? Does he distort the facts? For what purposes?

5. The story of Hester's life as a branded adulteress is preceded by a long introduction titled "The Custom House." Why do you think Hawthorne included this narrative? What purposes does it serve? Can the rest of the novel be read effectively without it?

6. Hawthorne sets the action of chapters 3, 12, and 23 at the scaffold in the town common. Compare the three scenes. What does each reveal about the principal characters in the novel? How do Hester and Dimmesdale change in the second and third scenes?

◆ Related Titles/Adaptations ◆

The Scarlet Letter has been filmed a number of times, with two particularly outstanding versions. The 1926 silent film version starring Lillian Gish (Hester) and Lars Hanson (Arthur) was an excellent, straightforward adaptation. Filmed several more times during the silent-film era, *The Scarlet Letter* was adapted as a talking film in 1934 but not filmed again until the 1979 PBS version. Filmed in Boston, this four-part mini-series boasted authenticity in every detail, researched by scholars of literature and American culture. Considered a masterpiece of documentary as well as commercial filmmaking, it starred Meg Foster as Hester and John Heard as Arthur.

Many of Hawthorne's short stories, especially "The Minister's Black Veil," "My Kinsman, Major Molineau," and "Young Goodman Brown," deal with the same themes as does *The Scarlet Letter*. Hawthorne's novel *The House of the Seven Gables* and many of his shorter works are set in New England and use the seventeenth-century Puritan setting to discuss universal human problems.

◆ For Further Reference ◆

Bloom, Harold, ed. *Nathaniel Hawthorne*. Modern Critical Views Series. New York: Chelsea House, 1986. Anthology of essays originally published in scholarly journals or monographs, providing a wide-ranging view of Hawthorne's methodology and of his central artistic concerns. Also contains a useful bibliography of secondary sources on *The Scarlet Letter* and other works by Hawthorne.

Fogle, Richard H. *Hawthorne's Fiction: The Light and the Dark*. Norman: University of Oklahoma Press, 1952. Seminal study of Hawthorne's imagery, giving special attention to the moral implications of the novels.

———. *Hawthorne's Imagery*. Norman: University of Oklahoma Press, 1969. Analyzes patterns of imagery in Hawthorne's work. Devotes a chapter to *The Scarlet Letter*, emphasizing the novelist's use of light and darkness to highlight his themes.

Gerber, John C. "Introduction" to *The Scarlet Letter*. New York: Modern Library, 1950. Astute analysis of the structure of the novel.

———, ed. *Twentieth Century Interpretations of "The Scarlet Letter."* Englewood Cliffs, NJ: Prentice-Hall, 1968. Excerpts of critical studies discuss the background of the novel; offer analyses of its form and of the techniques Hawthorne uses in the work; and provide interpretations of its themes.

Kaul, A. N. *Hawthorne: A Collection of Critical Essays*. Englewood Cliffs, NJ: Prentice-Hall, 1966. Collection of previously published essays and excerpts from studies that give a sense of Hawthorne's chief interests as a writer and assess his literary achievements. Includes two selections on *The Scarlet Letter*; one discusses the significance of "The Custom House" chapter.

Lee, A. Robert. *Nathaniel Hawthorne: New Critical Essays*. Totowa, NJ: Barnes & Noble, 1982. Essays on Hawthorne's novels and on several well-known short stories; includes some selections that offer an overview of Hawthorne's artistry. Two essays focus on *The Scarlet Letter*.

Rountree, Thomas J., ed. *Critics on Hawthorne*. Coral Gables: University of Miami Press, 1972. Collection of brief essays and excerpts of longer works by prominent authors and critics. Offers an excellent overview of Hawthorne's career; several selections discuss *The Scarlet Letter* in some detail.

Laurence W. Mazzeno
Mesa State College

THE SECRET GARDEN
Novel
1911

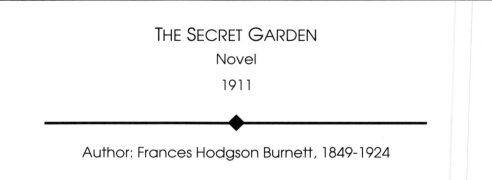

Author: Frances Hodgson Burnett, 1849-1924

Major Books for Young Adults

Little Lord Fauntleroy, 1886
Sara Crewe, 1886
Elizabeth and Other Stories, 1890
Giovanni and the Other, 1892
Piccino and Other Stories, 1894

Two Little Pilgrims' Progress, 1895
A Little Princess, 1905
The Secret Garden, 1911
The Lost Prince, 1915

◆ About the Author ◆

Frances Hodgson Burnett was born Frances Eliza Hodgson on November 24, 1849, in Manchester, England. In 1865 the family's ironmongery failed, triggering the Hodgsons' move to Knoxville, Tennessee. Burnett began writing to supplement the family income, and by the time she was twenty, she was writing and publishing as many as six short stories a month in a wide array of potboiler magazines. Soon Burnett's work was accepted by established magazines such as *Scribner's* and *Harper's*; her commercial success financed the first of many trips to England. In 1873, back in Tennessee, she married Dr. Swan Burnett, a prominent physician. Burnett, however, was unhappy in Tennessee and persuaded one of her editors to advance her enough money to move to Paris with her husband and young son, Lionel, in 1874.

Returning to the United States in 1877, Burnett published her first novel, *That Lass o'Lowrie's*, a story about miners in Lancashire. A tremendous success both in America and in England, the novel was adapted for the stage, the first of fifteen dramatizations of Burnett's fiction. Burnett became well known as she wrote and published adult fiction almost incessantly over the next six years. In 1883 Henry James, in a review of the London production of her play *Esmeralda*, suggested that Burnett's style and moral focus would make her a good children's writer. At this time Burnett was actually writing *Little Lord Fauntleroy*. Although originally written solely for her two sons' entertainment, the book was serialized by the magazine *St. Nicholas* in 1885. This novel, in part a portrait of her own sons, proved so successful that Burnett continued writing for young people as well as adults until her death in Plandome, New York, on October 29, 1924.

◆ Overview ◆

Although *The Secret Garden* depicts the dismal effects of a loveless home, its goal is to show how nature, coupled with positive thinking, can transform people's lives. The central characters, Mary and Colin, initially seem to be spoiled, mean-spirited, and completely self-absorbed characters. Although they do not recognize their own emotional emptiness, they are both hungry for affection and companionship. The novel concerns itself with the process of Mary and Colin's awakening to the world, other people, and their own feelings. In many ways the story has the texture of a fairy tale: the magical effects of a special and secret place save the children. However, the story is more satisfying than a fairy tale because Burnett's characters evolve into caring, sensitive beings through their own efforts, demonstrating that people are capable of changing their lives for the better.

◆ Setting ◆

The story begins in colonial India, where Mary Lennox lives with her mother and father. When Mary's parents die, the scene shifts to Misselthwaite manor, the Yorkshire home of Mary's reclusive uncle, with whom she has been sent to live. At Misselthwaite, Mary discovers a garden that her uncle has kept locked up and abandoned for ten years, ever since his wife suffered a fatal injury there. The garden has run wild and is choked with dead or dying weeds and grasses. Mary decides to make the garden her secret place and begins to try to revive it.

◆ Themes and Characters ◆

Mary Lennox and Colin Craven, the two main characters in *The Secret Garden*, are cousins but psychologically resemble twins. Both have been effectively orphaned—Mary by her parents' death, and Colin by his mother's death and father's subsequent abandonment. Brought up by servants who dislike and fear them, the two are unruly, nasty children, prone to temper tantrums whenever they do not get their way. The servants, however, meet only the children's physical needs and desires; they do not satisfy their need for love and affection. Without being aware of it, Mary and Colin are exceedingly lonely, isolated, and frightened that life will continue to bring them no genuine, lasting joy.

Mary, however, begins to understand herself and her needs when she is brought to the home of her uncle, Mr. Archibald Craven, and must learn how to dress and care for herself. Having no peers or playthings, Mary comes to identify with the craggy, angry gardener, Ben Weatherstaff, as well as with a robin who has been abandoned by his nest mates. She recognizes for the first time that she has always been lonely, yet she does not know how to bridge her isolation. With the robin's help she discovers the dying secret garden, and, because it too has been abandoned, Mary becomes determined to restore the garden to its former loveliness. The act of reviving the garden restores Mary's physical strength, and she is gradually transformed into a vibrant, healthy, happy young woman capable of looking beyond herself.

Colin does not appear until almost halfway through the novel, when Mary discovers him hiding from the world in his room. Colin's mother died in childbirth after a tree branch in the garden struck her and forced her into premature labor. Unable to recover from the shock and grief of her death, Mr. Craven has become reclusive and avoids seeing his son. Although he does not consciously wish Colin any harm, he cannot see him without remembering his deceased wife. Colin fears that he will develop a hunchback and die. A hysterical, angry young man who has been deeply hurt by his father's unthinking rejection, Colin needs companionship; he needs to learn how to love and be loved, and he needs to learn how to help himself. Mary, recognizing much of herself in Colin, forces him to see that there is nothing physically wrong with him except the debilitation brought on by spending most of his life in bed. Lashing out at him with her own very violent temper, she challenges him to recover and introduces him to the secret garden.

Dickon, the housemaid Martha's younger brother, is the exact opposite of Mary and Colin. A static character, he offers unqualified acceptance to the two troubled children and thus helps them grow. He has an uncanny, almost supernatural ability with wild animals and nature, drawing squirrels, rabbits, foxes, and lambs to his side by playing his pipes. A Yorkshire lad, he is at one with nature and at peace with himself. He has no doubts, no fears, no feelings of isolation, and no selfishness. Innately kind, he provides Mary and Colin with the first positive, nurturing friendship they have ever experienced. Dickon's character gently reinforces the novel's themes of rebirth and redemption through nature, and helps make *The Secret Garden* a novel of hope and joy fulfilled.

Illustration by Tasha Tudor for *The Secret Garden* by Frances Hodgson Burnett. J. B. Lippincott: New York (1962).

◆ Literary Qualities ◆

Although *The Secret Garden* has many of the characteristics of a fairy tale, its most elemental symbol is rooted not in fantasy but in nature. The abandoned garden's rebirth parallels the rebirth of Mary and Colin. Like them, it has been left to die of neglect, yet it still has the seeds—albeit hidden and buried—that will allow it to flower and grow if only someone will nurture it. As the garden grows, so too do the children who work there. Once the garden is revived, the children come to recognize its tremendous strength and power. Although they label this power "magic," they recognize that magic works "best when you work yourself." They sing hymns and chant incantations in the joyous knowledge that they, too, share in and help perpetuate the miracle of life.

Symbolically, Burnett draws on an old pastoral literary tradition that transforms the garden into a substitute, benign mother. The garden nurtures the children by offering them a safe, secluded spot in which to learn how to care for themselves and others. Indeed, the children spend approximately nine months—spring, summer, and fall—hidden behind the protective walls of the garden before they emerge triumphant.

But she was inside the wonderful garden and she could come through the door under the ivy any time and she felt as if she had found a world all her own.

The Secret Garden's tightly unified plot is controlled by the changing seasons, allowing the rebirth of both the garden and the children to take place smoothly and cohesively. Burnett also makes good use of dialogue: Colin's and Mary's increasing use of Dickon's Yorkshire dialect vividly illustrates the young pair's growth as they learn to see the world through their friend's eyes. Ultimately, the characters' growth and their ability to transform their lives makes this novel a story of redemption.

Some readers may be disturbed by Burnett's sentimentalizing of poverty and the class system, but her portrayal does not lack sensitivity. As Mary and Colin grow healthier, they learn what it means to be physically hungry and unable to satisfy their needs. For the first time, they understand how difficult it must be for Dickon's mother, Mrs. Sowerby, to feed her twelve children. When she sends them milk and freshly baked bread, they feel genuine gratitude, but they also recognize the cost to all of the Sowerbys. No longer are the two children oblivious to the needs of those less fortunate than themselves, and they find a way to help the Sowerbys in return.

The novel demonstrates that everyone needs love and understanding, but it stresses that these must be given in order to be received. The lessons the children learn—to care for others, to work to make others happy, and to understand the pain of others' lives—make *The Secret Garden* a sensitive and strong novel.

♦ Topics for Discussion ♦

1. When Mary learns that her nurse and both of her parents have died in the epidemic, she worries solely about who will take care of her. Why does she not display any expression of grief?

2. Why does Mary show no curiosity about her move to England, her uncle, or even about her future?

3. Mary's new life at Misselthwaite forces her to look at her behavior for the first time. What role does Dickon's

sister, Martha, play in Mary's self-examination?

4. Mary recognizes herself in the old gardener, Ben, and in the robin. What do they have in common? Why is Ben so reluctant to speak with Mary?

5. Why is Mary so curious about the secret garden? What does it represent to her?

6. Mary has always shunned other children; why, then, does she want to meet Dickon? What, other than her interest in restoring the garden, enables her to become friends with him?

7. When Mary and Colin first meet, both are startled, and both think that the other is a ghost. Why do they think this? In what ways have the two actually been like ghosts?

8. At first, Colin is a spoiled, obnoxious boy. What draws Mary to him? Why does she tell him about the garden? Why does she help him? How is she able to convince him that his fears of dying are exaggerated?

9. Why do Colin, Dickon, Mary, and Ben go to great lengths to keep the restoration of the garden a secret?

10. Colin declares that his and Mary's growing strength is caused by the "magic" of the garden and insists that each of them must help the "magic." What is the "magic," and how do they help it?

11. Colin intends to hide his return to good health until his father returns from Europe, and then he plans to march into his father's study to surprise him. Instead, his father discovers Colin running out of the garden straight into his arms. Colin then takes his father into the secret garden to explain all that has happened. Is this ending more satisfying than the one Colin intended? If so, how? Why is it important for Mr. Craven to go back into the garden after ten years? Why are Mary and Dickon absent from the last few pages of the book?

♦ Ideas for Reports and Papers ♦

1. Frances Hodgson Burnett liked happy endings so much that she called herself "Mrs. Romantick." She believed that it was possible to transform reality by thinking positively. How does positive or negative thinking affect the lives of Mary, Colin, Dickon, and Mr. Craven?

2. How does the garden function as a metaphor for the way Mary and Colin are at the start of the novel? Trace the ways this metaphor is realized or fleshed out in the course of the novel. In what ways does the garden's transformation into a mother figure that protects, nurtures, and teaches, alter this metaphor?

3. Some critics believe that the novel's shift from Mary to Colin makes it ultimately Colin's story. Others claim that the story is really that of Mary's triumphant transformation of herself and of Colin. Whose story is *The Secret Garden*? Why?

4. At the time *The Secret Garden* was written, children were rarely presented in a negative way. More typical of the time is Burnett's *Little Lord Fauntleroy*, whose central character is a sweet, ideal child. Compare both works, paying particular attention to which characters grow the most and how they do so.

Which of the central characters is most satisfying: Mary, Colin, Little Lord? Why?

5. Although Dickon is an important character, he remains one-dimensional: he does not change dramatically during the story. What is his role in the novel? Why is it necessary that he remain a one-dimensional character?

♦ Related Titles/Adaptations ♦

The Secret Garden was made into a film by Metro-Goldwyn-Mayer in 1949. The screenplay was written by Robert Ardrey and Fred Wilcox directed. The film starred Margaret O'Brien as Mary, Dean Stockwell as Colin, and Brian Roger as Dickon. This film does not capture the subtleties of the novel, and it emphasizes sentimentality. A better adaptation is the 1987 Hallmark Hall of Fame made-for-television movie from Rosemont Productions. Filmed at Highclere Castle, Newbury, England, it stars Gennie James as Mary, Barret Oliver as Dickon, and Jadrien Steele as Colin. Blanche Hanalis wrote the screenplay, and Alan Grint directed this adaptation.

♦ For Further Reference ♦

Bixler, Phyllis. *Frances Hodgson Burnett.* Boston: Twayne, 1984. A thorough study of Burnett's adult and children's novels which pays particular attention to her depiction of female characters.

Burnett, Constance Buel. *Happily Ever After: A Portrait of Frances Hodgson Burnett.* New York: Vanguard, 1969. Based largely on Burnett's autobiographical *The One I Know the Best of All* (1893), this work is an entertaining, positive examination of Burnett's life that appeals primarily to young people.

Gohlke, Madelon S. "Rereading *The Secret Garden.*" *College English* 41 (April 1980): 894-902. While comparing her reading of *The Secret Garden* as an adult and as a sickly child, Gohlke examines the themes of death, rebirth, health, and illness in the novel.

Keyser, Elizabeth Lennox. "'Quite Contrary': Frances Hodgson Burnett's *The Secret Garden.*" *Children's Literature* 2 (1983): 1-13. Examines the shift in focus to Colin at the end of the novel.

Koppes, Phyllis Bixler. "Tradition and the Individual Talent of Frances Hodgson Burnett: A Generic Analysis of *Little Lord Fauntleroy, A Little Princess* and *A Secret Garden.*" *Children's Literature: An International Journal* 7 (1978): 191-207. A well-conceived, thorough comparison of the three novels.

Thwaite, Ann. *Waiting for the Party: The Life of Frances Hodgson Burnett 1849-1924.* New York: Charles Scribner's Sons, 1974. An exceptionally complete biography that provides a bibliography of Burnett's English and American plays.

Marlene San Miguel Groner
SUNY at Farmingdale

A SEPARATE PEACE
Novel
1960

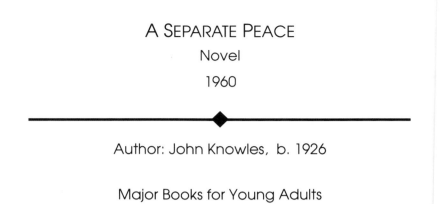

Author: John Knowles, b. 1926

Major Books for Young Adults

A Separate Peace, 1960
Phineas: Six Stories, 1968
Peace Breaks Out, 1981

◆ About the Author ◆

John Knowles was born on September 16, 1926, in Fairmont, West Virginia. He lived there until he enrolled at Phillips Exeter Academy in 1941, where he was on the swimming team. He entered Yale University in 1945, continuing to compete as a swimmer in addition to editing the *Yale Daily News* and contributing short fiction to the Yale magazine *Lit*. He graduated with a bachelor's degree in English in 1949, and he worked briefly as a reporter for the *Hartford Courant* before joining the Curtis Publishing Company. At Curtis, he eventually became the associate editor of *Holiday* magazine. He spent much of his free time traveling extensively in Europe, the Near East, and the islands of the Aegean. During this time, he contributed many essays to travel journals and began to publish his short stories in popular national magazines. In 1960 *A Separate Peace*, his first novel, was published. It met with widespread critical acclaim and enthusiastic public

response. More than nine million copies have been sold since its publication. The book won the Rosenthal Award from the National Institute of Arts and Letters and the William Faulkner Foundation Award (the forerunner of the prestigious PEN/Faulkner Award), and it enabled Knowles to declare himself a "full-time writer." He lived primarily on the French Riviera for the next eight years (although he undertook stints as a writer-in-residence at Princeton University and at the University of North Carolina at Chapel Hill) and proceeded to publish *Morning in Antibes* (1962), *Double Vision: American Thoughts Abroad* (1964), *Indian Summer* (1966), and *The Paragon* (1972).

None of these books approached the critical or commercial success of *A Separate Peace*, but each displayed Knowles's intrinsic command of language and style. *Morning in Antibes* is marked by Knowles's characteristic facility with mood and atmosphere, while *Double Vision* presents his belief "that living in, not just visiting, foreign countries is the best education." *Indian Summer* and *The Paragon* both have their origins in Knowles's experiences at Yale and the seven years he spent living in Connecticut, while a later work, *Spreading Fires* (1974), takes place on the French Riviera.

In recent years, Knowles has lived in East Hampton on the outer edge of Long Island. In 1981 he published *Peace Breaks Out*, in which the narrator returns to the Devon School in New Hampshire (the site of *A Separate Peace*) after World War II to begin teaching at his alma mater. Most critics felt that the book was strongest in its depiction of the atmosphere of the school and in its rendering of life among the students, aspects of Knowles's writing that have had a continuing appeal for young adults.

◆ Overview ◆

A Separate Peace was recognized immediately as an extremely sensitive account of a young man's self-discovery through the process of maturation, and the passage of time has not lessened its universal appeal. John Knowles identifies and examines some of the crucial questions a young man might ask about himself and the world during his later teen-age years. Knowles's evocation of the moods of developing manhood is deeply felt, precisely rendered, and exceptionally incisive. The novel captures a period of life in which everything seems intense and important, in which decisions must be made that may affect one's entire life, in which action is seen with rare moral clarity, and in which an almost desperate sense of potential loss (of innocence, of uniqueness, of importance) underlies every act.

In addition, Knowles uses an extremely effective method for organizing this narrative of self-discovery. At the core of the story, the narrator undergoes an epiphany, a moment of irrevocable displacement that haunts the remainder of his life and reverberates throughout the book. Unsure of its meaning at the instant it occurs, the narrator finds that the incident symbolizes for him the awesome power of revelation, the moment of vision that shapes a life and defines existence, offering access to the secrets of the innermost self. The progress of the narration is controlled by a concentration on the full meaning of this incident and, by implication, on the universality of such events.

Beyond this, *A Separate Peace* may recall for older readers the special qualities of existence in those years when one is "green and dying," in Dylan Thomas's words. The novel reconnects the mature reader to that period in life when the demands and rewards of friendship and love were new and noble, and it helps to explain why idealism is so valuable a quality, and one so difficult to sustain. At the same time, the book articulates these feelings for all readers who may have been unable to express them.

◆ Setting ◆

The values that John Knowles emphasizes in *A Separate Peace* reveal his belief that an appreciation of nature's wonders is fundamental to a life of moral integrity and spiritual satisfaction. Consequently, the novel is set in the beautiful countryside of New England, not far from the Atlantic coastline at a New Hampshire prep school called Devon. The year is 1942, and the United States is increasing its involvement in World War II. The early reverses the Allies suffer seem to imperil the very values of Western civilization. The war is presented first as a distant source of uneasiness, but its presence gradually grows into an emblem of the encroachment of the adult world's most mundane elements onto an unspoiled realm of youth and beauty.

That realm lies within the protected sanctuary of the school, a place of privilege run by quasi-British masters who espouse "continuity" but have ceased to provide the inspirational energy that keeps tradition vital. Although Knowles admires the school's overall aims and holds it in higher esteem than he does most other institutions in American life, he also recognizes its tendencies to mold and limit its students, draining them of the creativity and spontaneity that make life so vivid for his exceptional, artistic, and slightly eccentric characters. Still, in the "gypsy summer" that produces the book's freest and happiest moments, it is the school grounds, glowing like a marvelous garden of Eden, that provide the setting for the idyll that precedes the "fall" into the "real" world. Knowles sees this moment in history, this place in the country, as the last vestige of a vanishing era, and the school's location on the banks of two rivers—the clean, pure Devon and the "turbid, saline Nagaumsett"—illustrates its pivotal place at a turning point in time.

◆ Themes and Characters ◆

The opening pages of A Separate Peace serve as a prologue in the "present" when the book is being written, fifteen years after 1942, the critical year in the life of the novel's narrator, Gene Forrester. A mood of philosophical reflection develops as the narrator describes a visit back to his prep school. His memory soon takes him back to the days of his seventeenth year, at the convergence of youth and manhood in a timeless moment when "feeling was stronger than thought." This return enables Knowles to place the action within an introspective frame so that both "feeling" and "thought" are employed in the service of understanding. In addition to the perspective provided by the passage of time, another kind of framework emerges as Gene, the central subject of his own narrative, also becomes the narrator of a hero's life, the poetic story of the extraordinary Phineas.

Knowles has created a friendship that parallels that of Nick Carraway and Jay Gatsby in F. Scott Fitzgerald's novel The Great Gatsby (1925). Gene, like Nick, records his friend's exceptional qualities and singular style. The parallel is particularly appropriate since Knowles, like Fitzgerald, is writing about the American dream and the loss of idealism. Gene's involvement with Phineas, however, is more intimate than Nick's relationship with Gatsby, and his own actions are more intricately connected with Finny's destiny. Gene's participation in Finny's fate irrevocably changes his own character.

This change in Gene's character structures the narrative and gives it a sense of progression, but the central core around which it revolves is the character of Phineas, Gene's roommate and best friend. In creating Phineas, Knowles builds a character upon an idea of excellence that a young man might aspire to, and he has succeeded in making Phineas a plausible person where he might easily have remained a wooden icon or symbol. Finny is the center of all social situations, the energy-giver who instigates and directs action. His wild imagination makes him a bold explorer of new possibility, and his sheer joy in existence contributes to his natural leadership. He is most at home in the world of sport—triumphing in traditional games with an almost casual competence, serving as the spirit of inspiration in games he creates to enchant his friends. Because he is so good at handling conventional social arrangements, he loves a challenge and often dares himself to go beyond the limits set by authorities. He is both a rebel and a faithful supporter. He loves Devon School "truly and deeply," and he directs his rebellion against blind order that prohibits the establishment of the perfect order he envisions. Clever and audacious, he enjoys the effect of proclaiming the unsayable, yet he always remains within the bounds of genuine good taste as defined by the totally democratic (that is, not class-conscious) world he longs for.

The tree was tremendous, an irate, steely black steeple beside the river.

The reader sees Phineas in the book through the eyes of his closest friend, Gene, who adores and, unfortunately, also envies him. Gene is Knowles's projection of his own early artistic consciousness. While reconstructing the formation of this creative intelligence, Knowles concentrates on the contradictions and uncertainties of a young man gradually coming to terms with the imperfections of his character and of the world. Because of Gene's doubts, he cannot fully and freely accept Finny's gift of unrestricted friendship and unrestrained candor, hiding his own fear behind a shield of fashionable sarcasm. Because he is unable to express his own feelings, he distrusts Finny's motives and ascribes to Finny his own competitive ambitions.

At the beginning of the narrative, Gene has a sense of himself as the center of the world. By the conclusion, he has been compelled to accept his own relatively insignificant position in a vast cosmos. Interestingly, this adjustment, essential to the process of maturity, enables him to understand Finny's gift for empathy and sharing. This understanding is the beginning of a real strength in Gene's character—a strength born of disappointment, pain, and loss, as well as insight.

While a confrontation with the dark dimensions of his own psyche is crucial for Gene's growth, it is only one aspect of his life. To balance the psychic struggle, Knowles skillfully evokes the beauty of a New England summer for a young man temporarily transfixed by a perfect moment in time. Gene is the embodiment of the heightened emotion, instinct, and candor that make youth such a poignant, precious, and, of course, temporary state of existence. The fleeting nature of these qualities is underscored by Gene's degree of change at the end of the book. At the end of the school year in June, Gene has prepared himself for the adult world—specifically the war—by consciously creating a gulf between his former pure joy in existence and his newly-formed guarded attitude as he faces the coming tumult.

But in a final reflection on Devon, the bruised, wary seventeen-year-old merges with the adult's narrative consciousness to try to come to terms with the transforming power of his friendship with Finny. What remains with him is Finny's wonderful and singular presence. The legacy of their shared moments is Gene's sense of the best side of himself and his understanding that one does not have to give in to the worst ways of the world to survive. The "separate peace" that Gene arranges is with that part of himself that was corrupted by fear, and as he realizes on his return, he remains at least somewhat at peace because of this accommodation. And although he will always resent the world that drove him to compete with and not fully accept Finny, Gene has made peace with that enemy also, recognizing that resistance through hate is negative and self-destructive, an impediment to the preservation of Finny's finest and most cherished gift, the life he bequeathed to his friend.

◆ Literary Qualities ◆

None of the books John Knowles has written since A Separate Peace has achieved nearly the critical or popular success of his first novel. The reason is not that Knowles has exhausted his knowledge of the world but that A Separate Peace has a rare unity of subject and style. Knowles is a graceful and lucid writer, but his ability to use language most effectively seems to require a specific focus to prevent style from becoming merely decorative, an end in itself. His task in A Separate Peace, to establish the authenticity of Gene's sensibility—that is, his heightened sensitivity to the beauty of the natural world and his capacity for intense feeling about human nature—required the

creation of a lyric voice to register the range of emotional response with poetic precision. Knowles's vivid descriptions of the countryside through four seasons enable him to echo the psychic landscape of his narrator in powerful imagery, and the clarity of his descriptions of certain key locations—a marble staircase, the testing tree, the pure river—offers an anchor and a context for the novel's most important events. Because Gene's voice throughout the narrative is generally sober and reflective, when Knowles shifts into a different rhythm the effect is often striking by contrast.

Knowles also knows the atmosphere of the school very well, and his unobtrusive presentation of details gradually gives the reader a full sense of the school's grounds. The other boys in Finny's "circle" are not presented with much depth, but they are drawn from familiar types, and Knowles has invested each one with enough personality to make him distinct. Knowles masterfully recreates the conversation of young men in groups, complete with all of the self-conscious, artificial linguistic apparatus. His ear for the telling phrase or the right slang gives his depiction of life in the dorms a convincing authenticity. As Gene grows throughout the year, the other boys are also affected by the changing times; but their transformations are mostly background for Gene's development. Still, the sense that they have grown, too, reinforces Gene's progress.

The first-person narrative draws the reader very close to Gene, an identification crucial to a full involvement in his quest. Knowles's skillful alternation between action and reflection, confrontation and relaxation, and seasons of ease and seasons of stress, prevents Gene's story from becoming routine or too predictable. Against these changes of pace, Gene's engaging desire to learn everything he can about all he encounters drives the narrative forward. Because Gene is such an open vessel, each setback has serious consequences, but because he has an essentially positive outlook, he can rebound quickly. The structure of the book follows this pattern of crisis and resolution until its conclusion, at which point it has been established that Gene will eventually become the man who can tell the story.

◆ Social Sensitivity ◆

It is a testament to Knowles's ability that a story about relatively privileged young men in the 1940s, written from the perspective of the quiet, almost humdrum days of the Eisenhower era, has not become dated at all. Knowles has written what appears to be a real "classic" of youthful ardor that so perfectly captures the poignance of a young man's feeling that it will continue to transcend its temporal and social bounds. The book's portraits of youthful aspirations, fears, frustrations, and revelations remain apt decades after Knowles painted them. Gene's progress from the protected environment of a friendly, unified school setting to his first encounters with the demands of an indifferent or hostile world has the resonance of an archetype of human behavior.

Yet, there is one aspect of the relationship between Gene and Phineas that looks a bit different now than it did thirty years ago. In the 1940s, it would be very unusual for boys of this background to discuss sex at all, and the absence of women from their thoughts is a function of the cultural reservations more than anything else, a fact still essentially operative in 1960 as well. Also, the virtual elimination of any interest in women might be regarded as Knowles's choice to remove a factor that would not particularly contribute to the themes he is considering. Still, the absence of any sexual curiosity tends to be rather conspicuous in the 1980s, in which sexual awakening is almost a requisite theme in many young adult stories. In addition, the almost total exclusion of any women from the narrative (besides a comment on "Hazel Brewster the professional town belle"), combined with several derogatory references to unattractive women, skews the male focus a bit further. An obligatory pinup of Betty Grable appears, but it does not elicit much interest compared to the boys' passionate responses to so many other things.

◆ Topics for Discussion ◆

1. How do the boys at Devon feel about the adults they know?

2. Why and how is the school and its setting important for Gene and the other boys at Devon?

3. What is the meaning of war for Gene and his friends? How does their attitude change? Does it affect all of the boys the same way?

4. How does the concept of friendship control and influence the lives of the boys at Devon?

5. Why does Gene fear the tree that Finny wants him to climb? How does his behavior in the tree reflect this fear?

◆ Ideas for Reports and Papers ◆

1. What is the "separate peace" that Gene feels he has achieved? How has it affected the rest of his life?

2. Find several examples of the way in which Knowles uses the natural world (e.g., the tree, the rivers) to introduce and express the novel's important themes. Do you think these images work well as symbolism? Why?

3. What is the place of sports in the life of the boys at Devon? How does Knowles use sports to help portray his characters?

4. What kind of picture of American society does Knowles develop in his portrait of the United States in the early days of World War II? How might his writing the book in the 1950s affect his description of the 1940s?

5. Gene is described with considerable psychological insight, but Phineas is presented primarily from Gene's perspective. How does Phineas see himself? How might Phineas's self-image differ from Gene's image of him?

◆ Related Titles/Adaptations ◆

In 1972 A Separate Peace was filmed by Paramount. The studio was unable to find a writer or director with the requisite cinematic genius to find images to correspond to the moods of Knowles's writing. Aside from the title and some scenes taken directly from the book, the film bears little resemblance to the novel and has been deservedly forgotten.

Knowles based A Separate Peace on a short story entitled "Phineas" that he had written about ten years earlier. The short story ends at the point where Gene goes to confess to Finny that he is responsible for Finny's fall from the tree. Knowles published "Phineas" in 1968 as part of the short story collection *Phineas: Six Stories*. The follow-up novel to A Separate Peace, Peace Breaks Out, serves as an interesting commentary on the post-World War II era.

◆ For Further Reference ◆

Ellis, James. "*A Separate Peace*: The Fall from Innocence." *English Journal* 53 (May 1964): 313-318. A good character study of the protagonist and his relationship with his best friend.

Halio, Jay. "John Knowles's Short Novels." *Studies in Short Fiction* 1 (Winter 1964): 107-112. Explores the relationship of A Separate Peace to Knowles's other works, with commentary on similarities in theme, style, and approach.

Knowles, John. "Musings on a Chameleon." *Esquire* (April 1988): 174-183. An interesting and revealing account of the author's friendship with Truman Capote, providing some previously unknown information about Knowles's career and writing.

MacDonald, James. "The Novels of John Knowles." *Arizona Quarterly* 23 (Winter 1967): 335-342. An intelligent overview of Knowles's work.

Mengeling, Marvin. "*A Separate Peace*." *English Journal* 58 (December 1969): 1322-1329. A good general discussion with particular emphasis on the mythic aspects of the character of Phineas.

Morgan, Neal. *Wilson Library Bulletin* 39 (December 1964): 343-344. A brief but informative sketch of the author's early life and career.

Raven, Simon. "Review." *Spectator* 202 (May 1, 1959): 630. An appreciative review of *A Separate Peace* by an English critic.

Theroux, Paul. "Review." *New York Times Book Review* (July 14, 1974): 4-5. An essay on Knowles, concentrating on *Spreading Fires* but reflecting on his earlier work as well.

Witherington, Paul. "*A Separate Peace*: A Study in Structural Ambiguity." *English Journal* 54 (December 1965): 795-800. An examination of meaning and structure in the novel.

Wolfe, Peter. "The Impact of Knowles's *A Separate Peace.*" *Ohio Review* 36 (March 1970): 89-98. Comments on the social and artistic impact of the novel.

Leon Lewis
Appalachian State University

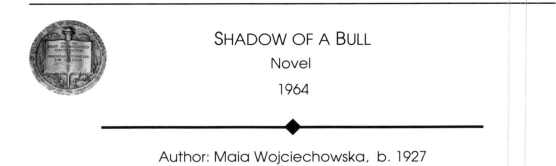

SHADOW OF A BULL
Novel
1964

Author: Maia Wojciechowska, b. 1927

Major Books for Young Adults

Market Day for 'Ti Andre, 1952 (written as Maia Rodman)
Shadow of a Bull, 1964
A Kingdom in a Horse, 1965
The Hollywood Kid, 1966
A Single Light, 1968
Tuned Out, 1968
Hey, What's Wrong with This One?, 1968

Don't Play Dead Before You Have To, 1970
The Life and Death of a Brave Bull, 1972
Through the Broken Mirror with Alice, 1972
Winter Tales from Poland, 1973
How God Got Christian into Trouble, 1984

◆ About the Author ◆

M aia Wojciechowska was born on August 7, 1927, in Warsaw, Poland. She came to the United States in 1942 with her parents and two brothers when her father received an assignment as air attaché to the Polish Embassy. Wojciechowska attended schools in Poland, France, and England, graduated from Sacred Heart Academy in 1945, and attended Immaculate Heart College in Los Angeles from 1945 to 1946. After moving from Los Angeles to New York, she met author Selden Rodman, who encouraged her in the craft of writing. They married in 1950 and spent time in Haiti, where she wrote her first published book for young readers, *Market Day for 'Ti Andre*. She and Rodman divorced in 1957, and

Wojciechowska married Richard Larkin, a poet and antique dealer, in 1970. Their marriage ended in 1981.

In 1960 and 1961, while Wojciechowska operated her own literary agency and was publicity manager of Hawthorn Books, she began writing in earnest. *Shadow of a Bull*, the result of this concentration, was a *New York Herald Tribune* Children's Spring Book Festival Awards honor book in 1964 and won both the Newbery Medal in 1965 and the Deutscher Jugenbuchpreis in 1968. This success made it possible for Wojciechowska to devote all her time to writing and traveling. She has published adult fiction and poetry as well as drama for television. In addition to her native Polish, Wojciechowska speaks several other languages—French, Spanish, Italian, Portugese, and English—and

Illustration by Alvin Smith for *Shadow of a Bull* by Maia Wojciechowska. Atheneum: New York (1972).

has translated books from Polish to English. When she is not traveling, she resides in Sante Fe, New Mexico.

Shadow of a Bull traces the story of a young man, Manolo, who defies everyone's expectations that he will become a great bull-fighter in the image of his dead father. Wojciechowska effectively conveys Manolo's dread that the villagers, who expect him to be as brave and heroic as his father, will discover his self-perceived cowardice and low self-es-

teem. Because of his fear, Manolo resists confronting the bull.

Wojciechowska uses her knowledge and love of Spain to write lucid descriptions of its people and culture. Her portrayal of bullfighting is clear and accurate: the mothers resignedly give their sons over to this futile pursuit, the village men revel in the excitement and grandeur of it, and while some young men love it, some, such as Manolo, feel the despair of failing at the sport.

Manolo finds the courage to proclaim that he does not choose to be a bull-fighter, announcing that he wants to be a doctor like the one he saw treat "El Magnifico," a young boy who fought bravely but was gored. In making this choice, Manolo sets himself free. There are all kinds of bravery, the story reveals, but to be true to oneself is the most courageous act of all.

◆ Setting ◆

The story takes place in the province of Andalusia, southern Spain, which is characterized by "majestic mountains, lacey olive groves, the round symmetry of the bullrings, and the pointed church steeples." Arcangel, the village, bordered on three sides by olive groves and on one side by the Guadalquivir River, is isolated and so small that all of the villagers know each other. Although an exact date for the story's action is never given, the activities and attitudes of the people suggest modern times.

◆ Themes and Characters ◆

The main character, Manolo Olivar, is the son of Juan Olivar, a famous bull-fighter whose statue adorns the town square. Because Manolo looks like his father—dark, thin, with a long nose (considered a mark of bravery) and sad, brooding eyes—everyone expects Manolo to behave just like his father. But Manolo refuses to make himself into the bullfighting hero that the townspeople of Arcangel envision.

Manolo struggles to follow his personal ambitions and desires but faces pressure from a community deeply entrenched in the rituals surrounding bullfighting. For example, six men, dedicated bullfighting fans called *aficionados,* share one determination: to prepare Manolo for his destiny as a bullfighter. One of them, the seventy-year-old Count de la Casa, lives in France but comes to Spain once a year to see his olive groves and observe the testing of the young bulls and heifers. Respected by the citizens of Arcangel, the Count sees Manolo each year, and it is he who decides that Manolo will begin his bullfighting career at age eleven, instead of at age twelve as his father did.

Jaime García is Manolo's best friend. Only when he is with Jaime can Manolo forget about bullfighting and enjoy going to movies, fishing, climbing roofs, and setting carrier-pigeons loose. Jaime tells Manolo about his bull-fighter brother, Juan, who goes to the pastures in the dark to cape the bulls because he is too poor to have the bulls readied for him. Manolo and Juan meet, and as the time approaches when Manolo must fight his first bull, Juan coaches him. Juan also takes Manolo to visit "El Magnifico," a boy who has been gored by a bull, and while they are there, a doctor arrives to attend to the wounded boy. Manolo assists the doctor, and while doing so decides, "This is what a man should do with his life: cure the wounded, bring health back to the sick, save the dying."

Manolo's mother, Señora Olivar, a strong, proud, quiet woman, allows her son to make his own decisions. She tells him about the private side of his famous father, confiding that this renowned bull-fighter enjoyed the winters and being sick because these things provided respites from the usual training and fighting. She says he died honorably, in the ring. Through her understanding and support, Manolo's mother helps to free him from his fear of not living up to expectations.

Alfonso Castillo, a famous bull-fighter critic, also educates Manolo about his father. He shows Manolo a portrait of his father, Juan Olivar, the famous matador, and "Patatero," the bull who pierced Juan Olivar's heart when Manolo was only three. Castillo tells Manolo that before a boy becomes a man he has to make some choices: "to do the right thing or the wrong thing, to please himself or to please others; to be true to his own self, or untrue to it." He also helps to free Manolo from fear. Manolo looks at the picture of his father and vows that he, too, will become a daring man.

The theme of a young boy reaching maturity is the thrust of *Shadow of a Bull.* Manolo prepares himself as best he can to fight the bull. His dilemma of choosing between loyalty to his heritage and loyalty to himself, combined with his longing for understanding, creates a powerful conflict in the story. Manolo wrestles with the fear of being labeled a coward, but he manages to conquer this fear when he realizes that honor and nobility can be achieved in many ways.

◆ Literary Qualities ◆

Wojciechowska's descriptive style, which vividly portrays the beauty of the Andalusian country, has been compared to Ernest Hemingway's in its construction and simplicity of language, as well as in its depiction of bullfighting. Wojciechowska, who has resided in both Spain and Mexico and even fought a bull once herself, draws on her experiences to depict Andalusia and the customs of its people. A valuable glossary of bullfighting terminology is included. The author's use of short sentences and of conversation that is direct and to the point moves the story along swiftly. The climax's gripping suspense encourages empathy for the protagonist, helping the reader to experience Manolo's sense of danger and to care about his safety and his future.

A giant head of a black bull looked down at Manolo. Its horns were long and sharp; its eyes, open, stared glassily.

◆ Social Sensitivity ◆

The theme of the book is socially sensitive because adolescents confront fears in many different ways. Manolo tries to hide his fear that he is a coward, but as the plot unfolds, he changes and faces his situation with courage. Manolo's plight of having to conform to others' expectations provides the means by which he matures, and should initiate a good discussion of social conformity. The violence of bullfighting is described but not excessively, although some readers will inevitably raise the issue of cruelty to animals. The killing of

bulls is inherent to the action of the novel and is therefore unavoidable, but it is not too graphic. Even the description of tending the wounded "El Magnifico" is more clinical than gory.

◆ Topics for Discussion ◆

1. If you were expected to follow your father's vocation, would you conform or rebel? What would you do if you were expected to follow your mother's vocation? How would you resolve these situations?

2. What conflicts between traditional and modern ways exist in Andalusia as portrayed in *Shadow of the Bull*?

3. What do you think Manolo would have done if Juan had refused to fight his bull?

4. Do you recognize people who resemble Manolo's mother or the six *aficionados* in your world?

5. What are some of the ways that Manolo tries to conquer his fear? How do you deal with your own fears?

6. What are the various interpretations suggested by the title?

7. Does the book have a satisfying ending? Did you suspect what would happen ahead of time? Would you have ended the book differently if you were the author?

8. Is Manolo too young to decide his vocation? Why?

9. When does Manolo begin to have self-doubts? Is he responding to his own

expectations or to the expectations that others have for him?

10. Manolo and Jaime's friendship is very important to each of them. Why?

11. How will Manolo use his skills as a doctor in Andalusia? Do you think he will remain in Andalusia?

◆ Ideas for Reports and Papers ◆

1. Write a report about the kind of career you want to have and your reasons for this selection.

2. *Shadow of a Bull* was first written as a short story. Do you think it would work as well in a shorter format? Write a paper about which parts of the narrative you think the author lengthened to turn it into a novel.

3. Think of another book you have read in which the hero grows up. Compare the two books, and show how each treats the problems of familial or community expectations.

4. Bullfighting is a violent sport. Do any of the characters in the novel display moral objections to the nature of the sport? Do you have any objections to bullfighting? Why or why not?

5. Write about the importance of expressing feelings of fear. Cite examples from the book.

◆ Related Titles/Adaptations ◆

The theme of ascertaining independence is also examined in Wojciechowska's *Hollywood Kid*, in which Bryan, a troubled, lonely boy, is torn between concern for his mother and a secret need to break free of her and be on his own. Another of Wojciechowska's works that addresses some of the same themes as *Shadow of a Bull* is *A Single Light*. Set in Spain, it is the empathetic story of a hearing impaired Andalusian girl's love for a priceless statue of the Christ child, and of how this leads to violence and tragedy in her village. Another influential work, *Tuned Out*, examines the use of drugs by adolescents. It is Wojciechowska's most controversial book and in 1981 was made into a movie entitled *Stoned: An Anti-Drug Film*, starring Scott Baio.

◆ For Further Reference ◆

Commire, Anne, ed. *Something about the Author*. Vol. 28. Detroit: Gale Research, 1982. Presents five pages of revealing autobiographical statements from Wojciechowska.

Dalgliesh, Alice. "Spring Brings the Winners." *Saturday Review* (March 27, 1965): 32. Review of *Shadow of A Bull*.

De Montreville, Doris, and Donna Hill, eds. *Third Book of Junior Authors*. New York: H. W. Wilson, 1972. Provides an autobiographical sketch of Wojciechowska and a list of her other works. Related articles about the author are also cited.

Gillespie, John, and Diana Lembo. *Juniorplots: A Book Talk for Teachers and Librarians*. New York: R. R. Bowker, 1967. Contains an evaluation of the novel and a list of related readings.

Moritz, Charles, ed. *Current Biography Yearbook*. New York: H. W. Wilson, 1976. Contains a brief but comprehensive discussion of Wojciechowska's life and works.

Norton, Donna E. *Through the Eyes of a Child: An Introduction to Children's Literature.* Columbus: Charles Merrill, 1983. Norton analyzes emotional maturity and the ways it is achieved in *Shadow of a Bull*; she also discusses how self-esteem and stereotypical behaviors are portrayed in realistic fiction.

Catherine Blanton
South Georgia Regional Library

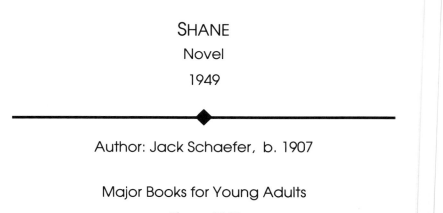

SHANE
Novel
1949

◆

Author: Jack Schaefer, b. 1907

Major Books for Young Adults

Shane, 1949
Old Ramon, 1960

◆ About the Author ◆

Jack Warner Schaefer was born on November 19, 1907, in Cleveland, Ohio, an unlikely birthplace for a writer primarily concerned with the history and characters of the American West. He received a bachelor's degree from Oberlin College in 1929 and attended Columbia University in New York City before beginning a varied career as a United Press reporter, an educator in the Connecticut State Reformatory, an editor for a series of eastern newspapers, and finally an associate in a New Haven, Connecticut, advertising agency. Schaefer did not turn to free-lance writing until he was in his early forties, but he scored an immediate success with his first novel, *Shane*, most of which was written in Norfolk, Virginia.

That novel, perhaps the most famous and most celebrated of all westerns, had a difficult birth. Schaefer submitted an early version of the book to *Argosy* magazine, but he forgot to include return postage with his typescript, an oversight that could have resulted in the rejection of the work. Nonetheless, in 1946 *Argosy* published the tale under the title *Rider from Nowhere* as a three-part serial. Unfortunately, Schaefer's name was misspelled on the cover of the issue containing the first installment of his novel.

Subsequent years have been kinder to *Shane*. The publishing house Houghton Mifflin put out the revised novel in 1949, and it has enjoyed solid sales ever since. By 1951 *Shane* was selling eight thousand hardbound copies a year; moreover, a Bantam paperback edition has averaged yearly sales of twelve thousand copies since 1950. The novel has been published in over seventy editions and has been translated into thirty languages. It was adapted into an excellent movie in 1953. The Western Writers of America honored *Shane* as the best western novel ever written. Schaefer himself was presented with a distinguished achievement award from the

Illustration by John McCormack for *Shane* by Jack Schaefer. Houghton Mifflin: Boston (1949).

an inevitable showdown between good and evil or, more accurately, between a new way of life and the established codes of the Old West.

Young readers easily identify with Bob Starrett, the story's narrator, who is an adolescent at the time of the action. Young Bob is drawn both to Shane and to his own father, Joe, and he grows toward manhood by emulating these two father figures. Although Shane is a self-sufficient loner, while Joe is committed to the valley's community of farmers, both men share common qualities of fortitude, courage, and a determination to stand up for what is right. Early in the novel, for example, these two very different men labor together to wrestle a monstrous tree stump out of the ground. Bob Starrett witnesses this epic struggle and begins to understand and take on the best aspects of both his "fathers." Like Bob, young readers may find admirable role models in these hardy characters of the American West.

Western Literature Association in 1975. He now lives on a ranch outside Santa Fe, New Mexico.

◆ Overview ◆

Shane's enduring and widespread popularity attests to the novel's compelling and exciting plot, which pits a greedy, land-hungry range baron against an embattled but valiant family of homesteaders in a fight for control of a Wyoming valley. When Shane, a mysterious gunfighter struggling to live down his violent past, joins forces with the Starrett family, the stage is set for

◆ Setting ◆

The setting of *Shane* is of central importance to the novel's themes and characters. Like American writer Stephen Crane before him, Schaefer deals with a transitional period in American history, the twilight of the western frontier as it gave way to the more cultivated, domesticated, and settled ways of the industrialized East. The Starretts and the other farming families in the valley represent this new wave of domesticity and civilization that spread across the country in the late 1800s. On the other hand, the gunfighter Shane and the greedy cattleman Luke Fletcher exemplify the frontier way of life that is about to be displaced by the advent of the "New West." Ironically, both Shane, the hero of this novel, and Fletcher, his antagonist, have outlived the historical period in which they grew up and flourished. The West's future, Schaefer makes clear, belongs to people such as the Starretts who can adapt to their new and civilized world.

◆ Themes and Characters ◆

Shane is filled with familiar character types that appear again and again in movies, television shows, and books about the West. Joe Starrett is a typically stalwart farmer, for example, while his wife Marian is a supportive and "house-proud" frontier woman, a type that the reader of western lore has encountered on many occasions. Shane himself, dressed all in black and trailing behind him a mysterious past, is a similarly familiar character, as are Fletcher and the malevolent Wilson, the land baron's hired gun.

Jacket illustration by John McCormack for *Shane* by Jack Schaefer. Houghton Mifflin: Boston (1949).

As he spoke the gun was in his hand and before his father could move he swung it, swift and sharp...

Schaefer sparks new interest in many of these stock characters, however, by evoking their humanity through their capacity for change, growth, and full emotional lives. For example, Shane continually struggles to cast off his violent past and assume the settled life of a farmer. Therefore, Fletcher's threat to the security of the Starretts and the other farming families sparks internal conflict for Shane: should he simply accept the outrages of Fletcher and carry on with his new life, or should he take up his ebony Colt .45 once again and confront the family's enemy? There is no easy answer to this dilemma, and it continues to pull at Shane throughout much of the novel.

Further, Shane's relationship to the Starretts is complex and often subtle. He genuinely admires and even venerates Joe Starrett; indeed, it is Fletcher's threat to Joe's life that finally compels Shane to reassume his old heroic stature as a gunfighter. Shane is similarly drawn to young Bob, to farming itself, and to the sense of belonging that he finds in his new life among the homesteaders. But when Shane agonizingly discovers that he is also falling in love with Marian, he realizes that he may ultimately destroy the very family that has adopted him. By exploring these competing aspects of the human heart, Schaefer elevates his stock characters and rescues them from stale familiarity.

◆ Literary Qualities ◆

The surface plot of *Shane* is rather typical of the western story: the conflict between cattleman and homesteader, leading inevitably to a fiery showdown, has become a kind of permanent American myth. But *Shane* upsets some expectations about this myth by altering its usual outline. In classical mythology, for example, the hero is called out of a static, settled environment at the beginning of the story and embarks on his great adventure. In *Shane*, though, the already heroic gunfighter continually tries to regain a settled existence by identifying with the Starretts; only at the end of the book does he find that he can never fit in with the farming life and that he must reassume his discarded role of gunman and deliverer.

Early reviewers sought to compare Schaefer's novel to the works of such western writers as Owen Wister (especially his *The Virginian* [1902]), Mary Hallock Foote, and Helen Hunt Jackson. More recently, similarities have been seen between Schaefer's themes and those of Stephen Crane. In any event, critics have consistently admired Schaefer's prose style for its directness, conciseness, and clarity—qualities that

probably reflect his years as a journalist. Moreover, Schaefer demonstrates his mastery of many literary techniques—including symbolism, foreshadowing, and characterization—all of which make *Shane* an unusually rewarding reading experience several notches above the "blood and bullets" fare offered by the more typical western novel.

◆ Social Sensitivity ◆

Shane, of course, culminates in an inexorable and violent showdown in which the gunfighter expertly dispatches Fletcher and Wilson; the novel's narrator, Bob Starrett, witnesses these killings. Nevertheless, the violent episodes in *Shane* are brief and never milked for sensationalism. Indeed, there is always a sense in *Shane* that such violence has been "earned" through Schaefer's manipulation of plot and character: the gunfire at the novel's end is far from gratuitous. Shane himself is perhaps the most reluctant gunfighter—and the most reluctantly violent man—to be found in any modern western. The profanity in the 1949 edition of *Shane* has been largely excised in every edition since 1954. Further, a special edition of the novel aimed specifically at juvenile audiences is available.

◆ Topics for Discussion ◆

1. The tree stump, introduced in chapter 2, seems to symbolize many central concerns of the novel: nature's stubbornness, Shane's commitment to farming, even the land itself. What is important about Joe and Shane's struggle with the stump? What do the two

men—and Marian and Bob as well—gain from that struggle?

2. Most readers realize early on that Shane will eventually take up his gun again in defense of the Starretts. How does Schaefer nonetheless maintain an atmosphere of considerable suspense throughout the novel?

3. As the family returns from town in chapter 6, Bob Starrett observes that "the closer we came [to the farm], the more cheerful [Shane] was." What accounts for this feeling in Shane?

4. In chapter 8, Shane seems to lose his serenity in the face of the looming conflict with Fletcher. By chapter 14, however, Shane is again reconciled to "the simple solitude of his own invincible completeness." Trace Shane's movement toward this acceptance of who and what he is.

5. The events of chapter 15 take place after Shane has left the Starretts. What is the purpose of this short chapter? What is the nature of Shane's enduring gift or legacy to the Starretts?

◆ Ideas for Reports and Papers ◆

1. Read Stephen Crane's short story "The Bride Comes to Yellow Sky." Compare Crane's theme or central idea in that story to the theme of the declining West in Schaefer's Shane. Although on the surface they are very different, what similarities are shared by Shane and Crane's Scratchy Wilson? How are Joe Starrett and Marshal Potter alike? Marian and the marshal's wife?

2. When Shane struggles with the tree stump or fights with Morgan, Fletcher, and Wilson, it is clear who his antagonist is. But what, precisely, are the terms of his inner conflict? That is, what competing needs and desires make their various claims on the gunfighter? How are Marian and Joe involved in some of these conflicts?

3. Western novels, mystery stories, Gothic romances, and much of science fiction are often dismissed by critics as examples of "escapist" literature, unconcerned with the realities of everyday life. In this sense, is Shane "escapist," or do you find that the book does say things that are universally and permanently true about the human condition?

4. The enigmatic Shane is described at various times in the novel as "a man apart," "just different," and "fiddle-footed." What other heroes in American fiction are similarly alone, anxious to "move on," and cut off from a meaningful sense of community with more settled, domesticated folk? What do these heroes have to tell us about the ways Americans typically view their world?

5. In myth, the quest of the hero commonly results in benefits for the community that he serves. Discuss, in specific terms, the ways in which Shane's struggles assist both the Starretts and, more generally, the community of homesteaders in the valley.

6. In one sense, Shane is the story of Bob Starrett's initiation into adult values and insights. How do both Shane and Joe Starrett contribute to this initiation? What positive values does Bob learn from the gunslinger?

7. Shane is told from the point of view of a grown man, Bob Starrett, looking

back on the events of one pivotal summer of his youth. How would the novel be different if narrated by Bob when he was still a child?

8. Given your reading of *Shane*, how does Schaefer feel about the decline and eventual fall of the Old West and its people? Does he view this fall as historically inevitable? Does he seem to regret the loss of the wide-open prairie and of men like Shane?

◆ Related Titles/Adaptations ◆

Schaefer has been a prolific writer of novels and stories, but his themes and characters remain fairly consistent throughout his works. In his short novel for young people, *Old Ramon*, the title character, an aging shepherd, shares Shane's Old West skills and his spirit of rugged individualism. In *Monte Walsh* (1963), Schaefer's most ambitious novel, the predominant theme once again is the gradual capitulation of the western wilderness to the forces of eastern civilization. In that novel, Monte is an expert cowboy, "a good man with a horse," who cannot adapt to the brave new world of the "autymobile" and the evolution of the cattle business into a corporate enterprise. Like Shane, Monte belongs to the "wild" West of his childhood; unlike Joe Starrett and his own friend Chet Rollins, Monte cannot find a meaningful place for himself within the confines of his new environment.

In 1953 *Shane* was made into an excellent and well-received film, starring Alan Ladd in the title role, Van Heflin as Joe, Jean Arthur as Marian, Brandon De Wilde as Bob (renamed "Joey" in the movie), and perhaps most memorably, Jack Palance as the evil Wilson. Lloyd Griggs's cinematography won an Academy Award. Released by Paramount Pictures and directed by George Stevens, with a screenplay by A. B. Guthrie, Jr., the film remains generally true to the plot of Schaefer's novel, and it does a good job of portraying Shane's futile quest to become part of the Starrett family. Inevitably, some of the complexity of the characters is lost in the screen adaptation, but the movie has become one of the most familiar and highly regarded of the countless westerns turned out over the years by Hollywood studios.

◆ For Further Reference ◆

Albright, Charles, Jr. "*Shane.*" In *Magill's Survey of Cinema*, English Language Films, First Series, edited by Frank N. Magill. Englewood Cliffs, NJ: Salem Press, 1980. A sound, intelligent review of the film version of *Shane*.

Beacham, Walton, and Suzanne Niemeyer, eds. *Beacham's Popular Fiction in America*. Washington, DC: Beacham Publishing, 1986. Entry on Schaefer examines his chief works, especially *Shane*, *Monte Walsh*, and *Old Ramon*.

Haslam, Gerald. *Jack Schaefer*. Western Writers Series, no. 20. Boise, ID: Boise State University, 1975. A brief, sympathetic discussion of Schaefer's works and themes.

Scott, Winfield Townley. Introduction to *Collected Stories of Jack Schaefer*. New York: Arbor House, 1966. A concise look at Schaefer, his debts to earlier writers, and his place in the literature of the American West.

William Ryland Drennan
University of Wisconsin Center—
Baraboo/Sauk County

SHELLEY'S MARY: A LIFE OF MARY GODWIN SHELLEY

Biography

1973

◆

Author: Margaret Carver Leighton, 1896-1987

Major Books for Young Adults

Judith of France, 1948
The Story of Florence Nightingale,
   1952
Comanche of the Seventh, 1957
Journey for a Princess, 1960

Bride of Glory, 1962
Cleopatra: Sister of the Moon, 1969
*Shelley's Mary: A Life of Mary God-
   win Shelley*, 1973

◆ About the Author ◆

Like the real-life heroine of *Shelley's Mary*, Margaret Carver Leighton grew up in a learned family where history-making ideas were frequently discussed by important scholars. Leighton was born on December 20, 1896, in Oberlin, Ohio, to Dr. Nixon Carver, a college professor, and his wife, Flora Kirkendall Carver. Early in Leighton's life, her father obtained a position at Harvard University, and Leighton's earliest memories are of the tree-lined streets of Cambridge, Massachusetts. Like Mary Shelley, Leighton took great pleasure as a young girl in reading, writing, drawing, and attending the theater.

During her father's sabbaticals, Leighton attended schools in France and Switzerland, countries she would revisit when writing *Shelley's Mary*. Leighton graduated from Radcliffe College in 1918 and served as an army nurse just before World War I ended. While living

in Westfield, New Jersey, in the 1930s, she served on the local board of education and later was a trustee of the Santa Monica, California, public library.

When Leighton met her future husband, Herbert Leighton, she was working in the advertising department of a publishing company. During their happy, fourteen-year marriage, the Leightons had four children, James, Mary, Thomas, and Sylvia. After her husband's death in 1935, Leighton moved with her four children to a rambling, seaside house in Santa Monica. Her love of beautiful, natural environments is reflected in her fiction, where she devotes much attention to environmental influences on character. In Santa Monica, Leighton began to write books for young people and occasionally modeled characters after her own children. In 1958, Leighton's *Comanche of the Seventh* won the Dorothy Canfield Fisher Memorial Children's Book Award. She eventually wrote more than twenty books for children and young adults. Leighton died on June 19, 1987, in Santa Monica.

◆ Overview ◆

Mature readers should read *Shelley's Mary* because it brings to life the sensitive young woman who wrote *Frankenstein*. The biography exposes readers to the exhaustive allusiveness of *Frankenstein* and familiarizes them with the relationships and tragedies that touched Mary Shelley's life. This knowledge awakens readers to serious cultural and ethical problems still unsolved.

By titling this biography *Shelley's Mary*, the author calls attention to one of the most important relationships of Mary Shelley's life: her love affair and marriage with Percy Bysshe Shelley, the celebrated free-thinking romantic poet. Implicitly the title signifies both the depth of Mary's devotion to the poet and the subordinate literary position her work has traditionally held when compared with her husband's. Through the details that Leighton provides, the reader is able to grasp the cost of that devotion and subordination to Mary's emotional and professional life. The complex ethical problems caused by Mary's relationship with Shelley suggest that in writing about Frankenstein's monster, she may have been writing—in a symbolic way—about the monsters of guilt and frustration that haunted her own life.

Mary Shelley was born to brilliant, famous, unstable parents. Her mother died when Mary was born, and her father's remarriage imposed on Mary a stepmother and a demanding, parasitic stepsister. When Mary eloped with Percy Shelley, he was married to another woman who was pregnant at the time and whose eventual suicide may have been triggered by Shelley's rejection. Mary herself soon became an unwed mother; she experienced five pregnancies during her eight-year relationship with Shelley, but only one of her children lived to adulthood. Her novel *Frankenstein*, like her life, is filled with sorrows and premonitions of tragedy. Only four years after its publication, Percy Shelley drowned in a sailing accident.

When read in association with the deeply moving *Frankenstein*, this account of Mary Shelley's tragic early life alerts the reader to the risks involved in pursuing romantic dreams at the expense of practical values. Leighton's biography also instills a sense of respect for the sensitivity and perceptiveness of *Frankenstein*, qualities that have made it one of the most influential novels of the past two centuries.

◆ Setting ◆

Leighton's biography reflects the significance of setting to Mary Shelley's life. Like most writers of the romantic era, Mary assigned almost a mystical power to the forces of nature. During the eight years Mary spent with poet Percy Bysshe Shelley, she and their entourage moved frequently from one scene of natural, awe-inspiring beauty to another. The biography begins at her birth in London on August 30, 1797. The account moves back and forth from England to the Continent—primarily Switzerland and Italy—from 1814, when the sixteen-year-old Mary elopes with the eccentric young Shelley, until 1823, when, soon after Shelley's death, Mary and her only surviving child return to London.

One of the most significant settings in *Shelley's Mary* is the Villa Diodati on Lac Leman in Switzerland. Here Mary and Percy Shelley, along with Mary's stepsister, Claire Clairmont, are guests of the poet Lord Byron, who is attended by his physician, Dr. Polidori. During the summer of 1816 the party of young romantics entertain themselves during rainy evenings by reading and composing ghost stories. Both the villa and the mountain lake scenery contribute to the mysterious atmosphere that inspires their stories. After one ghost-tale evening, Mary has a nightmare that she eventually reworks into *Frankenstein.*

Leighton also describes other settings that hold important memories for Mary, such as a villa on Lake Como in Italy, and the field and flower-starred meadows near Leghorn, Italy, where she and Shelley walk happily together. The Lake Como setting appears in Mary's novel *The Last Man*, and the Leghorn Meadows bloom eternally in Shelley's "Ode to a Skylark." After Shelley's death in a sea storm on the lake between Leghorn and Pisa in 1822, Mary returns to London. Except for a tour abroad from 1840 to 1843, which she chronicles in *Rambles in Germany and Italy*, she remains there until her death in 1851.

◆ Themes and Characters ◆

The themes of Mary Shelley's novels often parallel the path of her personal experience. She probes issues in her work that she explores in her life, asking whether total devotion to individual liberty and the unrelenting pursuit of knowledge through experimentation benefit either individuals or societies. That she spends her life asking and acting out these questions is not surprising, for she is surrounded by radical free-thinking romantics all her life.

Her mother, Mary Wollstonecraft, is a pioneer feminist writer who dies shortly after Mary's birth. Mary reveres her mother's memory and frequently visits her mother's gravesite. But her father, William Godwin, makes an even deeper impression on Mary. Godwin, a tremendously influential political philosopher, an artist, and an anarchist, claims to have unshakable faith in the powers of reason to bring about ethical behavior. As depicted in Leighton's book, Mary remains devoted to her father despite his remarriage to a cold, domineering woman and despite his opposition to Mary's elopement with Shelley. Although Godwin's attitude toward the elopement is understandable, his frequent insistence that Shelley provide him with financial aid is less easy to accept. Overall, Godwin appears to be a petulant, egocentric man who lacks the strength of his own convictions.

Next to her father, the most influential character in Mary's life is Percy Bysshe Shelley. An ardent disciple of Godwin's, Shelley falls in love with Mary while visiting the Godwin household. Mary's devotion to him seems complete, although her frequent bouts of depression may be caused by the insecurity of their life together. Extravagant, politically radical, volatile, and somewhat fragile, Shelley is financially irresponsible and subject to irrational outbursts. He often chooses to soothe his fears by moving the family to new lodgings. His great generosity usually pleases Mary, but at times—such as when he invites Claire Clairmont along on their elopement—upsets her greatly. Impetuous, moody, and demanding, Claire always manages

Shelley and Mary in St. Pancras Churchyard by W. P. Frith reprinted in *Mary Shelley* by Emily W. Sunstein. Little, Brown: Boston (1989).

to be around when she is least welcome. Claire's liaison with Lord Byron causes great hardships and heartbreak both for herself and for the Shelleys.

Mary soothes her husband's spirit and is able to serve, for her father, as a living reminder of her determined, feminist mother. But underlying these admirable strengths, always tapped by others, are her own fears, insecurities, and frustrations. Bookish and bright, tender and kind, Mary consistently subordinates her own nature in order to gratify those around her. She views her own writing as less important than Shelley's; always subdues her misgivings about the irresponsible lifestyle they lead; and retreats within herself to deal with the deaths of three of her four babies.

◆ Literary Qualities ◆

Like most of Leighton's biographies of famous women, *Shelley's Mary* is marked by strong characterizations and accurately detailed historical background. Leighton has managed to convey the spirit of Mary Shelley without compromising objective detail. She manages to include enough dialogue and description to give this biography the feel of a novel, although the reader has the sense of always being anchored in reality. If anything, Leighton's sympathetic attitude causes her to overpraise Mary.

Leighton offers insightful suggestions for interpretations of Mary Shelley's works, drawing parallels between Mary's life and her literature, especially *Frankenstein*. For example, Leighton suggests that although Mary outwardly declares her loyalty to her father and even dedicates *Frankenstein* to him, the disastrous effects of Victor Frankenstein's radical experiments in the novel reproach Godwin's impersonal, rational attitude to human relationships. In Leighton's biography, Mary expresses her personal feelings through her fiction, and only in her fictional creations—beginning with *Frankenstein*—is she able to express her misgivings about the direction her own life and the intellectual life of Western culture have taken.

◆ Social Sensitivity ◆

For the astute young reader, this biography provides a commentary on almost every so-called "modern" young adult problem. Drugs, teen-age pregnancy, parental rejection, suicide, peer influence, and jealousies all enter Mary Shelley's life. Her handling of these problems may not always coincide with the choices of a conscientious parent, but Mary seems to have accepted responsibility for her choices. Indeed, Mary is represented as the most conscientious and loyal member of her circle. Mary's life, like her novel *Frankenstein*, may be read as a cautionary tale, warning readers against rash and selfish actions, even when those actions are apparently meant to lead to idealistic ends.

◆ Topics for Discussion ◆

1. Mary's education is unconventional by our standards. Is it adequate for her day?

2. Is Mary in any way responsible for the death of Harriet Shelley?

3. How does William Godwin's attitude toward his daughter affect her?

4. Is the relationship between Claire Clairmont and Mary a beneficial one for Mary?

5. Should the quality of a poet's writing—like Lord Byron's, for example—be judged in any way by the quality of his life?

6. How would you describe the character of Percy Shelley?

7. What can you infer about the quality of medical services in the early nineteenth century from this book?

8. How do you think most modern versions of the *Frankenstein* story differ from the original?

9. What part of Mary's life would you describe as the happiest? Why?

◆ Ideas for Reports and Papers ◆

1. Make a map showing the various places the Shelleys lived or visited during their eight-year relationship. Make a list of those places, including a brief description of the events of Mary's life that occurred there.

2. List all of the works written by members of Mary Shelley's family that are mentioned in the novel. Briefly describe the subject matter of each work.

3. Write a report on the artistic and intellectual movement known as romanticism that includes an explanation of Mary Shelley's and Percy Shelley's contributions to that movement.

4. Read *Frankenstein* and write a plot summary of it. What parallels can you find between its lessons and those of Mary Shelley's life?

5. Read a biography of Percy Shelley and report on the contradictions between *Shelley's Mary* and the biography you have chosen.

◆ Related Titles ◆

Margaret Leighton wrote several other biographies of women aimed at mature young readers. These books demonstrate Leighton's exceptional ability to integrate historical background with personal detail, and in each Leighton confronts controversial issues—such as violence or drug use—with honesty and decorum. Among these titles are *Judith of France*, the story of Charlemagne's granddaughter, who makes two royal marriages before she finds true love; *Journey for a Princess,* the story of Estrid, daughter of King Alfred of England; *The Story of Florence Nightingale,* a sympathetic portrayal of Florence's early years; and *Cleopatra: Sister of the Moon,* one of Leighton's most celebrated works.

♦ For Further Reference ♦

Fuller, Muriel, ed. *More Junior Authors.* New York: Wilson, 1963. Includes a biographical sketch of Leighton.

Spark, Muriel. *Child of Light: A Reassessment of Mary Wollstonecraft Shelley.* Essex: Tower Bridge, 1951. An insightful interpretation of Mary Shelley's life and works.

Levine, George, and U. C. Knoepflmacher, eds. *The Endurance of "Frankenstein": Essays on Mary Shelley's Novel.* Berkeley: University of California Press, 1979. Offers a variety of compelling analyses of Shelley's most famous novel.

Mary Lowe-Evans
University of West Florida

THE SIGN OF THE BEAVER
Novel
1983

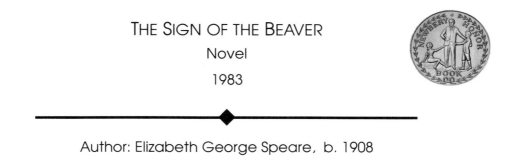

Author: Elizabeth George Speare, b. 1908

Major Books for Young Adults

Calico Captive, 1957
The Witch of Blackbird Pond, 1958
Bronze Bow, 1961
Life in Colonial America, 1963
The Sign of the Beaver, 1983

◆ About the Author ◆

Elizabeth George Speare was born on November 21, 1908, in Melrose, Massachusetts. She began composing stories as a child during lonely summers in the countryside. After completing her undergraduate work at Smith College, she earned her master's degree in English from Boston University and then taught English in Massachusetts high schools.

In 1936 she married Alden Speare. The couple had one daughter and one son. In order to care for her children, Speare retired from teaching, but when her son and daughter entered high school, she began writing seriously.

Her first novel, *Calico Captive*, was based on the memoirs of a settler who was captured by Native Americans in colonial times. Her second novel, *The Witch of Blackbird Pond*, also set in colonial America, won the Newbery Medal in 1960. Two years later Speare won that prestigious prize a second time for *The Bronze Bow*, a story of ancient Jerusalem. *The Sign of the Beaver* was a 1984 Newbery Honor Book and in 1984 won the first Scott O'Dell Award for historical fiction.

◆ Overview ◆

The Sign of the Beaver is an excellent introduction to life among pioneers and Native Americans in the eighteenth-century American colonies. Full of precise detail concerning the tasks and objects that filled everyday life, the novel also contains a good deal of adventure and suspense. Most notable is Speare's insightful and sensitive portrayal of the relations among white settlers and Native Americans. Intertwined with the exciting plot is a strong but not didactic commentary on the tragedy that ensued when settlers forced the Native Americans from their lands.

The story takes place in the late 1760s. The northeast coast of America has already been settled by Europeans, and the colonists are gradually cutting down forests, establishing farms, and pushing the Native Americans into Canada.

Twelve-year-old Matt Hallowell is alone in the woods of Maine. He and his father have cleared some land and built a log cabin, while his mother and sister have remained in Quincy, Massachusetts. As the novel opens, it is summer and Matt's father has gone to fetch the rest of the family, leaving Matt to look after their new home for several weeks.

• Themes and Characters •

The Sign of the Beaver relates how Matt Hallowell matures from a child to an adult in the course of several weeks that he lives alone in the wilderness of Maine. Early in the novel, Matt supplies a vagrant trapper named Ben with food and lodgings only to have his gun stolen by the blustery old trapper. Soon after, a bear raids the Hallowell cabin, leaving Matt with almost no food to sustain him while he waits for his family to return. Deprived of his provisions, Matt must rely on his own resources to survive. An early attempt to fend for himself fails miserably when he tries to retrieve honey from a beehive and ends up with multiple bee stings and a sprained ankle. Two Native Americans—Saknis and his thirteen-year-old grandson Attean—rescue the injured Matt, and Matt agrees to teach Attean to read English in exchange for their help.

Attean plays a vital role not only in Matt's survival but also in his maturation, though the reading lessons that

Matt devises, first using a copy of Daniel Defoe's *Robinson Crusoe* and then the Bible, fail. *Robinson Crusoe* proves to be a particularly disastrous choice when Attean becomes offended by the assumptions of white supremacy that underlie the portrayal of Crusoe's relationship with Friday, a Native American from South America who becomes Crusoe's faithful servant. Matt is shocked to realize that a novel that he has always regarded as a harmless adventure story contains such assumptions. The failure of the reading lessons—which Saknis hopes will enable Attean to understand treaties drawn up by settlers and thus check the white encroachment on his people's hunting grounds—reflects the historical reality that most attempts at fair negotiations between the whites and the Native Americans eventually failed.

The friendship between Attean and Matt develops slowly and is an idealized version of relationships between Native Americans and settlers. Neither of the boys understands the culture of the other whatsoever when they first meet. Attean is generally aloof and mistrustful, an attitude that Matt understands when Attean tells him that white men killed his mother in order to make money from selling her scalp. Attean's father has never returned from his mission to avenge her death. When Attean tells Matt about his mother's scalping, Matt argues that the Native Americans treat the settlers similarly, but is at a loss when Attean points out that the whites are destroying Native American hunting grounds.

Matt makes a tremendous effort to impress Attean, who scorns the white boy's ineptitude in the wilderness. But Matt gradually learns much more about the wilderness from Attean than Attean learns from Matt about reading. Matt

Jacket illustration by Robert Andrew Parker for *The Sign of the Beaver* by Elizabeth George Speare. Houghton Mifflin: Boston (1983).

if that difficulty is not overcome. Matt's mistaken assumption that the paint Attean dons for the bear feast is war paint points out how easy it is to misinterpret the intentions of a culture that one is not familiar with. The murder of Attean's mother and the fate of his fellow villagers—who are all eventually forced to move further west because of white encroachment on their hunting grounds—suggests the tragedy that can result from ignorance about other cultures.

◆ Literary Qualities ◆

The Sign of the Beaver is in many ways a retelling of Daniel Defoe's early eighteenth-century novel *Robinson Crusoe*, the novel Matt chooses for Attean's ill-fated reading lessons. Like Crusoe, Matt is stranded in a wilderness. But for the most part, Speare switches the roles of the white man and his Native American companion: "[Matt] remembered Robinson Crusoe and his man Friday. He and Attean had sure enough turned that story right round about." In Defoe's novel, Crusoe rescues Friday, and Friday becomes the white man's faithful servant; in Speare's novel, Matt realizes that it is always Attean who is "leading the way, knowing just what to do and doing it quickly and skillfully," while Matt, "a puny sort of Robinson Crusoe, tagged along behind, grateful for the smallest sign that he could do anything right." Defoe depicts most of the Native Americans that Crusoe encounters as ruthless cannibalistic savages. Speare, on the other hand, depicts the Native Americans as having great regard for the sanctity of life. Attean's people take only what they need from nature, find a use for every part of

begins to earn Attean's respect when Matt helps to kill a bear that attacks the boys. Attean acknowledges Matt's progress when he leaves Matt to find his way back to the Hallowell cabin from the Native American village on his own, a compliment that is not lost on Matt. Attean pays Matt an even greater compliment later by inviting him to accompany the men of his village on a hunt and calling him his "white brother," but it is at this point that Matt decides that he must remain loyal to his own heritage. Matt declines the invitation, choosing to stay at his cabin in case his family, several weeks late already, arrives.

The novel shows that it can be very difficult to understand another culture and that tragic consequences can ensue the animals they hunt, and solemnly apologize to the animals' spirits.

The Sign of the Beaver is told by a third-person limited omniscient narrator who relates Matt's thoughts and feelings. Nothing is wasted in the carefully crafted narrative. Speare unobtrusively weaves details about life in eighteenth-century America into the plot, selecting those details that provide insight into either Native American or white culture. For example, the settlers make conspicuous blazes on trees with knives, while the Native Americans create subtle signs by perhaps pushing two stones together or breaking a twig.

◆ Social Sensitivity ◆

Speare handles difficult cultural conflicts with sensitivity and tact. The story is told primarily from the perspective of Matt, a young white settler and a sympathetic character. As Matt begins to understand and appreciate Attean's culture, he realizes the enormity of the problems that the settlers are causing for Native Americans. The Native Americans do not have concepts of land ownership as the settlers do, but they have definitely marked hunting territories. Because the Native American ways of staking out territory differ from the settlers' ways, the settlers simply ignore them. As the settlers take over their hunting grounds, the Native Americans must move further west, as Attean's people do at the end of the novel. Matt knows that he and his family are part of the influx of settlers responsible for driving away the Native Americans, but he does not know what to do about it other than try to explain his friendship with Attean to his family, who are startled that he has befriended a Native American. Speare offers no easy solutions for the complex problems she presents in *The Sign of the Beaver*, but she does suggest that solutions are possible only if people of different cultures or backgrounds first make an effort to understand one another.

◆ Topics for Discussion ◆

1. Children in colonial America had to grow up much more quickly than children do today. Matt and Attean become adults by the age of thirteen. Why was this possible?

2. How would you like to have lived in colonial America instead of the present time? What would you have missed or enjoyed?

3. Why is Matt so concerned about earning Attean's respect? How does he finally succeed in doing so?

4. Attean goes off by himself to find his *manitou* or guardian spirit, so he can become a man. Does anything similar happen to Matt?

5. After Matt offers Ben hospitality, Ben steals his gun. Should Matt have refused to let Ben in? What might have happened then? What could Matt have said or done to ease the situation?

6. What do you think will happen to Attean and his people after they move further west? What do you think life will be like for Matt and his family after Maine becomes more populated?

7. Why does Matt have to skip parts of *Robinson Crusoe* when he tries to teach Attean to read? Would the lessons have gone better if he had started with the Bible instead of *Robinson Crusoe*?

8. Throughout the story Attean is seen from Matt's point of view. How do you think Matt appears to Attean?

9. Much of Native American culture was eventually destroyed by the development of white settlers. How much blame should be placed on settlers such as Matt and his family for this tragedy?

◆ Ideas for Reports and Papers ◆

1. Many Native American communities identified themselves with totem animals such as the beaver or the turtle. What was the significance of these animals?

2. Research and report on the initiation ceremonies of Native Americans, in which a child passed to adulthood.

3. How were log cabins like that of Matt's family built? What tools were used?

4. What chores were young people in colonial America expected to perform? How might they spend a normal day?

5. How were holidays celebrated in the families of pioneers?

6. How was work divided between men and women among the pioneers? Among the Native Americans?

7. What impressions did the colonists have of the Native Americans? How did Native Americans regard the white men?

8. Write a sequel to the story in which Matt and Attean meet again many years later. How have they changed? Can they still be friends?

◆ For Further Reference ◆

Fuller, Muriel, ed. *More Junior Authors.* New York: H. W. Wilson, 1983. Contains a brief autobiographical sketch by Speare.

Kirkpatrick, D. L., ed. *Twentieth Century Children's Writers.* 2d ed. New York: St. Martin's Press, 1983. The entry on Speare summarizes her career, lists her publications, and gives brief critical comments on her major works.

Sloan, Eric. *Diary of an Early American Boy.* New York: Ballantine, 1984. A historical reconstruction of the daily life of a young man who lived in the same era as Matt Hallowell.

Boria Sax
Pace University

THE SILVER SWORD

Novel

1956

Author: Ian Serraillier, b. 1912

Major Books for Young Adults

They Raced for Treasure, 1946
Flight to Adventure, 1947
*Captain Bounsaboard and the
    Pirates*, 1949
There's No Escape, 1950
The Ballad of Kon-Tiki, 1952
Belinda and the Swans, 1952
Jungle Adventure, 1953
The Adventure of Dick Varley, 1954
Beowulf the Warrior, 1954
Making Good, 1955
Guns in the Wild, 1956
The Silver Sword, 1956 (also pub-
    lished as *Escape from Warsaw*)
Poems and Pictures, 1958
The Ivory Horn, 1960
*The Gorgon's Head: The Story of Per-
    seus*, 1961
*The Way of Danger: The Story of
    Theseus*, 1962
The Windmill Book of Ballads, 1962

*The Clashing Rocks: The Story of
    Jason*, 1963
*The Enchanted Island: Stories from
    Shakespeare*, 1964
The Cave of Death, 1965
Fight for Freedom, 1965
*A Fall From the Sky: The Story of
    Daedalus*, 1966
The Challenge of the Green Knight,
    1966
Robin in the Greenwood, 1967
Chaucer and His World, 1967
Havelock the Dane, 1968
Robin and His Merry Men, 1969
The Ballad of St. Simeon, 1970
The Tale of Three Landlubbers, 1970
The Bishop and the Devil, 1971
Suppose You Met a Witch, 1973
I'll Tell You a Tale, 1973
The Robin and the Wren, 1974

◆ About the Author ◆

Ian Serraillier was born on September 24, 1912, in London, England. He received his master's degree from St. Edmund Hall, Oxford, in 1935, and then taught at Wycliffe College in Stonehouse, Gloucestershire from 1936 to 1939. He continued his teaching career at Dudley Grammar School in Dudley, Worcestershire, from 1939 to 1946, and at Midhurst Grammar School in Midhurst, Sussex, from 1946 to 1961.

Serraillier has published many books for young adults and children, including numerous works of poetry. He has retold the myths and legends of classical and medieval times, often in the

Illustration by C. Walter Hodges for *The Silver Sword* by Ian Serraillier. Criterion Books: New York (1959).

form of narrative verse, and most of his stories demonstrate his taste for tales of high adventure. He received the Boys' Clubs of America Junior Book Award for *The Silver Sword* in 1960.

◆ Overview ◆

The Silver Sword realistically presents the problems of war as seen through the eyes of a Polish family torn apart by World War II. The novel's main characters include three children—Ruth, Edek, and Bronia Balicki—who are left to live as best they can in the streets of Warsaw when their father is sent to a prison camp and their mother is taken away to do forced labor in Germany. Serraillier explores the meaning of courage, unselfishness, loyalty, and honesty as the children try to survive in a world made brutal by war. Violence is never depicted graphically, however, and more than half the novel takes place immediately after the war. The hardships the children endure arise from the deprivations war imposes on all members of their society. The feelings of hatred that result from the war must be overcome in order to produce a society in which people from once-hostile countries can live together in peace.

Serraillier stresses that peaceful societies must be founded upon love and trust and demonstrates this theme most concretely in the relationship between Ruth, the model of "courage, self-sacrifice, and greatness of heart," and Jan, an orphan who has learned that he can survive and remain self-sufficient only by stealing. Ruth's love gradually brings Jan from a state of selfishness to one of loyalty and self-sacrifice. *The Silver Sword* is a story of hope and love in which the children undertake a journey of discovery in search of their parents that brings out the essential qualities in each of them.

◆ Setting ◆

The story is set against a backdrop of destruction in Europe during and after World War II. Much of the early action takes place in Warsaw and other areas of Poland. The opening chapters describe the South Polish prison camp where the children's father, Joseph Balicki, has been sent. The novel then switches to Warsaw under the Nazi occupation, where Joseph has returned to hunt in vain for his splintered family. The children's experiences living on their own in Warsaw provide further glimpses of the war-torn city. The Warsaw uprising of 1944 and the virtual destruction of the old city are vividly described. The locale shifts during the last two thirds of the book as the children journey to Switzerland to find their parents. As the book progresses, Serraillier paints a vivid portrait of western Poland, Berlin, and rural Germany in the aftermath of the war, depicting the long lines of migrating refugees, refugee camps, soup kitchens, cities devastated by bombing, and finally the beauty of Switzerland unscarred by the war, where the family's reunion finally occurs.

• Themes and Characters •

The experiences of the Balicki family reflect those of many others caught up in the war, although their story admittedly ends unusually happily. The novel focuses briefly on Joseph Balicki, the father, but for the most part concentrates on the children and Jan, an orphan whom they make part of their family. Joseph Balicki is an idealistic, courageous, and resourceful man. The headmaster of a school, he is sent to prison for defying Nazi rule soon after the Germans take over Poland. His ingenuity helps him escape from the prison camp where he has been held for two years, and after making his way back to Warsaw, he hunts for his missing wife and children. During his search he encounters Jan, a ragged orphan boy. Joseph gives Jan the only trace of his home he has found, a silver paperknife shaped like a sword, on the

condition that if Jan ever meets Joseph's missing wife and children he will tell them that Joseph has gone to Switzerland. Joseph's sympathy and willingness to trust Jan win over the usually reclusive boy. This meeting between Joseph and Jan sets up not only the plot line but also one of the novel's major themes: the need for mutual trust and its ability to heal the emotional ravages of war.

Ruth, Joseph's oldest daughter and the novel's main character, embodies the virtues necessary to survive the war with hope and dignity. At first bewildered by the difficulties of survival in Warsaw without her parents, she matures as she takes on the role of substitute mother—first to her siblings, and eventually to a larger group of children who come to a school she starts. When her students find Jan lying sick out in the street, Ruth takes him under her care, and love and discipline slowly begin to heal Jan's psychological wounds. Emotionally and morally strong, she inspires Jan's love and trust.

The war has twisted Jan's perceptions of human relationships, making him distrustful, hateful, and angry. Soldiers particularly symbolize the suffering he has undergone, and he fears and hates them all so much that he can make no distinction between soldiers of different armies. Because animals cannot betray trust the way humans do, they are the only creatures Jan can find any affection for until Joseph, and then Ruth, break through the barriers he has set up. Jan becomes fiercely loyal to Ruth, who tries to instill in him some of the moral values the war has extinguished. As Jan becomes more attached to Ruth and Bronia, he becomes less self-centered. He continues to behave dishonestly toward other people, but his intentions improve. At the climax of the novel Jan finally puts the needs of others before his own. In the midst of a storm, he must choose between going after the dog he has adopted and helping Ruth save Edek from drowning. By deciding to help Ruth and Edek, Jan breaks free of his self-imposed isolation and puts his trust in human ties and responsibilities. Like Ruth, he too begins to mature when he accepts responsibility for others. As love and trust take root, Jan abandons his habits of stealing and violence.

The children receive help during their trip from people of many nationalities, illustrating the book's themes of reconciliation and the deeply rooted bonds among civilized peoples. Serraillier demonstrates the willingness of the victorious Allies to work toward the restoration of Europe in his portraits of the Russian soldier, Ivan, who helps the children get started; the British officer who nearly runs over Jan but later saves the silver sword; the American Captain Greenwood, who is lenient with Jan after the boy has broken the law; and the Polish-American G.I. Joe, who gives the children a lift to the border of Switzerland at the end of their journey. A less conventional and more touching episode is the children's experience with Herr and Frau Wolff, a German farmer and his wife whose son was killed in Warsaw fighting against the liberating Russian army. Jan has trouble connecting the couple that shows him so much kindness with the soldiers he has hated so much. This sympathetic portrait of the Germans is unusual for a World War II novel. It reflects Serraillier's commitment to showing that civilians on all sides of the conflict suffered, and that all people ought to work together in peace to repair the damage done by the war. This belief is illustrated by the building of the international children's village at the end of the novel.

◆ Literary Qualities ◆

The Silver Sword is a realistic novel about war that depends heavily on description for its literary effect. Because the setting of war-torn Europe shapes the children's experiences, Serraillier gives detailed and vivid descriptions of the ravaged countries and of the hardships the children endure. The role these problems play in building the children's characters is revealed several times by biblical parallels. Ruth tells Bible stories to the children in her school, and their favorite is the one which most inspires her as well: Daniel in the lions' den. She sees the hardships she faces every day as the lions, and she believes that if she is patient and trusting like Daniel, she too will be delivered. Switzerland, as the children's destination, becomes the promised land that they reach after long wandering in the desert of the war.

The silver sword itself provides a recurring symbol of hope. The only vestige of the Balickis' home, the sword symbolizes the family's unity before the war. Joseph offers the sword to Jan as a pledge, and through Jan the sword serves as the crucial connection between Joseph and his children. It inspires Ruth to undertake the journey to look for her parents, and it spurs the children on as they travel. When the sword gets left behind at the Wolffs' farm, the children's luck changes for the worse; when the sword is returned, it cuts through the red tape of Swiss immigration and leads to the children's reunion with their parents. Jan firmly believes that the sword is responsible for the group's survival in the storm on the lake at the climax of the book. When his treasure box, symbolizing all the secrets of his past, finally sinks to the bottom of the lake, the sword alone remains, hanging from a string around his neck. He offers it, the most precious of his treasures, to Joseph's wife, Margrit, if she will be his mother. And so the pledge between Joseph and Jan is redeemed, and the sword brings the family back together.

◆ Social Sensitivity ◆

As a novel about the effects of war, *The Silver Sword* confronts the effects of violence on a large scale and depicts a great deal of suffering. Although Serraillier never minimizes the hardship the family endures, he never graphically depicts the worst violence of the war. The novel shows that goodness and courage continue to exist in individuals, despite the evils of war. Jan is a special example of this theme; he is an attractive and sympathetic character, particularly in his special touch with animals, but his various misdeeds often create added difficulties for the other children. His good intentions and genuine repentance make him forgivable even when he breaks the law. The final promise of a new society with peaceful ideals brings the book to a hopeful conclusion.

◆ Topics for Discussion ◆

1. *The Silver Sword* has been published with a different title, *Escape from Warsaw*. Which title do you think fits the book better? Why?

2. Why is it important to Jan that Joseph *gives* him the sword? What function does the sword serve in the story?

3. The night that Mrs. Balicki is taken away by the Germans, Edek shoots at the soldiers. They come back later and blow up the house. Should Edek have shot at the soldiers? Why or why not?

4. Jan steals things throughout the book. He apparently feels justified in stealing, even when he gets caught. Why does he need to steal? Is he justified or not? Why?

5. The son of Herr and Frau Wolff was a German soldier in Warsaw, the sort of soldier Jan particularly hates. The young Wolff was killed trying to keep Warsaw under German control. Why do the Wolffs help the children? Why is Jan able to accept their help?

6. Why does Jan finally decide to help Ruth save Edek instead of going after Ludwig?

7. Why does Jan have trouble settling down after the war is over and life no longer presents as many struggles?

◆ Ideas for Reports and Papers ◆

1. *The Silver Sword* is set in Poland and Germany during and just after World War II. The author includes much description of the damage the war has done to the two countries. What effect do these descriptions have on the story?

2. Ruth, Edek, and Jan must all try to act like adults when their parents are no longer around to take care of them.

Where in the story do you see signs of how they are growing up? What adult qualities do they display?

3. Read the autobiographical book *Anne Frank: The Diary of a Young Girl*, written by a girl hiding from the Nazis with her family. How do Anne's experiences compare with those of the children in *The Silver Sword*? Why do you think Serraillier gave his book a happy ending? Do you feel that the ending of *The Silver Sword* makes light of the real tragedy suffered by millions of children, such as Anne?

4. Read one of the other books written about children's experiences during World War II (try *Summer of My German Soldier* by Bette Greene, *They Didn't Come Back* by Hans Peter Richter, *The Machine Gunners* by Robert Westall, or *I Am David* by Ann Holm.) How do these novels portray people from the different countries involved in the war, especially those on the "enemy" side? How do the experiences of the children in these books compare with those of the children in *The Silver Sword*?

5. Trace the development of the silver sword as a symbol in the novel. What does it represent thematically, and how does it function as a plot device?

◆ For Further Reference ◆

Commire, Anne, ed. *Something About the Author*. Vol. 1. Detroit: Gale Research, 1971. Contains a biographical sketch of Serraillier.

MacCann, Donnarae. "Militarism in Juvenile Fiction." *Interracial Books for Children* 13 (1982): 18-20. Includes *The Silver Sword* in its discussion of young adult books dealing with war.

Taylor, Anne. "A Comparative Study of Juvenile Fiction Dealing with the Second World War." *Emergency Librarian* 11 (November 1983): 13-21. Compares various books for young adults that are set during or otherwise examine the issue of World War II. *The Silver Sword* is discussed in the context of other works.

Kara K. Keeling
Indiana University

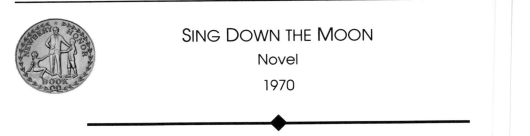

SING DOWN THE MOON
Novel
1970

Author: Scott O'Dell, 1903-1989

Major Books for Young Adults

Island of the Blue Dolphins, 1960
The King's Fifth, 1966
The Black Pearl, 1967
Dark Canoe, 1968
Journey to Jericho, 1969
Sing Down the Moon, 1970
The Treasure of Topo-el-Bampo, 1972
The Cruise of the Arctic Star, 1973
Child of Fire, 1974
The Hawk That Dare Not Hunt by Day, 1975
Zia, 1976

The Two Hundred Ninety, 1976
Carlota, 1977
Kathleen, Please Come Home, 1978
The Captive, 1979
Sarah Bishop, 1980
The Feathered Serpent, 1981
Spanish Smile, 1982
The Castle in the Sea, 1983
The Amethyst Ring, 1983
Alexandra, 1984
The Road to Damietta, 1985
Streams to the River, River to the Sea: A Novel of Sacagawea, 1986

◆ About the Author ◆

Scott O'Dell was born on May 23, 1903, in Los Angeles, California. Although he traveled widely, he made his home in southern California, the region in which many of his books are set. O'Dell attended Occidental College, the University of Wisconsin, Stanford University, and the University of Rome but never completed a degree. Believing that he did not need an academic degree to become a successful writer, he attended these institutions to study the subjects that interested him most: history, philosophy, psychology, and literature. In addition to being a prolific novelist, O'Dell worked briefly as a movie cameraman, served in the Air Force, and pursued journalism. He married Jane Rattenbury in 1948.

After publishing several adult novels, O'Dell began a career as an author of novels for young readers with *Island of the Blue Dolphins*. He went on to write more than twenty novels for young adults, most of which received awards and achieved popularity. One of the best of these is *Sing Down the Moon*, a Newbery Honor Book. O'Dell's other awards include the 1961 Newbery Medal for *Island of the Blue Dolphins*, a 1968 Newbery Honor Book citation for *The Black Pearl*, and the 1972 Hans Christian Andersen Award for lifetime contribution to children's literature. Two of his novels—*Island of the Blue Dolphins* and *The Black Pearl*—were adapted to feature-length films. O'Dell died on October 15, 1989, in Mount Kisco, New York.

◆ Overview ◆

O'Dell called *Sing Down the Moon* an adventure about loyalty. Bright Morning, a young Navaho woman, remains loyal to her family, her homeland, and her people. The book opens with Bright Morning remembering the first time she took her family's sheep onto the mesa at Canyon de Chelly to begin the spring grazing. When a late spring blizzard strikes, she secures the sheep in a grove of trees but becomes frightened and abandons the flock. Although the sheep survive, Bright Morning feels that by leaving, she has betrayed both them and her family. Looking back on the incident a year later and recalling her family's disapproval, Bright Morning understands the importance of loyalty. Her experiences throughout the novel— being captured as a slave, being forced to participate in the Navaho "long walk" into exile from Canyon de Chelly, marrying the recently crippled Tall Boy, and returning with her new husband to the canyon—test and strengthen her loyalty to the people and places that are part of her identity and her integrity.

◆ Setting ◆

Sing Down the Moon takes place mainly in Arizona and New Mexico between 1863 and 1865. The story begins and ends in Canyon de Chelly, now a national monument. O'Dell is a careful historical novelist. In addition to giving his readers the pleasure of adventures set in another time and place, he offers a glimpse into the life and culture of Navahos in the nineteenth-century Southwest. He creates a vivid sketch of traditional Navaho life, basing his story of "the long march" on an actual historical event. In 1863 the U.S. government removed all the Navahos from the Four Corners region of the Southwest (where the borders of Arizona, Utah, Colorado, and New Mexico all meet) to Fort Sumner, southeast of Santa Fe, New Mexico. Colonel Kit Carson led U.S. Cavalry troops in destroying Navaho villages and crops and killing those who resisted the three-hundred-mile walk. About ten thousand Navahos were removed; about eighty-five hundred reached Fort Sumner alive. Another fifteen hundred died during two years of exile. *Sing Down the Moon* captures the horror of this long march from a young Navaho woman's point of view.

◆ Themes and Characters ◆

In his portrayal of Bright Morning, the novel's protagonist and narrator, O'Dell lives up to his reputation for sensitive depictions of strong female characters. Fifteen years old when the novel opens, Bright Morning is compassionate, nurturing, and physically and mentally tough. She feels strong ties to her people, to her homeland, and to nature. When Bright Morning is exiled twice— first Spanish slave traders capture her and her friend Running Bird, and then she is forced on the long march to Fort Sumner—her greatest regret is being separated from her home.

Bright Morning hopes from the novel's outset to marry Tall Boy, a courageous but arrogant young warrior. Tall Boy's

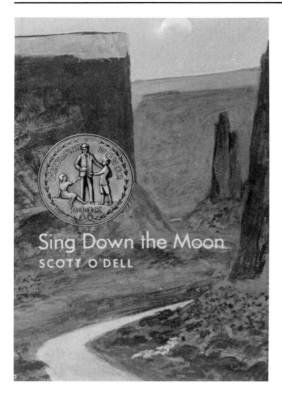

Jacket for *Sing Down the Moon* by Scott O'Dell.
Houghton Mifflin: Boston (1970).

as she teaches him that the human spirit can be imprisoned by neither a broken body nor other people.

The other characters in the novel—such as Bright Morning's sister, Lapana; her parents; and her friends Running Bird and White Deer—function primarily to further the plot. When Bright Morning is taken into slavery, though, she meets two contrasting characters whose differences serve to underscore the novel's message about the value of freedom. Rosita is from Navaho country, and Nehana is a Zuni; both are slaves in the same household as Bright Morning. Initially, Rosita appears to be a potential friend, but Bright Morning soon realizes that Rosita enjoys being a slave. Rosita comes from a poor family and has become enamored with the comforts of "civilization." Nehana, on the other hand, seems unfriendly at first, but she masterminds an escape for herself, Bright Morning, and Running Bird. Nehana refuses to sacrifice her freedom at any cost and emerges a noble figure; Rosita's submission to slavery, along with her willingness to forsake her cultural heritage, has destroyed her personal integrity.

The importance of remaining loyal to one's cultural heritage constitutes the novel's major theme. O'Dell shows that when the Navaho are forced to abandon their traditional ways during the long march and their subsequent imprisonment, they wither both physically and spiritually. The high value that Bright Morning places on loyalty is partially revealed through her relationship with her black dog, who, against all odds, manages to find Bright Morning whenever they are separated. O'Dell contrasts the dog's loyalty with the disregard for bonds between humans and animals displayed by the Jicarilla Apache woman who eats dog stew. The Navaho,

inordinate pride is tempered only after he cripples his right arm in a fight while helping Bright Morning escape from slavery. His disability means that Tall Boy must relinquish his position as leader of the warriors and assume the lowly status of a woman in the tribe. Bright Morning marries the devastated Tall Boy anyway, because she values his capacity for loyalty and love more than she did his prowess at hunting and fighting. In this regard, she rejects traditional Navaho ideals, which place a high value on a man's abilities as a hunter and a warrior, and teach women to be submissive. Bright Morning gradually instills a new sense of pride in Tall Boy says Bright Morning, "never eat stew made of dog meat." But once the spirits of the starving Navaho are broken during the long march, many of them begin to eat their dogs, and Bright Morning is forced to become fiercely protective of her black dog. Her determination to remain true to her culture culminates when she and Tall Boy return to their homeland with their infant son even though their village has been burned to the ground.

In the novel's final scene in the Canyon de Chelly, O'Dell makes his strongest statement about the preferability of peace over war, a theme that he weaves throughout the novel. The family has made a home in a hidden cave and Tall Boy, the former warrior, has fashioned a toy lance for his son and made up a song about using the lance to kill soldiers. Bright Morning takes the lance from her son and breaks it, and the child laughs and touches a lamb, a symbol of peace.

◆ Literary Qualities ◆

Bright Morning tells her story in a straightforward first-person account. O'Dell uses the pattern of exile and return to express his theme of the connections between loyalty and identity, and to criticize cultures that damage these connections by tearing people away from one another and from their homes. When Bright Morning is thrust into white culture, she often reflects on how it differs from her own culture, a device that allows O'Dell to unobtrusively insert many revealing details about Navaho life. The wistful but dignified tone of Bright Morning's narrative as she recalls her past life makes these details vivid. O'Dell's inclusion of such details in a fast-paced adventure story lends richness and depth to the novel and brings Bright Morning's character to life.

Bright Morning's adventures generate a great deal of suspense. When great misfortune is about to befall a character, O'Dell often hints at the forthcoming event and then shifts to an idyllic description of nature just before disaster strikes. For instance, before the slavers abduct Bright Morning and Running Bird, Bright Morning lapses into a revery about the tranquil spring day: "Clouds drifted in from the north, but they were spring clouds, white as lamb's wool. In the stream that wandered across the mesa speckled trout were leaping." Then Bright Morning's dog barks, and minutes later the girls are bound and gagged. Similarly, just as Bright Morning and Running Bird forget about the threat posed by soldiers camped near their village and try to coax a squirrel down from a piñon tree, Bright Morning notices a puff of smoke and realizes that the soldiers are burning the village. In addition to creating suspense, this technique of juxtaposing a tranquil scene with a violent event underscores the impact of the violence.

◆ Social Sensitivity ◆

O'Dell said that he was concerned with the way in which children grow up in American society and with the failures of different cultures to understand and appreciate one another. These concerns are apparent in *Sing Down the Moon*.

O'Dell shows Bright Morning growing from the girl who abandoned her sheep into the mature woman who can break the lance her husband makes for their son. Her rejection of a tradition of warfare promises a new cultural direction for her people. A feminist theme is implicit both in O'Dell's choice to make a young woman his narrator and main character, and in the direction the story takes. In traditional Navaho society, masculine interests dominate, and these interests help to provoke "the long march." Despite warnings from the U.S. government that Navaho raids against the Utes will bring reprisals, the Navaho are unable to give up warfare as a means of gaining extra food, territorial advantage, and personal honor. Though Bright Morning and other women understand how foolish such behavior is and emphasize the importance of protecting their precious, fertile canyon, the men will not listen. Rather, they insist upon the traditional way, in which women submit and avoid contradicting husbands and fathers. While women have a voice in tribal affairs, they lack the power to change the men's foolish behavior. Tall Boy's loss of the use of his arm and the couple's sufferings in exile lead to Bright Morning's assertion of a new ideal that promises a beneficial change for her people.

In *Sing Down the Moon,* much suffering results from the failures of cultures to understand and appreciate one another. The Navaho are unable to give up their long rivalry with the Utes even though they have all they need. The Spanish-American civilization of New Mexico tears young women away from "savage" tribes to gain slaves and servants. The U.S. soldiers who move the Navaho think of them as primitives that need and desire autocratic control. In each case, cruelty arises from ignorance and a lack of effort to overcome the ignorance. To use people or force them to conform always seems the easier choice, unless it is seen from the point of view of the victims. By telling the story from Bright Morning's point of view, O'Dell insures that his readers will see how unnecessary and wrong are such brutalities as the Navaho long march and the exile at Fort Sumner.

◆ Topics for Discussion ◆

1. What does Bright Morning learn from her mistake of leaving the sheep in the snow storm?

2. Why can't Bright Morning live happily in the pleasant house where she is a servant after she is first captured?

3. What do you think of the way Tall Boy handles the men who pursue Bright Morning and her friends to regain their horses?

4. Why does the U.S. Cavalry remove the Navahos from the Canyon de Chelly area?

5. What meanings do you see in Bright Morning's taking care of the baby that dies on the way to Fort Sumner?

6. How does the forced move to Fort Sumner affect the Navaho? Think about both the physical and the spiritual changes they undergo.

7. Why does Bright Morning want to return to Canyon de Chelly from Fort Sumner?

8. What similarities do you see between Bright Morning's first and second exiles? What important differences do you see?

9. What meanings do you see in Bright Morning's breaking her son's toy spear at the end of the story?

10. In the postscript, we learn that this novel is based on actual historical events. Does this make a difference in the way you think about the novel?

♦ Ideas for Reports and Papers ♦

1. Tall Boy's loss of the use of his right arm may be seen as a symbol. Review what we learn about that arm, how it is hurt, what the loss means, and what he says about the wound. Write a paper explaining how the wound functions as a symbol in the novel. What does Tall Boy learn from Bright Morning's response to his injury?

2. O'Dell has said, "I'm not interested in the Navajos particularly—they're not my favorite tribe even. They were marauders—they rode in and took the crops of other Indians, after harvest sometimes." Does his attitude towards the Navaho show in the story? Write a paper discussing the weaknesses of Navaho culture that most seem to influence how the story is told.

3. Think about the married life of Bright Morning and Tall Boy. Write a sketch of what this life would have been like had the two married as they originally planned—she wealthy in sheep and he a successful hunter and warrior. Describe and explain the most interesting similarities and contrasts between this picture and the actual situation.

4. Use an encyclopedia and other sources to learn about the culture or history of the Navaho. Write a report about how O'Dell incorporates this information into his novel. Note any new facts that surprise you.

5. Use an encyclopedia and other sources to learn about the Navaho's long march to Fort Sumner in 1864. Explain the differences between the historical account and the one presented in *Sing Down the Moon*.

6. O'Dell refers briefly to one of the most horrendous acts of violence by white settlers against Native Americans: the nighttime massacre, led by J. M. Chivington, of an entire village of three hundred Arapaho and Cheyenne. Research the historical events that led to this massacre.

♦ Related Titles ♦

O'Dell did not write any other books about the characters in *Sing Down the Moon*, but *The King's Fifth* takes place in the same region. This novel, which is about the sixteenth-century Spanish search for gold, includes Native American characters. Several other O'Dell novels are set in the Southwest, Mexico, and Central America, and concern interactions between Native Americans and Europeans.

♦ For Further Reference ♦

Estes, Glenn E. *Dictionary of Literary Biography*. Vol. 52. Detroit: Gale Research, 1986. Contains a discussion of O'Dell's career with detailed descriptions and reviews of his young adult books.

Townsend, John Rowe. *A Sense of Story: Essays on Contemporary Writers for Children*. New York: Lippincott, 1971. Includes a brief overview of O'Dell's early novels and an excerpt from an essay in which he discusses his aims as a writer for young people.

Wintle, Justin, and Emma Fisher. *The Pied Pipers: Interviews with the Influential Creators of Children's Literature.* New York: Paddington, 1974. Contains an interview with O'Dell about *Sing Down the Moon* and his other novels, his reasons for writing books for young people, and his views about the function of young adult literature in modern American society.

Terry Heller
Coe College

SLAUGHTERHOUSE-FIVE
Novel
1969

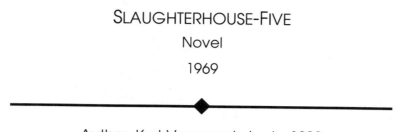

Author: Kurt Vonnegut, Jr., b. 1922

Major Books for Young Adults

Player Piano, 1952
The Sirens of Titan, 1959
Mother Night, 1961
Canary in a Cat House, 1961
Cat's Cradle, 1963
God Bless You, Mr. Rosewater, 1965
Welcome to the Monkey House,
   1968

Slaughterhouse-Five, 1969
Breakfast of Champions, 1973
Wampeters, Foma & Granfalloons,
   1974
Slapstick, 1976
Jailbird, 1979
Deadeye Dick, 1982
Galapagos, 1985

◆ About the Author ◆

Kurt Vonnegut, Jr., was born in Indianapolis, Indiana, on November 11, 1922, the son of accomplished German immigrants. His grandfather held the distinction of being the first licensed architect in Indiana; his father was also an architect, while his mother's side of the family owned prosperous breweries. Prohibition's outlawing of alcoholic beverages, which went into effect in 1919, had already curtailed the brewery business at the time of Vonnegut's birth, but he enjoyed an affluent, privileged childhood nonetheless. Family finances suffered, however, during the Great Depression, as the demand for new building construction tapered off.

Vonnegut attended high school in Indianapolis and began his writing career on the school newspaper. He continued his journalistic endeavors with the *Cornell Daily Sun*, the college newspaper of Cornell University, where he majored in biochemistry. Vonnegut left school to enlist in the U.S. Army in 1942. Arriving home on special leave for Mother's Day in 1944, Vonnegut found that his mother had committed suicide the night before by taking an overdose of sleeping pills. After returning to his unit, he was captured at the Battle of the Bulge (fought in France from December 16, 1944, to January 16, 1945) and imprisoned in Dresden, Germany, for the remainder of the war. Held captive in an underground meat storage cellar, Vonnegut survived the British and American bombings that leveled the city. He was liberated by the Russians and awarded one of America's highest military honors, the Purple Heart.

Vonnegut attended the University of Chicago after the war and then worked as a police reporter. From 1947 to 1950 he was a publicist for General Electric Corporation in Schenectady, New York, where he learned much about the technology that would later permeate his fiction. Leaving General Electric in 1950, Vonnegut turned to writing full-time, gaining a minor reputation as a science fiction writer but receiving little acclaim. It was not until the publication of *Slaughterhouse-Five* in 1969 that Vonnegut received any serious critical attention. After the success of this novel, however, his earlier works were republished, and he came to be regarded as one of America's most original and provocative writers.

◆ Overview ◆

Vonnegut's dramatic, tragic younger life greatly influences his fiction and establishes a framework for most of his themes. His immigrant family achieved the grandest of American dreams, only to have its success shattered by economic and political change. Traditional American values such as common sense, self-reliance, and practicality are juxtaposed in his fiction with the absurdity of fate and the folly of humankind. Such folly is epitomized by the bombing of Dresden (now part of East Germany) on February 13, 1945, only a few months before the end of World War II. Dresden was an unarmed, historic city of no military importance, and the motive for the Allied decision to bomb it into oblivion is still a mystery. The two-hour bombing killed 135,000 people.

It is against the backdrop of the bombing of Dresden that the dark world of *Slaughterhouse-Five* emerges. The hauntingly innocent main character, Billy Pilgrim, exudes a childlike wonder that such an atrocity could have been perpetuated. The mythical world of

Jacket for *Slaughterhouse-Five* by Kurt Vonnegut, Jr. Dell Publishing (reprinted by arrangement with Delacorte Press/Seymour Lawrence): New York (1969).

Tralfamadore, a product of Billy's innocence and perhaps of his insanity, stands as an alternative to a world in which nuclear weapons have given humankind the ability to obliterate life on earth.

◆ Setting ◆

For many years categorized strictly as a writer of science fiction, Vonnegut has a propensity for mixing the ordinary and the otherworldly in his fiction. Structured in "the telegraphic schizophrenic manner of tales of the planet Tralfamadore," *Slaughterhouse-Five* jumps backward and forward in time, and back and forth across the universe in setting. Snippets of events, seemingly unconnected either chronologically or geographically, follow one another; Vonnegut suggests that the cataclysmic devastation of modern warfare has deadened human sensitivity and that modern technology has outstripped the reach of human comprehension. The novel follows Billy Pilgrim, who "has come unstuck in time," to the battlefields of World War II, the slaughterhouses of Dresden, the suburban comforts of Ilium (modeled after Schenectady), and the zoos of distant Tralfamadore. In an age when progress frequently means destruction, the Tralfamadorian concept of time—which, essentially, states that all moments exist and always have existed, all at once—seems the only antidote to a maddening sense of helplessness.

◆ Themes and Characters ◆

A novel about man's folly, *Slaughterhouse-Five* traces the wanderings through time and space of Billy Pilgrim, a survivor of the fire bombing of Dresden. Billy marries an optometrist's daughter, fathers two children, and finds himself a kidnap victim on the night of his daughter's wedding. His kidnappers are green creatures from outer space who place him in a zoo and provide him with a mate, a luscious pornographic film star named Montana Wildhack. According to the Tralfamadorians, earthlings are the only creatures in the universe to believe in the concept of free will. Thus, although Billy adopts the Tralfamadorian notions about time and shuttles among past, present, and future events, he must come to terms with the knowledge that he has no control whatsoever over his immediate actions or his ultimate fate. His motto—"God grant me the serenity to accept the things I cannot change, courage to change the things I can, and wisdom always to tell the difference"—points up the value of maintaining composure in the face of stark destiny.

Billy is spastic in time, has no control over where he is going next, and the trips aren't necessarily fun.

The mass destruction of Dresden by Allied forces serves as Vonnegut's metaphor for the absurdity of life. An underlying theme is the extent to which technology has magnified humankind's capacity for cruelty; Vonnegut is appalled by the idea that a bombing raid could destroy a civilization hundreds of years old and kill 135,000 people in less than two hours. At a deeper level the novel explores the moral vacuum in which contemporary human life exists. Vonnegut's outrage is compounded by the lack of public attention given the Dresden bombing. He subtitles his book "The Children's Crusade," implicitly comparing Billy and his fellow soldiers to the twenty thousand children who set out from France during the summer of 1212 with the expectation of walking to the Holy Land and peacefully reclaiming it for Christianity. Most of the children died en route or were captured and sold into slavery; none reached their destination.

At the heart of the novel's theme is the question of free will versus deter-

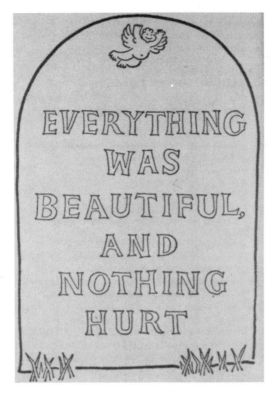

Illustration for *Slaughterhouse-Five* by Kurt Vonnegut, Jr. Dell Publishing (reprinted by arrangement with Delacorte Press/Seymour Lawrence): New York (1969).

no characters and no dramatic confrontations because "most of the people in it are so sick and so much the listless playthings of enormous forces." That is to say that the narrator believes personality is crushed by larger forces, such as war. But the writer-narrator himself develops into a character, with each of the novel's players representing a fascinating side of his personality; his individualism is not obliterated as long as his imagination remains active.

◆ Literary Qualities ◆

Vonnegut's title page statement that *Slaughterhouse-Five* is written in a "telegraphic schizophrenic manner" is a fairly accurate description of the novel's stylistic approach. Drawing on the literary devices of "flashback" and "flash-forward," Vonnegut ignores the restrictions of linear time and fixed space to fashion a novel that, despite its sometimes extraterrestrial setting, displays less affinity with science fiction than it does with psychological drama. Vonnegut, the writer-narrator, moves freely through narrative time, mixing descriptions of historic Dresden and his personal wartime experiences with Tralfamadorian fantasy and characters from his earlier fiction. Playing Tralfamadorian time against sequential Earth time allows Vonnegut to establish the psychic disorder of both Billy and the society that has produced him.

Vonnegut denies being a science fiction writer, and some critics have argued that *Slaughterhouse-Five* is a novel of "science reality" rather than science fiction. Vonnegut describes a world in which technology has rendered an event such as the annihilation of 135,000 people both possible and almost beneath notice. Although *Slaughter-*

minism. The Tralfamadorians teach Billy that events, such as death, represent only one moment in time's continuum, and that to dwell on any particular moment is to miss the point. The novel suggests that moments of serenity exist regardless of an individual's ability to conjure them up or to direct the flow of time. Life for Billy is not futile—it may be senseless, but it is not without its pleasures. If the novel contains any message other than a condemnation of war, it is that people must come to peace with themselves by knowing how to respond to the moment.

The narrator of the novel, presumably Vonnegut himself, states that there are *house-Five* does not fit neatly into any one genre, it stakes a place for itself in the literary canon with a combination of startling originality and thought-provoking literary allusion. Billy Pilgrim's name implies a connection to John Bunyan's seventeenth-century allegory, *Pilgrim's Progress.* Like Bunyan's Christian explorer, Billy is exposed to the evils of the world, but unlike Bunyan's pilgrim, Billy is not supported by the vision of a Celestial City at the end of the journey. Instead, he envisions the moment of his own death. Vonnegut's adaptation of this famous Christian allegory, combined with his ironic references to the ill-fated Children's Crusade, clearly indicates his belief that modern religion has failed humankind. As for the novel's protagonist, it is unclear whether Billy has really become "unstuck in time," or whether, like so many madmen in literature before him, he has merely denied reality and has thereby released himself from the horrors of his world.

symbol of such madness, but he has stated that his purpose in writing the novel was to make Americans more aware of the absurdity of the Vietnam War. Vonnegut consciously wanted to avoid writing a novel that glamorized the brutality of war and thus, as the subtitle suggests, portrays war as fought by young and uncomprehending innocents.

Although *Slaughterhouse-Five* remains an enormously popular novel some two decades after its publication, it has not been without its critics. Some readers are offended by the book's black humor and irreverent attitude, and charge that Vonnegut's view of life is so slanted by his personal experiences that he is incapable of serving as a legitimate social critic. Vonnegut uses vulgar slang, but before condemning Vonnegut's books parents and teachers should note that the vulgarity serves the stylistic purpose of interjecting humor and flippancy into discussions of dark situations.

♦ Social Sensitivity ♦

The 1960s produced a string of novels of the absurd that reflect the bleakness of a time when unabated optimism was checked by the assassinations of President John F. Kennedy in 1963 and of Robert Kennedy and Martin Luther King, Jr., in 1968. By the end of the decade, the Vietnam War had reached its height, and the mood of the country had sunk to one of abject pessimism. Many people believed that society had gone berserk and that a few world leaders exercised control over the destiny of millions. Vonnegut's expressed theme in Slaughterhouse-Five is the madness of war. In his novel he uses the senseless bombing of Dresden as the

♦ Topics for Discussion ♦

1. Describe the Tralfamadorian philosophy of life. How do the Tralfamadorians describe the fate of the universe? How do they react to this vision of the future?

2. Billy thinks of himself as a prophet. Do you agree that he is? Is he in any way a Christ-like prophet?

3. Is Billy's life in Tralfamadore heaven, hell, or just an extension of life on earth?

4. At the beginning of the novel, why does the writer-narrator compare himself to Lot's wife, who defied God by

looking back at Sodom and for doing so was turned into a pillar of salt?

5. What is the symbolic significance of telegraphs in the novel?

6. Cite evidence from the novel to support the position that Billy has lost touch with reality and that his time travel is just a function of his madness.

7. Billy is an optometrist whose job it is help people see better by prescribing corrective lenses. Does his profession influence his attempts to look at the world through a Tralfamadorian framework of ideas?

◆ Ideas for Reports and Papers ◆

1. Read St. Luke's Gospel in the Bible and demonstrate how it has influenced Billy's "Tralfamadorian adventure with death."

2. Research and describe the bombing of Dresden. Include information about the cultural history of Dresden up until the time it was bombed.

3. Research and explain the philosophical concept of determinism.

4. Research the Children's Crusade and explain why Vonnegut found it an appropriate subtitle for his novel.

5. Research the type of twentieth-century literature referred to as "the absurd," and explain some of the "absurd" characteristics of *Slaughterhouse-Five.*

◆ Related Titles/Adaptations ◆

Just as Vonnegut mixes history and fantasy in *Slaughterhouse-Five,* he also combines new material with characters and references to his earlier fiction in the book. The fictional city of Ilium is the setting for *Player Piano;* the Tralfamadorians are the central focus of *The Sirens of Titan;* Howard Campbell is the protagonist of *Mother Night;* and Eliot Rosewater and Kilgore Trout return from *God Bless You, Mr. Rosewater.*

The apocalyptic nature of *Slaughterhouse-Five* is echoed in many of Vonnegut's other works. In *Mother Night* Howard Campbell defends the Holocaust; in *Cat's Cradle* the Earth is destroyed by a substance called "ice-nine"; in *Deadeye Dick* the citizens of Midland City are inadvertently killed by a neutron bomb; and in *Galapagos* the narrative takes place in the distant future, long after humankind has been wiped out by a virus.

The film version of *Slaughterhouse-Five,* with a screenplay by Stephen Geller, was directed by George Roy Hill and starred Valerie Perrine, Michael Sacks, and Ron Leibman. The film was released by Universal Pictures in 1972 and won a special jury prize at the 1972 Cannes Film Festival.

◆ For Further Reference ◆

Giannone, Richard. *Vonnegut: A Preface to His Novels.* Port Washington, NY: Kennikat Press, 1977. Analyzes Vonnegut's novels, concentrating on his development as an artist.

Goldsmith, David H. *Kurt Vonnegut: Fantasies of Fire and Ice.* Bowling Green, OH: Bowling Green University Popular Press, 1972. Examines visions of the Apocalypse in Vonnegut's writing.

Klinkowitz, Jerome. "The Literary Character of Kurt Vonnegut, Jr." *Modern Fiction Studies* (Spring 1973): 57-67. Analyzes incidents and characters in *Slaughterhouse-Five* and shows how they are based on events from Vonnegut's life.

———. *Vonnegut.* London: Methuen, 1982. Surveys nine of Vonnegut's novels, emphasizing their relation to American culture.

Klinkowitz, Jerome, and John Somer, eds. *The Vonnegut Statement.* New York: Delacorte, 1973. Collection of essays that analyze Vonnegut's popularity.

Lundquist, James. *Kurt Vonnegut.* New York: Frederick Ungar, 1977. Argues for the essential midwestern quality of Vonnegut's work.

Reed, Peter J. *Kurt Vonnegut, Jr.* New York: Warner Paperback Library, 1972. Biography and analysis of the novels through *Slaughterhouse-Five.*

Schatt, Stanley. *Kurt Vonnegut, Jr.* Boston: Twayne, 1976. Outlines the concurrent development of Vonnegut's style and language.

Tanner, Tony. "The Uncertain Messenger." In *City of Words.* New York: Harper & Row, 1971. Analyzes the themes and examines the ambiguity of communication in Vonnegut's first five novels.

Carl Brucker
Arkansas Tech University

THE SLAVE DANCER
Novel
1973

Author: Paula Fox, b. 1923

Major Books for Young Adults

How Many Miles to Babylon?, 1967
Portrait of Ivan, 1969
The King's Falcon, 1969
Hungry Fred, 1969
Blowfish Live in the Sea, 1970
Good Ethan, 1973

The Slave Dancer, 1973
A Place Apart, 1980
One-Eyed Cat, 1984
The Moonlight Man, 1986
Lily and the Lost Boy, 1987
Village by the Sea, 1988

◆ About the Author ◆

Paula Fox was born April 22, 1923, in New York City, the daughter of Paul Hervey and Elsie de Sola Fox. Fox moved frequently as a child and at the age of eight went to Cuba to live with her grandmother for a while. Fox had attended nine different schools by the time she was twelve; she later attended Columbia University, left before receiving a degree, and studied piano at the Julliard School of Music. Her first marriage ended in divorce in 1954, and she remarried in 1962. Her sons from her first marriage were ten and twelve when she began to write *Maurice's Room*, her first book for children. Fox has won numerous awards, including the Newbery Medal in 1974 for *The Slave Dancer*, the Hans Christian Andersen Medal in 1978 for her lifetime contribution to children's literature, the American Book Award in 1983 for *A Place Apart*, and the Christopher Award in 1985 for *One-*

Eyed Cat. She writes complex, rich, and compelling tales that often develop themes from her own childhood. Her books' realistic plots and characters make her work popular with young readers and professional critics alike.

◆ Overview ◆

Jessie Bollier, the narrator of *The Slave Dancer*, relates how he was kidnapped at age thirteen and made to play his fife on a slave ship, how he endured a journey to West Africa and back, and how he and the young slave Ras survived a shipwreck. He resists the moral corruption of the sadistic men on the slave ship and eventually triumphs over the poverty of his childhood by becoming an apothecary, or druggist. These victories are not easily gained, though. Jessie vividly records his struggles with the slave dealers and the elements of

Illustration by Eros Keith for *The Slave Dancer* by
Paula Fox. Bradbury Press: Scarsdale, NY (1973).

American society. The novel is rich with
facts about the slave trade, about the
debate over banning slavery, and about
living conditions and customs of the
time.

The Slave Dancer moves among
various geographical settings—New Orleans, West Africa, the Gulf of Mexico,
and the mobile setting of the slave ship
itself. Jessie is kidnapped from his
home in New Orleans in 1840 and
voyages to West Africa on the slave ship
The Moonlight; on the return trip, his
ship is wrecked in the Gulf of Mexico
somewhere near New Orleans. Jessie
and Ras, the young slave he has
befriended on the ship, then live in Mississippi with Daniel, an elderly black
man, for a short while before Jessie
walks back to New Orleans and Ras
begins his trip to the North. Jessie then
briefly summarizes the rest of his life to
the time he tells the story—his becoming an apothecary, his moving to Rhode
Island, and his fighting for the Union
Army in the Civil War.

nature, and carries with him a
permanent psychological scar: never
again is he able to listen to music.

The Slave Dancer is a novel about
ideas and history in the guise of a superbly told adventure story. The novel is
thought-provoking; it encourages
readers to ask themselves how they
would have reacted if they were in
Jessie's place. Because of Fox's careful
research, the novel gives a realistic view
of life aboard a slave ship. It also shows
what life was like for poor people living
in the American South during the
1840s, revealing the extent to which
slavery pervaded and corrupted

◆ Themes and Characters ◆

The Slave Dancer focuses on a young
man's search for self-knowledge.
Caught up in the machinations of a
corrupt society, thirteen-year-old Jessie
Bollier must define himself through his
actions while living in psychological,
moral, and physical isolation from his
family and friends. Jessie is the only
musician on board the ship and the only
white character who cares about the
slaves as human beings. To his horror,

though, Jessie finds himself adopting some of the older men's attitudes as the voyage progresses. He cannot resist the slavers physically, but he resists morally and intellectually and both survives and grows because of this resistance.

The ship's officers and crew compose a rogue's gallery of characters. They range in moral quality from the bluff but honest sailor Clay Purvis, to the conniving, treacherous sailor Benjamin Stout, to the sniveling, savage mate Nicholas Spark, to the unpredictable, sadistic, and selfish Captain Cawthorne. The other adult sailors are less sharply drawn, their characters largely defined by the moral corruption brought on by their work on a slave ship.

Ras, the young slave who survives the shipwreck with Jessie, is the only slave in the novel given a name. Fox does not develop the characters of the other slaves; individuals emerge from the crowd only as they become the victims of specific cruelties. Daniel, the old black man who helps Jessie and Ras after the shipwreck, stands in marked contrast to the sailors and officers on *The Moonlight*. He does not judge people because of race; he simply sees two young men who need help and provides them with water, food, and shelter. Daniel, Ras, and Jessie's mother and sister are minor characters who echo Jessie's indifference to race and abhorrence of slavery.

Several subordinate themes cluster around the central theme of Jessie's conflict with society. Among the issues that Fox explores are struggles with conscience, coming of age, lack of communication with older people, repression of emotions, alienation, and perhaps most poignantly the ambiguity of justice in a universe where a slave ship is destroyed but nearly all of the slaves drown.

◆ Literary Qualities ◆

The Slave Dancer, a superb historical novel that probes complex questions of morality, deserves study for its stylistic brilliance and structural excellence. The telling is rich with dialogue and movement; the prose speaks directly to the reader's sensory perceptions. Even in the shortest of passages, Fox evokes the fundamental essence of the natural world that surrounds her characters: "Everything except the dark smudge of shore was gray now, sky and water and dull clouds. It looked like rain....Except for the mutter of Purvis' voice, I heard only the fluttering sound of water about the hull of the ship. A man passed me wearing a woolen cap, his gaze on the horizon." The novel deals with feelings, thoughts, and moral ambiguities, but these issues are all developed through concrete external action.

Jessie is deeply scarred by his trip on *The Moonlight*. Retelling his story as an adult, he reveals that he can no longer listen to music: "At the sound of my instrument, a fiddle, a flute, a drum, a comb with paper wrapped around it played by my own child, I would leave instantly and shut myself away." Furthermore, there are signs that the psychological scarring extends beyond his aversion to music, for he writes formally and frequently uses odd syntax. This style shows Jessie's reserve and reveals his cautious approach to life following his traumatic voyage on *The Moonlight*.

Structurally, specific actions advance the plot forward to an inevitable conclusion. Fox opens her novel with a page titled "History," under which heading she lists the characters aboard *The Moonlight* and states the fate of the ship. It is interesting to note that, excluding Jessie, the officers and crew of *The*

Illustration by Eros Keith for *The Slave Dancer* by Paula Fox. Bradbury Press: Scarsdale, NY (1973).

escape fully the society that has formed him. He survives his journey on the slave ship only to be plunged back into the antebellum South. He later moves to the North and sees his moral dilemmas reflected in the upheavals of the Civil War, all the while carrying with him the internal scars of his personal struggle.

◆ Social Sensitivity ◆

Various aspects of *The Slave Dancer* have come under fire, including the slaves' passivity and the abruptness of the novel's ending. But the novel has survived this criticism and has become an important work about slavery.

The novel is rooted in a sordid port of American history, and Fox has taken great pains to depict slavery in its full viciousness. She is not a revisionist and refuses to rewrite history to reflect contemporary social standards. As a result, the characters display the attitudes of the period and use such highly objectionable words as "nigger." But Fox's moral commitment is clear throughout the novel. She wants her readers to know the awful effect of slavery on slaves, slave-holders, and the entire nation. She stated her perspective on the issue in her Newbery Award acceptance speech: "There are those who feel that slavery debased the enslaved. It is not so. Slavery engulfed whole peoples, swallowed up their lives, committed such offenses that in considering them the heart falters, the mind recoils. Slavery debased the enslavers, and self-imposed ignorance of slavery keeps the mind closed."

Because of the book's historical accuracy and moral clarity, it can be used to illustrate the progress in civil rights

Moonlight number twelve—a typical size for the Chorus in Greek tragedy. Traditionally, the Chorus voiced the attitudes and opinions of the community; across the web of this group's often judgmental utterances, the playwright would weave the struggles of the play's major characters. In *The Slave Dancer*, the crew of *The Moonlight* represents the voice of a repressive and prejudiced society. Jessie's search for moral standards is played out against the siren song of this corrupt but privileged company, a grotesque Chorus that would accept him—if only in the role of musician—simply because the color of his skin matches its own. Like Greek heroes of old, Jessie is ultimately unable to made in America since the 1840s. *The Slave Dancer* should remind all readers that this progress came about only as a result of conscious effort.

◆ Topics for Discussion ◆

1. In later life, Jessie cannot listen to music. Does this reaction seem reasonable to you? Have you had a bad experience that has caused you to dislike or fear something you associate with it?

2. Fox has been criticized for the passivity of her black characters. Do you think the black characters in *The Slave Dancer* should have been more forceful? If so, do you think Jessie, a white character, should have been stronger as well? What might have happened to the characters if they had more actively fought the circumstances of their life aboard the ship?

3. Both *The Slave Dancer* and William H. Armstrong's novel *Sounder* (1969) deal with painful issues in black history, yet the authors of these books are white. Some people have objected to these novels because they think that these white authors lack an adequate perspective on black history. How do you respond to this criticism?

4. Some people have criticized the novel because the main characters are male. Do you think Fox should have included more significant female characters? How would the novel have differed if Jessie had been a girl?

5. Jessie plays his fife while the slaves "dance." How important is his playing? Do you think the slaves would have "danced" equally well without the

music? If so, why does Captain Cawthorne want Jessie to play?

6. Cawthorne orders Jessie to play his fife immediately before the drunken dance near the end of the book. Why do Cawthorne and the rest of the men want to dance with the slaves who are dressed in fine costumes? Is this dance symbolic in showing similarities between the captors and the captives?

7. Cawthorne calls Jessie "Bollweevil." What is a bollweevil? Why does he give Jessie this name?

8. Jessie's mother works as a seamstress to make a living, although the hours are long and the pay is low. What other jobs might she have held in the mid-nineteenth century, considering what you know about her and about working conditions for women at that time?

9. Do you think Fox should have included humor to soften the novel's grimness?

◆ Idea for Reports and Papers ◆

1. Jessie writes that he "spent three months in Andersonville, surviving its horrors, I often thought, because I'd been prepared for them on *The Moonlight*." What was Andersonville? Write a paper explaining how Andersonville's horrors were like the horrors on board *The Moonlight*.

2. Jessie records major places along the route of his journey, such as New Orleans, Bight of Benin, Whydah, and Cuba. On the basis of these references

to places, what was the approximate route of *The Moonlight*? Was this a usual route for slave ships? Write a report tracing Jessie's route, and draw his route on a map along with other major nineteenth-century trade routes.

3. *To Be a Slave* (1968) by Julius Lester was a Newbery Honor Book in 1969; *Sounder* received the Newbery Medal in 1970; and *The Slave Dancer* received it in 1974. All three books deal with the mistreatment of blacks in American history—*To Be a Slave* and *The Slave Dancer* during the time of slavery, and *Sounder* during the Depression of the 1930s. Write a paper describing the social changes in America during the 1960s and early 1970s that make it possible for authors to address painful issues in black history. Before the civil rights movement in America, do you think these books would have received such positive recognition?

4. Write a paper comparing *The Slave Dancer* to either *Sounder* or *To Be A Slave*. In what ways are the books alike? Explain which book you prefer and why.

5. Some critics have said that Fox conveniently got rid of all the evil on *The Moonlight* by ending the book with a shipwreck. Do you think Fox resolved the problem of the evils of the slave trade adequately? Do you think Jessie should have grown more from his experience, rather than suffering the permanent scars to which he refers at the book's end? Rewrite the conclusion of the book if you find it disturbing; explain why you think your conclusion is better than the book's.

6. Early in the book, Jessie records that "this very day I'd seen six Africans offered up for sale as cane hands. They had been dressed as if they had been going to a ball, even to the white gloves they were all wearing. 'These niggers are matchless!' the auctioneer had cried, at which instant I was picked up bodily by a man as hairy as a dray horse, thrown to the pavement and told to keep away from the slave market until I had something better in mind than nasty peeking." Jessie is again picked up roughly when he is kidnapped, and later in the novel, the slaves are dressed up for the drunken dance before the storm. Note some of the other actions or words that recur in the novel. What does this repetition serve?

7. Early in the book, Jessie's Aunt Agatha tells him he should be "apprenticed and learn a trade," and after his voyage he is apprenticed to an apothecary. What did apprenticeship mean during the nineteenth century? Are young people still apprenticed today? Write a paper describing a typical nineteenth-century apprenticeship, and compare it to how a young person might learn a similar trade today.

8. Paula Fox did not rewrite history in *The Slave Dancer* to conform to modern social standards. In what ways do the book's characters illustrate attitudes that most people now find objectionable? What does the book show about how attitudes have changed in America between 1840 and the present?

9. Fox wants Jessie's narrative to resemble nineteenth-century speech and writing. How does she make his prose sound dated? Notice the formal and archaic words Jessie uses, and the length, construction, and punctuation of some of his sentences. Try to write a book report about *The Slave Dancer* using this same kind of "old" language.

◆ For Further Reference ◆

Baker, Augusta. "The Changing Image of the Black in Children's Literature." *Horn Book* 51 (February 1975): 84-87. This article sets *The Slave Dancer* in a larger context.

————. "Paula Fox." *Horn Book* 50 (August 1974): 351-353. This article introduces Fox and her work.

Fox, Paula. "Newbery Award Acceptance." *Horn Book* 50 (August 1974): 345-350. The author discusses her work and her motivation for writing *The Slave Dancer* and answers some of the criticisms directed at the book.

Harold Nelson
Minot State University

SMITH
Novel
1967

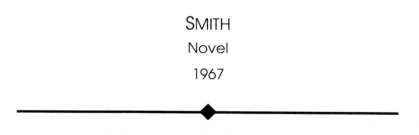

Author: Leon Garfield, b. 1921

Major Books for Young Adults

Jack Holborn, 1964
Devil-in-the-Fog, 1966
Smith, 1967
Black Jack, 1968
Mr. Corbett's Ghost and Other Stories, 1969
The Boy and the Monkey, 1969
The Restless Ghost: Three Stories by Leon Garfield, 1969
The God Beneath the Sea, 1970 (written with Edward Blishen)
The Drummer Boy, 1970
The Ghost Downstairs, 1970
The Strange Affair of Adelaide Harris, 1971

The Captain's Watch, 1971
Child O'War: The True Story of a Sailor Boy in Nelson's Navy, 1972
Lucifer Wilkins, 1973
The Golden Shadow, 1973 (written with Edward Blishen)
The Sound of Coaches, 1974
The Prisoners of September, 1975
The Apprentices, 1978
Footsteps, 1980 (also published as *John Diamond*)
The Wedding Ghost, 1985 (written with Charles Keeping)
The December Rose, 1986

◆ About the Author ◆

Leon Garfield was born in Brighton, England, on July 14, 1921. He wanted to become an artist, but his training was interrupted by his service in the Medical Corps during World War II. After the war he worked as a biochemist in hospitals for twenty years before deciding to write full-time. He has produced novels, short stories, and works of nonfiction, many of which are set in eighteenth- and nineteenth-century England. *The God Beneath the Sea*, a retelling of Greek myths, earned the 1970 British Library Association's Carnegie Medal for best children's book of the year published in the United Kingdom. *Footsteps* won the Whitbread Award of the British Booksellers Association for best children's book of 1980, and *Smith* was given the Phoenix Award of the Children's Literature Association in 1987.

Many of Garfield's novels cannot be strictly classified as adult or children's books. The majority are adventure tales in which children or adolescents play the central roles. His protagonists usually embark on quests staged against the backdrop of a historically accurate setting.

Garfield has said that *Smith* was a book that took a great deal of effort to write. For *Smith*, as with his other works, Garfield did all of his own research, and in the process turned up many interesting facts and incidents that helped make his work lively and appealing to both adults and children.

◆ Overview ◆

From the moment that Smith, a ragged eighteenth-century London urchin, witnesses the murder of an old man whose pocket he has just picked, he lives between hope and fear: hope that the document he stole from the old man will spell his fortune, and fear that the old man's assailants will murder him next. Smith cannot read and thus is unable to decipher the document. His journey toward enlightenment takes him through the alleys and shadowy corners of London, from thieves' dens to the homes of the wealthy. Smith brings to his quest shrewd common sense, the quickness of a scurrying rat, and a half-developed sense of human kindness. While pursuing the meaning of the document, he learns a great deal about justice of all kinds, and he acts with a desperate courage that makes the unexpected ending appropriate and satisfying.

The book's characters exhibit the limitations to be expected of those who have suffered from poverty, ignorance, or crushing misfortune. Mr. Mansfield, the blind justice; his daughter, torn between the need for a life of her own and the demands of her father; and the swashbuckling Lord Tom, highwayman and friend, all come to life in Garfield's tale, helping or hindering Smith in his efforts to uncover the document's secrets.

◆ Setting ◆

Garfield has received consistent critical praise for the effective settings of his books. In *Smith* he depicts eighteenth-century London with an eye for accuracy and atmosphere, rendering in vivid detail the sights, smells, and sounds of The Red Lion Tavern, where Smith lives with his two sisters; the murky back streets, where he drifts and dodges like "a sooty spirit"; and the bitter, snowy reaches of Finchley Common, where he thwarts a coach robbery and saves the life of Mr. Mansfield.

◆ Themes and Characters ◆

Smith and the blind judge, Mr. Mansfield, are the most effectively drawn and carefully balanced characters in the novel. Smith is motivated by the need to survive; he is a clever and quick pickpocket but has a sense of compassion that leads him to offer a helping hand to old Mr. Mansfield. Smith has no scruples about his pickpocketing and even aspires to be a highwayman like Lord Tom for the excitement and treasure that such a life will bring—even if it also brings a death by hanging. His sisters call him "Smut," and at first he appears as little more than a grimy scrap of a boy. On the other hand, Mr. Mansfield—large in build, rich, and possessing the power and status of a judge—has only a rigid, abstract sense of justice to cling to in his blindness. This compels him to imprison Smith even though he is drawn to the boy and is in debt to him for his kindness.

Ilustration by Antony Maitland for *Smith* by Leon Garfield. Pantheon/Random House: New York (1967).

Few people in the novel are who they seem to be at first. Because Smith lives by his wits, he is more perceptive than the others, reading character from people's faces. He instinctively distrusts Mr. Billing, the lawyer, and wonders about Miss Mansfield, whose face and flashing eyes contradict the gentle words and actions she shows her blind father.

Smith's determination to learn to read so that he can decipher the stolen document and his subsequent pursuit of the document when it vanishes provide the driving forces of the narrative. But it is his reluctant kindness and boyish courage that provide the theme. Smith proves that, contrary to Mr. Mansfield's initial belief, justice is not a matter of clinging to abstract principles. Instead, justice must be tempered by understanding and compassion. When Mr. Mansfield finally lies about Smith's identity in order to protect the boy, he has learned a more important lesson than has Smith when he learns to read.

Adventure novels usually depend on a series of exciting events that culminates in the success of the protagonist, usually because of his or her courage and determination in the face of overwhelming odds. *Smith* is a more complex novel because although the hero is brave and resourceful, his ultimate success results from his ability to face the intellectual challenge of deciphering the written word. The suspense engendered by Smith's attempts to elude his pursuers is balanced by the equal urgency with which he throws himself into the task of learning to read. The theme of ignorance versus knowledge is carried out at two levels: Smith learns to read, and he solves the mystery of the old man's murder; both of these events lead to the happy ending.

◆ Literary Qualities ◆

The evocative atmosphere of the novel arises from Garfield's detailed descriptions of eighteenth-century London. The settings of the narrow, fog-shrouded alleys, the malodorous depths of Newgate Prison, the rough-and-tumble world of the Red Lion Tavern, and the rigid, unchanging Mansfield house all overflow with precise and picturesque detail. Garfield's use of slang and thieves' lingo, combined with his descriptions of dress and manners, defines the separate worlds of the upper and lower classes and highlights the contrast as Smith moves between these two worlds.

Garfield's settings also function as metaphors for action and character. The dark, twisting streets suggest the evil plottings of the lame man; the cold and blinding snowstorm echoes Smith's detachment from the conventional patterns and beliefs of Mr. Mansfield's world; and the narrow twisting ventilators in Newgate Prison symbolize the convoluted path that Smith must negotiate to escape the world of crime, poverty, and ignorance.

Critics have compared the characters in the novel to the larger-than-life figures created by nineteenth-century English novelist Charles Dickens. Living in an adult world that refuses to take him seriously, Smith is a complex combination of boyish enthusiasm, self-confidence, and vulnerability. His careless thievery contrasts with his kind heart, and his ingenuity contrasts with his inability to defend himself in the face of unjust accusations. Mr. Mansfield is both physically big—"a real giant of a gent" who "fairly towered over the tiny, helpful Smith"—and physically weak because of his blindness. He is morally rigid in denying Smith his trust, yet willing to change his deepest convictions when he realizes the inhumanity of this kind of justice.

Illustration by Antony Maitland for *Smith* by Leon Garfield. Pantheon/Random House: New York (1967).

◆ Social Sensitivity ◆

Eighteenth-century England, as re-created in Garfield's novel, is a lawless society. Traditional justice is shown to be mistaken, unkind, and inadequate. The reader's sympathy goes to the petty thieves, highwaymen, and debtors whose actions are depicted as attempts to survive in a hostile world and whose accomplishments, like those of Lord Tom, are glamorous and exciting. The Mansfields, who live by a less opportunistic code, are helpless, deluded, and often unhappy. The complex character of Miss Mansfield, for example, shows the strain of subduing her naturally "peevish" nature in order to treat her father with the gentleness that makes her appear a "saint" in his blind eyes. Garfield does not condemn the value system of traditional society, but he does emphasize that people should not be judged by class, appearance, or education. Both Mansfields are deluded about Smith's goodness and Mr. Billing's evil, suggesting that traditional morality is of limited worth unless it is infused with human sympathy.

◆ Topics for Discussion ◆

1. Meg, the Mansfields' servant, says that she is kind to Smith because her mother has always told her to "follow her heart." How is her motivation different from Mr. Mansfield's? What rules of behavior does he follow?

2. In the novel's opening chapter, London is seen in part from the perspective of the birds who perch on the roof of St. Paul's Cathedral. Why is this an effective way of setting the scene?

3. How is Mr. Mansfield's blindness an advantage to Smith? How is it a disadvantage?

4. A single incident often marks a change of fortune for a character. When Smith is brought to Mr. Mansfield's house, his layers of clothing are taken away and burned, and he is scrubbed to remove the layers of grime. How does this incident and the description of Smith after the bath suggest that his life is about to change?

5. Many characters indicate to Smith that learning to read will only get him into trouble, and that he will be better off if he remains ignorant. Why do they say this? What circumstances suggest, at first, that they may be right?

6. When Smith and Mr. Mansfield arrive frozen and exhausted at the constable's house, the man writes down their names and makes a list of everything he will give them. What does Mr. Mansfield think of the constable's need to measure carefully the help he gives to others? How does the constable's behavior influence Mr. Mansfield's decision to lie about Smith's identity?

◆ Ideas for Reports and Papers ◆

1. Although the story is set in eighteenth-century England, it does not concern itself with actual historical events. Instead, the details of eighteenth-century life create an atmosphere for the adventure that takes place. Show how the descriptions of the Red Lion Tavern and Newgate Prison help the reader understand Smith's personality.

2. Moral choice is an important element in *Smith*. Show how some of the events in the story teach Smith and the other characters that outward respectability, rank, and wealth are not always indications of honesty and goodness.

3. It is ironic that many of the characters in the story turn out to be the opposite of what they appear. Mr. Billing, a lawyer, turns out to be a lawbreaker, and the man who judges Smith cannot see. Discuss some other examples of irony, such as the actions of Lord Tom, and show how the reader, as well as Smith, learns not to judge by appearances.

4. Symbols in a novel often stand for feelings and attitudes the author wants to convey about situations and events. Discuss the way Garfield uses descriptions of fog and snow to show loss, confusion, or danger.

5. The names that an author gives to characters often reveal something about the characters. Why does Garfield give his protagonist only one name, and why

does he choose "Smith," a common last name? What is the effect of calling the highwayman "Lord Tom"? Discuss how other names in the novel reflect on characters and the way they are perceived by others.

6. Show how the author uses humor to lighten tense situations. Consider Smith's bath at the Mansfields', the character of the hangman, and the way Smith finally escapes from prison under Miss Bridget's hoop skirt.

ducing the violent aspects of eighteenth-century life to young readers.

Townsend, John Rowe. *A Sense of Story: Essays on Contemporary Writers for Children*. Philadelphia: Lippincott, 1971. The discussion of *Smith* indicates the ways in which the author has developed the narrative line to produce greater unity than exhibited in his previous works.

Ruth Anne Thompson
Pace University

♦ For Further Reference ♦

Carpenter, Humphrey, and Mari Prichard. *The Oxford Companion to Children's Literature*. Oxford University Press: Oxford, 1984. Contains a brief overview of Garfield's works, which summarizes *Smith*'s plot and literary qualities, and sets the novel in the context of the author's other novels.

Natov, Roni. " 'Not the Blackest of Villains...Not the Brightest of Saints': Humanism in Leon Garfield's Adventure Novels." *Lion and the Unicorn* (Fall 1978): 44-71. This article focuses on the way the author embraces humanity in all its weaknesses as well as all its strengths. Natov compares Garfield to some of the best nineteenth-century novelists and shows how *Smith* is both cynical and sentimental.

Stott, Jon C. *Children's Literature from A to Z: A Guide for Parents and Teachers*. New York: McGraw-Hill, 1984. The entry on Garfield suggests that his novels are effective in intro-

A SOLITARY BLUE
Novel
1983

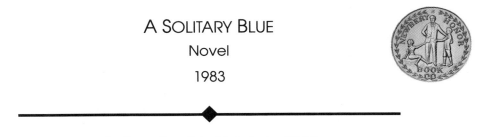

Author: Cynthia Voigt, b. 1942

Major Books for Young Adults

Homecoming, 1981
Tell Me If the Lovers Are Losers,
   1982
Dicey's Song, 1982
The Callender Papers, 1983
A Solitary Blue, 1983
Building Blocks, 1984

Jackaroo, 1985
The Runner, 1985
Izzy, Willy-Nilly, 1986
Stories about Rosie, 1986
Come a Stranger, 1986
Sons from Afar, 1987
Tree by Leaf, 1988

◆ About the Author ◆

Cynthia Voigt was born on February 25, 1942, in Boston, Massachusetts. She attended the Dana Hall School in Wellesley, Massachusetts, where she graduated with distinction. She earned her bachelor's degree from Smith College in 1963. After she married, Voigt received her teaching certificate from St. Michael's College (now called the College of Santa Fe) in Santa Fe, New Mexico, then moved to Annapolis, Maryland, where she began teaching at the Key School.

Voigt's books for young adults began appearing in the early 1980s and were soon winning praise and awards. *Homecoming* was nominated for an American Book Award; *Tell Me If the Lovers Are Losers* was named an American Library Association Best Book for Young Adults; and *The Callender Papers* won the Edgar Allan Poe Award for best juvenile mystery. In addition, *Dicey's Song* received the Newbery Medal, and *A Solitary Blue* was named a Newbery Honor Book.

◆ Overview ◆

Like most of Voigt's books, *A Solitary Blue* focuses on the theme of love and trust. It tells the story of Jeff Greene from the ages of seven to sixteen. The novel begins on the day he comes home from school to find that his mother has left him and his father, and it ends years later when Jeff, who has inherited his wealthy great-grandmother's estate, rejects his dishonest mother's overtures. Along the way, Jeff learns to overcome his insecurity, which results from the abandonment by his mother, the apparent indifference of his father, and the neglect of a series of live-in housekeepers/sitters. His ability to

A
SOLITARY BLUE
by Cynthia Voigt

Jacket painting c 1983 by James Shefcik for *A Solitary Blue* by Cynthia Voigt. Atheneum: New York (1983).

come to terms with his difficult childhood demonstrates the potential of the individual to learn from and triumph over painful experiences. Although it is hurtful, Jeff's psychological journey is fascinating, and the lessons he learns about the real nature of love and strength are valuable and convincing.

◆ Setting ◆

The setting of *A Solitary Blue* is integral to the story and its themes. The story begins in Baltimore, then moves between Charleston, South Carolina, and Baltimore, and finally ends in Crisfield, Maryland.

Baltimore and Charleston come to represent two extremes of Jeff Greene's confused and insecure life. In Charleston with his mother, where it is warm and sunny, Jeff feels loved. In Baltimore with his father, where the weather is colder, he feels self-sufficient and reticent. The house in Charleston is spacious and bright; in Baltimore, the house has small rooms and narrow halls. In Charleston, he is Jeffie (his mother's name for him) or Jefferson (his great-grandmother's name for him); in Baltimore he is Jeff Greene. On his first visit to Charleston, when he sees his mother for the first time in almost five years, Jeff feels "like a man must who has been kept in a dungeon for years and years, and he steps out into the sunlight for the first time." Just as he physically is shuttled back and forth between Baltimore and Charleston, Jeff is emotionally torn between his father and his mother; because Jeff has no identity of his own, he becomes what he thinks his mother wants him to be when he is in Charleston and what he thinks his father wants him to be when he is in Baltimore.

His mother seems the warmer, more loving character. She has told Jeff that his father is a poor parent, a cold, unloving, boring man; little in his shy, introspective father's behavior indicates otherwise to Jeff. But when, in the warm and happy atmosphere of Charleston, Melody betrays Jeff's love and trust yet again, he must find a retreat from the beautiful setting that is now tainted for him with the stains of sorrow and disillusionment. He finds an uninhabited island to which he can sail each day and be safe from hurtful human contact. The island represents Jeff's withdrawal from life, but what it symbolizes is not altogether bad. In solitude Jeff begins to recover from the shock of learning what his mother is really like; on the island, he can begin to muster his internal resources to fortify himself for a return to what he thinks is the unloving atmosphere of Baltimore. But in Baltimore he discovers that his father really does love him. The Professor does not say much about love, but he is reliable and trustworthy; he is always *there*.

Recognizing Jeff's unhappiness and his bad memories associated with the Baltimore house, the Professor discusses with Jeff the possibility of moving. They sell their house and move to a smaller one in Crisfield, on Maryland's Eastern Shore. The Professor, who is a man of few words but astute observation, knows that this house and the surrounding area remind Jeff of "his" island. This is the place where Jeff will be happy. Crisfield is home to Jeff. Charleston and Baltimore were places where he lived or stayed; they were never home.

Illustration by James Shefcik for *A Solitary Blue* by Cynthia Voigt. Atheneum: New York (1983).

◆ Themes and Characters ◆

Jeff Greene is the protagonist in *A Solitary Blue*; the reader sees everything that happens through his eyes. The novel begins when seven-year-old Jeff comes home from school and finds a note from his mother that says she has gone away and will not be coming back. In the letter she intimates that Jeff should try to do things for himself and not bother his father. This insures that Jeff will be afraid to grieve publicly and ask for help.

Jeff is a frightened, sensitive, and insecure boy; he feels as if his father might leave at any moment if he becomes a hindrance. Later, as Jeff matures, he takes chances: he tells his mother he does not like her lying, and becomes more open with his father. His sen-

sitivity will always leave him vulnerable to pain, but his love of nature and music will help him through such suffering. By the end of the book, his hard-won emotional maturity shows that he is a strong and brave young man willing to take the risk of loving and trusting again.

The Professor, Jeff's father, has been terribly hurt by his marriage to Melody; although he is extremely intelligent, he has a difficult time communicating with others. He is withdrawn and gives the appearance of not caring. Jeff bases his image of the Professor in part upon what Melody has told him and in part upon the Professor's own withdrawal from life. The Professor also grows as a person when he and Jeff are able to communicate with each other. Like Jeff, the Professor has been living behind a wall for protection.

Melody, Jeff's mother, may be the most simple character in the book: she is a type, like Mrs. Jellaby in Charles Dickens's *Bleak House*. She is full of concern for strangers, but oddly indifferent to the suffering of her own husband and son. She has gone off to try to save the world. She gives the appearance of being a loving person; unlike the Professor she is very demonstrative. When Jeff goes to visit her, she hugs and kisses him frequently. Starved for affection, Jeff assumes this is love. Even though she lies and manipulates people, Melody is not all bad. She wants custody of Jeff only after she finds out that Gambo, her grandmother, has made him the heir of her will. But Melody does not want the money for herself; she wants to put it into her crusades. When Jeff gives Melody Gambo's diamond engagement ring, she plans to sell it so that she can go on a charitable mission to Colombia, South America. In her own way Melody tries to make the world a better place. But the trail of pain and shattered illusions she leaves behind in her personal life is an ironic contradiction of her good intentions.

Among the minor characters are Brother Thomas, Gambo, and Miss Opal. Brother Thomas is a friend of the Professor's who also teaches at the university. He acts as a bridge between the Professor and Jeff by forcing them to talk and interact with one another. Gambo is Melody's grandmother and Jeff's great-grandmother. She is wealthy and very pleased to meet Jeff because he is the last of the Boudrault family line of men. Gambo fills Jeff with the history of his family. Even though Gambo and Jeff are not very close, she makes him the heir of her estate, an act inspired by pride rather than love. Her cold character helps the reader to understand Melody's personality. Miss Opal, Gambo's maid, gives up her house and moves in to take care of Gambo when she has a stroke. Jeff is amazed to learn that she is older than Gambo. After Gambo's death, Jeff asks the lawyer to give the house to Miss Opal so that she will have a place to live for the rest of her life.

The Tillerman family in Crisfield helps Jeff heal his emotional wounds and start to trust people again. The family includes Gram, the eccentric old woman who has taken her four grandchildren in; Dicey, the bright, tough, honest oldest girl; James, the oldest boy, a mixture of intelligence and raw curiosity; Maybeth, who is fragile and warm; and Sammy, a born fighter. Although the Tillermans are present only in the last third of the book, they are deftly drawn, and their role is important. Jeff sees in them what a family can be: a collection of individuals bound together by a tough and honest love.

The search for true love and trust is the most memorable theme in *A Solitary Blue*. It is most clearly shown in Jeff's experiences and development. Twice betrayed by his mother, Jeff becomes obsessed with protecting his heart. His father's less demonstrative but more reliable love finally reassures him, and he becomes a caring young man who is at last secure. Jeff has come full circle because he has learned to love and trust himself.

♦ Literary Qualities ♦

Voigt has been described in the *New York Book Review* as "a wonderful writer with powerfully moving things to say." The wide variety of images and symbols she uses can turn a realistic, everyday happening into something new and wonderful. Voigt knows that young people believe the possible to be real and writes according to her readers' expectations. Without being unrealistic, she presents the possibility of happiness, healing, and love.

The most obvious symbol in *A Solitary Blue* is the blue heron. Jeff appreciates the heron's beauty and its love of solitude. The blue heron does not want to be bothered and is frightened by sudden movement. The heron parallels Jeff, who, after being devastated by his mother's abandonment, becomes wary, untrusting, and withdrawn. The only time that people do not frighten the heron into flying away is when Jeff and Dicey are together in the sailboat.

Voigt uses simple but evocative diction, and her descriptions of the blue heron and Jeff's tranquil island are almost poetic. Her dialogue is strikingly appropriate to the characters. The Professor speaks almost in monosyllables until he and Jeff come to understand and trust one another; then he shows himself to be very articulate but never chatty. Melody, on the other hand, fairly gushes with words: light and funny dialogue when she is happy, appealing emotional language when she wants something, and bitter, harsh remarks when she is angry. This skillful use of language helps make the characters, even minor ones such as Miss Opal, fully rounded. This lends depth to the book, for even people with very small roles in Jeff's story are perceived as people, not cardboard cutouts.

◆ Social Sensitivity ◆

Melody's early abandonment of her child and her later betrayal of his trust create perhaps the most sensitive issue in *A Solitary Blue*. This negative picture of a mother reveals a harsh emotional truth: that some people, even parents, are never able to love maturely. The selfishness and narcissism of Melody's love is disturbing. But it is crucial to Jeff's development that he see Melody

for what she is. The relationship between Jeff and his mother never improves, but he finally reaches a stage where he expresses anger toward her. Jeff travels far to trust himself enough to afford the luxury of deciding his own fate.

> *A solitary blue heron stood...half-hidden in the pale marsh grass...Jeff felt as deep in his aloneness as the single blue heron.*

Voigt presents this situation with great sensitivity. Jeff rejects his mother because she repeatedly betrays his trust, and he does so only after a good deal of introspection. Neither Melody's final betrayal nor Jeff's rejection is malicious. After the final betrayal, Jeff finds an isolated island, and there, "he felt at ease with himself and as if he had come home to a place where he could be himself, without hiding anything, without pretending even to himself." But Voigt makes it clear that while such an escape may be part of the healing process for Jeff, it is not a solution to his problems. Jeff is still alone; he has found part of himself, but he has not integrated that part into a whole person who can function in society. When he returns to Baltimore, he keeps the image of the island with him at all times but finds that he is not capable of concentrating on anything else. The guitar that has been such an important part of his life lies unnoticed in his room, and his school-work suffers to the point that he gets suspended.

It is when Jeff finally manages to leave his "island" to share his feelings with the Professor that he realizes his father loves him. Once Jeff lets any feeling inside of his emotional fortress, he is able to feel everything. He still has bad memories, but he now can live a fuller life and treasure some good memories as well.

◆ Topics for Discussion ◆

1. Are Jeff's personality characteristics more like his father's or his mother's? Who do you think he wants to be more like at the beginning of the book? And at the end?

2. Why does Jeff call his father "the Professor"?

3. Why does Jeff continue to write Melody letters, even though she does not answer any of them? If Melody had written back, what do you think she might have written about—her own life or Jeff's?

4. Why does Gambo decide to make Jeff the heir to her estate?

5. What are the differences between the summer when Jeff is twelve and the summer when he is thirteen?

◆ Ideas for Reports and Papers ◆

1. Why do the Professor and Jeff decide to move to the small house on the Chesapeake Bay? How does this quiet setting affect Jeff?

2. Brother Thomas and the Professor are good friends even though they appear to be very different. What is the basis for their friendship? How are they alike?

3. What is the relationship between the book's title and its themes?

4. Analyze the attraction that the Tillerman family holds for Jeff.

5. Read another of Voigt's books that includes Jeff as a character. How does the way other characters see Jeff change your understanding of his personality?

◆ Related Titles ◆

A Solitary Blue is the third of six books that deal with the Tillerman family. Each book depicts many of the same characters but through different eyes. Jeff Greene figures in four of the six books. He first appears as a minor character in *Dicey's Song*, as an insecure, frightened, but likable teen-ager who is drawn to the Tillermans. *A Solitary Blue* is Jeff's story. Jeff surfaces next in *Come a Stranger*, where he is seen through Mina Smith's eyes. Mina describes Jeff as one of those rare people who have the capacity to love deeply, and she says that he has never fallen in love with anyone but Dicey Tillerman. In *Sons from Afar*, Mrs. Tillerman reflects briefly on Jeff's personality, and readers learn that he has gone away to college. The other two books in the Tillerman series are *Homecoming*, the first book about Dicey and her brothers and sister, and

The Runner, the story of Bullet Tillerman, Dicey's uncle.

◆ For Further Reference ◆

Donahue, Rosanne. "New Realism in Children's Fiction." In *Masterworks of Children's Literature*, edited by William T. Moynihan and Mary E. Shaner. Vol. 8. New York: Chelsea House, 1985. A critical survey of new realistic books and their impact on the field of children's literature. *A Solitary Blue* is discussed in the context of novels that depict children surviving on their own.

Irving, Elsie K. "Cynthia Voigt." *Horn Book* (August 1983): 410-412. Voigt's mother gives an insider's view of the author.

Jameson, Gloria. "The Triumph of the Spirit in Cynthia Voigt's *Homecoming, Dicey's Song*, and *A Solitary Blue*." In *Triumphs of the Spirit in Children's Literature*, edited by Francelia Butler and Richard Rotert. Hamden, CT: Shoe String Press, 1986. Focuses on how Dicey's and Jeff's spirits triumph as they struggle to survive and develop.

Lukens, Rebecca J., ed. *A Critical Handbook of Children's Literature*. 3d. ed. Glenview, IL: Scott, Foresman, 1986. Discusses the theme of love in *A Solitary Blue* and the way Jeff's internal conflict contributes to the book's plot.

Reed, Arthea J. S. "Transition from Childhood into Adulthood." In *Reaching Adolescents: The Young Adult Book and the School*. New York: Holt, Rinehart and Winston, 1985. This chapter discusses Jeff's two trips to visit his mother as symbolic of his emergence into adulthood.

Voigt, Cynthia. "Newbery Medal Acceptance." *Horn Book* (August 1983): 401-409. Voigt discusses her philosophy about quality literature for young people.

Voigt, Jessica. "Cynthia Voigt." *Horn Book* (August 1983): 413. A reflection on Voigt written by her daughter.

Rosanne Donahue
University of Massachusetts at Boston

THE SOUL BROTHERS AND SISTER LOU
Novel
1968

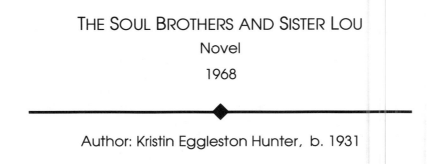

Author: Kristin Eggleston Hunter, b. 1931

Major Books for Young Adults

The Soul Brothers and Sister Lou,
   1968
Boss Cat, 1971
The Pool Table War, 1972

Uncle Daniel and the Raccoon, 1972
Guests in the Promised Land, 1973
Lou in the Limelight, 1981

♦ About the Author ♦

Kristin Eggleston Hunter was born on September 12, 1931, in Philadelphia, Pennsylvania. Her father was a school principal and U.S. Army colonel, and her mother worked as a pharmacist and teacher. Hunter earned a bachelor's degree in education from the University of Pennsylvania in 1951. Although she was trained to teach elementary school, she decided instead to pursue a variety of employment opportunities. She has worked as a copywriter for advertising agencies and, at different times, a research assistant, lecturer assistant, and lecturer in English at the University of Pennsylvania. Hunter has also held the post of writer-in-residence at Emory University.

Hunter's writing career began while she was still in junior high school. At the age of fourteen, she wrote a column for young people that appeared in the Philadelphia edition of the *Pittsburgh Courier*. Hunter's first novel, *God Bless the Child* (1964), illustrates her exceptional ability to capture the essence of black life in the inner city. An adult novel about a young black girl's struggle to escape the poverty and despair of Harlem, *God Bless the Child* introduces Hunter's particular interest in the plight of black females. Hunter's next novel, *The Landlord* (1966), is a light-hearted account of the problems a rich young man faces when he buys an inner-city apartment building. The novel's humorous tone does not detract from the author's serious reflections on the problem of poverty.

While Hunter's first two novels were written for adults, her later fiction is directed toward young adults. Her best-known novel for young readers, *The Soul Brothers and Sister Lou*, received an award from the National Council on Interracial Books for Children in 1968, and also was honored with the Mass Media Brotherhood Award from the National Conference of Christians and Jews in 1969, and the Lewis Carroll

Shelf Award in 1971. Hunter published a sequel, *Lou in the Limelight*, in 1981, and continues to write fine books for children and young adults.

◆ Overview ◆

The Soul Brothers and Sister Lou explores important questions involving sibling rivalry, racial antagonism between black teen-agers and white police officers, problems of self-acceptance, and a young adult's struggle to break free of parental control. The novel's central character, fourteen-year-old Louretta (Lou) Hawkins, confronts an array of conflicts within her family, school, and community, allowing Hunter an opportunity to examine several important themes.

The ideas that Hunter develops through her central and supporting characters are familiar to most adolescents. Many youngsters compete with their siblings for their parents' attention and affection, just as Louretta competes with her sister, Arneatha. Louretta is convinced that her mother gives Arneatha special privileges. Believing that Arneatha is her mother's "pet" causes Louretta to suffer tremendous emotional pain.

The teen-ager's need for some private space at home is another concern with which most adolescents can identify. Louretta has no privacy because she lives in a small house with ten family members and must share her room with two younger sisters. As she contemplates her severely crowded environment, she realizes that many of her friends live under similar conditions. She understands why teen-agers gather on street corners and in alleys after school. To alleviate this problem, Louretta decides to establish a clubhouse where she and her friends can meet after school for safe, wholesome fun. Much of the novel centers on Louretta's fight to gain support for her idea from her peers and from skeptical adults.

Hunter's novel also addresses the need to achieve self-acceptance. Some of Louretta's friends ridicule her reddish brown hair and light complexion, making her feel unattractive, self-conscious, and different. Fortunately, Louretta's mother helps her to understand and appreciate her diverse ethnic heritage. In *The Soul Brothers and Sister Lou*, Louretta embarks on a frequently painful but essential voyage of discovery, learning about courage, commitment, self-confidence, and ethnic pride.

◆ Setting ◆

The story is set in an area called Southside in an unnamed city in the northern United States during the 1960s. Plagued with gang violence, crime, and police brutality, Hunter's locale is reminiscent of many large, urban neighborhoods where the vast majority of the residents are poor and black. Arrogant, bigoted white police officers patrol the streets of the fictional Southside, harassing black teen-agers.

Most of the action in the novel takes place in the Southside clubhouse for teen-agers that Louretta helps to establish. Lou and her friends are sensitive to the racism in their community, and they are aware of the civil rights movement that is gaining momentum throughout much of the United States. While the level of organized social activism in Southside is low, a few militant youngsters involved with the clubhouse print a newspaper containing articles urging adults to join them in protests against police intimidation.

Jacket illustration by Ilse Koehn for *The Soul Brothers and Sister Lou* by Kristin Hunter. Charles Scribner's Sons: New York (1968).

Two other significant features of Southside include the ubiquitous storefront churches and a small group of Black Muslims whose presence in the community signals the emergence of black pride among the residents.

◆ Themes and Characters ◆

Louretta Hawkins and her older brother William are the most fully developed characters in *The Soul Brothers and Sister Lou*. A courageous fourteen-year-old, Louretta challenges gang leaders to reject violence and to pursue peaceful, productive goals. Louretta also reminds adults of their responsibility to teen-agers. She persuades parents and teachers to get involved with the clubhouse, and she encourages honest dialogue between teen-agers and adults. On a more

personal level, Louretta struggles to overcome the deep resentment that she feels toward her father, who abandoned his family when he could not find work so that his wife could qualify for welfare assistance. Louretta is a sensitive, dynamic character who triumphs over difficult problems during the course of the novel.

William, Lou's twenty-one-year-old brother, acts as a surrogate father for his siblings. Although his job at the post office provides enough income to support the family in his father's absence, William has studied printing in night school and dreams of opening his own printing business. But his goal seems out of reach because his domineering mother—fearful that the printing business would fail and force the family back onto the dreaded welfare rolls—insists that William keep his "safe" job at the post office. But Lou's faith in her brother's ability to build a successful business bolsters his self-confidence, and he decides to open his shop despite his mother's objections. William also plays a central role in Lou's efforts to establish the clubhouse for local teen-agers, providing a space in his shop for the club activities; moreover, he displays courage and integrity in dangerous confrontations with hostile police officers and belligerent gang members. Hunter's characterization William helps young readers understand the necessity of taking risks to reach self-fulfillment.

Eddie Bell, a blind, long-haired old man, plays a key role in the book. Hunter describes him as wearing "several layers of tattered clothing, carrying a white cane and a battered guitar case." He exerts a profound influence on Lou by teaching her to play the blues with feeling and by putting her in touch with her musical heritage. A once-famous musician, Blind Eddie experiences a new sense of purpose in his role as teacher and culture bearer. Under his wise instruction, Lou and her friends learn that the essence of "soul" is rooted in blues and gospel traditions. This knowledge gives them a heightened awareness of their cultural history.

The actions of Officer Lafferty, the central white character in the novel, symbolize the antagonistic patterns that often shaped relations between white police officers and the black citizens that they were ostensibly protecting in the 1960s. Throughout the book, Officer Lafferty and his men harass and intimidate the young people in Lou's neighborhood. Because the teen-agers witness daily examples of police brutality and wanton abuse of power, they hate and fear the officers who patrol their neighborhood. Officer Lafferty seems to derive a perverse satisfaction from provoking black youngsters into behavior that gives him cause to arrest them. In one incident, Lafferty physically assaults a pregnant teen-ager who belittles his complaints about excessive noise coming from the club-house. Hunter leaves no doubt that Lafferty and his fellow officers are racists who treat blacks with utter contempt.

Hunter also depicts a fascinating group of teen-agers who join Lou in her efforts to organize the clubhouse. Many of the youngsters are gang members who are tired of Lafferty's abusive tactics. Fess, the militant leader of the gang known as the Hawks, is also a poet. He wants to publish a newspaper that would inform and unite the community in an organized protest against conditions in the neighborhood. When a police officer accidentally kills Jethro, a popular youngster who sings tenor in Lou's group, the club's newspaper reports the tragedy, arousing the indignation of many Southside residents. A quiet unassuming teenager named Calvin uses the clubhouse activities to develop his skills as a visual artist. Calvin also shows incredible bravery in the face of threats from police officers. These teen-agers are representative of the young people that Louretta tries to save from the violent, negative influences of their environment.

Louretta's dream of rescuing her friends from the perils of the streets turns into a nightmare when police officers raid the clubhouse during a fund-raising dance, mortally wounding one of her schoolmates. This tragedy plunges Lou into despair and prompts her to charge her school and church with hypocrisy. Lou's white teachers had taught her to view police officers as friendly guardians of the public, but Lou's personal experience has created quite a different image. Moreover, Lou feels deceived by a church that continues to proclaim God's justice in the midst of chronic poverty, pervasive crime, and corrupt police offers. Lou's faith in her school is restored when she learns that several teachers, outraged by the senseless killing, persuade the mayor to allow the reopening of William's print shop and the resumption of clubhouse activities without further police harassment. Hunter's emphasis on perseverance, cooperation, and faith in human potential reinforces fundamental values that encourage young readers to develop a strong sense of self.

◆ Literary Qualities ◆

In *The Soul Brothers and Sister Lou*, Hunter creates a realistic and compelling picture of life in the inner city.

Hunter's carefully selected images and symbols evoke a complex world in which poverty, violence, and despair dominate the landscape. As a means of coping with these persistent features of their environment, many residents join youth gangs or storefront churches. By controlling certain sections of their neighborhood through verbal and physical intimidation, the gangs offer frustrated teen-agers a tempting illusion of power. Ironically, the gangs' influence does not extend to their most potent adversary, the white power structure. For many older blacks, the church, with its promise of a glorious life after death, also represents a desirable escape from the unpleasant realities of their surroundings. Lou's mother is one of countless such people who immerse themselves in religion as they strive to make sense of their narrow, blighted lives.

Hunter invests familiar objects and settings with symbolic significance. For example, when Lou first discovers an old piano left in a building once occupied by a storefront church, she is elated, for in the soft evening light the upright looks beautiful. But when Lou examines the piano in the daylight, she notices numerous scars and scratches on the old cabinet; some keys are missing, and the rest are discolored and dirty. Furthermore, the keys make sour, twanging sounds. Clearly, the old piano symbolizes the sharp contrasts that often exist between appearance and reality. This important idea is emphasized further in Hunter's portrayal of Blind Eddie Bell, the ragged, unkempt blues musician, who at first glance appears to be a worthless old tramp. A popular performer in his heyday, Blind Eddie apparently lost his audience when musical tastes shifted from blues to rock 'n' roll. Nevertheless, he is still an accomplished pianist who not only teaches Lou to play blues chords, but also serves as an invaluable source of black music history. Blind Eddie symbolizes the differences between appearance and reality, but more important, he represents the discarded elements of black culture that must be reclaimed and preserved.

Another effective use of images and symbols is Hunter's depiction of the hospital staff that Lou observes when she tries to donate blood for her injured friend. She notices that blacks wearing "dingy gray uniforms" work in the drab, dimly lighted basement, whereas white employees dressed in white work upstairs in cheerful, bright spaces. The workers in this hospital scene are meant to suggest the respective positions of blacks and whites in 1960s society at large.

◆ Social Sensitivity ◆

Socially relevant issues in *The Soul Brothers and Sister Lou* revolve around racism. Long-standing tensions between abusive white police officers and black residents point up the need for effective communication and mutual respect across racial and civic lines. Some readers may view Hunter's portrayal of the police officers who patrol the Southside as too harsh and consistently negative. But historical accounts of American race relations in the 1960s support Hunter's depiction. Hunter does not mean to imply that all black-white relations were antagonistic during this period in U.S. history. In fact, she is careful to indicate the crucial role that Lou's white teachers play in exposing the police officers' abuse of authority. One of Lou's white teachers also volunteers to help develop activities for the teen-agers who come to the clubhouse after school.

Another important social concern that Hunter addresses in the novel is sexism. Throughout the book Lou encounters young men who feel threatened by her self-confidence and intelligence. Indeed, one of the young men involved with a neighborhood civil-rights group tells Lou: "Women have a place in this movement, but they can't be the leaders." Lou rejects the limitations that her male peers seek to impose upon her, and she takes a leadership role in the general clubhouse activities. Lou also infuriates gang leaders when she denounces their violent tactics and persuades some gang members to try nonviolent means of resolving differences. Lou also wields considerable influence in the singing group known as "The Soul Brothers and Sister Lou." Lou is an excellent role model for young women who may suffer the effects of others' sexist attitudes.

◆ Topics for Discussion ◆

1. At the beginning of the novel, Lou dreads going home after school. Why does she take the long way home? Is she envious of the boys' freedom to gather on the sidewalks and in the alleys?

2. White police officers "constantly arrested Southside fellows whether they had done anything wrong or not." How does this abuse of authority affect the police officers' image in the Southside community?

3. Most parents encourage their children's efforts to achieve career goals. Why does Mrs. Hawkins oppose her son's plan to open his own print shop?

4. Blind Eddie Bell introduces Lou and her friends to the blues. Does Blind Eddie suggest a link between black gospel and the blues?

5. Lou sets Fess's poem, "Hungry Cat Blues," to music. What is the poem about?

6. Explain why Lou feels like an "outsider" after the policeman shoots Jethro. Is she disillusioned?

7. In what ways are sexism and racism similar? Find two examples of sexist attitudes in the novel, and compare them to examples of racism in the book.

8. Why did Lou's father abandon his wife and children? Does the welfare system bear some responsibility for the high incidence of absent fathers in poor black families?

9. Some critics view the novel's ending as contrived and unsatisfactory. What do you think of the ending? Does it ignore the serious social issues raised in the preceding chapters?

◆ Ideas for Reports and Papers ◆

1. For the most part, Hunter's black characters speak standard English but they are also fluent in street dialect. Is this dialect difficult to understand? Has it changed since the 1960s? Make a list of examples of street dialect from the novel.

2. Lou and her young friends strive to grasp the essence of "soul" and to express it through their music. Is black

English an aspect of "soul"? Explain. How would you define "soul"?

3. At one point in the novel, Lou attends a meeting of Black Muslims. Consult an encyclopedia or other general reference work for background information on Black Muslims (also known as the Nation of Islam). Who were Elijah Muhammad and Malcolm X? What role did these men play in the civil-rights movement of the 1960s? You may also want to consult some periodicals and report on the activities of the Black Muslims today, particularly in urban areas such as Washington, D.C., or Detroit.

4. Blind Eddie Bell identifies blind Lemon Jefferson and W. C. Handy as major figures in the history and development of the blues. Write a brief biographical sketch of these musicians, highlighting their achievements.

5. Realistic characters possess both good and bad personality traits. List some of the positive and negative traits that you see in Lou. Explain how they surface in the book.

◆ Related Titles ◆

After receiving numerous letters from young readers who wanted to know what happened to the characters in *The Soul Brothers and Sister Lou*, Hunter wrote a sequel called *Lou in the Limelight*. In the sequel Lou and the singing group have an agent and a recording contract, and they earn large salaries performing in Las Vegas. But their success exposes them to many temptations. For example, the boys develop an expensive gambling habit, and Lou becomes involved with drugs. Artistically, *Lou in the Limelight* suffers

from poor character development and a weak conclusion, but readers will appreciate the novel's exciting plot and the valuable moral lessons it teaches.

◆ For Further Reference ◆

Neufeld, John. "Review." *New York Times Book Review* (January 26, 1969): 26. The review praises Hunter's vivid description of the inner city but finds the book's ending unrealistic and contrived.

Sutherland, Zena. "Review." *Saturday Review* (October 19, 1968): 37. This review identifies Lou's struggle to achieve self-acceptance as a central theme in the novel.

Thompson, Judith, and Gloria Woodard. "Black Perspective in Books for Children." In *The Black American in Books for Children,* edited by Donnarae MacCann and Gloria Woodard. Metuchen, NJ: Scarecrow Press, 1972. This brief commentary applauds Hunter's depiction of inner city culture from a black point of view.

Elvin Holt
Southwest Texas State University

SOUNDER

Novel

1969

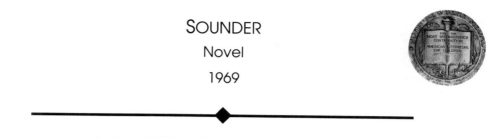

Author: William H. Armstrong, b. 1914

Major Books for Young Adults

Sounder, 1969
*Barefoot in the Grass: The Story of
    Grandma Moses*, 1970
Sour Land, 1971
*Hadassah: Esther the Orphan
    Queen*, 1972

The MacLeod Place, 1972
The Mills of God, 1973
The Education of Abraham Lincoln,
    1974
JoAnna's Miracle, 1978
Tawny and Dingo, 1979

◆ About the Author ◆

William Howard Armstrong was born September 14, 1914, near Lexington, Virginia. He was raised on a farm in the lovely, history-steeped Shenandoah valley, and the descriptions of southern life in his most famous novel, *Sounder*, reflect his Christian upbringing in the rural South. The strong individuals that play major roles in Armstrong's fiction can be traced back to the history of his neighborhood; Stonewall Jackson, the famous steel-willed Confederate general killed in the Civil War, had taught Sunday school at the same church Armstrong attended as a boy. Military history was a part of Armstrong's childhood because several Civil War battles had been fought near his home.

His love of history was cemented at the Augusta Military Academy, a private military high school that he attended from 1928 to 1932. According to his family, Armstrong wrote his first story as a cadet at Augusta, but the story was so good that his teachers falsely accused him of plagiarism. Later, the story was published in the literary magazine at Hampden-Sydney College, where Armstrong edited both this magazine and the college newspaper. He graduated from Hampden-Sydney with honors in history in 1936 and also studied history at the University of Virginia.

Armstrong married Martha Stonestreet Williams in 1942. Three years later, he became a history teacher at Kent School, a private school in Kent, Connecticut. His wife died when his children were very young and Armstrong raised his family as a single parent. He has been a teacher most of his adult life and also raises sheep on his farm.

During the 1950s and 1960s, Armstrong focused on writing history books and study skills guides rather

Illustration by James Barkley for *Sounder* by William H. Armstrong. Harper & Row: New York (1969).

In the early 1970s, Armstrong wrote two more books that echo the characters and plot of *Sounder*. *Sour Land* features Moses Waters, a black man of near-mythic goodness, as its hero. *The Mills of God* set in Appalachia during the Great Depression, has a boy and a dog as central figures and provides vivid descriptions of the era and setting.

During the 1970s, Armstrong wrote three books about historical figures: *Barefoot in the Grass,* a folksy biography of another strong individual he admired, the painter Grandma Moses; *Hadassah: Esther the Orphan Queen,* a fictionalized account of the Old Testament figure Esther who started life as an orphan but rose to become a queen; and *The Education of Abraham Lincoln,* which dramatizes Abraham Lincoln's early life. None of Armstrong's later historical portraits or novels were as highly praised or as popular as *Sounder*.

◆ Overview ◆

Sounder reflects Armstrong's personal history, his knowledge of southern rural life, and his admiration for strong individuals. Concentrating on an innocent child's perspective, the story provides graphic descriptions of the cruelties inflicted upon a black sharecropper family trapped by poverty and lack of education. *Sounder* is the tragic and moving story of an unnamed boy who is devoted to his family and their faithful hound, Sounder. His father, jailed for stealing food to feed the starving family, is put on a chain gang that is constantly moved around the state, and the boy sets out on a quest to find him. The story also involves the boy's loving relationship with Sounder, who is named for his resonant howl that reverberates across the countryside.

than fiction. He wrote his fictional masterpiece, *Sounder,* in 1969, in the heat of the civil rights movement of the 1960s. It won both the Newbery Medal and the Lewis Carroll Shelf Award in 1970, and was called the best children's book of the year by the *New York Times. Sounder* received high praise for its tragic and understated beauty, its fine descriptions, and its depiction of a boy's experiences with his dog and with the racism in his society. Like Armstrong's subsequent fiction for young adults, it portrays a strong individual who strives to overcome racial injustice.

Sounder begins shortly before Christmas, in a small cabin on a poor, desolate farm somewhere in the American South, where the boy lives with his parents and siblings. There are two dimensions to the setting—one psychological, the other physical. The exact place and time of the story are deliberately vague, but *Sounder* probably takes place around 1900, before tractors and machines were common on small farms. The psychological setting, the young boy's mind, is more precisely defined.

• Themes and Characters •

he unnamed boy is the book's central consciousness and only well-developed character. The boy is first seen as a lonely child, perhaps six or seven years old, who idolizes his father and loves to hunt with him and Sounder. Rather than providing a description of the boy, Armstrong allows the boy's thoughts and observations to reveal that he is strong, curious, and good-hearted. His family is illiterate, and he longs to learn to read. After Sounder is shot, the boy comforts and tries to help him, demonstrating his devotion to the dog. When his father is unfairly jailed, the boy is adventurous enough to leave his mother and his small cabin and embark on a quest to find his father and to learn how to read.

The boy eventually finds a teacher who becomes a substitute father. The boy develops into an unselfish, hard-working teen-ager who takes care of his mother and the other children. He never forgets his roots and returns from school in the summers to work the family farm and pay the rent. The boy

stoically endures pain and failure, overcoming all setbacks with a quiet nobility.

The courageous and faithful dog Sounder is "a mixture of Georgia redbone hound and bulldog." Both Sounder's bark and his heart are noble and larger than life. Armstrong describes Sounder's melodious bark as haunting the countryside: "But it was not an ordinary bark. It filled up the night and made music as though the branches of all the trees were being pulled across silver strings." The dog, a wonderful hunter, suffers a crippling gunshot wound when he bravely goes to his master's aid as the father is being arrested. By drawing parallels between the fates of Sounder and the father, Armstrong makes the point that humans are treated like dogs in the racist early twentieth-century South. Both are subjected to cruel and unprovoked violence that cripples and eventually kills them.

The boy's mother is a long-suffering and hard-working woman who believes that fate is too powerful a force to resist. She takes in laundry and shells walnuts to eke out a meager existence. Because she does not want her son to leave home, she discourages him from learning to read. The mother constantly hums or sings the woeful song "That Lonesome Road." A limited, sad figure, she talks, like everyone in the story, in short laconic sentences, and tries to hide her emotions.

The father appears only at the beginning and the end of the story. At the beginning, he is a strong, resourceful, and loving man who finds joy in hunting. He hunts not just for sport but to put meat on his family's table. As the story opens, game is scarce and the family is starving. In desperation, the father steals a ham and sausages to feed his family. The father loves his family passionately and risks his own freedom so they can eat. Brutally arrested and treated like an animal in front of his family, he is ashamed to speak to his son when the boy comes to see him in the county jail. At the end of the story, the father returns, crippled from a mining accident after years of labor on a chain gang. A man broken by his society's brutal response to a small crime, he dies while hunting with Sounder.

Armstrong uses the young boy and his family to dramatize the evils of racism and poverty. Notions of social injustice and unnecessary cruelty are developed through precise and realistic descriptions of the father's arrest, the boy's visit to him in jail, and the incident of the father's crippling. The boy's courage in confronting racism, his endurance in the face of opposition, his unselfish love for his family, and his love of learning are traits Armstrong promotes as necessary for the survival of humankind. The boy learns to read in order to help himself overcome his loneliness and to break the chains of ignorance that imprison his family. Thus, the book is also about the power of literature and stories to comfort people and to help them deal with hardships.

◆ Literary Qualities ◆

By leaving the family unnamed and by keeping the exact setting somewhat unclear, Armstrong makes the story more universal. The vagueness of the world outside the cabin reflects the limited vision and knowledge of the novel's illiterate protagonist. Armstrong uses a third-person limited omniscient point of view that focuses on how the boy thinks and reacts to events. This method of setting the story in a person's mind and trying to imitate the ways his mind works is called "psychological realism." The boy's consciousness and innocence form the lens through which readers view his world.

Armstrong's descriptive powers are a strength in *Sounder*. His precise images are especially effective in portraying aspects of the family's daily routine. For example, his vivid description of them harvesting walnuts elevates a mundane activity to an almost mystical ritual:

> Inside the cabin, the boy's mother sat by the stove, picking kernels of walnuts with a bent hairpin. The woman watched each year for the walnuts to fall after the first hard frost. Each day she went with the children and gathered all that had fallen. The brownish-green husks, oozing their dark purple stain, were beaten off on a flat rock outside the cabin. On the same rock, the nuts were cracked after they had dried for several weeks in a tin box under the stove. When kernel-picking time came, and before it was dark each day, the boy or the father took a hammer with a home-made handle, went to the flat rock, and cracked as many as could be kerneled in a night.

Armstrong also artfully links physical descriptions of farm life to the young boy's emotions, thus integrating elements of the natural landscape with the boy's inner life. One passage links the boy's loneliness at night to the wind blowing outside. By connecting loneliness, an emotion, to the natural force of the wind, Armstrong creates a striking contrast between the coldness and cruelty of the world outside the family to the warmth and light of the world of the family inside the cabin.

The story is also well plotted and uses parallelism between the crippled dog and the father especially effectively. The father almost disappears from the story after his arrest, and the boy's attention shifts to Sounder. The boy waits weeks for Sounder to return, and when the mangled dog hobbles home on three legs, he is nurtured by both the boy and the mother. The dog's maiming foreshadows the father's injury. The wounded Sounder becomes a kind of stand-in for the father who is gone, and he absorbs some of the family's love for their missing father.

◆ Social Sensitivity ◆

Because Armstrong attempts to realistically portray a racist society, he includes scenes of violence and racist language that readers may find offensive. Without excessive goriness, he graphically describes wounds to the dog and to the boy, and he also describes violent details of the boy's revenge fantasies.

Sounder has caused a controversy among critics over whether the depiction of the family is racist. In an article printed in Donnarae MacCann and Gloria Woodard's *The Black American in Books for Children: Readings in Racism*, Albert Schwartz attacks Armstrong for imposing a "white fundamentalist" style and belief structure onto his representation of black culture. Schwartz contends that a white author who leaves his black characters unnamed is unconsciously expressing a form of "white supremacy" that "has long denied human individualism to the Black person." But critic and young adult author John Rowe Townsend defends Armstrong, arguing that omitting the characters' names simply universalizes their experiences. Whatever side one takes on the issue, there is little doubt that *Sounder* is a powerful reminder of the pain and suffering caused by racism.

◆ Topics for Discussion ◆

1. What effect does Armstrong create by not naming any of the characters in this book? Do you think this makes the characters seem more timeless and universal, or does it make them seem like stereotypes?

2. What does the author gain by telling the story through the eyes of a child? Does the boy's innocence intensify your reactions to events?

3. Why is the dog's name used as the title of this book? What purposes does the dog Sounder serve in the novel and in the lives of the family?

4. In your opinion, is there as much racism today as there was in the time depicted by *Sounder*? Are there different ways of expressing racism today?

5. Can the unnamed boy who is the protagonist in *Sounder* be called a hero? If so, what are some of the heroic traits he displays?

◆ Ideas for Reports and Papers ◆

1. How does Armstrong draw the reader into the child's point of view in the novel? Describe how he uses his third-person limited omniscient point of view to move in and out of the boy's consciousness.

2. Compare the beliefs and attitudes of the boy and the mother in *Sounder*. In what ways do their similarities and differences help characterize each of them and make them individuals?

3. Twice in the novel the boy wishes for revenge against cruel lawmen. Select one of these revenge fantasies and demonstrate how the boy's desire for revenge helps make him a more convincing character.

4. Armstrong says that as a child he loved Bible stories. In what ways does he use biblical stories in the novel? What effect does the use of these stories have in the novel?

5. Some critics have said that Armstrong's portrait of the family in *Sounder* is flawed because he depicts the black men and women as powerless. Do you agree or disagree with these critics? Be sure to cite examples from the novel to support your position.

6. Even though *Sounder* is apparently set in a much earlier time, show how the novel reflects the events and sentiments of the 1960s, particularly the civil rights movement.

7. Compare the 1972 film version of *Sounder* with the novel. What are the major differences in the focus of the novel and of the film? Who is the most dominant character in the film? In the novel? How do you explain these differences?

◆ Adaptations ◆

The 1972 film version of *Sounder* is quite different from the novel. It stresses the unity of the black family and its strength, and the family members are given names. Paul Winfield plays the father, Nathan Morgan; Cicely Tyson plays the mother, Rebecca Morgan; and Kevin Hooks plays the boy, David Lee Morgan, who is older than the boy in the book. Also, a definite setting, Louisiana in 1933, is established. The mother is not the passive martyr depicted in the novel but is instead a courageous, powerful woman who encourages her son to learn to read. Nathan returns home after only one year and is not as horribly crippled as he is in the novel. Sounder is not as badly wounded either, and he accompanies the boy on his quest to find his father. The Hollywood version has a happy ending with the reunited family sending the boy to school. Several characters not in the novel appear in the film. Praised by most critics, the film is available on videotape.

A successful sequel to the film, *Part 2, Sounder*, was released in 1976 and starred Harold Sylvester, Ebony Wright, and Taj Mahal.

◆ For Further Reference ◆

Armstrong, Christopher, David Armstrong, and Mary Armstrong. "William Armstrong." *Horn Book* 46 (August 1970): 356-358. A short biographical article written by William Armstrong's three children.

Armstrong, William H. "Newbery Acceptance." *Horn Book* 46 (August 1970): 352-355. Armstrong's acceptance speech, in which he discusses his early reading habits and readers' reactions to *Sounder*.

Deutsch, Leonard J. "The Named and Unnamed." In *Children's Novels and the Movies,* edited by Douglas Street. New York: Ungar Publishing, 1983. An excellent comparison of the novel and film versions of *Sounder.*

Jordan, June Meyer. "Review." *New York Times Book Review* (October 26, 1969): 42. A very favorable review of *Sounder.*

MacCann, Donnarae, and Gloria Woodard, eds. *The Black American in Books for Children: Readings in Racism.* Metuchen, NJ: Scarecrow Press, 1972. Contains several articles that attack Armstrong's views of black people. The articles by Rae Alexander, Evelyn Geller, and Albert V. Schwartz give negative assessments of the novel.

Townsend, John Rowe. *Written for Children: An Outline of English Language Children's Literature.* Rev. ed. New York: Lippincott, 1974. Townsend defends *Sounder,* contending that the charges against the novel are misguided, and that the tale is both well told and well crafted.

David J. Amante
University of North Carolina, Charlotte

SPUNKWATER, SPUNKWATER!: A LIFE OF MARK TWAIN
Biography
1968

---◆---

Author: James Playsted Wood, b. 1905

Major Books for Young Adults

The Queen's Most Honorable Pirate,
1961
A Hound, a Bay Horse, and a Turtle-
Dove: A Life of Thoreau for the
Young Reader, 1963
Trust Thyself: A Life of Ralph Waldo
Emerson for the Young Reader,
1964
The Man Who Hated Sherlock
Holmes: A Life of Sir Arthur
Conan Doyle, 1965
The Lantern Bearer: A Life of Robert
Louis Stevenson, 1965
The Snark Was a Boojum: A Life of
Lewis Carroll, 1966

What's the Market?: The Story of
Stock Exchanges, 1966
Sunnyside: A Life of Washington Ir-
ving, 1967
Spunkwater, Spunkwater!: A Life of
Mark Twain, 1968
Mr. Jonathan Edwards, 1968
This Is Advertising, 1968
I Told You So!: A Life of H. G. Wells,
1969
The Unpardonable Sin: A Life of
Nathaniel Hawthorne, 1970
The Admirable Cotton Mather, 1971
This Little Pig: The Story of Market-
ing, 1971
Emily Elizabeth Dickinson, 1972

◆ About the Author ◆

James Playsted Wood was born on December 11, 1905, in Brooklyn, New York. He earned two degrees from Columbia University—a bachelor's in 1927 and a master's in 1933. Wood taught English for seven years at Du-Pont Manual Training High School in Louisville, Kentucky, where he also contributed book reviews for the Louisville *Courier-Journal.* From 1937 until 1946 he was a member of the English department at Amherst College in Massachusetts. A member of the U.S. Army Air Forces during World War II, he served in the Pentagon office of the chief of staff, General George C. Marshall. He became a major and earned the army commendation medal. During the war, on August 14, 1943, he married Elizabeth Craig, a teacher of Latin, French, and Greek.

In 1946 Wood left both the military and Amherst College to work as assistant to the director of research at the Curtis Publishing Company in Philadelphia. He stayed with the Curtis Company until 1962. During this period Wood became associated with the children's magazine *Jack and Jill*, first as a contributor of stories, articles, and poems, and later as managing editor (1954-1955) and contributing editor (1959-1964). A full-time writer since 1966, Wood has written extensively about magazines, advertising, and the stock market. Wood targets much of his writing for young people. For very young readers he has produced several fantasy books and for young adults he has written both historical fiction and literary biographies.

• Overview •

Mark Twain's *Huckleberry Finn* (1884) is considered by many to be one of the greatest American novels, a humorous, moving tale of American boyhood that has been interpreted as reflecting the development of a U.S. national identity. A knowledge of the life of *Huckleberry Finn's* author is of great importance in understanding this classic book and its impact, for in Mark Twain, Samuel Langhorne Clemens (Twain's real name) created his most flamboyant character. In *Spunkwater, Spunkwater!* Wood presents the essential Mark Twain, and he does so with a verve that both shows his own appreciation of the man and makes this biography a satisfying and informative reading experience.

• Setting •

Because Mark Twain roamed the world, this biography is set across continents, spanning rivers and oceans as it follows Twain on his travels. Born in 1835, Twain spent most of his boyhood in Hannibal, Missouri, on the Mississippi River, the same river that is the setting for much of his best fiction. He began working as a printer's assistant in Hannibal at the age of twelve; six

years later, he left home to become a roving printer, working in Saint Louis, New York, Philadelphia, and Keokuk, Iowa. In 1857 he began an apprenticeship as riverboat pilot, a career that ended when the Civil War broke out in 1861. After a few weeks as a Confederate soldier, he followed his brother, Orion Clemens, west to Nevada. Twain's energetic nature and curiosity made him a rambler; he worked first as a silver miner in Carson City, Nevada, and later as a reporter in Virginia City and San Francisco. In 1866 he made his first excursion out of the United States, visiting the Sandwich (Hawaiian) Islands. The next year he spent several months touring Palestine and the Mediterranean. Even after marrying in 1870 and settling in Buffalo, New York, and later in Hartford, Connecticut, Twain was often away from home on lecture tours. He lived in Europe for most of the period between 1891 and 1900. As authentically American as he was, Twain was also a citizen of the world. The changing landscapes of his life are delightfully reflected in Wood's biography.

• Themes and Characters •

As a mature man, Mark Twain would always look to the past as a happier and more innocent time than the present. He cherished and often wrote about his boyhood in Hannibal and his brief career as a Mississippi riverboat pilot. In his writings he gave these earlier periods of his life an almost mythical coloring.

Over the years, Twain would also wrap himself in the trappings of mythology. As Wood makes clear, Twain was never deeply concerned with the literal truth

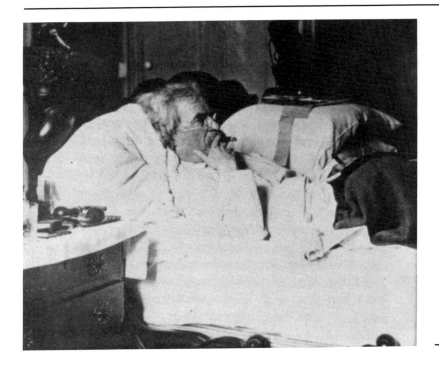

Photograph by Brown Brothers in *Spunkwater, Spunkwater!* by James Playsted Wood. Pantheon: New York (1968).

about his own life, especially if his imagination could improve upon its events. Humor was also part of these exaggerations—a humor that Twain learned on the fringe of the frontier in his Missouri days, and later on the frontier itself in the far West. Wood details Twain's development as an unsurpassed humorist, revealing that the passionate Twain was capable of making both love and hatred appear equally funny.

After a poor but happy childhood in Missouri, Twain worked as a printer, a riverboat pilot, a reporter, and finally, a writer and lecturer. He married Olivia Langdon, a New York heiress, in 1870, in Elmira, New York. The couple had four children: Langdon, who died in infancy, Clara, Susan, and Jean. At the age of forty, Twain was afraid that he had exhausted himself as a writer, but he was most productive during his middle age, when he published *Life on the Mississippi* (1883), *Tom Sawyer* (1876), and *The Prince and the Pauper* (1882). *Huckleberry Finn*, generally recognized as Twain's best novel, was published in 1884. Twain suffered severe financial losses in the late 1800s, and in the early 1900s endured personal tragedy as well with the death of his wife and two of his daughters. Twain died on April 21, 1910, in Redding, Connecticut.

Wood portrays Twain as lovable but self-centered and cantankerous. He believes that the pessimism of Twain's later works, as seen in *The Mysterious Stranger* (written in 1898 but published posthumously) and *What Is Man?* (1904)—both indictments of what Twain called "the damned human race" in his final years—has been taken too seriously by critics. While pessimism also darkened the tone of Twain's last great full-length novel, *A Connecticut Yankee in King Arthur's Court* (1889), Wood believes that this darkened outlook simply reflects the rage of a man who suddenly ran out of what once had seemed inexhaustible luck.

Wood's biography focuses on Twain's rambunctious, tempestuous character to the near-exclusion of other characters who figure prominently in Twain's life. Wood states, for example, that Twain's wife, Livy (Olivia), was the object of Twain's undying devotion, yet Wood's characterization of her is so thin that it becomes difficult to determine exactly what traits in Livy inspire Twain's adoration. Livy, from a wealthy, cultured family, was a quiet, sickly young woman whom Twain "looked on with awe and wonder as an ethereal being." Wood notes that Livy "adored" Twain, though she "could not always keep her unpredictable husband in order." Twain, did, however, trust Livy's editorial judgment and had her review all of his work before publication.

Another figure close to Twain was the writer and editor William Dean Howells, whom Wood describes as "almost as necessary to Twain as Livy herself." Howells's character is only superficially revealed, but he is portrayed as Twain's warm, generous, and loyal friend. Wood emphasizes the bond these men shared, noting that "Mark Twain was extravagantly, almost fiercely attached to Howells, and Howells was unreservedly convinced of the genius of Mark Twain." Quotations from the correspondence between these famous writers further illustrate the intimate nature of their relationship, as do Wood's descriptions of their friendly interaction with one another.

Other friends, family members, and historical figures are mentioned throughout the biography, but Wood concentrates on the development of Twain's character and the American qualities Twain embodied. Wood holds Twain up as an example of originality, vigor, and boldness; he sees in Twain "the voluble symbol of the kind of practical wisdom most Americans admired."

◆ Literary Qualities ◆

Wood says that he learned to read from listening to the works of nineteenth-century American authors Horatio Alger, Jr., and Winston Churchill. His grandfather often read aloud to him from Alger's famous rags-to-riches stories, and his father read him Churchill's novels at night. To Wood, writing a biography of Mark Twain must have seemed like telling a true-life Horatio Alger story. But whereas Alger's heroes are rather simple, Twain was a very complex man. Indeed, biographers are still trying to reconstruct the true events of Twain's life and finding that to do so they must often treat his own accounts of it with distrust. Wood's brief biography does not pretend to be a definitive work, but it remains adequate, entertaining, and especially accessible for younger readers.

Wood, aware that Twain preferred lively tales to the literal truth, creates a biography of the storyteller that is far from dull. Twain created a new idiom for literary English by adapting the patterns and rhythms of American speech to his narrative style, and Wood's style appears to be a reflection of Twain's. The quick-paced biography is marked by short declarative sentences and a clipped, repetitive style. Wood's first chapter, for example, opens with two paragraphs detailing the things Twain loved: "Mark Twain loved cats. He loved his wife almost beyond his ability to express the depth...of his adoration. He loved his three daughters. He loved money." He proceeds in the next paragraph to juxtapose the things Twain loved with the things Twain hated. Wood thus establishes from the onset the biography's affectionate, informal tone. He recounts the events of Twain's life in great detail, but his straightforward, humorous style—punctuated by occasional authorial intrusion—creates an easy-to-read, enthusiastic account of a great American personality.

◆ Social Sensitivity ◆

Although Mark Twain's outbursts and writings often created a sensation because of Twain's colorful language and impetuous style, Wood's treatment of Twain's life is generally inoffensive. Wood neglects to develop the significant female characters in the story, and he does not explore in any depth Twain's attitudes about social issues. But in portaying Twain's relationships with the people he loved, Wood's biography reveals a caring, if bitter, individual.

◆ Topics for Discussion ◆

1. Humor is very difficult to analyze, but nearly everybody agrees that Twain was a very funny man. What made him a great American humorist?

2. Wood correctly observes that Mark Twain was both Tom Sawyer and Huck Finn. Of the two, Twain seemed to prefer Tom. Why was this?

3. What is a *persona*? How did Samuel Clemens choose certain elements of his personality to become Mark Twain?

4. Mark Twain was very image conscious and wanted to be certain that future readers of his books got the right impression of him. Has this happened?

5. Twain, a professed atheist, had several ministers as friends, such as the Reverend Joseph Twichell. How were these unlikely relationships possible?

6. According to Wood, why did Mark Twain believe that Halley's comet had personal significance for him? Was this a joke or superstition?

7. Given his attitudes about the progress of "the damned human race," do you think Twain would have been surprised by Hitler's Germany or Stalin's Russia?

◆ Ideas for Reports and Papers ◆

1. Compare the writings of Mark Twain with those of Kurt Vonnegut, who has been called a modern-day Mark Twain. What do these writers have in common in terms of viewpoint, subject matter, and style?

2. Compare the accounts of the Mississippi River in *Tom Sawyer* and *Huckleberry Finn*. Is the river simply part of the background in these books or is it sometimes a character in its own right?

3. William Faulkner's novel *The Old Man* describes the Mississippi during the flood of 1927. Compare the struggles of Faulkner's unnamed convict as he battles the currents of the river with those of Jim and Huck in *Huckleberry Finn*. Are Huck and the convict at all similar?

4. *Roughing It* describes Mark Twain's travels by stagecoach to Nevada in 1861. It has been said that Twain and Charles

Dickens have provided the best descriptions of this type of travel in the nineteenth century. Compare Dickens's novel *The Pickwick Papers* (1837) to Twain's *Roughing It*.

5. *The Mysterious Stranger* is considered a minor masterpiece and possibly the best expression of Mark Twain's pessimistic final phase. What ideas does Twain express in this work? How do you think he arrived at such a bleak outlook on humanity?

♦ Related Titles ♦

Wood's other biographies for young adults have also been praised by critics as interesting and intelligent studies of some of America's best writers. Many of Wood's subjects are eighteenth-century writers, and when read as a group these biographies provide an insightful portrait of the social and literary life of that century. Wood enthusiastically endorses the individualism of Henry David Thoreau in *A Hound, a Bay Horse, and a Turtle-Dove*, as he does that of Ralph Waldo Emerson in *Trust Thyself*. He is equally effective in his study of the enigmatic poet Emily Dickinson. These books, along with his studies of Jonathan Edwards, Cotton Mather, and Washington Irving, also provide good supplementary reading for adults.

♦ For Further Reference ♦

Brooks, Van Wyck. *The Ordeal of Mark Twain*. New York: E. P. Dutton, 1920. Brooks's work is dated but still interesting, especially as an example of early Twain biographies.

Commire, Anne, ed. *Something about the Author*. Vol. 1. Detroit: Gale Research, 1971. Contains a biographical entry on Wood.

Etheridge, James M., ed. *Contemporary Authors*. Vols. 9-10. Detroit: Gale Research, 1964. Includes a biographical entry on Wood.

Geismar, Maxwell. *Mark Twain: An American Prophet*. Boston: Houghton Mifflin, 1970. Geismar believes that the works of Twain's final period have not had the recognition they deserve.

Lauber, John. *The Making of Mark Twain*. New York: American Heritage, 1985. This biography deals with Twain's apprenticeship as a writer.

Leary, Lewis. *Mark Twain*. Minneapolis: University of Minnesota Press, 1960. This is a good, brief introduction to Twain's writings.

Karl Avery

THE STONE BOOK QUARTET

Novellas

1976-1978

◆

Author: Alan Garner, b. 1934

Major Books for Young Adults

The Weirdstone of Brisingamen,
   1960
The Moon of Gomrath, 1963
Elidor, 1965
The Owl Service, 1967

Red Shift, 1973
The Stone Book, 1976
Granny Reardun, 1977
Tom Fobble's Day, 1977
The Aimer Gate, 1978

◆ About the Author ◆

Alan Garner was born on October 17, 1934, at Alderley Edge, Cheshire, in the northwest of England. He spent much of his first ten years bedridden, suffering from spinal and cerebral meningitis, diphtheria, pleurisy, and pneumonia. As a child, Garner entertained himself with stories inspired by the irregular walls of his room, which he viewed as a fantasy landscape. This period created feelings of resentment between young characters and an ineffectual or exploitative older generation in Garner's early novels. At the same time, the author's constant references to magic spilling over into ordinary life may be an enactment of the wishful fantasies of his childhood.

Garner put chronic illness behind him in his eleventh year, quickly distinguishing himself as a student and a fiercely competitive athlete at the local school in Alderley Edge and at Manchester Grammar School. Garner went on to Magdalen College, Oxford, where he studied classical Greek literature and archeology, and developed an interest in acting. He left Oxford without a degree when he became bored with academic life.

After leaving Oxford, Garner served as an officer in the Royal Artillery until, influenced by William Golding's recently published *Lord of the Flies* (1954), he decided to become a writer. Returning to Cheshire, Garner spent four years completing his first book and researching the folklore and archeology of the region. Today Garner lives and works in the Cheshire village of Blackden-cum-Goostrey in two houses built on an ancient burial mound, similar to the ones described in several of his stories.

◆ Overview ◆

Although each of these brief stories can be read separately, *The Stone Book* and its equally slender companion volumes, *Granny Reardun, Tom Fobble's Day* and *The Aimer Gate,* gain complexity and power when read in sequence. Taken together, the books read like sections of a single novel. The quartet traces the history of an unnamed working-class family (based on Garner's own) in Chorley, Cheshire, from the 1860s of *The Stone Book* to the dark days of World War II in *Tom Fobble's Day*. Each book is the story of one special day when a member of the rising generation faces decisions that will shape his or her life in a changing world. The formula enables Garner to catch four generations of young people, not just at a dramatic moment in their own lives, but also at a crucial time in the larger story of their family and society.

At first glance the stories seem undemanding, but they are hardly simple. To read the series is to sample some of the major social, economic, and political issues of the last hundred years. Each main character's personal search for a life's role illuminates universal problems, and the books produce a compelling sense of local and family tradition.

◆ Setting ◆

The Stone Book series is set in rural Cheshire in a region of long ridges and "mosses," or boggy lowlands, within a mile of the village of Chorley. Garner accurately describes the local landscape and weather, but he emphasizes the time—which ranges from the 1860s to the 1940s—and culture of the setting, presenting his village family against the broad backdrop of history. For all their seeming isolation, Chorley and its people are touched by the same historical currents that wash through the outside world during the nine decades covered by the stories.

◆ Themes and Characters ◆

The theme of constant, relentless change is a key element in the series, as Garner's villagers try to maintain local traditions in the face of upheaval. Progress strands the elderly by making their skills obsolete. Like the rest of the world, Chorley is steadily moving away from the familiar values of the past toward the impersonal standards of modern mass society. But if change is one of Garner's themes, stability is another. Members of the family remain profoundly loyal to their surroundings and to their class, their fortunes perpetually tied to those of their neighbors, the Allmans and Leahs. Everyone grows up knowing the same stories, landmarks, hills, and fields. By the end of the series so much has happened at some of the key places—St. Philip's and the chapel at Chorley, Glaze Hill and the jackacre at Lizzie Leah's—that they have almost become characters themselves.

The characters in *The Stone Book* must confront the relentless industrialization of their crafts. Uncle William is a weaver, a holdover from the days when individuals worked alone using their own rudimentary machinery. Cottage industries like Uncle William's died away as the new railroads concentrated production in industrial centers such as Manchester (just visible from the steeple of St. Philip's in Chorley). William's brother Robert, a stonemason, knows that trades rise and vanish—like species—through survival of the fittest. It is this struggle of the natural selection of industry that provides the backdrop for the book.

Joseph, Robert's grandson, decides in *Granny Reardun* to become a blacksmith because he has seen Robert bypassed just as William was. The railroad boom is over, and Joseph's search for a trade leads him to the smithy. Workers will always need tools, he reasons, hoping that because ironworking is "aback" of other trades, it will outlast them all. But in *The Aimer Gate*, set during World War I, Joseph is forced to toil daily making horseshoes for the army. He forges fifteen tons of shoe iron into 33,600 shoes in the course of the war. Once an independent craftsman, Joseph is reduced to imitating modern factory methods of mass production. This trend continues in *Tom Fobble's Day*, the last volume in the series. Great waves of industrial production and international conflict wash over Chorley in the form of German bombers, sweeping searchlights, and booming guns. Joseph's handwork at the forge is entirely outmoded. The outlook for the younger generation is as uncertain as ever, represented by Joseph's grandson, William, who to some extent symbolizes Garner himself.

Garner's characters come alive with all their quirks and faults. Old Robert, "a bazzil-arsed old devil," is proud and irritable. A drinker, he spent more than one night in a ditch in his younger days. While he is up-to-date on geology and evolution, he harbors a reactionary, anti-intellectual streak. Robert considers religion a plot to suppress workingmen and resists letting his daughter Mary learn to read. Mary is a bit of a mystery. A spunky, bright girl, she hopes to be a housemaid for the local aristocracy, a better life than stone-picking in the fields. Although Robert loves Mary's pluck, their wills seem destined to clash. In *Granny Reardun* Mary is apparently unmarried and looking after her son Charlie while her older son Joseph—the "granny reared one"—lives with Robert.

Joseph matures into a conservative and dour man, sharing Old Robert's powerful mind and difficult nature. Joseph's intuitions about mechanical forces are almost visionary, but he is unable to open himself to others. By mid-life he is a miser, and in old age he sums up his life in numbers: the distance he has bicycled to and from work over the years ("equivalent to two and a half times round the world at the equator" or the 33,600 horseshoes he made during World War I). On a carefully hidden level of his personality, he remains passionately devoted to his dead wife.

Joseph's son, also named Robert, is sweet natured and simple. When pressed in *The Aimer Gate* to name his life's work, he says only that he likes looking after the crippled Faddock Allman, whom he serves with heroic patience. Drawn to his cheerful Uncle Charlie, who is home on leave from France, Robert thinks of being a soldier, but no one could be less suited for the army than this gentle, almost saintly boy.

William, Joseph's grandson, is more self-seeking. He is physically timid and not overly blessed with imagination. But it is William, inspired by a triumphant vision of family, nature, and time, who ends the series by gloriously descending a dangerous hill on a sled built by his grandfather.

◆ Literary Qualities ◆

The Stone Book series confirms Alan Garner's mastery of plain language. Each book is rich in dialect, starting with the first lines of *The Stone Book*: "A bottle of cold tea, bread and a half onion. That was Father's baggin." Words such as "baggin" (for "lunch") establish the authenticity of Garner's style, yet their meanings are always clear and never slow the stories down. Equally authentic are idioms borrowed from mining, masonry, metalwork, farming, and other trades. When the Allmans' house is demolished in *Granny Reardun*, for instance, the workmen do not simply stack different sized roof slates on the site; they stack "Princesses, Duchesses, Small Countesses, Ladies, Wide Doubles, and the neat Jennie-go-lightlies from under the ridge."

Garner's descriptions are simple but brilliant. In *The Stone Book* Mary watches a half-eaten onion fall from the steeple: "The onion dropped off Father's knife and floated down to the lawns of the church. It had so far to fall that there was time for it to wander in the air." In these lines, Garner verifies the giddy height of the steeple, atop which Mary will shortly ride the weathercock. The passage turns on nothing more exotic than the words "floated" and "wander," two common verbs deployed here with scientific precision.

What sets the Stone Book sequence apart, however, are the intricate cross-references Garner develops among the stories, using echoes and recurring symbols to weave each volume into the series and build a network of associations. Thus, even commonplace items such as Faddock Allman's hammers or the handle of Joseph's bellows carry literary significance. In *The Stone Book*, for example, Mary's exultant moment on the weathercock as she looks out across the prosperous countryside is balanced by her descent into the Engine Vein and the subterranean room where footprints of centuries of her forebears draw her back into the distant past. These themes are then repeated with intriguing variations in *The Aimer Gate*, when the younger Robert climbs the tower of Chorley's other church, built by Old Robert at the opposite end of the village. Just when he feels most alone at the top of the tower, Robert discovers his own name in the stone, carved there by his great-grandfather. Robert's ascent recalls his grandmother's climb two generations earlier, but because Robert climbs inside the tower, his experience is linked to her cave walk as well.

The Stone Book sequence is crisscrossed by such recurring elements, woven into structures of striking complexity. *Tom Fobble's Day* ends with a culmination of sorts: William sleds down Lizzie Leah's with the clay pipe Old Robert buried in *The Stone Book* in his pocket. William's sled is made from the handle of Joseph's bellows and the remains of Old William's loom. The bump he must negotiate between the upper and lower fields was left there by Robert in *The Aimer Gate*. Beneath it are the remains of the Allmans' cottage, torn down in *Granny Reardun*. The family's lives and works are forged together in one shimmering moment of joy and motion as William glides down the hill.

◆ Social Sensitivity ◆

The deftness of Garner's touch should not disguise the range of issues he engages. From the rise of mass production to the stupendous violence of modern warfare, many leading concerns of the past century and a half are reflected in the lives of the Stone Book family. For example, the concepts of class conflict, religious arrogance, and thoughtless destruction of the past come together when the rector demolishes the Allman's cottage in *Granny Reardun*. The rector carries out this destruction merely because he wants the stone from the cottage to wall his wife's garden.

The books deal less sensitively with women. Regrettably, Garner creates a strong character in Mary, the protagonist of *The Stone Book*, only to let her life fade into uncertainty. When she reappears in *Granny Reardun* she is merely a shadowy figure on the fringes of the relationship between Joseph and Old Robert. The reader never learns how she fared in her efforts to better herself or how she copes with her unconventional life as an adult. No woman besides Mary in Garner's four stories is given more than passing mention. While this imbalance might be excusable in some fiction, Garner so clearly wants to make points about the real lives of working villagers that his failure to include a proportionate number of women and to treat them fairly is a notable omission.

◆ Topics for Discussion ◆

1. In *The Stone Book* Mary is frightened at first when she must climb St. Philip's steeple, but her fear gradually changes to a boldness that astounds her father, who is used to high places. How does Garner trace the steps of this transformation in Mary's feelings?

2. Each book in the series describes an important day for someone in the family. For instance, *Granny Reardun* takes place on Joseph's last day of school. What family turning points occur in the other stories? Why does Garner choose to base his stories on these particular events?

3. Garner's villagers are generally unsinkable: Uncle William makes light of his deafness; Faddock Allman lives cheerfully without legs; after each bombing run, the village children collect shrapnel as if the pieces were baseball cards. What other characters triumph over hardships? What gives them their strength?

4. Giving Mary a stone facsimile of a book, Old Robert says, "It's better than a book you can open....A book has only one story." Is this deep folk wisdom, or is Robert trying only to appease Mary, whom he does not want to go to school? Look especially at the last sentence in the book. Would Robert feel differently if Mary were a boy? Do you think Garner would have treated her character differently?

5. Young people around Chorley are taken seriously but never coddled. They have work to do, and adults are often brusque with them. Even breezy Uncle Charlie in *The Aimer Gate* coldly berates William for using his oil: " 'I don't care what you need,' said Uncle Charlie. 'And you don't touch, think on.' " What other passages and episodes in the stories help define young people's roles?

6. When William asks Joseph what to do when someone calls "Tom Fobble's Day" unfairly, Joseph wants to know if the caller is bigger than William. "Bigger," William says. "Then run like beggary," says Joseph. Find and discuss other examples of humor in the stories. Is there a particular style to the humor around Chorley?

◆ Ideas for Reports and Papers ◆

1. Inspect the handiwork in an old building in your area. What features

would be difficult to duplicate today? What sort of craftsmen probably worked on this job? Where did they learn their trades? If they were starting over now, how would their work be different? Write a report in which you carefully describe the building and speculate about its builders.

2. Look closely at what young Joseph says and thinks about his grandfather, Old Robert, in *Granny Reardun*. Write a detailed comparison between Joseph's reactions in that book and the feelings of William in *Tom Fobble's Day* as he thinks about his grandfather—the same Joseph, now grown old.

3. Joseph pushes his baby brother Charlie down Long Croft in his bassinet. Years later the bassinet has been recycled as Wicked Winnie, Robert's wagon, and follows the same route on Robert's record run to Chorley. Later still, Joseph rides on Long Croft on his bicycle, with his grandson William on the back. List and discuss other examples of variations on the same theme that migrate from story to story.

4. Some critics accuse Garner of sugar-coating the Stone Book stories, nostalgically idealizing the past while ignoring the advantages of modern times. Do you think Garner's picture of the past is realistic or idealized? Base your answers on specific examples from the books.

5. When he learns that Joseph has not told Old Robert he intends to become a smith, Jump James comments: "You're a previous sort of youth, aren't you?" Have you ever heard the word "previous" used this way? Is its meaning related to the Latin etymology of the word listed in dictionaries? What other words do Garner or his characters use in ways that differ from their common meanings?

◆ Related Titles ◆

Garner's early fantasies, *The Weirdstone of Brisingamen* and *The Moon of Gomrath* are generally cheerful adventure stories crowded with country scenery, wonderful characters, and thrilling events. They form an interesting point of comparison for his more mature works, such as *The Owl Service* with its plain style and somber vision. *Elidor,* a fantasy about a family of children from industrial Manchester, is a transitional work that arrives at a tragic conclusion.

Red Shift is a less successful experimental novel that intertwines three stories from different periods in the history of Cheshire. The modern protagonist, Tom compulsively ruins everything he believes in. Tom's story has flashes of humor, but the two other narratives woven into the text are grim. Garner's account of a brutal seventeenth-century massacre during the English Civil War and his violent depiction of the end of the Roman occupation of Cheshire are not clearly related to the affair between Tom and his girlfriend, Jan. Instead of adding tragic stature to Garner's present-day plot, the interwoven stories only make Tom and Jan's problems seem commonplace and unimportant. It is difficult not to be baffled by the book and repelled by its bleak outlook.

Garner has published rewarding collections of traditional stories and fairy tales, such as *The Hamish Hamilton Book of Goblins* (1969), *Alan Garner's Book of British Fairy Tales* (1984), and *The Lad of Gad* (1980). The last two books may shock readers familiar only with sanitized fairy tales, for Garner catches not only the spoken music but also the nightmarish violence of traditional stories.

◆ For Further Reference ◆

Chambers, Nancy, ed. *The Signal Approach to Children's Books*. Metuchen, NJ: Scarecrow, 1980. Contains a long, intense interview between Garner and Aidan Chambers on Garner's literary technique through *The Stone Book* and its sequels. A shorter version of this interview appeared in the periodical *Signal* (September 1978).

Eyre, Frank. *British Children's Books in the Twentieth Century*. New York: Dutton, 1971. Discusses Garner's work in the context of British children's literature.

Garner, Alan. "A Bit More Practice." *Times Literary Supplement* (June 6, 1968). Reprinted in *The Cool Web: The Pattern of Children's Reading*, edited by Margaret Meek, A. Warlow, and G. Barton. New York: Atheneum, 1978. Garner's own reflections on his craft and career up to 1968.

Inglis, Fred. *The Promise of Happiness: Value and Meaning in Children's Fiction*. Cambridge, England: Cambridge University Press, 1981. A distinguished critical evaluation of children's literature. Inglis finds Garner's fantasies "substanceless," part of an escapist trend that "heightens and intensifies emotional life without giving either these emotions or the images that provoke them a way back into experience."

Philip, Neil. *A Fine Anger: A Critical Introduction to the Work of Alan Garner*. London: Collins, 1981. A general appreciation, focusing on Garner's influences and the urge to excel that has driven him far beyond the easy appeal of his earliest work.

Townsend, John Rowe. *A Sounding of Storytellers: New and Revised Essays on Contemporary Writers for Children*. New York: Lippincott, 1979. Contains a generally sympathetic account of Garner's development through *The Stone Book* and its sequels.

————. *Written for Children: An Outline of English Language Children's Literature*. Philadelphia and New York: Lippincott, 1974. Discusses Garner and other fantasists.

Wintle, Justin, and Emma Fisher. *The Pied Pipers: Interviews with the Influential Creators of Children's Literature*. New York: Paddington Press, 1974. Contains a revealing interview with Garner that focuses chiefly on his early life.

Joe Glaser
Western Kentucky University

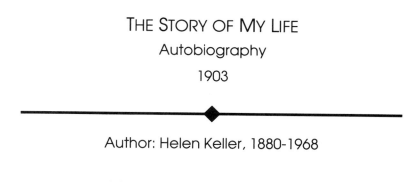

THE STORY OF MY LIFE
Autobiography
1903

Author: Helen Keller, 1880-1968

Major Books for Young Adults

The Story of My Life, 1903

◆ About the Author ◆

Helen Adams Keller was born on June 27, 1880, in Tuscumbia, Alabama, the daughter of Captain Arthur Keller, a former Confederate officer, and his second wife, Kate Adams Keller. She lived as a normal, healthy child for the first eighteen months of her life. In February 1882, however, she became ill with what doctors called "acute congestion of the stomach and brain." A conclusive diagnosis of the exact disease has never been made, but her family discovered shortly after her recovery that she had lost both her sight and her hearing.

She spent the next five years unable to communicate by using language but showing a lively intelligence in her use of signs to make her wishes known. Her parents refused to institutionalize her, as many of their friends recommended, and instead kept her as an active member of the household. But their pity for Helen caused them to spoil her badly, and by the time she was seven she was becoming a formidable adversary. Realizing that something must be done

before she grew absolutely uncontrollable, her parents consulted eye and ear specialists in the hope of finding a cure. None of the doctors could heal the damage the illness had caused, but Dr. Alexander Graham Bell suggested that the Kellers contact the Perkins Institution for the Blind to see if Helen could be educated. The director of the institute, Mr. Michael Anagnos, offered one of its recent graduates as a teacher for the child, and Helen Keller's life and success are linked inextricably to the life of her famous teacher.

Anne Mansfield Sullivan was born in 1866 into an Irish-American family that lived in extreme poverty, and after her mother's early death, her father abandoned his three children. Anne, already partially blinded by an eye disease that thrived in the poor living conditions of her family's home, was sent with her younger brother, Jimmie, to the Massachusetts State Infirmary. Her brother died shortly afterwards, but Anne remained in the infirmary for four years, her eyes growing worse until she was almost completely blind. Finally, during a state investigation of the infirmary,

Photograph of Helen Keller and Anne Sullivan in *The Story of My Life* by Helen Keller. Doubleday: New York (1954).

In spite of her handicaps, Sullivan possessed qualities that helped her relate to Helen. She knew what it was like to be blind. At Perkins she had known Laura Bridgman, the only deaf-blind person who had ever been taught to communicate, and she had studied the notes of Bridgman's teacher. Sullivan's infinite drive, determination, and a passion for excellence also contributed to her success. During her first month, she instilled the discipline Helen needed to enable her to learn, and on April 5, 1887, Helen finally made the connection between the words that Sullivan had been teaching her to finger spell and the objects that they named. Once she broke through this barrier to communication, Sullivan based her teaching on the principle that Helen should acquire language and knowledge like any hearing and seeing child, and she turned all Helen's experiences into opportunities for learning.

Helen Keller's success was largely a result of Anne Sullivan's unflagging teaching. Both were eager for Helen to interact and compete with seeing and hearing children. Interacting with other children required speech, and the greatest ambition of teacher and pupil was for Helen to learn to speak aloud properly. She began taking speech lessons when she was ten, and although she learned how to talk, her vocal chords had never been properly developed, and her speech was almost unintelligible to those who did not know her well. As an adult, her speech improved, but she needed an interpreter when speaking to strangers.

After studying for two years at Perkins, four years at the Horace Mann School for the Deaf, and two more years at the Wright Humason School for the Deaf, sixteen-year-old Helen entered a regular preparatory school for college:

she begged one of the commissioners to send her to a school for the blind. Soon after, in October 1880, at age fourteen, she was transferred to Perkins Institution for the Blind. Anne had a difficult time at Perkins, for she had received almost no formal education until then, and she had an ungovernable temper that almost got her expelled from the school several times. But she was keen to learn and made good academic progress. After two eye operations, she recovered her sight, although it remained weak for the rest of her life. So when she arrived in Tuscumbia, on March 3, 1887, "Teacher" (as Helen would later call her) had poor eyesight and only six years of formal education behind her.

the Cambridge School for Young Ladies. Here and at Radcliffe College, which Helen entered four years later, Sullivan kept up the herculean effort of spelling all the lectures and much of the required reading into her student's hand. It was while she was attending Radcliffe that Keller wrote *The Story of My Life*. She graduated cum laude in 1904.

For several years after her graduation, Keller tried to support herself and Sullivan through her writing. Unfortunately, the public most wanted to hear Keller talk about herself, a subject that she felt she had exhausted. Instead, she wrote essays expressing Socialist views on issues that many people felt were not proper for her to discuss, such as the need for doctors to put nitrate of silver in the eyes of newborns to prevent the blindness that venereal disease often caused. Some people even accused Sullivan and her husband, John Macy, of being the originators of Keller's ideas. Unable to earn enough money by writing, Keller turned to lecturing in 1913 and continued on the lecture circuit for three years.

Still plagued by a lack of money, Keller began working in vaudeville, presenting a short act with Teacher on how she had been taught and advocating the right of the handicapped to a normal life. This drew a storm of criticism that she was exhibiting her handicap for profit, but Keller was finally earning enough to support herself and Sullivan. She worked on and off in vaudeville for several years until she finally found her real vocation in 1923 as a spokesperson for the American Foundation for the Blind.

For the rest of her life Keller campaigned for the foundation, crisscrossing the country and eventually the world, making speeches and visiting the blind. Her efforts on behalf of the blind,

deaf, mute, and handicapped people in general heavily influenced reforms that improved social and educational opportunities for the physically disabled. Sullivan's death on October 20, 1936, was a great blow to Helen, but she continued her speechmaking with the interpretation of Polly Thomson, the indispensable secretary and friend who had lived with Keller and Sullivan since 1914. Keller wrote two more books, *Helen Keller's Journal* (1938), a diary she had kept for the first six months following Teacher's death, and *Teacher: Anne Sullivan Macy* (1955). She actually had to write *Teacher* twice, for the first manuscript was burned, along with all her letters from Anne and her notes, in a fire that destroyed her home in 1946. Helen Keller died on June 1, 1968, widely acknowledged as one of the twentieth century's leading humanitarians. She is buried beside Anne Sullivan and Polly Thomson in the National Cathedral in Washington, D.C.

◆ Overview ◆

Keller's ability to communicate despite her handicaps has always fascinated people. To read her autobiography is to experience that communication as closely as possible. Readers gain a sense of what it would be like to be both deaf and blind, and of how a normal human being faced extraordinary difficulties with courage and grace. It is important to remember that Keller wrote this book while still in college, when she was about twenty-two years old. Covering only her childhood and young womanhood, this "story of her life" is an incomplete one, for she had over sixty years yet to live.

The story of Keller's early life takes place during the late 1800s, a time when people's understanding of the physically disabled was much more limited than it is today. Physically disabled people were routinely institutionalized and often assumed to be mentally disabled as well. Efforts to teach them to overcome their disabilities and lead normal lives were extremely limited. But Keller was fortunate enough to have parents who refused to institutionalize her, an extraordinary teacher, and a burning desire to learn. Her accomplishments led to a greater public understanding of the handicapped. Her autobiography traces her progress over the first two decades of her life, following her from her parents' home in Tuscumbia, Alabama, through a succession of schools for the handicapped, and concluding when she is a student at Radcliffe College.

Jacket for *The Story of My Life* by Helen Keller. Doubleday: New York (1954).

◆ Themes and Characters ◆

In one sense, Keller is really the only character in *The Story of My Life*. The other people are secondary to her story except as their actions affect her life. Anne Sullivan, as the person who makes it possible for Helen to communicate with other people and who serves as the primary mediator between Helen and the world, is the only other character that develops somewhat in the course of the narrative. Yet even she remains shadowy.

Keller interests people because she overcame great handicaps, and her fight is both the focus and theme of her autobiography. Although loosely organized and episodic in structure, the book follows Helen's gradual growth from a helpless blind and deaf girl to an intellectually independent woman, and it emphasizes her constant striving to lead as normal a life as possible. The first chapters deal with Helen's life before the arrival of Sullivan and show how the absence of language skills imprisons her alert mind. Later chapters describe how she explores the world in the months after she acquires language. They also illustrate how capable she is of participating in all the activities of other girls her age. Keller continually focuses on her abilities, not her disabilities, so that the reader shares her discoveries with joy rather than pity.

Helen's excitement about learning is one of her most appealing characteristics. Coming to language later and with more difficulty than most people sharpens her conscious awareness and enjoyment of learning. Keller's narrative reveals how Sullivan uses all their daily experiences for educational purposes, and it conveys the curiosity and joy with which Helen explores her new world. Keller's account of her formal education at the Cambridge School for Young Ladies and at Radcliffe College does not make light of the difficulties she faces in competing with seeing and hearing women in regular classes, but it also communicates her enthusiasm for her studies, particularly through her critiques of the books she reads and their impact on her.

◆ Literary Qualities ◆

Because *The Story of My Life* is an autobiography, it tends to be episodic and anecdotal rather than tightly plotted; after all, an individual's life seldom takes the form of a well-plotted novel. This structure also partly results from the circumstances of its composition. Keller wrote many of the chapters as themes for the English composition course she took while attending Radcliffe. Consequently, there is little connection between chapters, although Keller's progress towards leading a normal life provides a thematic framework for her story.

Modern readers may find Keller's style old-fashioned, for she describes her experiences and feelings with sentimental Victorian language. Her writing is full of literary allusions, especially biblical references. Her imagery is so vivid and extraordinarily visual that many of her contemporary readers refused to believe that she had written the book. They failed to understand that language is inherently visual and that Keller's style

was formed by reading the works of seeing authors. Furthermore, by using tactile analogies, such as heat, she could grasp visual concepts such as color and even intensities in color, so these elements in her writing are not unnatural.

◆ Social Sensitivity ◆

Because Keller focuses on her abilities rather than on her deprivations, *The Story of My Life* serves as a model for what the physically disabled can accomplish. She stresses her normalcy—she enjoys the same activities that seeing and hearing people do. Her story shows readers that the physically handicapped are not "different," a message that was particularly relevant in her era, when people often assumed that the physically disabled were also mentally disabled. In part because of Keller's remarkable career, that attitude has decreased considerably, and modern society is more accepting of both physically and mentally disabled people. Young adults are often curious about the lives of the disabled, and *The Story of My Life* provides a firsthand account.

◆ Topics for Discussion ◆

1. Why is Helen so frustrated by her desire to communicate before Anne Sullivan arrives?

2. Helen learns that the word "w-a-t-e-r" means what comes out of the pump in the wellhouse. Why is this such a significant discovery?

3. Why is learning to speak with her mouth important to Helen? Why does her joy in speaking make her family

respond to her accomplishment in silence?

4. In her descriptions of what she has "seen," Helen often uses words that suggest visual images she is incapable of actually seeing, or sounds she cannot hear. Find some instances of this and explain how, as a blind or deaf person, she could use these words to describe her experience.

5. When Helen writes "The Frost King" she genuinely believes she is making up her own story. Explain why it is not actually her story and how she plagiarizes it. What do you think about how the adults react?

6. What difficulties does Helen encounter when she goes to schools for seeing and hearing students?

7. Does the number of activities in which Helen participates surprise you? Why or why not?

◆ Ideas for Reports and Papers ◆

1. Keller worked to make the world more accessible to physically disabled people. What programs does your community have that carry on her work? What are their purposes and accomplishments?

2. Sullivan was as remarkable a woman as her student Helen. Read a biography about her and discuss how her background affected her work with Helen.

3. Learn the manual alphabet. Compare it with American sign language.

What are their similarities and differences? What advantages and disadvantages does each one have?

4. Many editions of *The Story of My Life* include the letters Sullivan wrote to people at Perkins Institution for the Blind during the first years she worked with Keller. After reading these, explain her philosophy of education. What were her methods? Why were they successful?

5. Watch the film *The Miracle Worker*. How does it portray Helen Keller? Anne Sullivan? What are some differences between the movie account and the account Keller gives in *The Story of My Life*?

◆ Adaptations ◆

Although several biographies had been written about Keller since her emergence into the public eye, it was not until 1953 that anyone attempted serious adaptations to other media. After reading *The Story of My Life*, William Gibson wrote a ballet with vocal accompaniment based on the book. Although the ballet was never produced, director Arthur Penn commissioned Gibson to use the subject matter for a television production for the drama series "Playhouse 90." Starring in the television production were Teresa Wright as Anne Sullivan and Patty McCormack as Helen. With public interest aroused through this production, Gibson revised the film into a Broadway drama, which opened in October 1959 as *The Miracle Worker*. Anne Bancroft played Anne; Patty Duke played Helen. For Duke, this was her first major appearance as an actress; for Bancroft, it was the first important role she had been given in a decade. When the play was adapted back to film in 1962, Bancroft and Duke again played the leads, winning enormous critical acclaim, as well as Oscars for their emotionally charged portrayals of teacher and student.

While the book traces Keller's life through her college years, *The Miracle Worker* focuses only on the first month of her life after Sullivan becomes her teacher. Keller is portrayed as a spoiled terror who dominates her weak father and indulgent mother. Uncontrollable because no one knows how to communicate with her, she throws tantrums, breaks china, and fights with people. Sullivan, who is tough yet empathetic, believes that Helen must be tamed before she can be taught, and the two push each other to their limits. Finally, after Helen deliberately spills a pitcher of water at the dinner table and Anne drags her outside to the water pump to refill it, Helen makes connections between water and the letters "w-a-t-e-r" that Anne spells out in her hand, and this breakthrough marks the beginning of Helen's new life.

The 107-minute film obviously embellishes and dramatizes Keller's account, and the drama is as much Anne's story as Helen's. But for whatever liberties they take with the autobiography, the play and film galvanize the audience with the power of these women's commitments and the bonds that make it possible for Helen to escape her isolated world.

◆ For Further Reference ◆

Braddy, Nella (Henney). *Anne Sullivan Macy: The Story Behind Helen Keller*. New York: Doubleday Doran, 1933. Braddy was a close friend of both Keller and Sullivan and wrote her book based on her conversations with Sullivan. Braddy was the first person to deal with Sullivan's accomplishments, rather than just Keller's.

Brooks, Van Wyck. *Helen Keller: Sketch for a Portrait*. New York: Dutton, 1956. Brooks was a well-known historian as well as Keller's good friend. He brings discipline and style to a subject he knows well, and produces a fine biography of Keller up to the point of middle age.

Davidson, Margaret. *Helen Keller*. New York: Scholastic Book Services, 1969. A biography for children ages five to eight.

Gibson, William. *The Miracle Worker: A Play for Television*. New York: Alfred A. Knopf, 1957. This is a famous and moving dramatization of Sullivan's first month with Keller, climaxing with Helen's discovery that everything has a name.

Hickok, Lorena A. *The Story of Helen Keller*. New York: Grosset and Dunlap, 1958. An engaging biography for young children.

———. *The Touch of Magic: The Story of Helen Keller's Great Teacher, Anne Sullivan Macy*. New York: Dodd, Mead, 1961. A good biography for young adults.

Lash, Joseph P. *Helen and Teacher: The Story of Helen Keller and Anne Sullivan Macy*. New York: Delacorte Press/ Seymour Lawrence, 1980. This is the best researched and most extensive biography of either Keller or Sullivan. Lash deals in depth with the complexities of their personalities and their relationship, showing them as full human beings rather than saints, a temptation many other biographers have fallen prey to—especially many of those who write for children. Lash gives a full account of Keller's later years and her relationship with Polly Thomson, who became her full-time companion after Sullivan died.

Peare, Catherine Owens. *The Helen Keller Story*. New York: Crowell, 1959. A biography for young children.

Waite, Helen Elmira. *Valiant Companions: Helen Keller and Anne Sullivan Macy*. Philadelphia: Macrae Smith, 1959. A good biography of both women for older children.

Kara K. Keeling
Indiana University

STRAWBERRY GIRL
Novel
1945

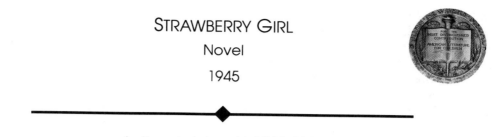

Author: Lois Lenski, 1893-1974

Major Books for Young Adults

A Little Girl of 1900, 1928
Phebe Fairchild, Her Book, 1936
A-Going to the Westward, 1937
Bound Girl of Cobble Hill, 1938
Ocean-Born Mary, 1939
Blueberry Corners, 1940
Indian Captive: The Story of Mary
　　Jemison, 1941
Bayou Suzette, 1943
Puritan Adventure, 1944
Strawberry Girl, 1945
Blue Ridge Billy, 1946
Judy's Journey, 1947

Boom Town Boy, 1948
Cotton in My Sack, 1949
Texas Tomboy, 1950
Prairie School, 1951
Mama Hattie's Girl, 1953
Corn-Farm Boy, 1954
San Francisco Boy, 1955
Flood Friday, 1956
Houseboat Girl, 1957
Coal Camp Girl, 1959
Shoo-Fly Girl, 1963
To Be a Logger, 1967
Deer Valley Girl, 1968

◆ About the Author ◆

Lois Lenore Lenski was born on October 14, 1893, in Springfield, Ohio, the daughter of a Lutheran minister and a former schoolteacher. She grew up in a small town in Ohio, the fourth of five children in a family that placed a high value on education and religion. After graduating from Ohio State University with a teacher's degree, she pursued a career in art. For four years she studied at the Art Students League in New York, working odd jobs to pay living expenses. She painted greeting cards, made fashion drawings for ads, clerked at a gift shop, and worked for one of her teachers, Arthur Covey, helping him

with mural paintings. During this time in New York, she sold illustrations for four softcover children's coloring books. The following year she studied at the Westminster School of Art in London, and it was at this time that she began illustrating hardcover books.

Two weeks after returning from her year in London, in 1921, Lenski married her former teacher, the widower Arthur Covey. During the first years of her marriage, she cared for her two step-children, making time for her own artistic work and attending art classes on Saturdays. Lenski hoped to illustrate books written by other people. When she showed her drawings to a New York editor, the editor said she had no manuscripts at that time to fit them but suggested that Lenski write a story of her own.

In 1927, Lenski published her first book, *Skipping Village*, the story of her childhood in Ohio. *A Little Girl of 1900* followed in 1928, also chronicling her childhood. After completing picture books for her son, Stephen, she turned to writing historical novels for young adults, doing extensive research in libraries and courthouses. Although her historical novels were well received, Lenski grew tired of the research necessary to gather material and turned instead to writing contemporary regional stories.

By visiting different parts of the United States, drawing pictures of people and places, and listening to local speech patterns, Lenski was able to capture regional life in words. Her first regional novel, *Bayou Suzette*, set in Louisiana, won the Ohioana Medal in 1944. In 1946 *Strawberry Girl* won the Newbery Medal. Another regional novel, *Judy's Journey*, won the Child Study Association of America Children's Book Award in 1947. In all, Lenski wrote seventeen regional books, each presenting a realistic pictures of life among poorer people.

During her career, Lenski wrote a hundred books for children and illustrated them all herself. She also illustrated another fifty books written by other authors. She died on September 11, 1974, in Tarpon Springs, Florida, two years after publishing her autobiography.

◆ Overview ◆

The United States is so large that people in one part of the country sometimes have difficulty understanding people in other parts. Lenski's regional books explore the differences in climate, food, dialect, and work that characterize different regions. In *Strawberry Girl* the personality of Birdie Boyer comes alive, and the reader understands how a girl from early twentieth-century rural Florida might have lived, thought, and felt. The book is richly illustrated by the author. Her black-and-white drawings accurately portray the region and complement the straightforward text.

◆ Setting ◆

The story takes place in the early 1900s in the Florida backwoods. This is strawberry country; school runs through the summer months but closes during berry picking season in January, February, and March. Most of Birdie Boyer's time is spent at home, working in the berry patch, doing housework, taking care of her younger siblings, or studying. Birdie is proud, as are her neighbors, to be a "Cracker"—a Florida native—and not a Yankee from up north. The town closest to Birdie's home boasts an open town square with a railroad depot on one side and houses and shops along the other sides. Going to town is an event that requires a ride in the mule-drawn wagon.

◆ Themes and Characters ◆

Birdie Boyer is ten years old and full of optimism and love of life. She and her parents, three brothers, and two sisters have just moved to the area from northern Florida when the story opens. She is excited to be in a new place and is hoping to make new friends. Initially she is disappointed when she meets her closest neighbors, the Slaters.

Cover illustration by Lois Lenski for *Strawberry Girl.*
Lippincott: New York (1945).

Shoestring. Birdie is definitely portrayed as the good character, but she occasionally feels hatred for the Slaters. On the other hand, Shoestring, the supposedly bad character, has moments when he feels remorseful and yearns to straighten out the feud between the families.

Lenski focuses on the poor working class in *Strawberry Girl.* The Boyers are not as impoverished as the Slaters, but they are poor and live on the same economic level as other members of the community. The Boyers' work ethic is important to the development of the theme, and hard work is identified with the good characters. Although the novel portrays very realistic problems and feelings, good does triumph over evil and all the problems are resolved neatly at the end.

The Boyers are a hard-working family whose members love one another and try to be kind to others. The Slaters, on the other hand, are lazy, dirty, and unkempt. The father goes on drunken binges, and the older boys beat up the schoolteacher. Mrs. Slater does the best she can with a husband and sons she cannot control. Her twelve-year-old son, Shoestring, is at times vindictive but often seems regretful for the behavior of his family.

The feud that ensues between the two families—primarily between Mr. Boyer, a farmer who believes in fencing in land and Mr. Slater, a cattleman who believes in open range—pits good against evil. While the distinction between good and evil is clear in the conflict between the fathers, it is less clear in the relationship between Birdie and

◆ Literary Qualities ◆

Regional stories have a long heritage in American literature. The earliest books written in America were regional ones explaining explorations in Virginia or hardships in New England. As the country expanded westward, stories of the new regions fascinated readers, and pockets of American literature developed in various territories. Place, more than time, became the essential ingredient in American fiction, especially in literature about the American South. The southern novel moves slowly through time and, unlike the western novel, puts less emphasis on plot and action than on place and characters. Lenski, who said she wanted to depict different regions accurately, has incorporated some characteristics of the southern novel in *Strawberry Girl.* Using the characters' dialect to establish the region's isolation, she attempts to illustrate the complicated layers of a society untouched by the outside world. Lenski explores southern character types similar to those found in the fiction of William Faulkner and Erskine Caldwell, two prominent southern writers of adult fiction at the time of *Strawberry Girl*'s publication. The world that Lenski documents often features people made mean by hard times; fiercely proud and independent people; people embroiled in family feuds; and people dependent on farms that cannot support them. Lenski's strength as a writer is her ability to render a vivid portrait of the world in which her characters live; her weakness is her failure to fully develop her characters as distinct personalities.

♦ Social Sensitivity ♦

American society has changed so much since the publication of *Strawberry Girl* that attitudes acceptable in those times may now be offensive. Although Lenski writes sympathetically about the rural poor and has captured much flavor of the region, she is a privileged outsider who presents characters as stereotypes. The problems that these poor people face are the direct result of character flaws, rather than of circumstances. Lenski seems to believe that anyone who works hard and has faith in God will lead a good life. Contemporary readers may find this belief not only naive but the product of an elitist mind.

For this reason, *Strawberry Girl* should be read as a "period piece." It was not until after World War II that most Americans began to acknowledge the existence of its minorities, its poor, and its uneducated. The novel provides an excellent view of the way Americans once thought, and should provoke stimulating discussions about how a society changes.

♦ Topics for Discussion ♦

1. Birdie's sense of responsibility is illustrated by her attitude toward her chores. Cite examples from the story that demonstrate her work ethic. What is Shoestring's attitude towards chores?

2. What is the significance of the title?

3. The question of fences or open range is uppermost in the minds of most of the characters in *Strawberry Girl*. Present both sides of the issue. With which side do you agree?

4. "Gettin' biggety" is mentioned time and again. What does it mean and who uses the expression?

5. Mrs. Slater holds a "chicken pilau." What is it and why does she have it?

6. What types of food are staples in this novel? Do they differ from the types of food you eat?

7. What does Mrs. Boyer use in the strawberry field to scare off the Slaters? Why does it work?

♦ Ideas for Reports and Papers ♦

1. A great deal of time goes into the strawberry business. Report on the process, from planting to picking, as described in the novel and in other sources.

2. Lenski uses regional expressions and dialect in her book. Cite examples.

Does this help you to understand the characters? Why or why not?

3. The Boyers and Slaters have different ideas about the treatment of animals, from rabbits to dogs to cattle. Why? Cite examples.

4. Realism was still an evolving concept in young adult literature when this book was written. Explain how realism is used in this book and give examples.

5. Which character did you like the most? Which did you like the least? Why?

6. Do Lenski's illustrations capture the spirit of the story? Why or why not? Give examples.

◆ Related Titles/Adaptations ◆

Each of the seventeen regional books by Lenski focuses on a young person. Lenski visited every region about which she planned to write, and patterned her characters and their actions after real life. Joanda Hutley of *Cotton in My Sack* and Felix of *San Francisco Boy* resemble Birdie Boyer in that they are particularly well-drawn, insightful characters.

Strawberry Girl was produced as a filmstrip with record by Miller-Brody Productions in 1973.

◆ For Further Reference ◆

Cech, John, ed. *American Writers for Children, 1900-1960*. Detroit: Gale Research, 1983. *Dictionary of Literary Biography*. Vol. 22. Includes an overview of Lenski's life and assesses her major works.

Commire, Anne, ed. *Something about the Author*. Vol. 26. Detroit: Gale Research, 1982. Contains an interview with Lenski.

Kinsman, Clare D. ed. *Contemporary Authors*. Permanent Series. Vol. 1. Detroit: Gale Research, 1975. Brief biographical information is included in this entry along with a complete list of Lenski's works.

Kirkpatrick, D. L., ed. *Twentieth Century Children's Writers*. New York: St. Martin's Press, 1983. Entry on Lenski states that her plots center on modest success stories.

Kunitz, Stanley J., and Howard Haycroft, eds. *Junior Book of Authors*. New York: H. W. Wilson, 1951. Entry on Lenski is a short autobiographical sketch.

Lenski, Lois. *Journey into Childhood: The Autobiography of Lois Lenski*. New York: Lippincott, 1972. Lenski's life story makes interesting reading. She includes her reasons for writing regional novels.

Roginski, Jim, editor. *Newbery and Caldecott Medalists and Honor Book Winners: Bibliographies and Resource Material through 1977*. Littleton, CO: Libraries Unlimited, 1982, pp. 169-173. This entry lists background reading for Lenski's works.

Veda Jones

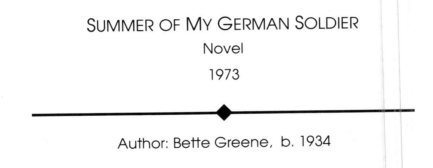

SUMMER OF MY GERMAN SOLDIER

Novel

1973

Author: Bette Greene, b. 1934

Major Books for Young Adults

Summer of My German Soldier, 1973
Philip Hall Likes Me, I Reckon Maybe, 1974
Morning Is a Long Time Coming, 1978

Get On Out of Here, Philip Hall!, 1981
Them That Glitter and Them That Don't, 1983

◆ About the Author ◆

Bette Greene was born Bette Evensky on June 28, 1934, in Memphis, Tennessee. A few years later, her family moved to Parkin, Arkansas, located just beyond the Tennessee-Arkansas border, where she attended elementary school. Her father, a merchant, operated a traditional country store in Parkin during World War II.

When Greene was thirteen years old her family returned to the Memphis area. She graduated from Memphis Central High School in 1952 and went to France, where she attended the Alliance Française in Paris. Later she attended several other universities in the United States: Memphis State University, the University of Alabama, Columbia, and Harvard. While at Memphis State, Greene worked for the school newspaper, as well as the Memphis *Commercial Appeal* and the *Hebrew Watchman*. She became a full-time reporter for the *Commercial Appeal* from 1950 to 1952 and was affiliated with the Memphis bureau of the United Press from 1953 to 1954. Greene served as public information officer for the American Red Cross in Memphis from 1958 to 1959 and for the Boston State Psychiatric Hospital in Massachusetts from 1959 to 1961. She married Donald Sumner Greene, a physician, on June 14, 1959. They have two children, Carla and Jordan Joshua, and they live in Brookline, Massachusetts.

After publishing several short stories and newspaper and magazine articles, Greene turned to novel writing. Her first published novel, *Summer of My German Soldier*, is autobiographical, with material borrowed from her childhood days in Arkansas. It won several awards including a *New York Times* Outstanding Book award, an American Library Association Notable Book citation, and a Golden Kite Society children's book award, all in 1973. *Summer of My*

German Soldier was also nominated for the National Book Award in 1974.

◆ Overview ◆

Summer of My German Soldier deals with an important period in American history, the armed conflict between Germany and America in World War II. Prisoner-of-war camps were established in many American towns to incarcerate captured German soldiers. *Summer of My German Soldier* describes how the citizens of an imaginary town react to the prisoner-of-war camps located in their community.

Patty Bergen, the twelve-year-old central character, finds growing up painful. Tension within her family compounds her anxiety and her low self-esteem. Abused and all but rejected by her callous parents, Patty befriends a peace-loving escaped German prisoner of war, Anton Reiker. Patty helps Anton hide from the authorities, and the two develop a caring, trusting relationship. What makes this relationship unusual is that Patty is Jewish and Anton is a former Nazi. Both, however, disregard these affiliations when they are together. Each seeks to escape from a violent, oppressive environment, and in each other, Patty and Anton find sources of warmth and comfort. A complex and emotionally wrenching novel, *Summer of My German Soldier* explores Patty's struggle for approval, affection, and identity.

◆ Setting ◆

The action takes place during the early 1940s in the fictional Jenkinsville, Arkansas, an eastern Arkansas town located in the heart of the Bible Belt. It is typical of the towns where the U.S. Army set up prisoner-of-war camps in World War II. The incongruity of a prisoner-of-war camp being located in a sleepy Arkansas town sets up the novel's central plot twist: Anton Reiker, a former member of the German Army escapes from the Jenkinsville prisoner-of-war camp and is assisted by a twelve-year-old Jewish girl. A Jew befriending a Nazi, whose party plotted the wholesale destruction of Jewish people, seems outrageous and highly unlikely. But the intense personal relationship between the main characters transcends hate and destruction, and illustrates Greene's main concern: that the universal values of love, trust, and respect cross national and religious boundaries.

◆ Themes and Characters ◆

The cast of characters in *Summer of My German Soldier* includes a variety of vivid personalities. Patty Bergen, the central character, is a twelve-year-old who perceives herself as plain and outspoken and thus "living with a disadvantage." Although frequently rebuffed when she tries to express love to her parents, she doggedly devises stories and scenarios designed to win their lasting affection. Her father brutally beats her, and her mother ridicules her appearance and behavior, but Patty too often blames herself for their abuse, rationalizing that if only she were prettier or more talented, her parents would love her the way they do her younger sister, Sharon. Patty's father considers Sharon—a cute, pampered little girl—the next Shirley Temple.

Photograph of Bette
Greene courtesy of
E. P. Dutton.

Patty's first-person narration of the story reveals her wit, imagination, and intelligence. Her favorite pastime is reading the dictionary, and she seriously applies herself to a study of language. Patty, demands precision of meaning: "When I read a book," she says, "I want to understand precisely what it is the writer is saying, not just almost but precisely." After meeting Charlene Madlee, a newspaper reporter who encourages her interest in writing, Patty aspires to a career in journalism.

Harry Bergen, Patty's father, puts running his dry goods store ahead of caring for his children. He is portrayed as a monstrously cruel man, but Greene hints that his violent behavior is the result of deep insecurities and psychological instability. Patty's mother, Pearl,

is depicted as a cold, controlled, and consistently unsympathetic character.

Anton Reiker, the prisoner and the son of a German professor, serves as a counterpoint to Patty's father. Where Mr. Bergen is brutal and sadistic, Anton is sensitive and understanding. Unlike Mr. Bergen, Anton, who was a medical student before the war, accepts "plain" Patty as "a person of value." With Anton, a former soldier for an army that kills Jews, Patty ironically finds someone who can comfort her, someone who considers her important. Anton even risks his life for Patty, coming to her defense during a particularly savage beating by her father. During World War II, many Americans fiercely hated the Germans and refused to consider them as individuals. Anton, who does not approve of Hitler and who is a kind, caring person, is the victim of social prejudice in Jenkinsville.

Ruth, the Bergens' maid, is loving, loyal, and constant like Anton. When Patty befriends Anton, Ruth assists her, and when Patty is incarcerated at the Arkansas Reformatory for Girls, Ruth is her only visitor. She teaches Patty to like and respect herself. For her love and loyalty, however, Ruth loses her job, another of Greene's comments on injustice. Ruth lives in Nigger Bottom, the black neighborhood in the segregated town of Jenkinsville. In addition to suffering the effects of generations of racial persecution, Ruth also bears the anxiety of knowing that her only son, Robert, whom she has painstakingly prepared for college, is now a conscripted soldier, fighting overseas. Her strong faith in God and her compassion for others help her endure these trials.

Greene sets her story about a girl's coming of age in a violent family against a backdrop of social oppression and world war. Her book explores these layers of conflict and weaves them into a tightly unified story that focuses on Patty's struggle to accept herself as a worthwhile person.

Although Anton and Patty seem to be extremely dissimilar—he is a good-looking, confident former Nazi soldier who has led a privileged, cultured life; she is a plain, insecure, Jewish girl from a small-town, abusive family—Greene structures her story around the parallels between them. Greene likens the cruelty and injustice Patty experiences at the hands of her father to the pain suffered by those—such as Anton and

his father—forced to bend to Hitler's will. Anton articulates this similarity when he asks Patty, "Would your father's cruelty cause him to crush weak neighboring states? Or would the Führer's cruelty cause him to beat his own daughter? Doesn't it seem to you that they both need to inflict pain?" Both Anton and Patty are prisoners seeking escape from this cruelty, seeking a chance to rise above distinctions of race, to be individuals interacting compassionately with one another. But Anton dies in his final attempt at freedom, and Patty is sentenced to a reformatory as punishment for assisting him.

Despite Anton's death and Patty's incarceration, Greene shows that Patty has changed as a result of her encounter with Anton. In a powerful, metaphorical passage, Greene conveys Patty's sense of hope and determination at the end of the novel. As Patty watches Ruth leave the reformatory after a visit, she experiences sudden panic, "like watching my very own life raft floating away towards the open sea." But Patty soon realizes that she has the strength to control her own future; she remarks, "maybe that's the only thing life rafts are supposed to do. Taking the shipwrecked, not exactly to land, but only in view of land, the final mile being theirs alone to swim."

Because the novel is about prejudice and family relations, it might raise provocative or painful observations that readers recognize in their own lives. Patty, who is extremely attractive as a person but considered an outcast by her family, turns to an "enemy" for acceptance and is punished by society for helping someone she loves. The moral questions posed by this dilemma will raise contemporary questions of right and wrong. An equally strong theme is the hypocrisy of the townspeople who, while outraged that the Nazis are persecuting the Jews, practice segregation.

◆ Topics for Discussion ◆

1. Why does Patty incriminate herself by showing the store clerk, Sister Parker, the ring Anton gave her?

2. Would you end this novel in the same way the author does, with Patty in jail, or would you construct some other conclusion?

3. How does Bette Greene achieve humor in her narrative? What purpose does the humor serve?

4. To what extent is Patty an ideal person rather than a realistic one?

5. Are Patty's parents portrayed fairly? Why does Patty feel that she is to blame for their abusing her?

◆ Ideas for Reports and Papers ◆

1. Write a paper on the establishment and maintenance of German prisoner-of-war camps in the United States during World War II.

2. Compare *Summer of My German Soldier* with its sequel *Morning Is a Long Time Coming*. Which is better? Why?

3. What was life like in America's prisoner-of-war camps during World War II?

4. Find as much biographical information about Bette Greene as you can. To what extent does *Summer of My German Soldier* reflect Greene's real-life experiences?

5. Are Patty's observational abilities beyond those of a twelve-year-old? To what extent, therefore, is the voice of Patty credible? Choose another character in the book and retell a chapter from this person's point of view.

◆ Related Titles/Adaptations ◆

Morning is a Long Time Coming, a sequel to *Summer of My German Soldier*, continues the adventures of Patty Bergen. Like the original novel, the sequel incorporates the author's personal experiences and is narrated in the first person. The story is set in Arkansas and Tennessee, and it begins when Patty graduates from high school, a few years after her fateful encounter with Anton Reiker. *Morning Is a Long Time Coming* chronicles Patty's trip to Europe and her meeting with Anton's family in Germany.

Greene also wrote *Philip Hall Likes Me, I Reckon Maybe* and its sequel, *Get On Out of Here, Philip Hall!*, both told by an eleven-year-old black girl. A fifth novel, *Them That Glitter and Them That Don't* has as its central character an eighteen-year-old gypsy girl. Despite their different religious and ethnic backgrounds, the central characters in Greene's novels share the same values: consideration, generosity, thoughtfulness, and love.

Greene wrote the screenplay for the 1978 television production of *Summer of My German Soldier*, with Kristy Mc-Nichol in the central role and Esther Rolle as Ruth. Rolle earned an Emmy

Award for her performance. Greene says she was able to keep the television production "emotionally true" to the story.

♦ For Further Reference ♦

Commire, Anne, ed. *Something about the Author*. Vol. 8. Detroit: Gale Research, 1976. Gives a brief biographical sketch and a listing of Greene's writings.

Evory, Anne, ed. *Contemporary Authors*. New Revision Series. Vol. 4. Detroit: Gale Research, 1981. Provides a brief overview of the author's life and lists her publications.

Kirkpatrick, D. L., ed. *Twentieth Century Children's Writers*. New York: St. Martin's, 1978. The article on Greene summarizes her life, provides a revealing quotation from Greene about her childhood, and includes short critical commentary.

Reilley, Carolyn, ed. *Contemporary Literary Criticism*. Vol. 30. Detroit: Gale Research, 1984. Contains excerpts from criticism of *Summer of My German Soldier*, *Morning Is a Long Time Coming*, and *Them That Glitter and Them That Don't*.

Lyman B. Hagen
Arkansas State University

THE SUMMER OF THE SWANS
Novel
1970

◆

Author: Betsy Byars, b. 1928

Major Books for Young Adults

The Midnight Fox, 1968
The Summer of the Swans, 1970
The House of Wings, 1972
After the Goat Man, 1974
The TV Kid, 1976
The Pinballs, 1977
The Cartoonist, 1978
Good-bye, Chicken Little, 1979
The Night Swimmers, 1980

The Cybil War, 1981
*The Animal, the Vegetable, and
    John D. Jones,* 1982
The Two-Thousand-Pound Goldfish,
    1982
Cracker Jackson, 1985
The Not-Just-Anybody Family, 1986
The Golly Sisters Go West, 1986
*The Blossoms Meet the Vulture
    Lady,* 1986

◆ About the Author ◆

Betsy Byars was born on August 7, 1928, in Charlotte, North Carolina, the daughter of George Guy and Nancy Rugheimer Cromer. She attended Furman University from 1946 to 1948, and received her bachelor's degree in English from Queens College, Charlotte, North Carolina, in 1950. She married Edward Ford Byars that year. The Byarses live in South Carolina and have four children.

When her husband was a graduate student at the University of Illinois, Byars began her writing career, publishing articles in the *Saturday Evening Post, T.V. Guide,* and *Look* magazines. As her family grew, she began writing books, and in 1962 her first book for young people, *Clementine,* was published. Nine years later she won the Newbery Medal for her novel *The Summer of the Swans.* Many of the ideas for her books spring from her children's personal experiences. Byars writes during the winter months and spends her summers pursuing an interest in gliders and antique airplanes with her husband.

◆ Overview ◆

The Summer of the Swans is unusual because the narrative provides an extremely perceptive look at the perspectives of two characters: Sara and her mentally retarded younger brother, Charlie. The opening chapters focus on

Sara's typical adolescent problems, but when Charlie becomes lost her personal problems become secondary to her concern over her brother's whereabouts. The narrative alternates its focus between Sara and Charlie, and as Charlie's story unfolds the reader sees his desperation in being cut off from those who care for him. Byars provides compassionate insight into Charlie's feelings of frustration and his sense that he is unloved and suspended in time. The novel also adeptly explores the emotions of Sara, who feels awkward, confused, unwanted by her father, unattractive, and judgmental.

◆ Setting ◆

Byars chose her home of twenty years, West Virginia, as the setting for *The Summer of the Swans*. Her abiding appreciation of the locale's natural beauty permeates her descriptions, making them authentic. She says that she set the novel in West Virginia "to give the reader the feeling of the power of the land over the individual." The idea for the swans in the story came from a newspaper article in her college alumni magazine that told about the swans at Furman University that left their own beautiful lake each year and flew to less desirable ponds. The setting in time is not particularly important to the story, but the action probably takes place around the time the novel was published, 1970.

◆ Themes and Characters ◆

Sara Godfrey is a fourteen-year-old who feels awkward, ugly, and unattractive because she has large feet, skinny legs, and a crooked nose. Her moods shift unpredictably: one minute she is "up" about something, the next she is "down" about the same situation. Her ten-year-old brother, Charlie, who has been brain-damaged and mute since the age of three, is loved by everyone in the community. Wanda, their older sister, spends much of her time with her boyfriend, Frank. Sara idolizes, but does not envy, her beautiful older sister. The children's mother is dead, and their father stays away as much as possible—even when he knows Charlie is lost—possibly because he cannot accept the reality of a mentally retarded child.

He looked blankly at the sky, unable to associate the heavy awkward birds with the graceful swans he had seen on the water.

Sara learns much about herself, her friends, and her acquaintances when Charlie becomes lost while searching for swans. Her friend Mary turns out to be loyal only to the extent that it does not interfere with her own fun. Joe Melby, on the other hand, proves how wrong Sara has been about him. Believing that he took Charlie's watch, Sara has hated him for several months. Actually, Joe returned the watch to Charlie after some other boys took it. After learning of Joe's good deed, Sara reluctantly accepts his offer to help look for Charlie. Joe and Sara find that they like one another, and once the crisis is resolved, they attend a party together.

Sara's sister Wanda and her Aunt Willie play minor roles but add humor and drama to the story. Wanda, nineteen years old, is a pretty, social girl. She exhibits some exasperation with Sara when Sara complains about being awkward and undesirable, but she tries to be a supportive sister. Sensible, good-natured Aunt Willie takes care of Wanda, Sara, and Charlie in their father's absence. She worries about the children but knows when to relax her overprotective tendencies toward them.

The novel has dual themes. The first is the teen-ager's capacity for maturity as exemplified by Sara's growth of character when she becomes personally responsible for finding Charlie, an experience that changes her outlook on life. The second theme is the need for compassion and understanding for the mentally retarded, as evidenced in the guilt, remorse, frustration, and discomfort that the other characters feel when it seems that Charlie may be lost forever.

◆ Literary Qualities ◆

Byars's style is simple, straightforward, and easy to read. She uses very short chapters and successfully builds suspense until the climax. She develops each character subtly through dialogue, everyday circumstances, or conflict. Byars generally omits adults from the plots of her works so that she can explore how her adolescent characters make decisions and act on their own, away from adult influences.

In *The Summer of the Swans* many characters interact to reveal a change in the life of Sara. The book's third-person omniscient narrator focuses on Sara's thoughts and feelings through most of the novel. Byars increases the novel's suspense by shifting to the distraught Charlie's point of view when he becomes lost.

Byars's use of symbolism adds depth to the story. Sara feels gawky and insecure at the beginning: her big orange sneakers symbolize her assessment of herself as unattractive and odd. But by the end of the book, Sara feels more confident and is ready to discard the sneakers. Once she realizes she is not an "ugly duckling," she conducts herself with the gracefulness of the swans she and Charlie watch at the lake.

Sara also learns to accept her father's inability to deal with Charlie's disability, and Byars explains Sara's new understanding in metaphorical terms:

> [Sara] suddenly saw life as a series of huge, uneven steps, ... and she had just taken an enormous step up out of the shadows, and she was standing, waiting, and there were other steps in front of her ... and she saw Charlie on a flight of small difficult steps, and her father down at the bottom of some steps, just sitting and not trying to go further.

Sara's newfound ability to put her life in perspective and to view her future with hope and determination signal her maturation. Byars convincingly captures this change in her character.

◆ Social Sensitivity ◆

Byars's compassionate approach to mental disability in *The Summer of the Swans* results from her work with learning disabled children at West Virginia University in 1968. While there, she researched histories of children with brain damage caused by high-fevered illnesses. This subject so fascinated her that she enrolled at West Virginia University to obtain her mas-

Illustration by Ted CoConis for *Summer of the Swans* by Betsy Byars. Camelot/Avon: New York (1970).

ter's degree in special education. At the time that Byars's novel was published, mental disabilities were a particularly sensitive subject that few books examined. Byars's treatment of the mentally handicapped is very touching, though not overly sentimental.

The novel emphasizes adolescents' great, though often untapped, capacity for maturity. Over the course of one summer, Sara convincingly grows from a self-absorbed, judgmental teen-ager to a capable, independent young adult. Most parents and teachers will find her to be an appropriate role model for adolescents, and Sara's actions may inspire adolescents to have more confidence in their abilities.

◆ Topics for Discussion ◆

1. What are Sara's memories of her father? Where does he live? Why do you think Sara's father does not come to rescue Charlie?

2. Why does Sara hold a grudge against Joe Melby? Is she justified in doing this?

3. Does Sara apologize to Joe? How does she convey her forgiveness?

4. Do you like Aunt Willie? Why does Aunt Willie regret not sewing on Charlie's button? Why does she call the television "a devil"?

5. Can you cite uses of imagery that intensify the story?

6. Why does Charlie's watch play such an important part in the story? Why is Charlie so attracted to the swans?

◆ Ideas for Reports and Papers ◆

1. Discuss the devices the author uses to heighten the conflict in the story.

2. Two of the novel's important themes are the teen-ager's ability to act maturely and the need to treat the mentally disabled with compassion and respect. Choose one of these themes and discuss how Byars develops it.

3. Cite sections of the novel that are humorous. Why do you think the author introduces humor in so serious a plot? Do you think that this is an effective device?

4. What incidents cause Sara to grow up this particular summer? Has any specific incident in your life caused you to change? Write about one incident that changed your life.

5. Do you like the way the author shifts the point of view from Sara's to Charlie's? What effect does relating the thoughts and feelings of both characters have on the story?

◆ Adaptations ◆

Several of Byars's novels have been adapted to television as ABC "Afterschool Specials." Based on *The Summer of the Swans*, "Sara's Summer of the Swans" is a particularly fine production. Produced by Martin Tahse Productions and first broadcast in 1974, it stars Heather Totten as Sara, Reed Diamond as Charlie, and Christopher Knight as Joe. This production is available on videocassette.

◆ For Further Reference ◆

Cullinan, Bernice E. *A Study Guide to the Novels of Betsy Byars.* New York: Viking Penguin, n.d. Provides literary analysis of several of Byars's novels, including *The Summer of the Swans*.

De Montreville, Doris, and Donna Hill, eds. *Third Book of Junior Authors.* New York: H. W. Wilson, 1972. The editors provide an autobiographical sketch by Byars and a bibliography of her works and related articles.

Glazer, Joan, and Gurney Williams III. *Introduction to Children's Literature.* New York: McGraw-Hill, 1979. Discusses the book with insight into Sara's sensitive feelings about Charlie.

Kingman, Lee, ed. *Newbery and Caldecott Medal Books, 1966-1975.* Boston: Horn Book, 1975. Offers a glimpse of the author through her Newbery Award acceptance speech and through her husband's comments.

Morowski, Daniel G., ed. *Contemporary Literary Criticism.* Vol. 35. Detroit: Gale Research, 1985. Excerpts criticism of Byars's novels.

Norton, Donna E. *Through the Eyes of a Child: An Introduction to Children's Literature.* Columbus: Charles Merrill, 1983. Contains a brief analysis of *The Summer of the Swans.*

Sutherland, Zena. *Children and Books.* 6th ed. Glenview, IL: Scott, Foresman, 1981. Discusses family life as portrayed in several books, including *The Summer of the Swans.*

Catherine Blanton
South Georgia Regional Library

THE SUN ALSO RISES

Novel

1926

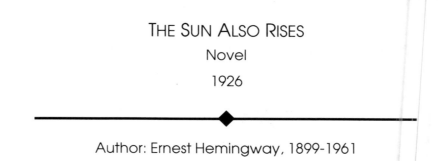

Author: Ernest Hemingway, 1899-1961

Major Books for Young Adults

In Our Time, 1925
The Sun Also Rises, 1926
A Farewell to Arms, 1929

The Old Man and the Sea, 1952
The Nick Adams Stories, 1972
The Complete Short Stories of Ernest Hemingway, 1987

♦ About the Author ♦

Ernest Hemingway was born on July 21, 1899, in Oak Park, Illinois, the son of Clarence Edmonds and Grace Hemingway. Hemingway first published his writing while he was a student at Oak Park High School, and he began his journalistic apprenticeship as a teen-age reporter for the Kansas City *Star* in 1917. Although his family expected him to attend college, Hemingway was drawn instead toward the excitement of World War I. In the spring of 1918 he volunteered with the American Red Cross as an ambulance driver on the front-line in Italy; in July 1918, two weeks shy of his nineteenth birthday, he was severely wounded in battle.

After recovering from his wounds, he supported himself as a journalist until he was able to make a living writing fiction. In the early 1920s, he lived in Paris and worked as a foreign correspondent for the Toronto *Star*. His first important work of fiction, a collec-

tion of short stories entitled *In Our Time*, appeared in 1925, followed in 1926 by *The Sun Also Rises*, considered a classic novel of the twentieth century. For the next three decades, Hemingway published one best-selling volume after another, including *A Farewell to Arms*, *For Whom the Bell Tolls* (1940), and *The Old Man and the Sea*. This string of successes established Hemingway as one of the most famous and influential novelists in history, widely recognized for his precise, innovative prose style and his unique vision of experience.

Hemingway married Hadley Richardson in 1921; following their divorce, he married Pauline Pfeiffer in 1927. That marriage also ended in divorce, and Hemingway married Martha Gelhorn in 1940, divorcing her and marrying Mary Welsh in 1945. His macho public persona—he was known as a hunter, aficionado of bullfighting, drinker, and womanizer—made him a celebrity. Constant media attention tended to de-emphasize Hemingway's actual writing,

The Sun Also Rises

and many readers, caught up in the superficial and glamorous aspects of his life and career, missed the fact that his fiction is firmly anchored in timeless, fundamental values such as courage, honor, truthfulness, and compassion. The Hemingway code has often been summed up by his phrase "grace under pressure," yet many observers fail to see that this "grace" is not only physical and aesthetic, but moral and spiritual. Much of Hemingway's important fiction is value-centered and profoundly religious.

None of Hemingway's fiction was written specifically for young adults. Yet, as with many classic authors, some of his works have crossed over, appealing widely to adults and young adults alike. Hemingway received numerous awards for his writing, including the Pulitzer Prize for *The Old Man and the Sea* in 1952, and the Nobel Prize in 1954. In January 1954, he was in two plane crashes in Africa and suffered severe injuries from which he never recovered.

On July 2, 1961, Hemingway committed suicide at his home in Ketchum, Idaho.

◆ Overview ◆

The First World War, with its chemical weaponry and trench warfare, killed millions of soldiers and shattered the ideals of countless survivors. As the world prepared to enter a new decade, both those who had and those who had not seen combat shared a numbing sense of devastation. In *The Sun Also Rises*, his first published novel, Hemingway sketches the relationships among a group of young people in 1920s Europe who attempt to fill their empty lives with travel, whiskey, and love affairs.

When the plot of *The Sun Also Rises* is summarized, the novel sounds more like a soap opera than a classic work of literature; what elevates the book is Hemingway's keen portrayal of characters adrift in a world that cannot satisfy their needs. In their relentless pursuit of pleasure, and in their quest to replace old, lost ideals with new ones, Hemingway's characters demonstrate a yearning to connect with some sort of universal order. For Hemingway and his protagonist, Jake Barnes, this higher order is symbolized by the honor and pageantry of bullfighting. Jake and his friends visit the city of Pamplona, Spain, for the annual Fiesta de San Fermín, and it is here—their dissipation set in sharp contrast to the purity of the bullfight—that they must confront the moral emptiness of their lives.

◆ Setting ◆

The novel opens in Paris in the early 1920s. The Left Bank of the Seine River was a magnet for philosophers, artists, and writers during the decade following the First World War; this era and place inspired some of the greatest artistic works of the modern age. Hemingway himself lived in Paris as a young man, and mingled with such literary figures as F. Scott Fitzgerald and Gertrude Stein.

Although *The Sun Also Rises* opens in Paris and is informed by the sensibility of the American and British community there, its venue ranges across the European countryside. Jake and his friend Bill Gorton leave Paris by train to go fishing in the Basque country of Spain; then they join the other members of their party. The symbolic focus of the festival in Pamplona is the bullfight; ordinary citizens risk their lives every morning to "run with the bulls" through the streets of the city. Jake and his friends are expatriates and wanderers all, unable to call any one place home.

Even Jake, who considers himself a true "aficionado"—one who understands and believes passionately in the bullfight—has his convictions shaken by the events that unfold over the course of the week; by the time he leaves Pamplona, he is a changed man. The novel ends in Madrid, where Jake and Brett ponder the changes they have undergone at the festival.

◆ Themes and Characters ◆

As the story begins, Jake Barnes, an American journalist and war veteran, is leading a somewhat bohemian life in Paris. He is in love with a young English war widow, Lady Brett Ashley, but their relationship is complicated by Jake's having sustained a war injury that has left him sexually incapacitated. Brett has become engaged, as a matter of convenience, to Michael Campbell, an Englishman. Robert Cohn, a young American writer who was once a boxing champion at Princeton University, is also attracted to Brett. The expatriates journey to Pamplona for the Fiesta de San Fermín and there meet the young matador Pedro Romero, who performs "without falsity" and thus upholds the pure standards of the bullfight. Sexual intrigue, most of it centered on Brett, provides the catalyst for Jake's reevaluation of his generation's moral standing.

Hemingway chooses two contrasting epigraphs—that is, opening quotations—for *The Sun Also Rises* and, through their juxtaposition, establishes a clear, simple theme. Gertrude Stein, herself a writer and the mentor of many young artists in Paris during the 1920s, once said of the American expatriates: "You are all a lost generation." Stein's observation suggests the transience of humankind; Hemingway took her statement to mean that his generation no longer had recourse to the ideals and structural order of pre-World War I civilization.

> *She was looking into my eyes with that way she had of looking that made you wonder whether she really saw out of her own eyes.*

Hemingway draws the book's second epigraph from the Old Testament Book of Ecclesiastes: "One generation passeth away, and another generation cometh; but the earth abideth forever...The sun also ariseth, and the sun goeth down." This prophecy suggests a cosmic order: in God's scheme of the world there is no "lost generation," and the self-centered, fragile human ego appears insignificant next to the cycles of the sun and the passing of time. Until Jake, Brett, and the others realize that they are indeed lost, but lost only because they lack the moral fortitude to subordinate individual desires to universal truths, their lives will lack meaning. Hemingway said that he did not intend for *The Sun Also Rises* to be "a hollow or bitter satire, but a damn tragedy with the earth abiding forever as the hero."

Against the backdrop of tragedy, Hemingway strings scenes of happiness and celebration: the gaiety of Paris nightlife; the splendor of Pamplona at festival time, with its bustling crowds and noble matadors; and the serenity of the Basque countryside where Jake and Bill Gorton hike and fish. Behind the nightlife stands the alcoholism, behind the bullfights the tragic realities, and behind the fishing a generation's unconscious quest for simplicity. The fishing scenes, far from being a mere pastoral interlude in an otherwise frenzied novel, serve to reinforce Hemingway's primary theme; Jake recognizes that he is missing some element crucial to his happiness, and he undertakes a quest to discover his generation's lost values.

Jake is most content fishing, observing the bullfight, or riding atop a dilapidated bus, drinking wine, and practicing his Spanish on the locals; the proprietor of the Hotel Montoya in Pamplona understands Jake better than do any of his "friends" because of the camaraderie the two share as aficionados. He ultimately sacrifices his most precious possession, his status as an aficionado, by exposing young Romero to Brett's seduction. As such, Jake is emblematic of a generation that has come of age only to find individual peace more elusive than world peace.

An idea that gives form to much of Hemingway's fiction is the notion of "grace under pressure," a code by which individuals might bring honor upon themselves. Simply put, this code requires that, no matter what the circumstances, a person must not break. The grace referred to is a physical, aesthetic, moral, and spiritual matter; the circumstances to be withstood include the complexity of moral choice, the chaos of violence, and, above all, the presence of death that gnaws at every human being. The primary incarnation of death in *The Sun Also Rises* is the bullfight; exemplary behavior—rooted in courage, honor, and passion—is demonstrated by the matadors. In the ritual of the fight, the bull and the matador face uncertainty with equal dignity, and death with equal courage.

Hemingway once remarked that *The Sun Also Rises* was the most moral book he had ever written; that it was a kind of "tract against promiscuity." Although at first it seems that Brett will sleep with anyone, in the end she realizes that she must not corrupt Romero. By recognizing the importance of setting standards, Brett echoes the novel's principal theme—the necessity of discovering, or rediscovering, those values that define a morally satisfying life.

◆ Literary Qualities ◆

Examined in the context of early 1920s literature, Hemingway's writing in *The Sun Also Rises* displays a combination of conventional and groundbreaking techniques. The chronological, first-person narrative structure of the novel is relatively standard, whereas the intense, almost poetic style is unique. Hemingway eliminates ornamentation—such as excessive adjectives or adverbs—from his writing and employs rigorous word selection in an effort to unite action, emotion, and text.

Hemingway carefully modulates the rhythm of the text, often through the use of repetition and short sentences. When Brett turns up on Jake's doorstep at 4:30 a.m., she explains why she has left her escort:

> ...Then he wanted me to go to Cannes with him. Told him I knew too many people in Cannes. Monte Carlo. Told him I knew too many people in Monte Carlo. Told him I

knew too many people everywhere. Quite true, too. So I asked him to bring me here.

The dialogue in *The Sun Also Rises*, like that in all of Hemingway's works, reveals character, carries the movement of the story, and generates tension. Brett's breathless rundown of her evening's activities highlights her flip, world-weary, and often drunken outlook on the world; whereas Cannes and Monte Carlo traditionally conjure up images of glamour and romance, behind Brett's offhand mention of these locales lies the unspoken fact that she and Jake can never be lovers. Throughout the novel, Hemingway's highly stylized dialogue contributes immensely to the book's power.

Hemingway uses the symbolic landscape to reveal the psychological and emotional workings of his characters. Landscapes are full of history and mirror the souls of the characters who traverse them. As Jake and Bill drive through the Basque country, Jake observes "squares of green and brown on the hillsides. Making the horizon were the brown mountains. They were strangely shaped." For Jake, as well as for his companions, travel is neither a novelty nor a means of escape; the peaceful countryside ringed by foreboding mountains represents the dark realities that mold human experience.

◆ Social Sensitivity ◆

From the start, *The Sun Also Rises* has stirred controversy. When the novel was first published, high society attempted to match characters in the book with certain well-known celebrities from the expatriate world. The thrill of this guessing game soon subsided, however, leaving Hemingway's characters to be examined in their own right. Although promiscuity, apathy, and alcoholism figure prominently in the behavior of Brett and the other expatriates, most readers deemed their actions more chic than immoral. Thus, while *The Sun Also Rises* explicitly criticizes expatriate society for lacking a moral foundation, public reaction to the book over the years has pointed up the hypocrisy of society at large for refusing to cast harsh judgment on those people it considers sufficiently glamorous.

◆ Topics for Discussion ◆

1. Describe Brett's relationships with Jake, Mike Campbell, Robert Cohn, and Pedro Romero. Do you think she treats men badly?

2. Robert Cohn, a former collegiate boxing champion, beats up Romero when he finds him with Brett. What does Brett think about Cohn after this incident? What does she think about Romero, and why does she decide to avoid further romantic involvement with him?

3. Hemingway regards the bullfight as a religious experience of sorts. Why? What are some of the similarities between religious ritual and bullfighting ritual?

4. Compare Hemingway's descriptions of Paris, the Basque countryside, and Pamplona. How do the different landscapes reflect the characters' actions and emotions?

5. At the end of the novel, Jake and Brett see the sights of Madrid from a taxi. How is this characteristic of their

relationship? What does it suggest about the fate of their generation?

6. Jake drinks a great deal of alcohol. Discuss the ways in which alcohol serves as a destructive force or an escape from reality, and the ways in which it serves as a medium for communion with nature. Analyze the last two pages of the novel in this regard.

◆ Ideas for Reports and Papers ◆

1. The Fiesta de San Fermin is a real festival held every year from July 6 to July 14 in Pamplona. Research and report on the history of bullfighting in Spain and the traditions associated with this festival in particular.

2. Research and report on the American literary colony in Paris during the 1920s. A few of the better known writers who made up this community are Hemingway, F. Scott Fitzgerald, Ford Madox Ford, and Gertrude Stein. You may wish to consult Hemingway's memoir *A Movable Feast* or Stein's *The Autobiography of Alice B. Toklas* for firsthand accounts of expatriate society.

3. Brett refers to herself as Circe, a temptress from Greek mythology. Research the Circe myth and discuss the aptness of Brett's comparison. Explain Jake's role in the Circe legend as it appears in Hemingway's novel.

4. In chapter 17, a man is gored to death while running with the bulls through the streets of Pamplona, prompting a waiter to comment to Jake: "A big horn wound. All for fun. Just for fun. What do you think of that?" How does Jake react to the waiter's comments? Do you think his attitude toward

bullfighting changes over the course of the book? Why is it significant that the bull that kills the man is later killed by Romero?

5. Read *Death in the Afternoon*, Hemingway's 1932 treatise on bullfighting. Compare his descriptions of the sport in this later work of nonfiction to those in *The Sun Also Rises*.

◆ Related Titles ◆

In a general sense, all of Hemingway's work is related, but the reader who wishes to gain a more thorough understanding of Hemingway's love for Spain is referred to the author's classic nonfiction study of the bullfight, *Death in the Afternoon*.

The Sun Also Rises is frequently studied in conjunction with Hemingway's novels *A Farewell to Arms* and *For Whom the Bell Tolls* and his novella, *The Old Man and the Sea*. In each of these later works, Hemingway's protagonist faces death or extreme deprivation, and learns the value of "grace under pressure." Read together, these books span nearly four decades and provide a glimpse of how Hemingway sustained and adapted his basic themes over the course of his career.

There have been many attempts to adapt Hemingway's work to film. *The Sun Also Rises* was made into a disappointing motion picture, directed by Henry King and starring Tyrone Power, Eva Gardner, and Errol Flynn, in 1957; in 1985 it resurfaced as a disastrous NBC television miniseries starring Jane Seymour, Hart Bochner, Zeljko Ivanek, and Robert Carradine. Neither version captured the spirit of the work or displayed any comprehension of the novel's themes.

◆ For Further Reference ◆

Baker, Carlos. *Ernest Hemingway: A Life Story.* New York: Scribner's, 1969. The first full-length biography of Hemingway, this volume remains the best and most reliable resource for a balanced portrait of the man and his career.

————. *Hemingway: The Writer as Artist.* Princeton, NJ: Princeton University Press, 1972. One of the earliest and still one of the best critical studies of Hemingway's works.

Bruccoli, Matthew J. *Conversations with Ernest Hemingway.* Jackson: University Press of Mississippi, 1986. A useful and convenient compilation of Hemingway interviews and statements.

Moore, Gene M. "Ernest Hemingway." In *Research Guide to Biography and Criticism,* edited by Walton Beacham. Washington, DC: Beacham Publishing, 1985. Contains a useful overview of Hemingway criticism and biography.

Oliver, Charles M., ed. *The Hemingway Review.* Most of the important new scholarly and critical work on Hemingway appears in this journal.

Reynolds, Michael. *The Young Hemingway.* New York: Basil Blackwell, 1986. The first volume in a multivolume biography of Hemingway, this judicious work is the most significant and substantive of the many biographies that have appeared since Baker's landmark study.

Wagner, Linda W., ed. *Ernest Hemingway: Six Decades of Criticism.* East Lansing: Michigan State University Press, 1987. Contains some of the best critical essays on Hemingway's work.

Waldhorn, Arthur. *A Reader's Guide to Ernest Hemingway.* New York: Farrar, Straus and Giroux, 1972. A useful guide to Hemingway's work.

Williams, Wirt. *The Tragic Art of Ernest Hemingway.* Baton Rouge: Louisiana State University Press, 1981. An interesting critical study of the tragic elements in Hemingway's work.

Jessica A. Dorman

H. R. Stoneback
SUNY-New Paltz

THE TALE OF BEATRIX POTTER

Biography

1946

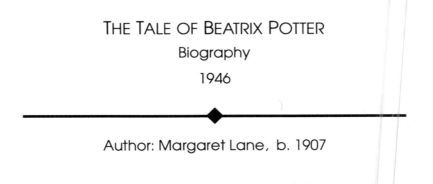

Author: Margaret Lane, b. 1907

Major Books for Young Adults

The Tale of Beatrix Potter, 1946, 1985

◆ About the Author ◆

Margaret Lane was born on June 23, 1907, in Cheshire, England. She was educated at St. Stephen's College, Folkstone, and St. Hugh's College, Oxford. Following in the footsteps of her father, a newspaper editor, she took up a career in journalism, working in London and New York from 1928 to 1938.

In 1934 Lane married Bryan Wallace, the eldest son of Edgar Wallace, the flamboyant and popular British novelist. She soon began to write novels also. Her first, *Faith, Hope and No Charity* (1935), won the Prix Femina-Vie Heureuse. A second novel, *At Last the Island* (1937), followed shortly, after which she produced a careful and well-received biography of her eccentric father-in-law, *Edgar Wallace: The Biography of a Phenomenon* (1938). Her marriage to Bryan Wallace ended in divorce in 1939.

Biographies of eccentric British characters have formed a major part of Lane's writing career. *Walk into My Parlour* (1941) is a biography of Emma Shardiloe, the nineteenth-century medium and spiritualist. *Life with*

Ionides (1963) concerns an Englishman who collected poisonous snakes in East Africa. In *The Brontë Story* (1953) and *Samuel Johnson and His World* (1975), she takes on somewhat better known but no less eccentric subjects.

In a way, Lane's most successful biographical find was Beatrix Potter, the shy and very private person who created the beloved characters of Peter Rabbit, Tom Kitten, and Hunca-Munca. When Lane wrote her book, few people knew much about Potter's life. Indeed, it rather surprised the public to learn that Beatrix Potter died in 1943; most would have said she had died years before. When she married Willie Heelis of Sawrey, Potter put aside her life as a children's author and became Mrs. Heelis, blunt country woman and sheep breeder. Her publishers were warned not to give out her address.

The Tale of Beatrix Potter remains the standard biography and has inspired a generation of Beatrix Potter scholars. Since it originally appeared in 1946, Lane has revised and enlarged her work several times, most recently in 1985, as new information has come to light.

Margaret Lane's second marriage was to Francis John Clarence Westenra Plantagenet Hastings, fifteenth earl of Huntingdon. She became the Countess of Huntingdon and had two daughters. She and her husband took up hunting for Zulu treasure on the border of Rhodesia and Mozambique. She describes it all in *A Calabash of Diamonds* (1961).

In the 1980s, Lane turned to children's books, composing a series of picture books for young children on the natural history of common creatures—*The Squirrel* (1981), *The Beaver* (1982), *The Fish* (1982), *The Fox* (1982), *The Frog* (1982), and *The Spider* (1982). The unsentimental, slightly humorous tone of these books recalls Beatrix Potter's works. Lane has been president of the Women's Press Club, the Dickens Fellowship, the Johnson Society, the Jane Austen Society, and the Brontë Society. She lives in Beaulieu, England.

Photograph of Beatrix Potter, age nine, in *The Tale of Beatrix Potter* by Margaret Lane. Frederick Warne: London (1968).

◆ Overview ◆

Most readers need no introduction to Beatrix Potter's nursery classics, which include *The Tale of Peter Rabbit* (1902), *The Tale of Squirrel Nutkin* (1903), *The Tailor of Gloucester* (1903), *The Tale of Benjamin Bunny* (1904), *The Tale of Mrs. Tiggy Winkle* (1905), *The Tale of Tom Kitten* (1907), and *Ginger and Pickles* (1909). These books have become a well-established part of the common culture. But few readers are familiar with the intriguing life of the woman who wrote and illustrated these books.

Lane's biography, begun shortly after Potter's death in 1943 at the age of 77, was the first and in some ways remains the best. Born into the deep conservatism of the Victorian middle class, Potter lived to see an almost modern assertion of the strength and capability of women in a masculine world. During her life, she fought against incredible obstacles to become economically independent and to free herself from demanding and rigid parents. Her small books, composed almost on the sly, were an important part of this struggle.

The Tale of Beatrix Potter is not written specifically for young readers, but readers of all ages have read and enjoyed this account of an extraordinary person. To some, her life may appear to have been excessively conservative. She was an exaggeratedly obedient daughter whose only open rebellion against her parents occurred when she married—at age forty-seven—a country solicitor and

Illustration by Beatrix Potter in *The Tale of Beatrix Potter* by Margaret Lane. Frederick Warne: London (1968).

collecting all sorts of things and sneaking them back into the house for further study.

Later, she wrote and published her "little books" and thrived on the details of business—something women were not supposed to do, and something her parents made every effort to stop. For each book she painstakingly matched every illustration with a real place or animal. By now she kept a veritable zoo of mice, hedgehogs, rabbits, snails, and ravens.

As she grew up, she did manage to make friends, although her parents' unrelenting views of propriety constantly stunted her social life. Not until late middle age did she ease her way out of London and away from her parents. She displayed a combination of great courage and incredible timidity, as she continued her role of dutiful daughter while building up an independent income and managing a successful farm and sheep breeding operation. When she died she left thousands of acres of land in the Lake District to the National Trust, a private land preservation group.

◆ Setting ◆

real estate agent. She was exceedingly shy and very private, but her interior life brimmed with humor, conflict, and even adventure.

Potter was never sent to school, was never permitted playmates, and very rarely participated in the social life of her parents, yet she grew neither sullen nor bored. Resourceful, intelligent, and creative, she developed interests that helped her combat the loneliness of her home environment. She taught herself to draw and enjoyed capturing precise details. She investigated natural history with astonishing care and accuracy,

Born in 1866, Potter grew up in London during the last decades of the nineteenth century, an era usually referred to as the Victorian period. In many ways her life, confined as it was, is but a reflection of this period's oppressive treatment of children and women. Her mother, for example, consistently refused to allow Beatrix to visit friends, for fear that these visits would upset Beatrix and make her ill. Nor would her mother allow young people to visit Beatrix at home because they might bring germs into the house. There is no evidence that Beatrix was a sickly child, and these extreme attitudes were symptomatic of a social culture that considered such protectiveness of the "weak" female health not only proper but a sign of parental love.

Overall, the obedience demanded of Beatrix and the discipline and routines that were imposed should be viewed as part of the middle-class Victorian culture. Beatrix, like most girls, was not sent to school. Instead her parents hired a governess who lived in their home and taught subjects considered appropriate for girls—languages, literature, a little history, and some drawing. Her younger brother, on the other hand, was sent away to boarding school at age seven, which was considered proper for boys of his social class.

Even the difficulty that Beatrix had in eventually leaving home, as well as her parents' unwillingness to allow her to marry, should be understood within the historical context. The Victorians sometimes appeared to have mixed feelings about their daughters. They wanted them to marry, and yet they did not want them to marry. If parents argued that a husband was not "good enough," it indicated how highly they valued their daughter. Beatrix's wealthy, but not aristocratic, parents considered neither Norman Warne (who died shortly after asking Beatrix to marry) nor William Heelis (the country solicitor she did marry) "good enough." In addition, one daughter in each family was supposed to sacrifice her own happiness and remain at home to take care of her parents in their old age. Beatrix was the only daughter, so this task fell to her.

◆ Themes and Characters ◆

The most important character in *The Tale of Beatrix Potter* is obviously Beatrix herself. In Lane's portrayal, Beatrix possesses a sturdy temperament and an inner self-sufficiency that allow her to find compensations in her lonely and rather unhappy childhood. Rather than succumbing to boredom, Beatrix develops during her solitude a life-long love of privacy and an ability to focus intensely on her own interests and fantasies. Shy, modest, and gentle, Beatrix has a subtle wit and an unsentimental innocence. Although the conventional formality of her parents' life irritates her, she remains patient and never openly rebels against it.

Rupert Potter, her father, is a dignified, whiskered, and punctual Victorian who does not share much of his daughter's life. Mrs. Potter is stern and stiff.

Some of the more positive influences in Beatrix's life include her grandmother, her brother, and her governess. Jessie Crompton, or Grandmamma Potter, is an old lady of seventy-five when Beatrix is five years old. She has sparkling eyes, like Beatrix's own, a lively wit, and a past filled with adventure and high-spirited romance. Beatrix's younger brother, Bertram, is her companion in the nursery and during summer vacations. The two remain friends throughout their lives, sharing interests in art and natural history. When Beatrix is seventeen, Annie Carter joins the Potter household as a German governess. Miss Carter is "sweet-natured, pleasant mannered, and—compared with Beatrix—splendidly emancipated." Although she soon leaves her job to marry and start a family in nearby Wadsworth, the friendship between Beatrix and Annie continues. Beatrix becomes known as "Auntie Bea" to Annie's children, whom she regularly visits. Beatrix brings them gifts, makes up stories for them, and draws pictures with them. When she cannot visit, she writes the children letters. She creates *The Tale of Peter Rabbit* as a picture-letter for Annie's son Noel Moore when he is in bed with a long illness.

When Beatrix is in her thirties, she develops a close friendship with Norman Warne, whose father founded the company that publishes her books. Shy, gentle, and imaginative, his personality is much like Beatrix's. When they become engaged, an awful row erupts in the Potter household because Beatrix's parents deem him an unsuitable husband. Norman dies in 1905 before a wedding can take place.

Beatrix's next suitor, William Heelis, a solicitor and real estate agent, meets with similar objections from her parents, but she marries him anyway, beginning what she describes as the happiest period in her life.

Many of the themes that Lane highlights in *The Tale of Beatrix Potter* are those that Potter herself chose to identify as important when she looked back upon her life during her later years. Lane also draws attention to the ironic conflict between Potter's conventional social behavior and her highly original inner life.

Tenacity and patience in the face of obstacles are important themes in this life. Beatrix's most obvious struggle is against her parents, but she also has to battle her whole society and its view of women as weak, unintellectual, and irresponsible.

Work and its relationship to happiness is another important theme. Work, not education or experience, helps Potter become self-sufficient and happy. Tucked away upstairs where she eats her meals alone, has few toys, no friends, and only an occasional lesson from a hired governess, Beatrix fills her hours with focused activity. She reads, makes up stories, trains mice,

memorizes Shakespeare's plays, and cultivates a highly sensitive eye for detail. Out of this solitude comes a distinctly unique and original personality. She overcomes her sorrows to find happiness and peace at last.

◆ Literary Qualities ◆

Lane, a novelist, uses many of the techniques of fiction to write *The Tale of Beatrix Potter*. She creates well-defined characters, draws detailed scenes, and even constructs a sort of dialogue through extensive quotations from Potter's own letters and diaries. Lane draws on the memories of William Heelis, friends, cousins, and local people from the village of Sawrey to give this biography a very personal quality.

The narrator's affectionate and admiring voice is strong throughout. Lane recounts with respect and awe how the scholar Leslie Linder worked for years to decode the alphabet cipher that Potter used to write her journal. The reader gets both a sense of how difficult the decoding task was and a portrait of the adolescent Beatrix composing long, detailed journal entries in elaborate code, not because she is being secretive, but because she enjoys the difficulty of writing in code.

◆ Social Sensitivity ◆

One of the most difficult tasks for some young readers of this book will involve coming to a fair understanding of Victorian attitudes toward children and women. These may appear very peculiar, if not cruel, to modern sensibilities. Readers may want to turn Beatrix's mother into a cruel, witchlike character. She was not. Lane is sensitive to this difficulty and offers some background on Victorian attitudes. She carefully paints the Potter parents as stiff and conventional rather than mean-spirited, noting that their daughter does not hate them, although she sometimes finds them irritating.

Young people may also have trouble understanding why Potter does not simply run away or rebel. In fact, this biography illustrates very well that open rebellion is often not necessary; Potter does get what she wants in the end. She is spunky and manages her parents remarkably well without causing too many outright wars. If she fails to change their attitudes, neither does she submit to them. This is the story of the success and triumph of a shy person.

◆ Topics for Discussion ◆

1. To be eccentric means to be unusual or "outside the center of things." In what ways do you think Beatrix Potter was truly an eccentric? In what ways was she not eccentric at all?

2. Potter believed in the importance of heredity in the formation of character, and as she grew older she liked to draw attention to "what she regarded as the outcroppings of native Crompton rock in her own character." How would you describe the influence of her grandparents and the Crompton family legends on Potter's life?

3. Potter once remarked, "I can't invent; I only copy." To what extent is this a true statement? How can one who copies also be creative?

4. A modern reader may be surprised to learn that Potter was outspokenly opposed to women's liberation. Can you explain this stand in terms of her character and upbringing?

5. In the later part of her life, Potter scorned English admirers who liked to emphasize her importance as an artist, while befriending American fans who emphasized her importance as a writer. Why do you think she felt this way?

6. Potter rejected many aspects of her childhood. She disliked Bolton Gardens and all it stood for. Yet in reading her biography, one feels a great strength of character and a unity of purpose. How would you tie together the interests of her youth with the interests of her maturity?

7. Friends are important to any person's development. Who were Potter's best friends and how did they affect her life?

◆ Ideas for Reports and Papers ◆

1. Critics often like to identify the people and places that inspired Potter's books. Try to separate the "fact" from the "fiction" in some of her books using this biography as a reference. Why do you think she was so careful to copy things from "real life"?

2. The Potter household is an example of late Victorian family life. Using this biography as an example, describe the Victorian attitude toward children and women. How has this attitude changed?

3. Potter's grandparents were religious and political nonconformists. How was this radical heritage reflected in Potter's own life?

4. Describe the influence of two or three people (other than her parents) on Potter's life.

5. "I cannot rest," Beatrix Potter wrote in her secret journal. "I *must* draw, however poor the result ... I *will* do something sooner or later." She appears to have been a very determined child who knew exactly what she wanted. In light of her entire life, what do you think she really did want? Did she achieve it?

6. Biographies sometimes bring up large questions that are relevant to many lives. How does Lane deal with the problem of happiness in the life of Beatrix Potter?

◆ For Further Reference ◆

Linder, Leslie. *The Art of Beatrix Potter*. 1955. Rev. ed. Middlesex, England: Frederick Warne, 1972. Contains reproductions of many of Potter's drawings, including her book illustrations, sketches from her notebooks, and the mushroom drawings she intended someday to make into a book.

Potter, Beatrix. *Beatrix Potter's Americans: Selected Letters*, edited by Jane Crowell Morse. Boston: Horn Book, 1982. The letters from Potter to her American fans, written during the latter part of her life, contain many reminiscences of her youth.

——. *The Journal of Beatrix Potter*, edited by Leslie Linder. Middlesex, England: Frederick Warne, 1966. This is the engaging journal that Beatrix Potter began at age fourteen and kept until she was nearly thirty years old.

Taylor, Judy. *Beatrix Potter: Artist, Storyteller and Countrywoman*. Middlesex, England: Frederick Warne/ Penguin Books, 1986. Contains plenty of pictures and provides a good overview of Beatrix Potter research since Lane's biography.

Linda Howe

A TALE OF TWO CITIES

Novel

1859

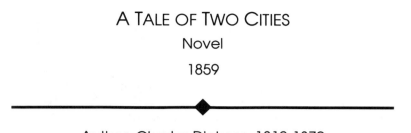

Author: Charles Dickens, 1812-1870

Major Books for Young Adults

Oliver Twist, 1837-1839
A Christmas Carol, 1843
David Copperfield, 1850

Hard Times, 1854
A Tale of Two Cities, 1859
Great Expectations, 1860-1861

◆ About the Author ◆

Charles John Huffam Dickens was born February 7, 1812, in Portsea, on England's southern coast. John Dickens, Charles's father, was a respectable, middle-class naval pay clerk. His family moved several times during Charles's youth, and the boy attended several schools, received instruction from his mother, and read voraciously. John Dickens received a reasonable salary, but he always spent more than he made. In 1824 he was imprisoned for debt. Two weeks before his father's imprisonment, young Charles was sent to work in a blacking warehouse, pasting labels on bottles of boot polish. He lived alone in poverty in rented lodgings while the rest of his family moved into prison with his father—a common practice at that time. John Dickens was released after three months, and Charles returned to school. Dickens always remembered and hated this period of his life and the degradation it seemed to entail. Yet here he first became familiar with the lower-class people who appear throughout his novels. Dickens also returns again and again in his books to prison scenes.

In 1827 Dickens left school for good and became an apprentice for an attorney's firm. He took a strong dislike to the law—a dislike that shows up in many of his novels, especially Bleak House (1852-1853). He studied legal shorthand after work and became a very successful court and parliamentary reporter, eventually working for several newspapers. In 1836 Dickens published his first book, Sketches by Boz, a successful collection of short sketches on London life previously published in a London newspaper. He married Catherine Hogarth that year, and the couple, though increasingly unhappy, had ten children. His first novel, The Posthumous Papers of the Pickwick Club, appeared in monthly installments in 1836 and 1837. It became an immensely popular best seller, making Dickens extremely famous at age twenty-four.

From this time on, Dickens worked full-time as a writer. He published fourteen major novels, several plays, numerous short stories, and many other books and articles. At times he was involved in writing as many as three novels simultaneously. A man of incredible energy and vitality, Dickens acted, edited a number of periodicals, and worked with various charitable organizations. He also gave impressive public readings from his own works. He twice toured America, giving readings to packed houses. Severe shocks and exhaustion from overwork contributed to the stroke that ended his life on June 9, 1870, in Rochester, England.

Dickens's novels dominated the Victorian literary scene throughout his life. He was arguably the most popular novelist ever to write in English. In addition to his books appropriate for young adults, Dickens's important works include *Bleak House* (1852-1853), *Little Dorrit* (1855-1857), and *Our Mutual Friend* (1864-1865). He left a final novel, *The Mystery of Edwin Drood*, unfinished at the time of his death.

◆ Overview ◆

Many critics consider Dickens the greatest novelist of the English-speaking world. Historically he is probably the most popular. Dickens is one of those rare writers—like Shakespeare—who has always appealed to a wide variety of readers. When each installment of a new Dickens novel appeared, people of all social and economic classes rushed out to discover what had happened to their favorite characters. Scholars estimate that for every copy sold, ten people read or heard the story. Often while the rich laughed over a Dickens novel upstairs, the servants were downstairs in the kitchen hearing the same story read with equal enjoyment. In America herds of people would wait on the docks for the boats carrying a new installment of Dickens's latest book.

Dickens's novels are still amazingly popular among a wide range of readers. Scholars publish articles and books on Dickens at a rate second only to that of Shakespeare criticism. Yet his stories and characters still delight readers of vastly different ages, backgrounds, and experience.

A Tale of Two Cities is probably the least typically Dickensian of all Dickens's novels. This is probably why many critics have called it either his best work or his worst. Shorter than most of his greatest achievements, *A Tale of Two Cities* lacks what Dickens called "elbow room." It includes few of the grotesque comic characters that populate his longer works, and it does not pause in its rapid pace to fill pages with humorous situations, pleasing descriptions, and hilarious details.

On the other hand, *A Tale of Two Cities* is certainly more direct and unified than many other Dickens novels. Its plot moves quickly toward climax, it contains few extraneous details, and everything serves a clear thematic purpose. Many passages create considerable suspense, and Dickens's language in this novel, written at the peak of his powers, amazes the sensitive reader with its aptness and power to make one seem to see and feel the events and people it describes. *A Tale of Two Cities* also provides particularly good opportunities to study such novelistic tools as allusion, foreshadowing, symbol, characterization, plot structure, repetition, tone and irony, and point of view.

◆ Setting ◆

Dickens sets *A Tale of Two Cities* primarily in Paris and London during one of the most turbulent periods of European history, the French Revolution.

The novel covers events between 1775 and 1793, referring also to incidents occurring before that time. The French Revolution began in 1789 and continued in various forms through at least 1795. Dickens takes most of his historical perspective from *The French Revolution* (1837), a three-volume description and philosophical discussion by his friend Thomas Carlyle. Carlyle's view was not objective or well documented; his intention was argumentative and dramatic. He portrays vividly the suffering of the poor and especially the Reign of Terror, best symbolized by the guillotine. Dickens greatly admired Carlyle and his work, and he read *The French Revolution* many times. Like Carlyle, Dickens cared less for accurate history and factual presentation than for vivid descriptions and the meanings he found behind the events. He did not concern himself with the revolution's immediate political or economic causes but focused on the human suffering that he believed warped the very humanity of individuals on both sides of the battle lines.

On the eve of the French Revolution, national debts and aristocratic unwillingness to sacrifice forced heavy tax increases on a populace already living at near-subsistence levels. Bickering between King Louis XVI and leading aristocrats revealed that the king could not effectively enforce his will through the military. In 1787 and 1788 excessive exports of already-scarce food caused near starvation among the poorer classes, and a bumper grape harvest depressed prices and further reduced the buying power of poor agricultural workers. Then came the winter of 1788-1789, probably the worst of the entire century. Inspired by political philosophers and the recent success of the American Revolution, many members of the middle and lower classes became

Illustration by Rafaello Busoni for *A Tale of Two Cities* by Charles Dickens. Grosset & Dunlap: New York (1948).

increasingly hostile to the system that seemed to cause their suffering. During these years members of the poorer classes working toward revolutionary action referred to themselves as "Jacques," as do the patrons of the Defarges' shop in Dickens's novel. On July 14, 1789, a large group of Parisian citizens attacked the Bastille, the large central prison that symbolized to the populace the worst aristocratic offenses. Dickens describes this event in part 2, chapter 21 of *A Tale of Two Cities*. Chapter 22, in which Foulon, an aristocrat, is captured by a mob and cruelly executed, illustrates what happened in France during the months that followed, as local bastilles were attacked and aristocrats murdered. In chapter 23 Dickens shows peasants burning the chateau of Charles Darnay's uncle. Power struggles for control of the country—both political and philosophical—dominated the next few years. In August 1792, when Darnay leaves England for France, the dominant political group passed a series of laws renouncing monarchy and proclaiming death for any returning aristocrats. During the months that followed, this political group used the infamous guillotine to behead aristocrats and others who opposed their policies. As Dickens shows, it became very dangerous even to voice opinions contrary to the prevailing ideas. During this period approximately 300,000 people were jailed, and about 17,000 of these were executed.

♦ Themes and Characters ♦

Just before writing *A Tale of Two Cities*, Dickens acted the leading role in a play called *The Frozen Deep* written by his friend Wilkie Collins. Dickens played a man in love with a woman who rejects him in favor of a rival. The character Dickens played sacrifices his own life to save the rival he despises—all because of his love for the woman who rejected him. *A Tale of Two Cities* works out a similar theme of self-sacrifice. Sydney Carton, a brilliant young lawyer, wastes his talents in drink and cynicism. Carton helps another lawyer, the self-centered and unintelligent Stryver, to win cases and "shoulder" his way up in the world, but he will not work for himself. "I am incapable of all the higher and better flights of men," Carton says. He describes himself as "a dissolute dog who has never done any good and never will." Yet, rejected by Lucie Manette in favor of the handsome Frenchman Charles Darnay, Carton tells her, "For you, and for any dear to you, I would do anything. . . . There is a man who would give his life, to keep a life you love beside you!" At the novel's end, Carton does exactly that, exchanging places with Darnay, who looks remarkably like Carton, just before his execution by guillotine. In willingly giving his life for Lucie—even to save the rival he dislikes—Carton performs a sort of Christlike sacrifice; he saves Darnay through his own death, and at the same time he redeems himself from his own sins. Carton dies with the famous last words: "It is a far, far better thing that I do, than I have ever done; it is a far, far better rest that I go to than I have ever known."

Part of this self-sacrifice theme depends on a recurring pattern of resurrection imagery. The novel opens with Dr. Manette, Lucie's supposedly dead father, being released from a French prison in which he was unjustly held in solitary confinement for eighteen years. Dickens's characters repeatedly describe Dr. Manette as being "recalled to life." Similarly, Carton twice rescues Darnay from prison and death. In London, where Darnay is tried as a French spy, Carton's legal brilliance discredits the prosecution's false witnesses and brings about an acquittal. Darnay is thus "recalled to life" after facing a death sentence if found guilty. In Paris, Carton drugs Darnay and again recalls him to life by taking his place at the guillotine. Before he dies, Carton repeatedly hears in his mind the words of Jesus, "I am the Resurrection and the Life." Dickens also includes several humorous or false resurrections. The comic Jerry Cruncher moonlights as a "resurrection-man," illegally digging up bodies to sell to medical researchers. The Old Bailey spy Roger Cly apparently dies and is buried, but as it turns out he has faked his own funeral to escape vengeful prisoners. Similarly, the French nobleman Foulon stages a funeral for himself to escape the French mob during the revolution, but he is eventually discovered, "recalled to life," and then cruelly executed.

Dickens portrays the French mob's violence in order to illustrate aspects of the relationship between rich and poor. The first half of *A Tale of Two Cities* shows examples of the French aristocracy's cruelty and insensitivity to the overtaxed, impoverished, starving lower classes. Following Carlyle's ideas, Dickens tries to show that when the rich and powerful of any country act as these French aristocrats did, the people will inevitably revolt. The French Revolution was the natural result of prolonged cruelty. Although he sympathizes with the sufferings of the French poor, Dickens disapproves of their violence and cruelty. But he primarily blames the corrupt aristocrats whose cruelty caused the poor to become inhuman. "Crush humanity out of shape once more, under similar hammers," Dickens writes, "and it will twist itself into the same tortured forms. Sow the same seed of rapacious license and oppression over again, and it will surely yield the same fruit according to its kind."

For Dickens, here as elsewhere in his writings, problems of human suffering will not be solved by changes in political or economic systems. Like Carlyle, Dickens believed that enough different systems had been tried over many centuries to prove that none would eradicate the suffering of the poor. Rather, he sought the kind of unselfish benevolence and self-sacrifice he illustrates in Lucie Manette, Charles Darnay, and Sydney

Illustration by Rafaello Busoni for *A Tale of Two Cities* by Charles Dickens. Grosset & Dunlap: New York (1948).

Carton. Only when individuals—especially leaders—adopt these virtues and really care about the poor will suffering and injustice end. Dickens contends that the important changes occur in individuals, not systems. So Carton goes to heaven, while the French revolutionary system only finds new ways to commit the same atrocities that spawned it.

Ironically, despite its emphasis on individuals, *A Tale of Two Cities* may include fewer individualized, believable characters than any other Dickens novel. Indeed, many of its characters seem to exist primarily to illustrate points or exemplify aspects of human nature. In a departure from his normal characterization techniques, Dickens writes that he intends in *A Tale of Two Cities* to create characters "whom the story shall express, more than they should express themselves by dialogue."

As often happens in Dickens's novels, the hero and heroine are among the book's least believable characters. Lucie Manette has almost no real depth of character: meek, pure, loving, inspiring to men, she represents Dickens's ideal

Victorian woman. Her husband, Charles Darnay, fares little better. Noble, honest, brave, and cultured, Darnay personifies the Victorian male virtues. He renounces his French aristocratic inheritance because of his relatives' cruelty and works in England teaching French. His ideas and actions command admiration and respect, yet he lacks real individuality and psychological depth. Sydney Carton is Darnay's double, both literally and figuratively. Carton sees in Darnay what he could have been, and this recognition contributes to his dislike of the Frenchman. Most readers find Carton believable and interesting through most of the book. Critics disagree, however, on whether his final sacrifice is convincing. Certainly Carton's character throughout the novel is essential to Dickens's purpose, and several incidents foreshadow Carton's final noble act.

Lucie's father, Dr. Alexandre Manette, seems at least somewhat more real than his daughter. As a prisoner in the Bastille, he fought despair by making shoes. For some time after his release, Dr. Manette cannot rediscover his old identity and finds it difficult to live without shoemaking materials and a locked door. His occasional relapses into his prison mode seem psychologically accurate and insightful.

The novel's most memorable characters are probably the French revolutionaries. Madame Defarge knits a coded history of aristocratic atrocities, storing up the wrongs committed against her class. As leader of the revolutionary women, Madame Defarge loses her best instincts and becomes thoroughly vengeful, unmerciful, and violent. The other women, too, show fascinating contrasts. They help storm the Bastille, destroying everything and killing everyone there, then return to home to nurse babies, prepare scanty meals, or play with their children. Despite her contradictions—or because of them—Madame Defarge stands out as a realistic, psychologically deep character. Her husband and the male revolutionaries have some depth as well. Lacking his wife's secret motives for hatred, Monsieur Defarge vacillates in his vengefulness. Yet he remains loyal to his revolutionary cause, refusing to help Darnay despite his sympathy.

It was the best of times, it was the worst of times, it was the age of wisdom, it was the age of foolishness, it was the epoch of belief, it was the epoch of incredulity...

Dickens does include a number of English characters who are more traditionally "Dickensian." These characters, usually comic and distinguishable by a repeated peculiarity of speech or humorous quirk, add a lighter touch to an otherwise dark and serious novel. Mr. Jarvis Lorry is an aging bachelor who represents Tellson's bank first and himself only afterward, if at all. Lorry pretends to consider everything from a purely business perspective, but he does this partly to modestly deny credit for his many acts of kindness. Jerry Cruncher, a low-level employee at Tellson's, steals bodies from new graves at night to sell to surgeons doing medical research. Jerry's pious wife prays that he will stop doing such awful things, which Jerry interprets as praying against him and his financial success. In a darkly funny tone, Dickens shows Jerry berating his wife for her prayers ("flopping" he calls it). He calls her, in his uneducated English, "Aggerawayter" (Aggravator). Stryver is a disgustingly egoistic and ambitious lawyer whose success depends entirely on Carton's behind-the-scenes instructions. Stryver's whole life has been an attempt to "shoulder" his way in front of others on his path to success. Finally, Miss Pross, the Manettes' loyal English servant, has her strange quirks. But she stands up to Madame Defarge in a climactic scene in which the two converse at high volume, each in a language the other cannot understand.

◆ Literary Qualities ◆

A Tale of Two Cities, though not typical of Dickens's writing in many ways, is a very strong novel. First, its remarkable use of language astounds the careful reader. The opening passage, beginning "It was the best of times, it was the worst of times," has become justly famous. Throughout the novel Dickens creates powerful moods, manipulates tone brilliantly, and portrays characters with unusual but precise descriptions (such as Miss Pross, whose hat looks like "a great Stilton cheese"). He satirizes pomposity, as in his account of the legal document accusing Darnay of spying "wickedly, falsely, traitorously, and otherwise evil-adverbiously." Dickens often describes characters metaphorically, then refers to them primarily by their metaphorical identifications thereafter. For example, he calls Carton the jackal for the lion Stryver, then refers to the two characters as jackal and lion for several chapters.

A Tale of Two Cities also provides excellent examples of literary devices. The novel abounds with symbols: spilled wine as blood, the knitting Madame Defarge as the classical Fates, the sunset making everything red and foreshadowing the aristocracy's bloody end. Especially powerful are Dickens's repeated references to water and storm imagery that foreshadows the approaching violence in France. Indeed, Dickens foreshadows events to come throughout the novel, and many students enjoy working out some of these patterns.

This novel also provides many examples of literary repetition. Numerous parallels ask readers to compare various characters and events. Such parallels include the trials, prisoners, and similarities between London and Paris or between English and French characters. Also, Dickens often juxtaposes chapters in such a way that he offers observant readers interesting contrasts or divergent treatments of similar subjects in consecutive chapters.

To fully appreciate Dickens's achievement, readers should keep in mind that, as with all his novels, he published A Tale of Two Cities serially in a magazine, in this case, one or two chapters each week. This means that once an installment had been published, he could not go back and revise it. By this point in his career, however, Dickens had learned to plan his novels out in detail before he began writing. Given the constraints of serial publication, A Tale of Two Cities is remarkably coherent and unified.

◆ Social Sensitivity ◆

It is difficult to imagine anyone objecting to A Tale of Two Cities. The novel does contain explicit scriptural references, especially near the conclusion. But these can easily be viewed as a means of making historically relevant comparisons.

Some have criticized Dickens's works for emphasizing grave social injustices but not offering any solutions. But such criticism misses Dickens's point: believing history has proved economic systems to be incapable of relieving poverty, Dickens stresses the importance of individual responsibility and compassion for the plight of the poor and disfranchised. Indeed, *A Tale of Two Cities* teaches the important lesson that individual efforts are worthwhile, even if they make but a small difference in an often violent and unjust world.

Although Dickens does not hesitate to portray the violence inherent in his subject matter, he in no way glorifies it. He depicts the mistreatment of the lower classes that spurred the French Revolution, but he clearly condemns atrocities committed in the name of revolution. For Dickens, no cause is great enough to justify abandoning all vestiges of sympathy for one's fellow human beings.

♦ Topics for Discussion ♦

1. How is Lucie Manette the "golden thread" in the novel?

2. Why does Monsieur Defarge keep the door to Dr. Manette's room locked?

3. What causes the French mob to revolt? Do you think their actions are justified? How does Dickens feel about the revolutionary mob? How do you know?

4. How does Dickens use foreshadowing to prepare the reader for what will happen later in the novel? How does he foreshadow such important events as the revolution, Carton's final sacrifice, or the reemergence of Roger Cly?

5. In what way does Dr. Manette unintentionally testify against his son-in-law during Darnay's second French trial?

6. Why is Madame Defarge so intent on vengeance against Darnay and his family? What events lead up to her particular concern with him?

7. Contrast Miss Pross and Madame Defarge.

8. How does Carton persuade John Barsad to let him into Darnay's cell? What is Barsad's real name?

9. What coincidences do you find in the novel? Do they detract from the book's success?

10. Dickens is often described as a humorous writer. What humor do you find in *A Tale of Two Cities*? What does it add?

11. What symbols can you find in this novel? How do they help Dickens establish his themes?

12. Do you see any parallels between London and Paris? Why a tale of *two* cities?

♦ Ideas for Reports and Papers ♦

1. The idea of resurrection or rebirth pervades this novel. How does Dickens use this theme? What does Dickens seem to be saying with it?

2. Dickens seems to show that the French Revolution was inevitable, given the cruelty and greed of the upper classes at that time. But how does Dickens feel about the actions of the revolutionaries once they took power? What did the revolution accomplish? Does Dickens approve of the guillotine? How do you know?

3. Why does Sydney Carton change places with Darnay? What makes him sacrifice his life in this way? Does Carton's character change here, or has he always had within him the potential for such noble action? Do you find his act believable?

4. Carton and Darnay look remarkably alike. They also have many other things in common, yet in some ways they are complete opposites. Can they be seen as different sides of the same human personality? In what ways are they doubles?

5. Do the themes of resurrection and self-sacrifice, and the setting of the French Revolution have anything to do with one another? Why would Dickens set his story in this particular time and place?

6. How does Dickens use parallel situations and characters in the novel? What examples can you find, and what do they contribute?

♦ Adaptations ♦

A Tale of Two Cities has been adapted to film seven times. The most popular and enduring productions were released in 1917, 1935, 1958, and 1980. The well produced 1917 silent version was released by Twentieth Century Fox, directed by Frank Lloyd, and starred William Farnum, Jewel Carmen, Joseph Swickard, Herschell Mayall, and Rosita Marstini. The 1935 black-and-white film released by Metro-Goldwyn-Mayer was a huge commercial and critical success. Produced by David O. Selznick and directed by Jack Conway, the film's fine cast included Ronald Colman, Elizabeth Allan, Edna May Oliver, Reginald Owen, Basil Rathbone, Blanche Yurka, Isabel Jewell, Walter Catlett, Henry B. Wathall, H. B. Warner, and Donald Woods. A 1958 British production remained true to Dickens's story. Directed by Ralph Thomas, it starred Dirk Bogarde, Dorothy Tutin, Cecil Parker, Stephen Murray, Athene Seyler, Christopher Lee, Donald Pleasance, and Ian Bannen. The most recent film version was a 1980 made-for-television movie starring Chris Sarandon, Peter Cushing, Kenneth More, Barry Morse, Flora Robson, Billie Whitlaw, and Alice Krige. Directed by Jim Goddard and produced by Norman Rosemont, this version seldom departs from the events in the novel.

♦ For Further Reference ♦

Altick, Richard D. *Victorian People and Ideas: A Companion for the Modern Reader of Victorian Literature*. New York: Norton, 1973. Extremely useful for background on Dickens's times.

Beckwith, Charles E., ed. *Twentieth Century Interpretations of "A Tale of Two Cities"*. Englewood Cliffs, NJ: Prentice-Hall, 1972. Includes a number of useful critical studies of *A Tale of Two Cities*.

Davis, Earl. "Recalled to Life." In *The Flint and the Flame: The Artistry of Charles Dickens*. Columbia: University of Missouri Press, 1963. A useful discussion of the resurrection theme.

Johnson, Edgar. *Charles Dickens: His Tragedy and Triumph.* 2 vols. New York: Simon and Schuster, 1952. This Book-of-the-Month Club selection has become a standard biography. It includes good critical chapters on all the novels, including *A Tale of Two Cities.*

Miller, J. Hillis. *Charles Dickens: The World of His Novels.* Cambridge: Harvard University Press, 1958. A standard book on Dickens's novels. Includes a short but insightful discussion of *A Tale of Two Cities.*

Orwell, George. "Charles Dickens." In *Dickens, Dali, and Others: Studies in Popular Culture.* New York: Harcourt Brace Jovanovitch, 1946. A classic study of Dickens's novels.

Wilson, Edmund. "Dickens: The Two Scrooges." In *The Wound and the Bow.* Boston: Houghton Mifflin, 1941. An important discussion of Dickens's life as it relates to his novels.

David L. Cowles
Brigham Young University

THAT WAS THEN, THIS IS NOW
Novel
1971

◆

Author: S. E. Hinton, b. 1950

Major Books for Young Adults

The Outsiders, 1967
That Was Then, This Is Now, 1971
Rumble Fish, 1975
Tex, 1979
Taming the Star Runner, 1988

◆ About the Author ◆

Susan Eloise Hinton was born in 1950, in Tulsa, Oklahoma. While still in high school Hinton began work on *The Outsiders,* one of the first in the popular genre of "problem novels." Published when Hinton was still in high school, *The Outsiders* met with great critical acclaim. Profits from the novel enabled her to attend the University of Tulsa, where she graduated in 1970 with a bachelor's degree in education.

Hinton's novels deal with problems faced by most teen-agers: peer pressure, making choices about the future, and finding a place in society. Hinton often makes reference to drug or alcohol abuse in her books, especially *That Was Then, This Is Now* and *Rumble Fish.*

The Outsiders received the 1975 *Media and Methods* Maxi Award and was also an honor book in the 1967 *Chicago Tribune* Children's Spring Book Festival, as was *That Was Then, This Is Now* in 1971. Both books were on the American Library Association's Best of the Best book list in 1975, and *Rumble Fish* was one of the American Library Association's Best Books for 1975.

Hinton's books have been published in Denmark, Germany, Finland, and England, and four have been made into feature films. Hinton says that writing does not come easily for her, and she credits her husband, David Inhofe with instilling good work habits in her. When they were dating and she was working on *That Was Then, This Is Now,* he refused to take her out unless she had written at least two pages that day. Her husband's vigilance has paid off, and Hinton is now one of the world's best-selling authors of young adult fiction, having sold more than ten million copies of her books.

◆ Overview ◆

That Was Then, This Is Now chronicles the deterioration of a friendship between two young men who grow up and away from one another. Mark, Bryon's best friend since early childhood, has lived with Bryon and his mother ever since his own parents killed each other in a domestic dispute. The book describes the year when Bryon, who is sixteen, begins dating Cathy and has less time to spend with Mark. Fearful that the nature of their friendship is changing, Mark tries desperately to arrest the process of Bryon's maturation. Because Bryon's mother has had an operation and is unable to work, both boys are struggling to make ends meet, and the method Mark chooses to raise money—drug dealing—triggers one of the final rifts in the friendship.

Although drugs provide the catalyst for the book's plot and outcome, this is not solely a book about drug abuse. In the end, its central themes are the mutability of friendship and the limits of love. Realistic and haunting, the book is a favorite with young adults.

◆ Setting ◆

The story takes place in a rough, low-income, east-side neighborhood of Tulsa, Oklahoma, during the mid-1960s, an era of anti-war demonstrations and anti-establishment attitudes. In this neighborhood, streetwise Mark and Bryon, the two main characters, hustle pool in Charlie's Bar, drink, fight, and pick up girls. The toughs often consider the counterculture hippies easy targets for mugging, for the hippies do not fight back when attacked. Hinton evokes a sense of the setting less through explicit description than through repeated mention of places and people. The Ribbon is a cruising strip where kids can buy hot dogs or marijuana; the parking lot of the high school and the local bowling alley are teen-age meeting spots where violence often erupts; the hippie commune is a colorful but neglected and dirty place, where residents talk about love and take drugs. The setting of the novel adds realism and power to Hinton's work, although the problems that her characters confront could arise anywhere.

◆ Themes and Characters ◆

Bryon Douglas, the sixteen-year-old narrator of *That Was Then, This Is Now*, is caught up in a sequence of events that forces him to question his beliefs and relationships. As he examines his attitudes, he becomes more responsible, less willing to spend time looking for fights or parties, and less tolerant of his friend Mark's noncommittal, unquestioning attitude. Hinton portrays Bryon as a complex character; sexist, unethical, and often violent, he resembles an anti-hero more than he does a traditional hero. Mark, the novel's other central character, is described in the first chapter as a friendly lion and in the last chapter as "an impatient, dangerous, caged" lion. This change reflects Mark's transformation from a happy-go-lucky kid who "can get away with anything" to a bitter juvenile delinquent on his way to the state prison.

Among Bryon and Mark's peers, the most important are M&M and Cathy. M&M is a thirteen-year-old hippie living "in a hood's part of town." He suffers ridicule and, occasionally, physical abuse at the hands of the "hoods." Although M&M is of above-average intelligence, his father criticizes his hair, his clothing, and the "C" he earns in gym class. M&M finally runs away and has a bad reaction to the drug LSD, which permanently impairs his mental abilities, changing him from a trusting, innocent child into a cynical and suspicious person. Cathy, quite straight herself, is shocked when she learns that Bryon has smoked marijuana and is worried that M&M is becoming involved with drugs. Most important, Cathy makes Bryon question his values, and he changes as a result. Another influential character is Charlie, who acts as a big brother figure to Bryon and Mark. He gives advice, lends Bryon his car, and is generally concerned about the boys' welfare. He tries to teach them responsibility and self-respect but never preaches. Killed while trying to protect the boys from two men they have hustled, Charlie continues to influence Bryon's thinking, even after his death.

The changing nature of Bryon and Mark's friendship is the thematic focus of *That Was Then, This Is Now*. The process of maturing is painted in dark and foreboding tones in Hinton's book; as much as Bryon and Mark want their relationship to continue, the boys realize that they are growing apart. Bryon's increasing desire to know why things are the way they are, and his questioning of whether or not they must remain that way, becomes a wedge that separates the friends. Mark does not like to think in terms of "what if" scenarios. He believes that he can escape his problems by ignoring injustice and questions of morality.

Although his thinking is characterized by futility and immaturity, Mark's emotional confusion is understandable. His parents shot each another in an argument over Mark's paternity, and Mark witnessed the tragedy. Growing up on the east side of town, he has learned to mask his feelings, a useful skill when confronting muggers or trying to win a poker game. The macho image, which both boys have developed emotionally and physically, is unhealthy, but in

Jacket design by Hal Siegel for *That Was Then, This Is Now* by S. E. Hinton. Viking Press: New York (1972).

their neighborhood it seems necessary. Yet Bryon, unlike Mark, is able to shed this image as he gets older and opens up to Cathy. Bryon has spent his life settling gang disputes and personal grudges by fighting, and he finally decides to put an end to his part in the violence.

The theme of betrayal becomes apparent by the end of the book. Mark betrays Bryon by selling drugs and by refusing to take responsibility for his actions. Bryon, in return, turns Mark in to the police. This betrayal of Mark's trust has deep emotional repercussions. Bryon loses most of the ground he had gained through his love for Cathy, and is stuck on the one question that Mark despised: "What if?"

A secondary theme, that of forgiveness, lends the book its slight air of hope. Hinton depicts two characters, each severely beaten for something he did not do, who forgive their attackers. Mike, a white boy, rescues a black girl from a threatening situation and drives her home. Upon reaching her house, she implies that Mike was the one who hurt her, and her friends beat him almost to death. Yet Mike forgives the girl and her friends, and the experience does not lead him to hate blacks. Later, when Bryon is beaten up for cutting Angela Shepard's hair, he tells Mark not to get even with the Shepards. A willingness to show forgiveness and bypass the normal channels of revenge shows a level of maturity that Mark cannot understand.

Bryon's mother pleads with her son to channel his empathy for others into an acceptance of his own faults: "Bryon, you got even with Mark for Cathy, then you got even with Cathy for Mark. When are you going to stop getting even with yourself?" Bryon realizes she is right, and Hinton suggests that eventually he may forgive himself and continue on his journey toward adulthood.

◆ Literary Qualities ◆

That Was Then, This Is Now is written as a first-person narrative. Because Bryon is retelling the story a year after it happened, Hinton is able to make especially effective use of the writing device called "foreshadowing." This technique gives the reader a sense of future turns in the novel, usually by hinting at a major idea or event. An early example of foreshadowing is found at the end of the second chapter. When referring to the boys who beat Mike, Mark says, "Man, if anybody ever hurt me like that I'd hate them for the rest of my life." Bryon, as narrator, picks up on this statement and lets the reader know it is significant: "I didn't think much about that statement then. But later I would—I still do. I think about it and think about it until I think I'm going crazy." A similar idea is echoed in chapter 3, when Bryon fears that Cathy may be interested in Mark. All of a sudden, and only for an instant, he hates Mark. Commenting on this reaction, Bryon wonders what it would be like to be haunted by feelings of antagonism for the rest of his life. Bryon's early resentment of Mark foreshadows Mark's eventual hatred of Bryon, which Bryon fears will last for the rest of Mark's life. In the epilogue Bryon claims to feel nothing, but his earlier statement leads the reader to suspect that he feels more than he will admit.

Hinton's foreshadowing technique affects the book's tone, making it somewhat foreboding because of the reader's sense that something unpleasant is coming. The violence that permeates the characters' lives also creates a mood of suspense and wariness. This combination of foreshadowing and violence creates a powerful and lasting sense of despair.

Hinton manages to convey realistic conversation without using overly offensive language. Although most teenagers from Bryon's neighborhood would use more vulgarity than is found in Hinton's book, the lack of absolute realism does not detract from the overall sense of place and character. The only language-related misunderstandings that might arise stem from Hinton's use of outdated terms. She uses the words "Negro" and "chick," neither of which was considered derogatory during the hippie era. Other examples of 1960s jargon—"flower-child," "free love," "Peace!" and "Cat"—help to create a sense of the period.

◆ Social Sensitivity ◆

That Was Then, This Is Now is concerned more with questions of personal morality and ethics than it is with social problems. Nevertheless, social issues do arise. One of the more troubling aspects of the boys' personalities is racism. When a bored Mark sees a black man standing alone, he asks Bryon if he wants to jump the stranger. M&M intervenes and points out the hypocrisy in their actions: they saved M&M from being jumped because he was different, a hippie, but now they want to attack someone on the basis of race. Bryon feels ashamed when he thinks about the truth in M&M's statement, but this will not redeem him in most readers' eyes. Parents or teachers may want to discuss the problem of racist attitudes in the book, perhaps in connection with Mike's story and in Bryon's and Mark's reactions to that incident.

Two other sensitive issues raised in the book are drug abuse and violence among teen-agers. Many students who casually read Hinton's account of a bad acid trip may need to have reinforced the dangerous consequences of hallucinogenic drug experiences. Bryon and Mark also drink excessively, although they do not perceive this habit as drug abuse.

Perhaps the most disturbing problem, a result largely of environmental pressure, is the extreme level of violence to which the boys are accustomed. Fighting is entertainment for Bryon and Mark. Hinton attempts to address the issue of violence by recounting several disturbing incidents—such as M&M's mugging, Mike's beating, and, later, Bryon's experience with the Shepards—and then depicting various characters' reactions to this violence.

◆ Topics for Discussion ◆

1. Although the book's ending seems hopeless, do you think it is possible that Mark and Bryon will reconcile? What would have to happen first for this reconciliation to take place?

2. Should Bryon have called the police when he did, or should he have given Mark another chance?

3. What could help Mark develop a more ethical, mature attitude toward others and himself?

4. Discuss the pros and cons of looking back at past events and asking "what if?"

5. Cathy exerts a big influence on Bryon. Does Bryon influence her in any way? Does she change as a result of her relationship with Bryon?

◆ Ideas for Reports and Papers ◆

1. Research the history of LSD and other hallucinogenic drug use. What is the history of their use? What are the effects of these drugs on the brain and on the body?

2. Analyze Hinton's use of the technique of foreshadowing. When does Hinton use this technique? Does she ever give the story away? When is the foreshadowing most effective? Least effective?

3. How would the story change if it were told from Mark's point of view?

4. How do issues of race and gender influence relationships in *That Was Then, This is Now*? Consider Mike's story and the scenes in which Angela's hair is cut and Bryon is beaten up.

5. Betrayal is a major theme in the novel. Whose betrayal is worse, Mark's of Bryon or Bryon's of Mark? Is one more excusable than the other, or are both equally devastating?

6. What constitutes a literary tragedy? Is *That Was Then, This Is Now* a tragedy? What parts are most applicable to a tragic interpretation?

◆ Related Titles ◆

Those who have read Hinton's first novel, *The Outsiders*, will recognize Ponyboy Curtis and the Shepards when they reappear in *That Was Then, This Is Now*. Events related in *The Outsiders* took place several years before those in *That Was Then, This Is Now*, and some of these events are alluded to in the later book. A third novel, *Rumble Fish*, is set in the same neighborhood. Themes of fighting, violent retribution, and substance abuse, as well as the effects of poverty and social stigmatization, unite these books, as do their location, and, to a lesser extent, their characters.

That Was Then, This Is Now was made into a feature motion picture in 1985 and is available on videotape. Directed by Christopher Cain and starring Emilio Estevez, the film differs from Hinton's book in many ways. Because it is set in the 1980s, M&M cannot be a hippie. Instead he is characterized as a surly, oversensitive youngster, not at all trusting or innocent. The neighborhood seems more middle class, and the boys' need for money is less apparent. The racism that appeared in the novel is omitted; Charlie is black, as is Terry, and Mike's story is left out altogether.

The movie focuses more evenly on both Bryon and Mark, without the unavoidable bias of a first-person narration. Mark is portrayed more sympathetically, and his loneliness and jealousy are emphasized. The ending of the story is changed, too. The movie still deals with the themes of betrayal and growing up, but the plot is thin and not as realistic as the novel. It should be noted that the language in the movie is extremely graphic, and the film would thus be inappropriate for showing in most schools.

Other movies based on Hinton's books include *The Outsiders* (1983) and *Rumble Fish* (1983), both directed by Francis Ford Coppola and featuring Matt Dillon. *Tex* was adapted to the screen in a 1982 production directed by Tim Hunter and starring Matt Dillon, Jim Metzler, and Meg Tilly.

◆ For Further Reference ◆

Commire, Anne, ed. *Something about the Author*. Vol. 19. Detroit: Gale Research, 1980. Contains a good bit of autobiographical information, as well as some critical analysis of Hinton's work.

De Montreville, Doris, and Elizabeth D. Crawford, eds. *Fourth Book of Junior Authors*. New York: H. W. Wilson, 1978. An excellent source for autobiographical information. Contains an analysis of Hinton's career up to 1978, and lists the awards she has received.

Hinton, S. E. "Face to Face with a Teenage Novelist." *Seventeen* (October 1967): 133. Hinton talks about herself and her writing. Parts of this article are reprinted in Commire.

———. "Teen-Agers Are for Real." *New York Times Book Review* (August 27, 1967): 26-29. More Hinton on Hinton, and on young adult literature as well.

Kirkpatrick, D. L. ed. *Twentieth-Century Children's Writers*. New York: St. Martin's, 1978. Contains an overview of Hinton's writing career to 1978, with analysis of her themes and characters.

Locher, Frances Carol, ed. *Contemporary Authors*. Vols. 81-84. Detroit: Gale Research, 1979. Contains a brief overview of Hinton's work.

Robin, Lisa. "The Young and the Restless." *Media and Methods* (May/June 1982): 28, 45. Focuses on *Tex*. Includes a teacher's guide to *The Outsiders*, *That Was Then, This Is Now*, *Rumble Fish*, and *Tex* that offers many useful discussion questions.

Senick, Gerard J., ed. *Children's Literature Review*. Vol. 3. Detroit: Gale Research, 1978. Contains commentary by Hinton and excerpts from various pieces of criticism of Hinton's works.

Stine, Jean C., and Daniel G. Marowski, eds. *Contemporary Literary Criticism*. Vol. 30. Detroit: Gale Research, 1984. Provides excerpts from criticism of Hinton's works.

A. Abigail McCormick
Estill County Public Library

THIMBLE SUMMER
Novel
1938

---◆---

Author: Elizabeth Enright, 1909-1968

Major Books for Young Adults

Thimble Summer, 1938
The Saturdays, 1941
Then There Were Five, 1944
Spiderweb for Two: A Melendy Maze, 1951
The Four-Story Mistake, 1955
Tatsinda, 1963

◆ About the Author ◆

Elizabeth Enright was born on September 17, 1909, in Oak Park, outside of Chicago. Her father was Walter J. Enright, a political cartoonist, and her mother was Maginel Wright Enright, a magazine illustrator. Influenced by her parents' interest in art, Elizabeth began drawing at age three. Her pictures were often of her favorite children's stories. Once out of high school, she studied at the Art Students League in New York from 1927 to 1928. She spent part of 1929 in Paris, and in 1930 she married Robert Marty Gillham; they had three boys: Nicholas, Robert, and Oliver.

Enright began her career by illustrating children's books, most notably those by Marian King: *Kees* (1930), *Annan, a Lad of Palestine* (1931), and *Kees and Kleintje* (1934). Wanting to focus her illustrations on a subject of her own choosing, Enright wrote her first book, *Kintu: A Congo Adventure* (1935). For this book, she created the pictures first and then wrote the text. While working on *Kintu*, she discovered that she preferred writing over illustrating, and she turned her talents to writing *Thimble Summer*.

Accompanied by Enright's own illustrations, *Thimble Summer* was well received by the critics, and it won the 1939 Newbery Medal. As her career developed, Enright became one of America's most respected writers for both young adults and children. Her book *Gone-Away Lake* (1957), which is written for younger children, won the *New York Herald Tribune*'s Children's Spring Book Festival Award in 1957 and was a Newbery Honor Book recipient in 1958. *Tatsinda* was a *New York Herald Tribune* Children's Spring Book Festival Honor Book recipient in 1963. Enright was nominated for the Hans Christian Andersen Award, which is given for a writer's lifetime achievement.

In addition to writing for young readers, Enright wrote many stories for adults that appeared in such magazines as the *New Yorker, Saturday Evening Post, Harper's,* and *McCall's.* As with her fiction for young people, Enright's short stories feature a gentle sense of humor and keen insight into human nature. She died on June 8, 1968.

◆ Overview ◆

In *Thimble Summer* Enright projects a deep understanding of the concerns and emotions of young adults. Garnet Linden, her brother Jay, and their friends Citronella Hauser and Eric Swanstrom are complex, engaging characters, and their desire for adventure, their need for security, and their wish to be respected will touch responsive chords in most young readers.

Garnet enjoys living on a farm with her parents and brother, but she is curious about the world outside her small country home, and she longs to venture out on her own, seeking education and excitement. Her adventures in town and her interaction with the other characters in the novel make for an amusing, moving story about growing up.

◆ Setting ◆

Most of the book's events take place during a summer in the 1930s in Esau Valley, Wisconsin, where Garnet lives on her family's farm. The valley contains a river, marshland, and woods. Local farmers raise corn and oats, as well as cattle, pigs, and chickens. Some of the action takes place in New Conniston, a small town that, for a country girl like Garnet, glitters "like Bagdad and Zanzibar and Constantinople." New Conniston has a dime store, furniture stores, restaurants, and movie theaters. For Garnet, it is a place full of interesting

people, city luxuries, and prospects for adventure. New Conniston is also the location of the Southwestern Wisconsin Fair, held in early September. Complete with carnival sideshows and rides, the fair offers new sights and sounds.

At the beginning of *Thimble Summer,* southwestern Wisconsin is in the middle of a terrible drought. The 1930s brought hard economic times to America with the Great Depression, a problem that was compounded when much of the Midwest suffered from a disastrous drought that dried up farm crops. The soil, without plants to hold it together with their roots, blew away in great clouds of dust. In Enright's novel, the lack of rain leaves Garnet's father's crops withering, and for a while he stays up late every night worrying about paying his bills. Garnet and Jay sympathize with their father, and Jay vows never to be a farmer. Rain brings relief early in the novel, and with it comes the freedom for Garnet to explore her world.

◆ Themes and Characters ◆

The themes involving family and adventure unify *Thimble Summer.* These themes find their focus in Garnet Linden, a girl "between nine and ten" who craves independence and the respect of her family. A tomboy, Garnet goes barefoot most of the time, dislikes wearing dresses, and enjoys physical activities such as swimming and helping out with the farm work. Quick to anger and nearly as quick to forgive, she is a resilient, good-hearted character.

Garnet looks to her family for warmth and support, but she is an independent girl who wants adventures of her own and who sometimes acts without thinking. When her brother's teasing leads her to run off impetuously to New

Illustration by Elizabeth Enright for *Thimble Summer* by Elizabeth Enright. Holt, Rinehart, and Winston: New York (1966).

Conniston, she has a vague idea that maybe her family will be "sorry later on." This childish notion of punishing those who love her is forgotten in the excitement of hitchhiking and then riding a speeding bus on the way to town. Once in New Conniston, she is delighted with the shops and ends up buying small presents for her family. Having carelessly spent her money, she finds herself stranded and must walk some of the eighteen miles home before she finds a ride with a truck driver. Upon Garnet's return, her neighbor Mr. Freebody points out just how painful her thoughtlessness could have been to those who love and worry about her.

Garnet's situation is a difficult one. She needs to learn to think about how her actions could affect others, but she also has to satisfy her independent spirit and sense of self-respect. Much of the novel emphasizes how she develops self-control, and by the end of the novel, she is well on her way toward adulthood, having decided that she wants to follow in her father's footsteps and become a farmer. She demonstrates her independence by exhibiting her pig Timmy at the fair, then treating her family and friends to her own special party, paid for with the first-prize winnings of three dollars and fifty cents.

Citronella Hauser is Garnet's best friend. She shares several of Garnet's interests, including reading, but the novel emphasizes their contrasts: Citronella focuses on household chores, such as cooking, while Garnet is primarily interested in outdoor work, such as threshing; Citronella is primarily a talker, not a doer, while Garnet prefers action. Even the girls' names suggest a contrast between Citronella's mild manner and Garnet's fiery temperament. "Citronella" is the name of a bluish-green grass, whereas "Garnet" suggests the color of a dark red gemstone. Despite their differences, the girls are united by a common concern for each other's welfare.

It is through Citronella that Garnet meets Mrs. Eberhardt, Citronella's great-grandmother. She tells the girls stories of the times when farmers and Native Americans shared Esau Valley, and of her mischievous behavior as a young girl. The young Mrs. Eberhardt described in these stories resembles Garnet and suggests that *Thimble Summer* concerns universal values that remain constant over generations.

Garnet and her brother, Jay, are very close until Eric Swanstrom enters their lives. Jay turns his attentions to the new boy, and Garnet becomes jealous. But Garnet learns to like Eric and soon treats him like another brother. The other youngsters envy Eric because he has led an adventuresome life, but he emphasizes that his experiences were born of hard necessity after the deaths of his parents. Only thirteen years old, he has bounced around the United States, looking for work so that he can feed himself. When he first enters the story, Eric has not eaten for two days.

"I've seen rivers dried up and shrunk away to nothing," he says, "and the earth all full of cracks, and cattle dead for want of water." He has seen the misery of the Great Depression and has no more taste for wandering or adventure: "I want to stay here for years and years." His experiences and views help to strengthen the theme of family, emphasizing the value of close family ties and suggesting that adventures are best when they are shared with loved ones.

◆ Literary Qualities ◆

Thimble Summer features clear, unadorned prose. With descriptive power Enright creates moods and images that reflect Garnet's feelings, as in this passage that depicts Garnet's twinges of fear as she and Jay walk along the wooded riverbank at night:

> All along the wooded banks owls hooted with a velvety, lost sound; and there was one that screamed, from time to time, in a high, terrifying voice. Garnet knew that they were only owls, but still, in the hot darkness with no light but the solemn winking of the fireflies, she felt that they *might* be anything.

Although Garnet's growth and personality are the primary unifying factors of the novel, symbols also help pull together the episodes. One significant but simply presented symbol is the silver thimble Garnet finds beside the river: " 'it's solid silver!' she shouted triumphantly, 'and I think it must be magic too!' " Garnet keeps this thimble with her throughout her adventures, and by the end of the novel she declares, "*Everything* has happened since I found it, and all nice things! As long as I live I'm always going to call this summer the thimble summer." Throughout the novel, the thimble is a symbol of home, a reminder that special events are about to happen.

Garnet's symbolic name refers to both a dark red color and a gemstone. Jewels and jewelry figure often in the images of *Thimble Summer*. For instance, in her story of youth, Mrs. Eberhardt tells of her desire to own a particular coral bracelet with a coral heart hanging from it. Coral as a color is red, recalling Garnet's name; the heart is like a gem, again recalling Garnet. This symbolism helps to convey the idea that Mrs. Eberhardt's story of the past is related to the Garnet of the present. The overall impression created by Garnet's name is that she, herself, is a jewel—as bright and colorful and precious as a gem.

◆ Social Sensitivity ◆

Thimble Summer is set in the 1930s, the time of the Great Depression and the drought that afflicted many midwestern states. Eric is Enright's vehicle for introducing some of the horrors of the era. Readers may be interested to know that many people rode railroad boxcars the way Eric does and that hawking goods on the street was common. The drought made the tough times even worse for farmers, and many families lost everything they owned. Thus, the opening chapter of *Thimble Summer* presented to readers in 1938 a dark and fearful reality. *Thimble Summer* may help generate discussions of what life in the 1930s Midwest was like.

An issue that parents and teachers will want to discuss with readers of *Thimble Summer* is Garnet's hitchhiking. Although the story of Mrs. Eberhardt's girlhood adventure creates some suspense by suggesting that running away may have serious consequences—

the young Mrs. Eberhardt is robbed—Garnet meets only nice people and has an interesting adventure. Readers should know that even in the 1930s it was unwise to hitchhike, and that in the modern world, a young person alone and hitchhiking is in very real danger of being harmed.

◆ Topics for Discussion ◆

1. What does Garnet learn from running away to New Conniston? Is it safe for her to hitchhike?

2. How did midwestern farms in 1938 differ from farms today?

3. How do the illustrations contribute to the story?

4. Garnet wants to be a farmer like her father but Jay does not. What do we learn about each character from their attitudes about farming?

5. How do Eric's experiences help Garnet understand her life?

◆ Ideas for Reports and Papers ◆

1. Research the Great Depression of the 1930s. Compare the conditions you learn about with Enright's portrayal of those hard times.

2. Eric travels in railroad boxcars, as did many people during the Depression. Research other sources and explain what the life of a "hobo" was like in the 1930s.

3. Read another book set about life on a farm, such as Robert N. Peck's *A Day*

No Pigs Would Die, and compare it to *Thimble Summer*.

4. Make a list of the symbols in *Thimble Summer* and explain how they contribute to the story.

5. Mrs. Eberhardt tells of a childhood adventure that is similar to the one Garnet has when she goes to New Conniston. How are the young Mrs. Eberhardt and Garnet similar and different?

◆ Related Titles ◆

Enright's other works include four books about the Melendy children, three of which make up The Melendy Family trilogy: *The Saturdays, The Four-Story Mistake,* and *Then There Were Five.* In *The Saturdays,* the young people pool their allowances so that each one, in turn, can enjoy a special day with enough money to do what he or she wants. This first novel in the trilogy takes place in New York, but the others take place in the country, emphasizing the adventures and pleasures to be found there. These books feature good characterizations and a fine understanding of what it is like to be a young person. The other book about the Melendy Family is *Spiderweb for Two: A Melendy Maze.*

◆ For Further Reference ◆

Commire, Anne, ed. *Something about the Author.* Vol. 9. Detroit: Gale, 1976. Contains a brief outline of Enright's career and achievements.

Enright, Elizabeth. *Doublefields: Memories and Stories.* San Diego: Harcourt Brace Jovanovich, 1966. Includes autobiographical essays.

———. "Realism in Children's Literature." *Horn Book* 43 (April 1967): 165-170. A presentation of Enright's views on writing for young people.

Kirkpatrick, D. L. ed. *Twentieth-Century Children's Writers.* New York: St. Martin's, 1978. Includes a listing of Enright's books and a brief critical summary of her work.

Kunitz, Stanley J., and Howard Haycraft, eds. *The Junior Book of Authors.* 2d ed. New York: H. W. Wilson, 1951. Contains an autobiographical sketch explaining how Enright developed from an illustrator to an author. Includes a photograph of her.

Sutherland, Zena, and May Hill Arbuthnot, eds. *Children and Books.* 7th ed. Glenview, IL: Scott, Foresman, 1986. A summary of Enright's books.

Townsend, John Rowe. *Written for Children: An Outline of English-Language Children's Literature.* 2d. ed. Middlesex, England: Penguin, 1983. Briefly places *Thimble Summer* in the context of other 1930s writings for young people.

Kirk H. Beetz
National University, Sacramento

THOREAU OF WALDEN POND
Biography
1959

◆

Author: Sterling North, 1906-1974

Major Books for Young Adults

Plowing on Sunday, 1933
Night Outlasts the Whippoorwill,
   1936
Seven Against the Years, 1939
So Dear to My Heart, 1947
Reunion on the Wabash, 1952
*Abe Lincoln: Log Cabin to the White
   House*, 1956
*George Washington: Frontier
   Colonel*, 1957
Young Thomas Edison, 1958
Thoreau of Walden Pond, 1959

*Captured by the Mohawks, and
   Other Adventures of Radisson*,
   1960
Mark Twain and the River, 1961
*The First Steamboat on the Missis-
   sippi*, 1962
Rascal: A Memoir of a Better Era,
   1963
Raccoons Are the Brightest People,
   1966
*The Wolfling: A Documentary Novel
   of the Eighteen-Seventies*, 1969

◆ About the Author ◆

Although best remembered for his nature books for young children and young adults, Sterling North also wrote a number of biographies of American literary and historical figures that added to his reputation as one of the most popular twentieth-century writers for young adults. He was born on November 4, 1906, on a small farm overlooking Lake Koshkonong, near Edgerton, Wisconsin. North first found literary fame through his poetry, which he sold to literary magazines throughout his high school and college years. After graduating from the University of Chicago in 1929, North worked as a reporter for the *Chicago Daily News*. In

1932 he became the newspaper's literary editor, a position he later held at the *New York Post* and at the *New York World Telegram and Sun*. In 1957 he accepted a post with Houghton Mifflin, his primary publisher, as editor of North Star Books, a series of historical books for children. Sole author of twenty-six novels, biographies, and children's books, North edited over twenty other books and anthologies as well. He also contributed poems, articles, and stories to a variety of national publications, including the *Atlantic, Harper's, Poetry*, and the *Nation*.

Critical acclaim for North's work has centered on its appeal to all generations. This is especially true in the case of North's most famous works, *Rascal: A*

Memoir of a Better Era and *Raccoons Are the Brightest People*, both set near the author's rural home in New Jersey. *Rascal* was a Newbery Medal runner-up in 1964 and received the Dorothy Canfield Fisher Award and the Dutton Animal Book Award. *The Wolfling* also won a Dutton Animal Book Award. Sterling North died in Morristown, New Jersey, on December 22, 1974, after a series of strokes.

♦ Overview ♦

Thoreau espoused a simple way of life that exemplifies the American spirit of self-sufficiency and thrift advocated by Benjamin Franklin and Thomas Jefferson. The true measure of Thoreau's success is the influence he had on the moral and social philosophy of scores of famous Americans, as well as intellectuals in other parts of the world. North's biography seeks to inform its readers how unique this stoic New Englander truly was.

The book incorporates Thoreau's own lively and vivid prose to describe his tour of the Concord and Merrimack rivers and his simple existence at Walden Pond. This technique gives readers a personal view of Thoreau's philosophy and encourages readers to delve into the author's original works.

♦ Setting ♦

Born on July 12, 1817, Thoreau lived in one of the most intellectual communities of any era in American history, mid-nineteenth-century Concord, Massachusetts. He was friends with many of the authors and philosophers associated with the movement called New England transcendentalism, including Ralph Waldo Emerson, Bronson Alcott, William Ellery Channing, and Margaret Fuller.

Emerson, Thoreau's friend and mentor, is considered the father of New England transcendentalism, which championed nature over the city, the individual over the masses, and intuition over reason. Although Thoreau's literary philosophy is distinctly his own, it reflects the ideas of the transcendentalists. North emphasizes the influence of nature on Thoreau, describing the beauty and splendor of the region surrounding Concord, specifically Walden Pond. North also provides vivid descriptions of the Maine wilderness, where Thoreau developed into an ardent naturalist and conservationist.

♦ Themes and Characters ♦

North's biography of Henry David Thoreau concentrates on the theme of human interaction with nature and, as a corollary, on individualism. The book recounts Thoreau's quiet, pensive nature and his appreciation of the outdoors. Although he is a good student, Thoreau receives his real education from nature, which the transcendentalists called "the Academy of the Universe." North shows how Thoreau's individualism puts him closer to the natural world more than it pulls him away from society.

Ralph Waldo Emerson exerts a profound influence on Thoreau and his philosophy. Emerson, Concord's most prominent citizen, does more than just allow Thoreau to live on his land and become involved in the Concord Lyceum; he encourages and inspires young Thoreau to live a life of thrift and utility. North credits Thoreau's fascination with Emerson's *Nature* (1836) as the motivation behind the 1837 Harvard commencement address in which Thoreau proclaims that people should spend most of their days enjoying the "sublime revelations of nature."

Content to wander about the Concord countryside, Thoreau has few, if any, opportunities to develop intimate relationships besides the one that he maintains with Emerson; hence, few other characters appear in the book. The tragic death of Thoreau's older brother John in 1842 seems to make him wary of establishing close relationships. But North mentions as minor characters some of the famous Concordians who admire Thoreau, among them Louisa May Alcott, Bronson Alcott, William Ellery Channing, and Margaret Fuller.

◆ Literary Qualities ◆

Perhaps the greatest literary value of *Thoreau of Walden Pond* is that it covers Thoreau's entire life. The biography does not concentrate on the circumstances surrounding the composition of Thoreau's greatest work, *Walden*, but instead devotes considerable space to Thoreau's journey up the Concord and Merrimack rivers, his Harvard education, and his journeys to the Maine wilderness toward the end of his relatively short life. Such an overview of Thoreau's life is vital to an understanding of his work, for Thoreau's personal beliefs and experiences have a particularly profound effect on his writing.

In *Thoreau of Walden Pond*, North incorporates lively, crisp prose and succinct paragraphs that make even relatively complex ideas or situations easy to grasp. To further liven the narrative, North makes frequent use of quotations from *Walden, A Week on the Concord and Merrimack Rivers,* and Thoreau's fascinating journals.

The life and works of Ralph Waldo Emerson, Thoreau's friend, occasional employer, and frequent philosophical model, play an important part in North's biography. From the prefatory poem to the excerpt from the transcendentalist's great funeral oration for his friend, simply entitled "Thoreau," the biography takes great pains to depict the influence that Emerson has on Thoreau.

◆ Social Sensitivity ◆

A few of North's remarks in the book seem directed exclusively to young males, but this does not occur so frequently that readers of both sexes cannot relate to Thoreau's life and philosophy. Thoreau was a man of great conscience who was deeply concerned with the ills that plagued the society of his day, and North objectively and thoroughly recounts his subject's responses to social problems, particularly Thoreau's involvement in the abolitionist movement. North portrays Thoreau's love of solitude not so much as antisocial behavior but as evidence of his strong bond with the natural world. Overall, readers should find a positive example in Thoreau's strong principles and abiding respect for the worth of the individual.

◆ Topics for Discussion ◆

1. Why do you think that Thoreau is considered not merely a great American writer, but also a great American?

2. Describe Thoreau's personality. Is he an outcast? An introvert? Antisocial?

How does Thoreau's personality match his ideas concerning humankind's relationship with nature?

3. Is Thoreau wrong in not paying the poll tax? Is such "civil disobedience" justified and perhaps even necessary in certain situations? Explain. Can you think of any individuals in more recent history who have taken similar stances against what they felt was the infringement of government on their personal lives?

4. Why does Thoreau "abandon" civilization for almost two years and live at Walden Pond? What does he learn from the experience? What does he propose in *Walden* concerning nature? Economy? Materialism? Individualism?

5. Thoreau's attitude toward the killing of wild animals is unique for his time. Why does he object to such activity? Does Thoreau believe that there are situations in which hunting is justified? Explain.

◆ Ideas for Reports and Papers ◆

1. What was Thoreau's philosophy toward humankind's interaction with nature? Was nature a resource to be used to benefit humankind or was it something to be left alone, spared of all human intervention?

2. Ralph Waldo Emerson wrote a short philosophical book entitled *Nature*. Emerson and Thoreau shared many similar ideas concerning human interaction with nature. What examples of Emersonian philosophy as depicted in *Nature* can you find in Thoreau's own life?

3. Prepare a short biography on one or two of Thoreau's Concord friends, such as Bronson Alcott, Nathaniel Hawthorne, or Ralph Waldo Emerson. How did they differ from Thoreau in their attitudes and way of life? How were they similar?

4. Thoreau wrote poetry as well as prose. Select a few of his poems, decide on the main idea in each, and find similar ideas in *Walden* or *A Week on the Concord and Merrimack Rivers*. Suggested poems: "My Prayer," "The Inward Morning," "The Summer Rain," "Inspiration," and "The Fall of the Leaf."

5. Read Martin Luther King, Jr.'s "Letter from Birmingham Jail" and compare King's and Thoreau's ideas on civil disobedience.

◆ For Further Reference ◆

Harding, Walter. *The Days of Henry Thoreau*. New York: Knopf, 1965. Harding's biography remains the most accurate and representative treatment of Thoreau.

Harding, Walter, ed. *Thoreau: Man of Concord*. New York: Holt, Rinehart and Winston, 1962. Harding has compiled a selection of assessments of Thoreau by his Concord contemporaries. An excellent source for a good picture of this enigmatic individual.

Thoreau, Henry D. *The Illustrated Walden*. Edited by J. Lyndon Shanley. Princeton, NJ: Princeton University Press, 1973. This edition of Thoreau's greatest work contains photographs by Herbert Wendell Gleason, a nineteenth-century photographer who journeyed to Walden Pond and

Concord a few short decades after Thoreau lived there. His photographic journal, reproduced in the pages of this popular edition, gives the student a wonderful pictorial view of Walden as Thoreau might have seen it.

——— . *A Week on the Concord and Merrimack Rivers.* Edited by Carl Bove, *et al.* Princeton, NJ: Princeton University Press, 1980. A marvelously reproduced facsimile of the original edition.

Captain Richard S. Keating
United States Air Force Academy

THE THREE MUSKETEERS
Novel

1844

◆

Author: Alexandre Dumas, 1802-1870

Major Books For Young Adults

The Three Musketeers, 1844
The Count of Monte Cristo, 1844
Twenty Years After, 1845
The Man in the Iron Mask, 1850

◆ About the Author ◆

Alexandre Dumas was born on July 24, 1802, in Villers-Cotterêts, a small village in France. His grandfather was a nobleman, the Marquis de la Pailleterie, and his grandmother was a black slave, Marie-Cessette Dumas. After quarreling with the marquis, Alexandre's father renounced the family and enlisted in the army as Thomas-Alexandre Dumas, using his mother's name. In a remarkable career, Thomas-Alexandre rose from the rank of lieutenant to general under Napoleon in less than two years. His boldness in battle prompted the enemy to nickname him "the Black Devil." While serving in the army, Thomas-Alexandre married Marie-Louise-Elizabeth Labouret, the daughter of a prominent hotel proprietor, and the couple had one child, Alexandre. In 1806, when young Alexandre was four years old, Thomas-Alexandre was killed.

Just as Thomas-Alexandre had argued with the marquis, Alexandre argued with his mother about her wish for him to be educated as a priest. Rather than accepting her plans for sending him to the seminary, Alexandre ran away from home. Educating himself, Dumas began writing plays and in 1829 produced his first literary success, *Henri III.* He soon established himself as the most popular playwright in Paris, often producing plays in collaboration with other writers. His plays helped change the public's taste in drama from formal tragedies based on Greek drama to highly romantic works that reflected the rapidly changing modern society.

Although Dumas was best known in his own time for drama, he is best known now for his novels. Dumas's romantic plays were influenced by Sir Walter Scott's novels, and when Dumas was forty years old he decided to try writing fiction of his own. His first novel, *The Three Musketeers,* was a great success and was shortly followed by the immensely popular *Count of Monte Cristo.* Dumas capitalized on the success of the first novel by writing two sequels to it: *Twenty Years After* and *The Vicomte de Bragelonne* (the last third of which has been published as *The Man in the Iron Mask.*)

His plays and novels made Dumas a rich man. He built a fabulous mansion, called Monte Cristo, and traveled a great deal, writing many books about his adventures. Eventually, his generosity and extravagant lifestyle drained his fortune. One of his two sons, also named Alexandre Dumas and a novelist in his own right, looked after him in his last years. Dumas died in Puys, France, on December 5, 1870, of a stroke.

◆ Overview ◆

The Three Musketeers is a historical romance, filled with adventure. Its brave and gallant heroes are generous to those who need help, chivalrous to women, and above all loyal to each other as their famous motto proclaims: "All for one, one for all." Their adventures may sometimes appear far-fetched, but the musketeers believe in their own abilities so strongly and carry off their deeds with such style that the reader has little difficulty in believing them capable of all that they do. The individual characters are easily distinguishable, but they are not profoundly developed, for fast-paced and suspenseful action is more important to Dumas's storytelling than is character. Dumas clearly differentiates good and evil characters, although the novel's treatment of good and evil is not as straightforward as it might first appear. The society of the period differs considerably from today's, and the novel provides an interesting look at seventeenth-century social hierarchy, religion, and relationships between men and women.

◆ Setting ◆

The story is set in seventeenth-century France. Dumas's portrait of the time, which was already two centuries past when he wrote about it, is unquestionably idealized. The novel is intended to play on the reader's sense of nostalgia with a look back to a more romantic and picturesque time when men were gallant and chivalrous. Dumas constructs his tale around three historical events of the time: the affair of the queen's diamonds, the siege of La Rochelle, and the assassination of the Duke of Buckingham, each of which dominates approximately one third of the novel. Many of most famous and powerful people of the time appear in the novel as characters: King Louis XIII; his wife, Anne of Austria; his priest, Cardinal Richelieu; and Charles I's prime minister of England, the Duke of Buckingham. Dumas intertwines the lives and actions of his fictional heroes with those of these important historical figures, depicting the latter as genuinely human characters with a complex variety of motives, abilities, and faults. Many translations of the novel retain a smattering of French phrases and titles of address that add to the French atmosphere.

◆ Themes and Characters ◆

The Three Musketeers focuses on d'Artagnan, who is the hero of the book, and his three friends: the musketeers Athos, Porthos, and Aramis. D'Artagnan's great ambition in life is to become a musketeer, a member of the elite group of King Louis XIII's personal bodyguards. His three friends embody the best qualities of the corps. A rivalry that exists between the king's musketeers and Cardinal Richelieu's guards grows into the musketeers' active resistance to the cardinal himself, and to his servants.

Athos, Porthos, and Aramis appear to have little in common. Athos obviously belongs to the nobility. Silence, melancholy, and an aversion to women are his distinguishing attributes. He is a brilliant, honorable, virtuous man who hides a mysterious secret in his past. Porthos is his opposite: loud, coarse, vain, and ostentatious, his gifts lie in his enormous size and strength. He constantly boasts of his prowess with beautiful and highly placed women, but here, as with other aspects of his life, he exaggerates his good fortune. Aramis is handsome, charming, and elegant. His extreme discretion about his affairs makes him a mysterious figure. Although Aramis professes a vocation for the priesthood and seems pious, d'Artagnan discovers that he is the lover of one of the most highly placed ladies of the court and is involved in various intrigues. All three of the musketeers are spirited and gallant adventurers who share the traits of bravery and loyalty; they are united by their courage and a sense of common purpose.

D'Artagnan himself is a worthy companion of such men. Exceptionally proud and intelligent, he comes to Paris as a young man to earn his fortune. He brings with him no resources except his wits and his skill with a sword. He is both courageous and passionate, but these qualities are equally balanced by prudence. He is neither as well born nor as morally scrupulous as Athos; he is not as well bred as Aramis but admires the latter's elegance and manners. D'Artagnan's own cleverness exceeds that of Aramis, with whom he shares a talent for intrigue. D'Artagnan's poverty sharpens his pride so that he possesses a vanity almost equal to that of Porthos.

Illustration by Maurice Leloir for *The Three Musketeers* by Alexandre Dumas. Dodd, Mead: New York (1941).

He also has a healthy amount of ambition and some greed mixed into his character. But above all d'Artagnan has the energy, passion, and enthusiasm of youth, traits that make him a likable character despite his faults.

The novel focuses on two political factions in France: one headed by the king and the other by the cardinal. The musketeers serve their captain, Monsieur de Tréville, a perfect gentleman and courtier to King Louis XIII. Dumas depicts Louis as a weak and unintelligent ruler. Cardinal Richelieu's character is the exact opposite: he is shrewd and forceful, a penetrating judge of character. The power of the government really rests with him, and he possesses a vision of France's role and destiny. He commands both the respect and the hatred of the musketeers. Although not an evil man, Richelieu accomplishes his aims and rules efficiently by employing methods not quite in keeping with his position as a cardinal of the Catholic church. The musketeers' mortal enemies are two of the cardinal's favorite servants and spies: the Count de Rochefort and Milady de Winter.

Rochefort appears sporadically throughout the novel, but the truly evil person is Milady, who uses her beauty as a tool to seduce and destroy men and women. From the first moment d'Artagnan sees her at the beginning of the novel she fascinates him, and his fate becomes inextricably bound to hers.

Milady's deeds become progressively more villainous. She steals the diamond studs from the Duke of Buckingham, forcing the musketeers to journey to England to save the queen's reputation. She is responsible for the abduction of Constance Bonacieux, d'Artagnan's mistress. She is revealed as Athos's former wife, who ruined him when he discovered that she had been branded as a thief. She tries twice to murder d'Artagnan, and she seduces a young man and persuades him to assassinate the Duke of Buckingham. As her final crime, she poisons Constance Bonacieux. There is no doubt that she deserves her ultimate fate, although her trial by the musketeers and subsequent execution pose serious questions about the musketeers' ethical conduct.

The characters and actions of the musketeers express the overall themes of the book: the idealism of youth, the growth of maturity, the importance of loyalty and friendship, and the need for bravery in the struggle of good against evil. This struggle is summed up in the contrast between the two rivals for d'Artagnan's affections: the treacherous Milady and the good Constance Bonacieux.

◆ Literary Qualities ◆

The Three Musketeers draws on the literary conventions of the three genres to which it belongs: the romantic, the Gothic, and the historical novel. As a romantic novel, its main interest lies in action rather than character: love, adventure, and combat form the basis of all the episodes of the story. The period seems exotic because of its remoteness, and so possesses a nostalgic attractiveness. The characters appear heroic and larger than life, and the musketeers accomplish almost impossible deeds. At times the trappings are almost Gothic: damsels need to be rescued and won, enigmatic and inscrutable strangers come and go mysteriously, and the characters live under the threat of being arrested and locked in a dungeon.

The influence of the historical novel helps to balance these romantic and Gothic elements, and to add realism to the text. Although Dumas's picture of the seventeenth century is unquestionably idealized, he vividly captures the spirit of the age and presents a picture that feels authentic. The use of historical people as characters who interact with the fictional characters also lends plausibility to the musketeers' heroic deeds.

The basic frame of the story draws on a traditional fairy tale motif. The reader can easily recognize d'Artagnan at the outset of the tale as the idealistic poor boy setting off to seek fame and fortune. With the aid of his comrades he overcomes the dangers and obstacles that beset him. By the end of the novel he has attained renown and the rank of lieutenant in the band of musketeers. But success has its price. He has suffered, lost some of his idealism, and become a sadder and wiser man.

◆ Social Sensitivity ◆

Because *The Three Musketeers* takes place in the seventeenth century and was written almost 150 years ago, the standards and customs of the society pictured differ considerably from those of today. Twentieth-century readers, particularly American readers, may not always understand the social relationships of a complexly hierarchical society. The main characters almost all come from the upper classes and assume their superiority on the social scale quite unconsciously. The terms "gentleman" and "lady" had different connotations then than they do now, and they were applied only to nobility. Attitudes toward religion and the church differed then, too. France was an almost wholly Catholic country in which the Protestants were persecuted. The church was one of the few careers open to the younger sons of the nobility and had far more secular influence than it does now. Thus, Aramis's attraction toward it is based on more than just natural piety, and Richelieu's position as a cardinal is a logical stepping stone to his political career as the prime minister for King Louis XIII.

By modern standards, *The Three Musketeers* undoubtedly appears sexist: the main characters are men, and the women often seem passive and usually have to be rescued. Milady, the one woman who takes an active role, is a villain who hardly serves as an appropriate role model. The treatment of sexual relations in the narrative depends a good deal upon whether or not the reader has an abridged edition of the novel. In the unabridged edition, it is clear that d'Artagnan's relationships with Milady and her maid Kitty are not celibate. Abridged editions touch only obliquely on the sexual aspects of the love affairs. D'Artagnan's conduct in these two affairs is neither admirable nor gentlemanly, especially given that he is supposedly in love with the missing Constance Bonacieux at the same time. His behavior provokes the narrator to comment that d'Artagnan's lack of scruples springs mostly from two of his dominant characteristics, pride and ambition, but also from the looser morals of the era. Admitting that d'Artagnan is a flawed young man, the narrator tries to present him in the best light possible.

The novel also contains a great deal of violence because of the conventions of the romantic tradition into which it fits. Duels and battles occur regularly and usually end with casualties. But the violence is not sadistic; the musketeers and even most of their adversaries observe rules of fair play. The distant historical setting also tones down the impact of the fighting.

The execution of Milady at the climax of the novel raises major ethical questions. Although she has committed many monstrous crimes and unquestionably deserves to be punished, the fact that the musketeers privately try and execute her is deeply disturbing. Horrific as her crimes have been, her terror during the trial and on the way to her execution is also horrific—to the point that readers can feel some sympathy with d'Artagnan when he is moved by Milady's pleas for mercy.

1. The title of the book is *The Three Musketeers*, but the story seems to be mostly about d'Artagnan, who does not become a musketeer until late in the story. What point is Dumas making with the title?

2. Which of the three musketeers is your favorite? Why?

3. Athos, Porthos, Aramis, and d'Artagnan each keep a servant. How does each servant suit his master?

4. When he arrives in Paris, d'Artagnan unintentionally picks a fight with each of the three musketeers. What do the reasons for each quarrel tell you about the personality of each of the musketeers?

5. D'Artagnan's duel with Athos is interrupted by the cardinal's guards, who have a long-standing rivalry with the musketeers. Why does d'Artagnan side with the musketeers when the guards challenge them? This episode sets up the antagonism between the cardinal and the musketeers that runs through the rest of the book. Why do the musketeers oppose the cardinal?

6. D'Artagnan takes revenge on Milady partly because of her role in kidnapping the woman he loves, Constance Bonacieux, and partly because she has pretended to love him. He avenges these wrongs by doing what she has done to him: he pretends to be the man she loves, the Count de Wardes, and in this guise he insults her by telling her that he is not serious about her. Later he reveals his deception to her, thus increasing her hatred of him. Do you think d'Artagnan is justified in what he does?

7. One of the many deceptions in the novel is that d'Artagnan pretends to love Kitty in order to get at Milady. Why are deceptions essential to develop plot? In the context of romantic literature, is deception the same as dishonesty?

8. The book concludes with Constance Bonacieux's death, Milady's execution, d'Artagnan's promotion to lieutenant, and the breakup of the four musketeers. Is this an appropriate ending to the story? Why or why not?

1. How does d'Artagnan's character change from the beginning of the novel to the end? What episodes reveal these changes?

2. At the beginning of *The Three Musketeers*, neither d'Artagnan nor the reader knows who Milady is, but she becomes the main villain of the story. Trace Milady's development as the villain. When and how does Dumas reveal her as an evil character?

3. D'Artagnan falls in love with Constance Bonacieux, who is the heroine of the novel, but later he also becomes infatuated with Milady, who is the villain. Contrast the two women and the relationships d'Artagnan develops with them. How can he be attracted to both when they differ so completely?

4. *The Three Musketeers* is a historical novel, which means that it contains events that actually happened and uses as characters people who actually lived. The most accurate historical events in *The Three Musketeers* are the siege of La Rochelle and the assassination of the Duke of Buckingham, but the affair of

the queen's diamond studs has some historical basis too. King Louis XIII, Anne of Austria, and Cardinal Richelieu were all real people. What is the effect of using historical events and people in a fictional story? Do they simply form the background of this novel, or do they play a more essential role in the plot?

5. Find some books in the library that tell you more about one of the historical events or characters, and compare Dumas's portrait with what the other writers say. What differences do you find? What has Dumas changed or left out? Why do you think he made changes, and what effect do they have on the story?

◆ Related Titles/Adaptations ◆

Because of the huge success of *The Three Musketeers*, Dumas wrote two sequels to it. Both of them are set much later than the original novel and show the effects age has on the musketeers and the friendship they share. The events of *Twenty Years After* occur, as the title suggests, two decades after the events of the first book. France is suffering from political turmoil, and the musketeers, now in their forties, find themselves in opposite factions. Their differences threaten their former friendship and loyalty; even after resolving not to let politics destroy their unity, they often end up working against each other. They are no longer the invincible foursome of their youth. Readers who know little about French political history will probably find much of the book hard to follow, for the events are much more complex than those of *The Three Musketeers*. The portion of *Twenty Years After* that lovers of the original novel will probably enjoy most concerns

the musketeers' adventure in England, where they try to rescue Charles I from execution but are foiled by Mordaunt, the son of Milady.

The second sequel, *The Vicomte de Bragelonne*, is a massive, three-volume tome that is twice as long as the first two books put together. It is difficult to find in full length, but the last third has been published under the title *The Man in the Iron Mask* and is more readily available. It starts approximately ten years after the previous sequel, with the musketeers in their fifties, and follows their fortunes up through their deaths.

Since its earliest days, Hollywood has adapted Dumas's stories to film, and much of the popular image of *The Three Musketeers* derives from film and television productions. These vary in quality and often use only the most basic elements of the novel's plot, but they are good fun, filled with swashbuckling adventure, and enjoyable for viewers of all ages. Of the various motion-picture versions, the two most important are the 1948 Metro-Goldwyn-Mayer production and the 1973 British production. The first of these features a screenplay by Robert Ardrey that emphasizes action and swordplay, and provides a happy ending. Gene Kelly, playing d'Artagnan, turns swordfights into ballet. The movie also features Lana Turner as Milady, June Allyson as Constance Bonacieux, Van Heflin as Athos, Gig Young as Porthos, Robert Coote as Aramis, and Vincent Price as Cardinal Richelieu. Although much of the story has been cut out, this version of the novel, taken as it is, is highly entertaining.

The second important motion-picture adaptation of the novel was made into two films, filmed simultaneously in 1973 but released separately: *The Three Musketeers*, released in 1974 and *The*

Four Musketeers, released in 1975. Some of the events have been changed (Constance is strangled, not poisoned, for instance), but all the major plot elements are reproduced. George MacDonald Fraser's screenplay emphasizes the romance of the novel, and it includes much humor and fine wordplay. Director Richard Lester creates a minor masterpiece of rich images and earthy action. The movie features Michael York as d'Artagnan, Oliver Reed as Athos, Richard Chamberlain as Aramis, Frank Finlay as Porthos, Faye Dunaway as Milady, Raquel Welch as Constance, Charlton Heston as Cardinal Richelieu, and Christopher Lee as Rochefort. This superb version of Dumas's novel received an "R" rating when first released because of its bawdy humor and its violence. Parents may wish to preview these movies before letting their children see them, but most teen-agers will find them entertaining.

A 1935 film version of *The Three Musketeers*, directed by Rowland V. Lee, stars Walter Abel, Paul Lukas, and Ian Keith. A 1939 production, directed by Alan Dwan, stars Don Ameche, the Ritz Brothers, and Lionel Atwill.

◆ For Further Reference ◆

Hemmings, F. W. J. *The King of Romance: A Portrait of Alexandre Dumas*. London: Hamish Hamilton, 1979. This is the best of the more recent biographies of Dumas. It includes a brief critique of *The Three Musketeers*.

Maurois, Andre. *Alexandre Dumas: A Great Life in Brief*. New York: Alfred A. Knopf, 1955. Although older and difficult to find, this biography serves as the basis of many more recent ones. It

gives a very readable account of Dumas's life and includes a short section on *The Three Musketeers* and *The Count of Monte Cristo*.

McNair, William. *In Search of the Four Musketeers*. Sydney, Australia: Alpha Books, 1972. McNair takes his readers on an illustrated tour of all the places that the characters go in the three novels about d'Artagnan. He traces many of the historical elements in the stories and incorporates a good deal of criticism along the way.

Ross, Michael. *Alexandre Dumas*. London: David and Charles, 1981. This is another recent biography with a brief critical appraisal of *The Three Musketeers*.

Spurr, Harry. *The Life and Writings of Alexandre Dumas*. 1902. Reprint. New York: Haskell House, 1973. Includes an excellent critique of *The Three Musketeers* that traces the historical basis of the tale, examines Dumas's reworking of his sources, and discusses the reactions of other writers and critics, notably William Makepeace Thackeray and Robert Louis Stevenson.

Stowe, Richard S. *Alexandre Dumas, père*. Twayne's World Authors Series. Boston: G. K. Hall, 1976. Stowe furnishes the best critical evaluation of *The Three Musketeers* and its sequels. He compares Dumas's stories with his sources and analyzes the differences, studies the characters' development in each book and over the course of the series, and examines Dumas's plotting and literary techniques.

Kara K. Keeling
Indiana University

TO BE A SLAVE

Nonfiction

1968

---◆---

Author: Julius Lester, b. 1939

Major Books for Young Adults

To Be a Slave, 1968
Black Folktales, 1970
The Knee-High Man and Other Tales, 1972
Long Journey Home: Stories from Black History, 1972
The Tales of Uncle Remus: The Adventures of Brer Rabbit, 1985
This Strange New Feeling, 1985

◆ About the Author ◆

Julius Bernard Lester was born in St. Louis, Missouri, on January 27, 1939. His father, a Methodist minister, inspired Lester's interest in southern black folklore and culture, as did Lester's maternal grandmother from Arkansas, with whom the boy spent many summers. He was educated at Fisk University in Memphis, where he earned a degree in music and literature in 1960. Despite legalized racism and segregation in the South, Lester focused on the positive traditions of rural southern blacks in his writing.

Lester's editor for his adult books suggested that he try writing literature for children, which eventually led to his publishing *To Be a Slave*. Lester says that his hope in writing stories for young adults is to provide them with the kind of books he never had as a child. *To Be a Slave* became a best-selling work that received the Nancy Bloch Award and a *New York Times* Outstanding Book Award in 1968 and a Newbery Honor Book citation in 1969. Another of Lester's books for young adults, *Long Journey Home*, was honored as a National Book Award finalist in 1973 and won the Lewis Carroll Shelf Award in 1972. Lester's books have been translated into German, Swedish, Finnish, Japanese, and Spanish.

◆ Overview ◆

To Be a Slave fills a void in the documentation of American history by providing a concrete illustration of the culture and history of blacks in the Americas, particularly in the United States. The book focuses on the plight of blacks: their brutal capture in Africa, their confined passage to America in slave ships, and their subsequent

Photograph of Julius
Lester courtesy of
E. P. Dutton.

servitude. Rather than offering a dry summary of these events, Lester brings history to life, presenting the testimony of former slaves who describe their experiences in visceral detail. Because most slaves were illiterate, their stories were passed along orally, but most written historical accounts of slavery ignore this oral tradition, focusing instead on how slavery as an institution affected the white, mainstream society. Hence, Lester fills a historical gap by providing a black perspective on the same situation. The quote from an ex-slave that begins Lester's book indicates the significance of *To Be a Slave*: "In all the books that you have studied you never have studied Negro history, have you?...If you want Negro history, you will have to get it from somebody who wore the shoe..."

◆ Setting ◆

The story has no one certain setting since it consists of a series of separate narratives, many of which are attributed to anonymous sources. But because Lester arranges these selections in chronological order, beginning with the initial capture of the slaves and ending with their emancipation, the story begins in Africa in the early seventeenth century, when Europeans are in quest of black people whom they can capture. After a sea voyage to such places as South Carolina or Virginia, the slaves are auctioned and dispersed to various plantations across the South. Lester follows the destiny of his characters as they experience personal upheavals, and as America faces tremendous change through the 1860s and 1870s with the Civil War, emancipation, and Reconstruction.

◆ Themes and Characters ◆

To Be a Slave aims to educate readers about slavery in America and about the dehumanizing misconceptions about blacks that even the intellectuals of the day believed. Thomas Jefferson, author of the Declaration of Independence and statesman, supported the idea of the "natural inferiority" of blacks. Lester notes that corporal punishment by masters was commonplace, while lynching by the Ku Klux Klan was generally accepted by whites as a necessary practice. Religion, which many slaves used as a positive spiritual weapon against suffering, was misused by manipulative slave masters who hired preachers who maintained that God had created blacks to be slaves and servants, and that the greatest glory blacks could give to God was to accept their place in God's grand universal structure. Slaves were subjected to further psychological cruelty when they were forced to adopt the surname of their owner.

The large cast of characters in *To Be a Slave* consists mostly of the slaves and slave owners mentioned in the brief, dramatic narratives that make up the book. But Lester's focus is not on the development of any one character; rather he presents the reader with the distinct voices of a wide assortment of characters. Several characters stand out; among them is Uncle Silas, an elderly slave who questions the philosophy that eternal rest in heaven is earned by serving one's master on earth with unqualified loyalty. Another memorable character is Lew Cheney, a charismatic young slave who raises the expectations of the slaves on the Hawkins plantation by planning a revolt and a crusade to Mexico. But Cheney betrays his people, which results in the hanging of many innocent slaves. Powhatan Mitchell, a slaveowner, differs from many of the "master" characters in that he claims his mulatto child as his own son and teaches him that he is a white man's equal. Despite this gesture of humanity, Mitchell continues to hold slaves. Dozens of additional characters spring to life in the narratives, and though each is part of a separate story, they all serve as vivid illustrations of Lester's overall theme of the dehumanizing force of slavery.

◆ Literary Qualities ◆

As Lester explains in an introductory note, *To Be a Slave* sprang from his research of slave narratives, documented in the nineteenth century by abolitionists, and from interviews with ex-slaves, recorded in the 1930s by members of the Federal Writers' Project. Lester's voice mingles with those of the slaves as his commentary, woven throughout the book, sets the historical context for the narratives. He arranges the stories chronologically, dividing the book into chapters that tell the history of slavery from a black perspective, from the capture of blacks in Africa to their emancipation and continued persecution years later in the United States.

Lester's narration is deliberate and powerful, and his understated style underscores the dramatic effect of the slave narratives. The words of those who actually experienced the anguish of slavery create a vivid, wrenching historical account. These narratives contain most of the book's symbolism and imagery. In the following passage, for example, an ex-slave describes the frustration experienced by newly emancipated slaves—who faced restrictive laws, economic oppression, and the Ku Klux Klan—in terms of a metaphor: "Two snakes full of poison...The snake called slavery lay with his head pointed south and the snake called freedom lay with his head pointed north. Both bit the nigger and they was both bad." Lester's own voice never overwhelms such moving statements. He conveys his message through the words of the slaves and ex-slaves. Lester, writing during the civil rights movement of the 1960s, does not write the story of the slaves. He allows them to tell their own stories.

As a collection of slave narratives, *To Be a Slave* is part of a whole body of literature that historians see as a rich source of information on American history and life. Slave narratives, which began to appear in the mid-1700s as a unique form of literature, may have been encouraged by abolitionists in the North in order to portray the evil nature of slavery. The slave narratives published early on tended to be far more religious than those published later. The first published slave narrative was *The Narrative of the Uncommon Suffering and Surprising Deliverance of Briton Hammon, a Negro Man* (1760). Since then, many narratives have been published; among the most notable is Frederick Douglass's autobiography, *Narrative of the Life of Frederick Douglass* (1845).

◆ Social Sensitivity ◆

Although *To Be a Slave* depicts conditions of blacks during a time that has long passed, it raises many questions about the treatment of minorities in contemporary society. *To Be a Slave* shows the tragic effects that ensue when a society discriminates against people because of race, religion, or gender. *To Be a Slave* is a cry for equality and justice for all. If the injustices vividly depicted during the time of slavery threaten readers because they parallel injustices committed in modern times, then Lester's themes and techniques have accomplished their purpose.

◆ Topics for Discussion ◆

1. What were the most difficult aspects of being a slave, according to Lester?

2. Was Christianity a positive factor in the lives of the slaves? What were the differences between the Christianity preached by the slaves' owners and the religion fashioned by the slaves themselves?

3. What aspects of African culture did the slaves bring to the plantations, and what measures were employed by the slave owners to destroy this influence?

4. What is meant by the expression "Jim Crow"? How does it apply to the

period after the emancipation of the slaves?

5. Why did Thomas Jefferson believe blacks were inferior?

6. The NAACP (National Association for the Advancement of Colored People) protests flying the Confederate flag or singing "Dixie" because these are symbols of slavery. Explain your position, drawing on what you have learned from reading *To Be a Slave*.

◆ Ideas for Reports and Papers ◆

1. Research the Reconstruction period of American history (the twenty years following the end of the Civil War). Explain its significance, both positive and negative, to blacks in America.

2. Rhody Holsell, a slave in the book, says that if President Lincoln had lived, there would have been no violence perpetrated against blacks after the war. He thinks that Lincoln would have separated blacks from whites and given them their own nation. How do you think that this solution would have worked?

3. Read Harriet Beecher Stowe's *Uncle Tom's Cabin* and explain what the term "Uncle Tom" means to that book. Thomas Hall, an ex-slave quoted in *To Be a Slave* says of Stowe, "I didn't like her book and I hate her." Why might Hall have this response to the book?

4. Research and report on how the "underground railroad" functioned.

5. Write a rebuttal to Thomas Jefferson's doctrine of "natural inferiority."

◆ For Further Reference ◆

Butterfield, Stephen. *Black Autobiography in America.* Amherst: University of Massachusetts Press, 1974. Survey of black autobiography from the slave narratives to modern times. Includes detailed descriptions of the most important autobiographies, including those of Frederick Douglass, Richard Wright, James Baldwin, and George Jackson.

Davis, Charles T., and Henry Louis Gates, Jr. *The Slave's Narrative.* New York: Oxford University Press, 1985. A useful collection of critical works on the slave narratives as literature and history, written by notable scholars. Includes a chronological list of all published narratives and a bibliography.

Huggins, Nathan I. *Key Issues in the Afro-American Experience.* Vol. 1. New York: Harcourt Brace Jovanovich, 1971. Collection of essays by prominent Afro-American scholars. Particularly interesting are the essays in Chapter 3, including "The Daily Life of Southern Slaves" and "The Social Consequences of Slavery."

Mannix, Daniel P., and Malcolm Cowley. *Black Cargoes: A History of the Atlantic Slave Trade, 1518-1865.* New York: Penguin Books, 1976. An examination of the Atlantic slave trade from its beginning until abolition.

Osofsky, Gilbert, ed. *Puttin' on Ole Massa: The Slave Narratives of Henry Bibb, William Wells Brown, and Solomon Northup.* New York: Harper & Row, 1969. An anthology of slave narratives. The introductory chapters on the significance of slave narratives and a note on the usefulness of folklore are very useful. Includes an invaluable bibliographical note.

Starobin, Robert S., ed. *Blacks in Bondage: Letters of American Slaves.* New York: New Viewpoints, 1974. A collection of letters written by the slaves with some letters by their masters. Gives useful insight into the experience of the slaves.

Williamson, Joel R. *After Slavery: The Negro in South Carolina during the Reconstruction, 1861-1877.* A detailed study of the emancipation and Reconstruction periods.

Kwaku Amoabeng
State University of New York,
Stony Brook

Carrol Lasker
State University of New York,
Stony Brook

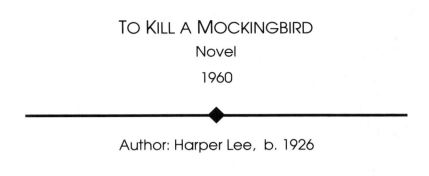

TO KILL A MOCKINGBIRD
Novel
1960

Author: Harper Lee, b. 1926

Major Books for Young Adults

To Kill a Mockingbird, 1960

♦ About the Author ♦

Nelle Harper Lee was born on April 28, 1926, in Monroeville, Alabama. The youngest child of Amasa C. and Frances Finch Lee, she attended public school in Monroeville before entering the University of Alabama to study law. After spending a year as an exchange student at Oxford University in England, Lee returned to school in Alabama but left in 1950 without completing her degree. She moved to New York City, where she worked as an airline reservation clerk and also wrote essays and short stories; at the urging of a literary agent, she soon quit her job to write full-time. Although Lee submitted a draft of *To Kill a Mockingbird* to a publisher as early as 1957, she worked on revisions of the story until its publication in 1960. In 1961 the novel received a Pulitzer Prize, and it was also awarded the Alabama Library Association award (1961), the Brotherhood Award of the National Conference of Christians and Jews (1961), and the *Bestsellers'* paperback of the year award (1962). Following the enormous success of the novel, Lee found herself the un-willing subject of public and critical attention. In 1961 she reported that she was at work on a second book about small-town life in the South, but she has yet to produce another novel. Lee currently lives and writes in Monroeville, Alabama.

♦ Overview ♦

To Kill a Mockingbird is at once a powerful indictment of racial injustice and a tender story about growing up. Narrated in the first person by the adult voice of Scout, who is almost six years old when the novel begins, the story weaves together two interrelated plots about life in Maycomb County, Alabama, in the 1930s. One story line involves the trial of Tom Robinson, a black man accused of raping Mayella Ewell, a white woman; the other follows the adventures of Scout, her older brother Jem, and their friend Dill, as they try to investigate the mysterious legend of the eerie Radley Place, which houses a "malevolent phantom" nick-named Boo Radley. Lee juxtaposes the

Photograph of Harper Lee by Truman Capote in *To Kill a Mockingbird* by Harper Lee. J. B. Lippincott: Philadelphia and New York (1960).

Mockingbird a poignant tale of small-town southern life.

◆ Setting ◆

To Kill a Mockingbird is set in the 1930s in Maycomb, Alabama, a town so small and insular that, according to Scout, her father is "related by blood or marriage to nearly every family in the town." Scout devotes the very beginning of her narrative to a description of her southern heritage, revealing that her English ancestor, Simon Finch, a slaveholding, enterprising skinflint, founded Finch's Landing, a cotton plantation where generations of Finches, including Atticus, grew up. Twenty miles east of Finch's Landing, Maycomb is home to old southern families whose roots, traditions, and biases run deep. Each family name carries its own accepted identity in town: the Haverfords, for example, have "a name synonymous with jackass"; the Cunninghams are considered poor but very proud; and the Ewells are cruel and lazy.

The town itself is slow, hot, and uneventful in Scout's memory; the men work from morning till evening, the women stay at home, and the children go to school and then play outside. In Maycomb, says Scout, "Men's stiff collars wilted by nine in the morning. Ladies bathed before noon, after their three-o'clock naps, and by nightfall were like soft teacakes with frostings of sweat and sweet talcum...There was no hurry, for there was nowhere to go, nothing to buy and no money to buy it with, nothing to see outside the boundaries of Maycomb County."

Racial segregation is an accepted way of life for the townspeople. The blacks in Maycomb live in their own part of town, attend their own churches and schools,

innocence and curiosity of the children with the ignorance and hostility of many of the adults, using the character of Atticus Finch—the children's father and a respected attorney who defends Tom Robinson—as a standard of reason, compassion, and fairness. Atticus helps the children leave behind their world of make-believe and come closer to understanding the mystery behind the Radley Place, just as he pushes the town of Maycomb County toward its own confrontation with bigotry and injustice. Combining dry humor with an evocative description of the various social groups, economic problems, and political issues of the time, Lee creates in *To Kill a* have low-paying, menial jobs, and are implicitly considered inferior by the majority white segment of the town. The whites use pejorative terms to refer to the black characters, and public buildings such as the courthouse have separate areas for the whites and for the "colored."

Much of the action, which occurs over the course of two years, takes place at the Finch home, where Scout lives with Atticus, Jem, and, during the day, their housekeeper, Calpurnia. Atticus has raised the children with Calpurnia's assistance since his wife died of a heart attack when Scout was two years old. Dill lives next door to the Finches during the summer, when he visits his Aunt Rachel Haverford. The rest of the action occurs at school, at the courthouse, and in the black part of town.

The Radley Place, a source of fear and drama for the children, is located down the street from the Finch home. According to local legend, the Radley Place was once home to Mr. and Mrs. Radley, an aloof, stern couple, and their son Arthur. While still a teen-ager, Arthur joined his buddies on a lark, in locking a town official in the courthouse outhouse one night. Although the offense was trivial, the Radleys disciplined their son by secluding him in their home for fifteen years. Then, the story goes, when Arthur was thirty-three years old, he nonchalantly stabbed his father in the leg with a pair of scissors. After this incident, Arthur was kept for a time in the courthouse basement and was eventually transferred back to his home, where he continues to live in isolation from the community. Although Arthur's cruel father has died, Arthur's older brother, Nathan Radley, an equally severe man, now occupies the Radley Place. Arthur, known as Boo to the superstitious, fearful neighbors, becomes a creepy object of fascination for the children, and the Radley Place is considered haunted property; as Scout explains: "People said that [Boo] went out at night when the moon was down, and peeped in windows. When people's azaleas froze in a cold snap, it was because he had breathed on them...A baseball hit into the Radley yard was a lost ball and no questions asked."

♦ Themes and Characters ♦

The central characters of *To Kill a Mockingbird* are Jean Louise (Scout), Jeremy Atticus (Jem), and Atticus Finch. Scout, precocious and outspoken, possesses a quick mind and a hot temper; her persistent desire to learn about and participate in the world around her frequently gets her into trouble at home and at school. When Walter Cunningham, a poor classmate of Scout's, is invited to lunch at the Finches', Scout watches in horror as Walter, unaccustomed to the formality of the Finches' noon-time meal, drowns his food in maple syrup. Without realizing her rudeness, Scout asks Walter what the "sam hill" he thinks he is doing; she receives a stern lecture from Calpurnia on the meaning of hospitality and good manners. Later, when her spoiled cousin Francis taunts her by criticizing Atticus, Scout—who has been trying to curb her combative tendencies—punches Francis in the mouth and is promptly punished. At school, when Scout tries to be helpful and educate Miss Caroline, her nervous, inexperienced first-grade teacher, about Maycomb County protocol, Miss Caroline disciplines her for impudence. Still, Scout remains a spunky, inquisitive, and loyal child whose love for her father and brother is evident through-

Jacket design by Shirley Smith for *To Kill a Mockingbird* by Harper Lee. J. B. Lippincott: Philadelphia and New York (1960).

around in it." He explains his treatment of his children to his brother, Jack: "When a child asks you something, answer him, for goodness sake. But don't make a production of it. Children are children, but they can spot an evasion quicker than adults, and evasion simply muddles 'em."

Nearly fifty years old, Atticus is older than most parents of Scout and Jem's friends; he differs from many of the adults in Maycomb in that he fights the entrenched ignorance and prejudice of the region. In his private life as a father and his public life as an attorney, Atticus champions honesty, fairness, and respect for the opinions and rights of others. His character seems believable despite his larger-than-life role as the moral center of the novel. Atticus also displays a dry sense of humor; when a drunken Bob Ewell threatens to kill Atticus and then spits in his face, Atticus's only comment about the incident is, "I wish Bob Ewell wouldn't chew tobacco." He shows fear when the children try to protect him from a mob intent on lynching Tom Robinson, and as a result of Aunt Alexandria's criticism, he exhibits temporary self-doubt about his ability as a single parent.

Jem has inherited his father's stubbornness and sense of righteousness. He is both playmate and protector to Scout, and in many ways her narrative seems to be a nostalgic reconstruction of the past in terms of her older brother's maturation. Likewise, Lee articulates many of her themes through her depiction of Jem's moral and emotional development. When the story begins, he is a bright, level-headed ten-year-old who loves to play imaginative games with Scout and Dill. But as he grows older, Jem becomes moodier; because he is four years older than Scout, he is beginning to understand, and thus

out the story; as the novel progresses, she develops the sensitivity and self-control that characterize the voice of the adult Scout who narrates the story.

Both Atticus and Jem shape Scout's development. Every night before she goes to bed, Scout reads with her father. He instills in her a love of reading so natural that Scout notes: "Until I feared I would lose it, I never loved to read. One does not love breathing." Atticus teaches Scout to behave with dignity and compassion; he never speaks down to her, but credits her with the intelligence to understand the point of such lessons as not to judge another person "until you climb into his skin and walk is more strongly affected by, adult realities such as racism, ignorance, and cruelty.

Jem's maturation is partially reflected in his changing attitude toward the Boo Radley game that the children play. The summer that Scout is six and Jem is ten, the children decide to try to make Boo come out of the Radley Place. Initially, Jem feeds the children's fear of Boo, describing Boo's bloodstained hands and rotting teeth, and confiding, "I've seen his tracks in our back yard many a mornin', and one night I heard him scratching on the back screen, but he was gone time Atticus got there." The children dare each other to touch the house, try to deliver a note to Boo, and despite strict orders from Atticus to stop playing the Radley game, try to peek in a window and catch a glimpse of Boo. But when Jem and Scout begin to find objects, such as an old spelling medal and carved soap figures of themselves, hidden for them in the knot-hole of a tree in front of the Radley Place, Jem realizes what Scout does not, that the objects are gestures of affection from Boo, who has been shut away in his house since he was a boy. Jem begins to understand that Boo is a real person who has been cruelly deprived of a normal life.

Just as his attitude toward Boo changes, so too do Jem's feelings for his sister, his father, and his town. Where he once accused Scout of acting too much like a girl, her now tells her to act more like one; where he was once embarrassed that his father is too old to play football, he now admires his father's courage in the courtroom; where he once took for granted the basic goodness and decency of the townspeople, he comes to a new realization about them after he witnesses the conviction of Tom Robinson. Jem tries to explain his disillusionment to Scout: "If there's just one kind of folks, why can't they get along with each other? If they're all alike, why do they go out of their way to despise each other? I think I'm beginning to understand why Boo Radley's stayed shut up in the house all this time...it's because he *wants* to stay inside." Jem's struggle to make sense of the Radleys' cruelty toward Boo and the town's persecution of Tom Robinson illustrates Lee's concern with personal and social injustice. She weaves together her dual themes—the bittersweet movement from childhood to adulthood and the painful awakening of a society to its own ignorance and bigotry—in her depiction of Jem's maturation.

The Radley place was inhabited by an unknown entity the mere description of whom was enough to make us behave for days on end...

To Kill a Mockingbird contains many minor characters who are vividly described. Charles Baker Harris (Dill), the children's seven-year-old playmate, is an eccentric, imaginative boy. Described by Scout as wearing "linen shorts buttoned to his shirt" and having white hair that "stuck to his head like duckfluff," Dill makes up fantastic stories about his family in order to hide the fact that his parents are separated and he feels unloved at his mother's home. Dill instigates many of the children's dramatic games, including the Boo Radley game. Literary rumor has it that Dill's character is based on the young Truman Capote, a famous American writer who grew up with Harper Lee.

Most of the adult female characters play maternal roles in the novel. Calpurnia, the Finches' housekeeper, maintains calm and order in the household. She is strict but loving with the children, and she helps them understand and respect the black community where she lives. Aunt Alexandria, Atticus's sister, comes to live with the Finch family in order to exert a bit of "feminine influence" on the children while Atticus is absorbed in the Robinson trial. Her presence creates much tension in the household, for she disapproves of Scout's tomboyish ways and tries to impose her snobbish, provincial ideas on the family. Miss Maudie Atkinson lives across the street from the Finches. A spry, fair-minded woman, she treats Jem and Scout with grandmotherly concern and adult respect. It is Miss Maudie who explains the significance of Atticus's statement that it is a sin to kill a mockingbird; she tells the children, "Your father's right. Mockingbirds don't do one thing but make music for us to enjoy. They don't eat up people's gardens, don't nest in corncribs, they don't do one thing but sing out their hearts for us. That's why it's a sin to kill a mockingbird." The mockingbird comes to symbolize Boo Radley and Tom Robinson, both of whom are persecuted by the townspeople.

Although Tom Robinson figures prominently in the plot of the novel, his character is one-dimensional. A humble, good-hearted black man, he is the victim of a racist white society. Mayella Ewell also plays a victim. Ignorance, poverty, and abuse at the hands of her father, Bob Ewell, lead Mayella to seek Tom Robinson's affection; when her overture toward Tom backfires, resulting in her father's brutal assault on her, she covers her shame and appeases her father by accusing Tom of rape. Bob Ewell plays the villain in the novel; he is a flat but menacing character, portrayed simply as a lawless, loathsome figure of evil.

◆ Literary Qualities ◆

Lee neatly structures her novel around a dual plot and dual themes; the novel is evenly divided into two parts. In her graceful, understated style, Lee weaves together a story about two children growing up in a small southern town, and a story about the children's father, a white attorney who defends a black man unjustly accused of raping a white woman. Because both stories involve Jem, Scout, and Atticus, Scout's first-person narration, with its focus on the development of these three characters, unifies the different story lines.

The narrator's emphasis on Jem is particularly significant to the structure and meaning of the story. Lee creates in Scout an immensely likable, funny character, but she invests Jem with the depth and literary complexity of a protagonist. Each section of the book begins and ends with a description of Jem as he matures and changes. Scout begins her narrative with the statement: "When he was nearly thirteen, my brother Jem got his arm badly broken at the elbow." The rest of the story follows from this simple revelation, and by the final chapters, when the injury actually occurs, the broken arm carries symbolic significance.

Through much of part 1, Jem is a child who plays make-believe games with Scout and Dill, but toward the end of the first section, he has begun to recognize the difference between right and wrong, good and evil. Scout's narration reflects this development; she begins part 2 by noting: "Jem was twelve. He was difficult to live with, inconsistent, moody." Hence, Scout sets the tone for the section of the novel that deals largely with the trial of Tom Robinson; just as Jem is entering a difficult stage, learning to confront conflicting emotions and beliefs, so too are the people of Maycomb feeling the tension of a trial that will shake the foundation of their racially-divided town. Near the end of the novel, Bob Ewell, who represents the backwardness and evil of prejudice, tries to kill Jem and Scout in a vengeful attempt to hurt Atticus. Jem's arm is broken during the attack, symbolizing the pain and disillusionment he has experienced while learning about Boo Radley and witnessing the Robinson trial.

Jem survives the attack but carries a permanent scar, a symbol of the disabling power of hatred and injustice. Scout says that as a result of his injury that night, Jem's left arm is "somewhat shorter than his right; when he stood or walked, the back of his hand was at right angles to his body, his thumb parallel to his thigh." In this way, Jem shares a bond with Tom Robinson, for Robinson's left arm is also shorter than his right. As a result of an accident involving a cotton gin, he is permanently crippled, and as Atticus argues at his trial, he is therefore physically incapable of beating Mayella Ewell in the manner that she describes. Yet Robinson's most damning handicap proves to be his race. Jem's broken arm serves as a reminder of this fact, and Lee

implies that Jem has been irreparably changed as a result of Tom Robinson's trial.

Lee also suggests, however, that Jem's disillusionment is not permanent and that he will grow up to be as fair-minded and compassionate as his father. Atticus acts as a guardian of justice throughout the novel, and Lee symbolically ends the story with the image of Atticus watching over his children. Scout's final passage states that Atticus "turned out the light and went into Jem's room. He would be there all night, and he would be there when Jem waked up in the morning."

◆ Social Sensitivity ◆

To Kill a Mockingbird is about two deeply disturbing subjects: rape and racism. Lee addresses both subjects with grave sensitivity. The details regarding Mayella Ewell's alleged rape come to light during the trial scenes, with Atticus gently guiding the proceedings. Although these details are not explicitly described, there is the suggestion of incest—that Bob Ewell not only beat his daughter but raped her as well. Since the story is being filtered through Scout, all of this information is related subtly and succinctly.

The novel also reflects the reality of racism in segregated southern towns in the 1930s, some thirty years before the civil rights movement. Blacks are commonly referred to as "niggers" and are considered below the law. Many members of the white society feel justified in inflicting their own form of justice on blacks, particularly on those, such as Robinson, whom they believe have violated racist sexual taboos. By confessing his sympathy for Mayella, Tom Robinson—a black man who has the gall to feel sorry for a white woman—offends the ignorant bigots of the town. A mob of townspeople gather at the jail in hopes of pulling Robinson from his cell and lynching him.

In her measured, deliberate style, Lee exposes the ugliness of this racist society and holds Atticus up as an example of enlightenment and compassion. Still, her comparison of Tom Robinson to a mockingbird, a harmless bird described as existing "only to sing his heart out for us," may strike some readers as patronizing and somewhat racist, for it reinforces the notion of the black man's role as servant, and does not allow for the intellectual equality of blacks.

◆ Topics for Discussion ◆

1. Scout describes her father's first law case in this way: "His first two clients were the last two persons hanged in the Maycomb County jail...The Haverfords had dispatched Maycomb's leading blacksmith in a misunderstanding...were imprudent enough to do it in front of three witnesses...They persisted in pleading Not Guilty to first-degree murder, so there was nothing much Atticus could do for his clients except be present at their departure, an occasion that was probably the beginning of my father's profound distaste for the practice of criminal law." How is this passage an example of Scout's style as a narrator? How would you describe this style? Find other examples of passages that illustrate her way of telling a story.

2. Many of the characters have unusual nicknames: Jean Louise is Scout, Jeremy Atticus is Jem, Charles Baker Harris is Dill, and Arthur Radley is Boo. How do you think these nicknames

developed, and how do they work as characterization devices?

3. Atticus's name is also unusual. Try to determine the origin of his name (it has Greek and Latin roots), and discuss its symbolic meaning in the story.

4. What role does Dill play in the novel? How is Dill different from Scout and Jem? Does he develop as a character in his own right, or does he merely serve as a contrast to Scout and Jem?

5. Scout's teacher, Miss Caroline, receives an education in the ways and means of Maycomb County on her first day of teaching. Who teaches her and what does she learn? Why does Lee include this scene early in the novel?

6. Both Calpurnia and Aunt Alexandria try to raise Scout and Jem properly. How do their values, rules, and methods regarding the children's upbringing differ?

7. The chapters leading up to and describing Bob Ewell's attack on Jem and Scout are full of foreshadowing and suspense. Discuss how Lee sets a mood of foreboding and tension, and show how she offsets this tension with humor.

◆ Ideas for Reports and Papers ◆

1. When Aunt Alexandria forbids Scout to associate with Walter Cunningham because she considers him "trash," Scout and Jem have a discussion about family background and what makes one type of family different from another in Maycomb. Jem tells Scout: "There's four kinds of folks in the world. There's the ordinary kind like us and the

neighbors, there's the kind like the Cunninghams out in the woods, the kind like the Ewells down at the dump, and the Negroes...Background doesn't make Old Family...I think it's how long your family's been readin' and writin'." Scout disagrees with him, saying, "I think there's just one kind of folks. Folks." Which character do you think is expressing the author's point of view, Scout or Jem? Cite examples from the book.

2. Research race relations in the South in the 1930s. Does Lee accurately depict the social tensions of the time? Research and report on specific incidents of racially motivated discrimination, protest, and violence in Alabama during the civil rights movement of the 1960s. Do you think that white racists in the South had to "pay the bill" for their oppression of blacks during this period of social uprising?

3. Watch the movie *To Kill a Mockingbird* and compare it to the book. Which do you like better, and why? Note what the director adds to or omits from the book and analyze the director's interpretation of the book.

4. Boo Radley's character is like a puzzle that the children put together in pieces throughout the novel. Trace the development of Boo's character from Scout's first description of him as a monster to his actual appearance in the last chapters as a gentle, heroic man, and explain his significance in the novel.

5. In the middle of the novel, Atticus is called upon to shoot a mad dog—Tim Johnson, considered the "pet of Maycomb"—that threatens the community. Explain the symbolic significance of this incident and relate it to

the fact that after Jem and Scout receive air rifles as gifts, Atticus tells them, "I'd rather you shot at tin cans in the backyard, but I know you'll go after birds. Shoot all the bluejays you want, if you can hit 'em, but remember it's a sin to kill a mockingbird."

6. When Scout learns that women in Alabama are not eligible for jury duty, she grows "indignant." Atticus tries to mollify her, explaining, "I guess it's to protect our frail ladies from sordid cases like Tom's. Besides...I doubt it he'd ever get a complete case tried—the ladies'd be interrupting to ask questions." Is Atticus completely sincere or slightly sarcastic in his explanation? Using his response to Scout as a starting point, analyze Lee's depiction of women in the novel. Focus especially on Miss Maudie Atkinson, Aunt Alexandria, Calpurnia, and Mayella Ewell, but also examine Lee's portrayal of minor figures as character types that help illustrate the setting and themes of her novel.

7. A pivotal and highly dramatic scene occurs when Scout, Jem, and Dill burst through an angry mob of men who are determined to remove Atticus from his place as guard in front of the jail so that they can lynch Tom. Atticus fears for the children's safety, but Scout breaks up the mob and violence is averted. Explain what Scout accomplishes in that scene, how she accomplishes it, and why it is important to the story as a whole.

◆ Adaptations ◆

In 1962 *To Kill a Mockingbird* was adapted as a motion picture with a screenplay written by Horton Foote. A winner of three Academy Awards, the film was directed by Robert Mulligan and starred Gregory Peck as Atticus Finch. The motion picture is remarkably faithful to the book and has received both popular and critical acclaim.

◆ For Further Reference ◆

Buelle, Edwin. "Keen Scalpel on Racial Ills." *English Journal* 53 (1964): 658-661. Discusses racial themes in Lee's novel and in Alan Paton's *Cry, the Beloved Country.*

Erisman, Fred. "Literature and Place: Varieties of Regional Experience." *Journal of Regional Cultures* 1 (Fall/Winter 1981): 144-153. Discusses Harper Lee, Robert Penn Warren, and Sarah Orne Jewett as examples of writers who use regionalism in literature.

————. "The Romantic Regionalism of Harper Lee." *Alabama Review* 26 (1973): 122-136. Discusses Lee's work in relation to southern romanticism.

Going, William T. *Essays on Alabama Literature.* University, AL: University of Alabama Press, 1975. Discusses *To Kill a Mockingbird* as a reflection of Alabama history and culture.

Kibler, James E., ed. *Dictionary of Literary Biography.* Vol 6, *American Novelists Since World War II.* Second Series. Detroit: Gale Research, 1980. Discusses Lee's life and writing, briefly analyzes her novel, and summarizes its critical reception.

Newquist, Roy. "Interview with Harper Lee." In *Counterpoint.* New York: Simon and Schuster, 1964. In this interview, Lee reveals much about her opinions and aspirations, her experience as a writer, and her feelings about the film version of her novel.

Visser, N. W. "Temporal Vantage Point in the Novel." *Journal of Narrative Technique* 7 (1977): 81-93. Discusses Lee's novel along with many others to show ways time is used and conveyed by novelists.

Wakeman, John, ed. *World Authors, 1950-1970.* New York: H. W. Wilson, 1975. An excellent brief article on Lee's life and book.

Mary D. Esselman
American University

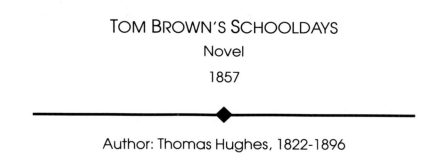

TOM BROWN'S SCHOOLDAYS
Novel
1857

◆

Author: Thomas Hughes, 1822-1896

Major Books for Young Adults

Tom Brown's Schooldays, 1857
Tom Brown at Oxford, 1861

◆ About the Author ◆

Thomas Hughes was born on October 20, 1822, near Uffington in southern England, the second of Margaret Wilkinson Hughes and John Hughes's eight children. The Hughes family were members of the rural squirearchy, a loose confederation of landed proprietors that provided traditional leadership in the community. John Hughes spent most of his life as a well-connected literary dilettante who enjoyed the traditional social and sports activities of the countryside.

Hughes had a conventional upbringing for his social class, beginning his education at home, attending Rugby, a "public school" (the British equivalent of an American private school), and eventually entering Oxford University at age twenty.

At Rugby, Hughes came under the influence of Dr. Thomas Arnold, father of the poet Matthew Arnold. Believing that his students would be the future leaders of the British Empire, Dr. Arnold hoped to transform the purposes and practices

of boarding schools in order that they might produce leaders distinguished for their intellectual achievements and moral strength. But in spite of Arnold's efforts to improve the academic rigor and moral tone of the school, Rugby was still an institution where the older boys exercised an often ruthless control over the younger students, and where learning took second place to sports and escapades.

Hughes flourished in the Rugby environment, excelling at both sports and academics. He was equally successful as a student at Oriel College of Oxford University. Upon completion of his studies, in 1847, Hughes married Frances Ford, the daughter of a well-connected clergyman.

During his time at Oxford, Hughes developed an interest in several progressive religious and social movements then current in England. From the late 1840s on, Hughes became a major advocate of Christian Socialism—which called for a merger of Christian and Socialist principles—as a means of improving the human lot. He helped establish a cooperative movement that called for economic reform of British retailing and manufacturing practices.

Hughes had studied law after leaving Oxford and was called to the bar in 1848, but he gradually found writing to be a more powerful means of effecting social change than litigation. His most popular work, though, proved to be *Tom Brown's Schooldays*, which he originally envisioned as preparatory reading for his eight-year-old son, who was about to enter school. Once published, the book received an enthusiastic response and was a best seller.

Buoyed by this success, Hughes set to work on other fiction, publishing *The Scouring of the White Horse; or, The Long Vacation Ramble of a London Clerk* (1859) and *Tom Brown at Oxford*. Neither met with the success of the earlier work, but Hughes's fame nonetheless continued to spread as *Tom Brown's Schooldays* became popular throughout the English-speaking world. His fame as an author helped publicize the various religious and reform causes with which he was affiliated, and in 1865 he was elected to the British House of Commons from a working-class district near London. He served in Parliament until 1874, and he was one of the founders of an institution called The Working Men's College, acting as its principal from 1872 to 1883.

During the last two decades of his life, Hughes gradually fell out of touch with growing extremism in both religious and labor circles, and saw both his influence and his fortunes decline. Defeated for re-election to Parliament in 1874, he turned his attention to religious matters, publishing *The Manliness of Christ* in 1879. This book publicized Hughes's faith in what came to be called "muscular Christianity." He then poured his financial resources into a cooperative society in Tennessee. Here he hoped to settle young British men who would learn to work with their hands and contribute to the experimental community. After initial success, the community collapsed, and Hughes suffered financial ruin. In 1882 his friends found him a post as a county court judge in Chester, England, where he spent his last years writing in support of liberal causes. Hughes died on March 22, 1896, in Brighton, England.

◆ Overview ◆

Despite Hughes's tendency to be didactic, his reticence about sexual matters, the remoteness of the time and school depicted in the novel, and the frequently obscure British schoolboy slang, *Tom Brown's Schooldays* still appeals to modern readers. Like modern young adults, Tom and the other boys at Rugby suffer pangs of separation from family, stand up against peer bullies, ponder the ambiguities of friendship and the finality of death, and gradually assume adult responsibilities. Tom is no saint; like his American contemporary Huckleberry Finn, he gets into trouble with authority, cuts corners when convenient, sees the hypocrisy of many conventional viewpoints, and relishes an active, outdoor life. Even when Tom is "civilized" under the indirect guidance of his headmaster, Thomas Arnold, he is not transformed into a prude or a snob. He is aware of his own weaknesses and feels great sympathy for those who do not possess his strengths. Thus, although the world that Hughes describes is one that modern readers will never enter, the characters and their internal struggles are relevant.

◆ Setting ◆

The novel takes place in the 1820s and 1830s in England. The opening chapters describe Tom Brown's early childhood in the rural county of Berks, west of London in the Vale of the White Horse. There Tom leads an active life under the tutelage of family retainers. Although he is a member of the upper classes, Tom associates with members of various social classes in the course of his daily activities. Hughes depicts a close-knit rural community just before the onslaught of the railways and the Industrial Revolution.

The scene shifts first to a small private preparatory school and then to the primary setting of the novel, Rugby, where Tom spends the next eight years. Located in a small, rural town, Rugby is a large, all-male public school run by Thomas Arnold, one of the great reformers in British educational history. Except for a brief reference to the urban parish work performed by the deceased clergyman father of one of Tom's classmates, George Arthur, Hughes ignores the political and economic ferment occurring at the time in England.

◆ Themes and Characters ◆

Written in part to inform Hughes's son about what lay ahead for him in school and in life, *Tom Brown's Schooldays* focuses on the theme of what it means to be a mature English citizen. Hughes, a devout Anglican, sees maturity resting ultimately on the individual's acceptance of the sovereignty of God as evidenced in the life and teaching of Jesus Christ. But Hughes does not associate Christian maturity with self-denial but rather with active involvement in life and all that it has to offer. For Hughes the ideal man is physically robust, intellectually alert, socially aware, and morally forgiving.

Hughes develops his theme primarily through Tom Brown, the novel's protagonist. Initially Hughes emphasizes the physical side of Tom's personality—he loves to play games, take jaunts, and make mischief. Academically, Tom does only what he has to do to pass his courses. Tom is joined in his endeavors by young Harry East, and the boys persist in neglecting their studies and stirring up trouble to the extent that the headmaster, Dr. Arnold, fears for their futures at the school. To deflect Brown and East from the potentially self-destructive course they are following, Arnold pairs off Tom with a new boy, the shy, physically weak, but brilliant George Arthur. Tom protects George from the school bullies, helps him make friends, and introduces him to sports. George, in turn, makes Tom and Harry aware of the satisfactions that can come from intellectual work and religious faith.

Hughes depicts an array of schoolboy characters—including the scientifically precocious Diggs and Martin, the leader Brooke, and the ultimate bully, Flashman—to illustrate different forms of human nature and different degrees of maturation. In addition, Hughes provides a fascinating gallery of supporting characters: the ancient Benjy who takes the young Tom fishing and to fairs, the coachman who talks endlessly on Tom's first trip to Rugby, and the farmers and gamekeepers who chase the schoolboys from off-limits swimming holes and chicken coops. Except for Dr. Arnold and one young master, the teachers at the school go unrecognized. The bulk of the learning that Hughes considers most important takes place outside the classroom, on the playing fields or in the surrounding countryside.

◆ Literary Qualities ◆

Except for his occasional use of authorial intrusions in order to ensure that readers grasp the moral point of certain episodes, Hughes propels *Tom Brown's Schooldays* along quickly with a straightforward, action-packed narrative. The book is not deeply analytical, and character development hinges on the events of the plot. Hughes's characters speak in a highly colloquial dialect, leading some critics to argue that the novel contains so much slang that reader comprehension suffers.

Perhaps Hughes's greatest achievement in *Tom Brown's Schooldays* is the vividness and timelessness of his schoolboy portraits. Tom and his friends engage in the same activities enjoyed by modern adolescents. Never the creations of an idealistic do-gooder, they learn about what helps or prevents an individual's reaching maturity as they progress through their schooldays.

Despite the excitement and humor of the narrative, Hughes's tone is serious. The boys are moving through a time that is bringing about great change for them, their circle of friends, and the society they inhabit. Although he seldom refers directly to political or social currents in mid-nineteenth-century Britain, Hughes nonetheless draws implicit parallels between the turbulence of his characters' adolescence and the havoc wreaked upon Victorian England by the Industrial Revolution. The boys gradually face the reality that their schooling has to end and that they must begin careers and assume responsibility for their lives. As each boy develops his own personality and interests, Hughes

depicts the character's relationships with peers and adults changing in believable ways. It is this literary re-creation of youth that continues to capture present-day readers.

◆ Social Sensitivity ◆

Tom Brown's School Days is a novel about upper-class boys developing into upper-class men. Women exist only on the periphery of the novel, mostly in the role of mothers and servants; young women are not mentioned. Because of this deliberate oversight, Hughes ignores a major part of the maturation process for most males: their relationships with females. More important, the female characters who are included in the story function only in relation to the men they nurture or serve. Hughes never portrays the women in the story as individual, fully developed characters. Thus, although Hughes viewed himself as a champion of social reform, his seemingly exclusive concentration on male issues—manifested in his advocacy of "muscular theology," his devotion to men's colleges and cooperatives, and his creation of books for and about boys—reveals his entrenched Victorian sexism. Moreover, despite his professed desire to improve the lot of all social classes, and despite his belief in human equality in the eyes of God, Hughes never questions the class system that permeates Rugby, the British public school system, and British society in general. Hughes and the boys he describes assume that their upper-class position is assured, and there is no indication in the novel that Tom Brown or his peers see anything wrong with the children of the poor being excluded from Rugby. The very popularity of *Tom Brown's Schooldays* has helped perpetuate boarding schools as bastions of social privilege in British society and in American society as well. The book also contains statements and terms that will offend modern readers because of the racist and colonialist attitudes reflected toward blacks and Asians.

♦ Topics for Discussion ♦

1. What social value does Hughes see in the village feast days? Has the importance of these days changed at all over the years?

2. Why does Hughes describe in such detail the history of the Brown family and the Vale of the White Horse? How would you explain the role of the Brown family in the social system of the vale? What features of this contained social system serve to diminish class differences?

3. What sorts of activities does Hughes consider appropriate for boys and young men? For girls and young women? Cite evidence from the book to support your answers. How might his views put him in conflict with modern critics?

4. Squire Brown debates at length over what advice he should give his son upon the boy's departure for Rugby. Do you think the squire offers Tom valid advice? Why or why not?

5. The maturation process is dramatized through various symbolic events in *Tom Brown's Schooldays*. What are some of the symbols Hughes uses? Do you think these symbols would be appropriate for a treatment of maturation in contemporary American society? If yes, why? If no, what symbols would you substitute?

6. Tom Brown's first days at Rugby are marked by dramatic events involving sports. How do the sports Hughes describes resemble or differ from modern athletics? What value does Tom's society place on athletics?

7. Little is said in the novel about the academic curriculum at Rugby, but much is said about the development of character. What sort of student does Tom's headmaster, Dr. Arnold, hope to nurture? Do you see any flaws in the concept of "character" as defined by Dr. Arnold?

8. The arrival of George Arthur changes the tone of the novel. In what ways does George mold Tom's attitudes and conduct?

9. Hughes's religious beliefs receive their fullest explanation in the summary of the life of George Arthur's father. What characterizes Mr. Arthur's faith and conduct?

10. In the chapter "The Fight," Hughes writes, "From the cradle to the grave, fighting, rightly understood, is the business, the real, highest, honestest business of every son of man." What does he mean? Do you agree?

11. Why does Hughes include a final chapter dealing with Tom's response to the death of Thomas Arnold? Would the book be better or worse if this chapter were omitted? Why?

♦ Ideas for Reports and Papers ♦

1. *Tom Brown's Schooldays* draws frequently on an academic, schoolboy, and sports vocabulary that may be un-

familiar to modern readers. Using the *Oxford English Dictionary* or other appropriate sources, develop a glossary of unfamiliar terms. Do you think that the inclusion of these terms stregthens or weakens the novel?

2. *Tom Brown's Schooldays* is the first of many so-called "prep school novels." The most famous American examples are J. D. Salinger's *Catcher in the Rye* and John Knowles's *Separate Peace.* Read one of these works and compare it to Hughes's novel.

3. Hughes wrote a sequel to *Tom Brown's Schooldays* called *Tom Brown at Oxford.* Read it and compare the two works. Which do you find more interesting? Why? Are Hughes's views consistent in the two books?

4. Hughes believed that team sports such as Rugby football and cricket were superior to individual sports such as running because team sports encouraged cooperation. Investigate the history of scholastic sports in nineteenth-century America.

5. Thomas Hughes was an advocate of Christian Socialism and the cooperative movement. Research and report on these movements. How do the philosophies that guided these movements resemble the principles Hughes outlines in *Tom Brown's Schooldays?*

6. Several film versions of *Tom Brown's Schooldays* have been made over the past five decades. Some are available on videotape. Find one or more of these film versions and compare the film director's handling with Hughes's work.

7. Research and report on British boarding schools for girls during the Victorian era. How did these schools differ from schools for boys?

◆ Related Titles ◆

The bulk of Hughes's writing addressed economic and political issues, but in 1861 he wrote a sequel to *Tom Brown's Schooldays* called *Tom Brown at Oxford.* The sequel gives a picture of life at a British university where sports and parties seem to overwhelm academic studies. The novel focuses on Tom's efforts to sort out his priorities.

Two notable motion-picture versions of *Tom Brown's Schooldays* were released in 1940 and 1951. The first of these was produced by David O. Selznick in America, but directed by an Englishman, Robert Stevenson. This movie reflects an Englishman's concerns about World War II and consequently emphasizes Tom's victory over Flashman as an example of right triumphing over might. Directed by Gordon Parry, the 1951 movie emphasizes period authenticity and Tom's school life, although Flashman remains a cruel antagonist. Of the two, the latter film better captures the mood of the novel and is likelier to interest the general audience.

◆ For Further Reference ◆

Cordery, Gareth. "*Tom Brown's Schooldays* and *Foreskin's Lament*: The Alpha and Omega of Rugby Football." *Journal of Popular Culture* 19 (Fall 1985): 97-104. A critical study of how the ethos of sports as presented in *Tom Brown's Schooldays* has permeated New Zealand society as depicted in *Foreskin's Lament*, a play.

Tom Brown's Schooldays

Gathorn-Hardy, Jonathan. *The Old School Tie.* New York: Viking Press, 1977. This comprehensive history of British public schools traces their evolution from the Middle Ages. Of special interest is chapter 4.

Mack, Ernest C., and W. H. G. Armytage. *Thomas Hughes: The Life of the Author of "Tom Brown's Schooldays."* London: Ernest Brown, 1952. A full overview of the life of Hughes. Chapter 6 deals with the writing and publication of the novel.

McLachlan, James. *American Boarding Schools.* New York: Charles Scribner's Sons, 1970. In this historical study of the emergence of American boarding schools in the nineteenth century, McLachlan shows the influence exerted by Hughes and Arnold on Americans attempting to establish schools comparable to Rugby.

Lawrence B. Fuller
Bloomsburg University

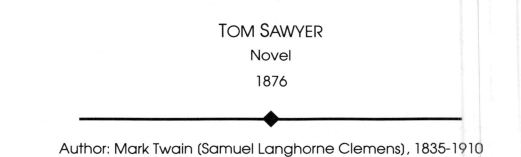

TOM SAWYER
Novel
1876

Author: Mark Twain (Samuel Langhorne Clemens), 1835-1910

Major Books for Young Adults

The Adventures of Tom Sawyer, 1876
The Prince and the Pauper, 1882
Life on the Mississippi, 1883
Huckleberry Finn, 1884
A Connecticut Yankee in King Arthur's Court, 1889

◆ About the Author ◆

Mark Twain's life is important to his writing, for his major works rely upon materials from his Hannibal, Missouri, boyhood and his careers as a Mississippi River pilot, a western miner, and a journalist.

Four years following his birth on November 30, 1835, in Florida, Missouri, Twain moved with his family to Hannibal, where he was shaped by experiences that would be transformed into such works as *Tom Sawyer* and *Huckleberry Finn*. When Twain was eleven his father died. Apprenticed as a printer, he began to contribute sketches to his brother's newspaper. As a young man he worked as a printer and journalist in a number of cities, including New York, but returned to the Mississippi River in 1857 to fulfill a childhood dream of becoming a river pilot. He held this job until 1861 when river traffic was halted by the Civil War.

After serving very briefly with the Missouri militia, he traveled to the Nevada Territory with his brother Orion, who had been appointed secretary to the governor. In Nevada he worked as a journalist and as a prospector for silver and gold. By 1864 he was a reporter in San Francisco, and in 1865 he published "The Celebrated Jumping Frog of Calaveras County" in a New York newspaper. Reprinted widely, the story gave him his first literary fame when it was reissued two years later. He delivered his first lecture in 1866, beginning a forty-year career as a performer whose public image became as famous as his books.

As a California correspondent, he traveled to Hawaii, then known as the Sandwich Islands, and later to Europe, the Mediterranean, and Palestine. His 1867 foreign travels became the basis of his first book, *Innocents Abroad* (1869). While enjoying the popular success of his writing, Twain settled in the East. In 1870 he married Olivia Langdon, daughter of a wealthy merchant from Elmira, New York, and became editor and part owner of a Buffalo newspaper.

A year later, he moved to Hartford, Connecticut, where he spent a large portion of his increasing income on a spectacular mansion (now restored as a memorial) on Farmington Avenue.

Twain's prolific writing career stemmed partly from the financial demands of his expensive life style. He turned to a variety of sources for his material: travel, his early life, and history. In 1872 he published *Roughing It*, a collection of irreverent sketches based upon his travels and his western experiences. While *The Gilded Age* (1873), written with Charles Dudley Warner, employed contemporary issues and provided a label for an era, *Tom Sawyer* made use of his Hannibal boyhood. *A Tramp Abroad* (1880) was another travel book, and *The Prince and the Pauper*, a historical comedy. *Life on the Mississippi* recounted the author's pilot days, and *Huckleberry Finn*, by most estimates his greatest work, was a sequel to *Tom Sawyer*.

By the time he produced his historical fantasy *A Connecticut Yankee in King Arthur's Court*, Twain had finished his most important work. The 1890s brought him great personal misfortune with a financial collapse resulting from his unprofitable investment in a typesetting machine and the bankruptcy of the publishing company he had founded to distribute his works. In 1896, while he was making a worldwide lecture tour to pay his debts, his daughter Susy died of meningitis in Hartford. Susy's death, like that of his first child and only son, Langdon, in 1872, devastated Twain, and the family never again resided in the Hartford house.

After *Following the Equator* (1897), another travel book, Twain worked on a variety of projects, many of which were published after his death. These works, most of which were overwhelmingly pessimistic, included "The Man that Corrupted Hadleyburg" (1900), "What Is Man?" (1906), and "The Mysterious Stranger" (1916). His final years were marked by increasing infirmity and unhappiness as he endured the deaths of his wife in 1904 and his daughter Jean in 1909. Toward the end of his life, Twain lived in New York, and he died at "Stormfield," his estate in Redding, Connecticut, on April 21, 1910.

At the time of his death, Twain had achieved international celebrity and was perhaps the most famous American. Like many famous people, he created a public image that masked inner conflicts. A complex and brilliant man, he was more than a simple humorist; as a social critic, historian, philosopher, novelist, and popular entertainer, he continues to fascinate readers and biographers.

♦ Overview ♦

Tom Sawyer introduces several significant figures in American mythology, including the hero of *Huckleberry Finn*, one of the central works of American literature. Nonetheless, *Tom Sawyer* is not just a dress rehearsal for its more powerful sequel. Allowing for nineteenth-century conventions of language and sentimentality in literature for young adults, the novel retains vitality and humor in exploring questions of freedom and responsibility. Like *Huckleberry Finn*, the book presents limitation, alienation, and horror as elements profoundly affecting a small Missouri town's young people, whose minds are shaped as much by superstition, romantic fiction, and nightmare visions as by social convention. It also resembles *Huckleberry Finn* in showing a painful moral growth that demands the risk of one's own welfare to assist another, while at the same time treating the reader to outlandish humor, melodramatic action, and a happy ending.

The intent of the novel, Twain states, is to entertain "boys and girls" and to "pleasantly remind adults of what they once were themselves." In order to appeal to such a wide audience, Twain chooses a setting that permits both adventure and nostalgia. The story takes place in "the poor little shabby village of St. Petersburg," the fictional equivalent of Hannibal, the Mississippi River town where Twain spent his early years. In his preface the author dates the action at "thirty or forty years ago," between 1836 and 1846, the era of his own boyhood. Twain also notes that Huck Finn is "drawn from life," and Tom Sawyer is a lifelike, though composite, character based on a number of boys.

The setting supports the major action and themes of the work. Institutions such as the home, the school, and the church provide a social order that Tom disrupts with pranks. Jackson's Island, where the boys camp and pretend to be pirates, offers the freedom of nature. But both the town and nature have their dark sides: the cemetery where the boys witness Dr. Robinson's murder, the "haunted" house where Injun Joe hides out, and the cave where Tom and Becky are lost and Injun Joe dies. Tom affirms social order when he returns from the island because of homesickness and guilt. He apologizes to his aunt for pretending to have drowned, and in the courtroom, another symbol of social order, he assumes responsibility by telling the truth about Dr. Robinson's murder. Later he and Becky escape the menace of the cave to rejoin the society of the village.

◆ Themes and Characters ◆

Tom Sawyer is a trickster figure who challenges the rules of conventional society. He and his younger half-brother Sid are wards of their highly conventional Aunt Polly, and Tom engages in a variety of ruses to escape from the impositions of adult society, particularly work and school. Although Sid cleverly sees through Tom's antics, his aunt is more easily fooled. Secretly indulgent of Tom's faults, she nonetheless punishes him dutifully when she discovers his deceptions.

> *Tom gave up the brush with reluctance in his face, but alacrity in his heart.*

Tom lives in a world defined by the customs and values of boys. He defends his territory, testing newcomers in fights, and participates in ritual exchanges of valueless, even repugnant, goods such as the dead cat he acquires from Huck. Bored by the solemnity of church, he disrupts the service with a pinchbug and trades to get tickets meant to be earned by memorizing Scripture. Subject to childhood romance, he falls in love with Becky Thatcher, a judge's daughter. His attempts to gain her approval, along with his general desire to be the center of attention, inspire him to show off unabashedly. Ultimately, however, he

Illustration by Ted Lewin for *The Adventures of Tom Sawyer* by Mark Twain. Julian Messner/Simon & Schuster: New York (1982).

assumes a hero's role, first taking the blame when Becky accidentally damages the schoolmaster's anatomy book, then rescuing her from the cave.

Huckleberry Finn appears in this book as a secondary character. Like Tom, Huck has lost a parent; unlike Tom, he lives a homeless life, sleeping at an old slaughterhouse. Further removed from social convention, Huck shares Tom's enjoyment of pranks and sharp dealing while lacking Tom's regard for respectability. At the end of the novel Tom demands that Huck accept "civilization" in order to remain a member of his gang, which he governs according to rules he interprets from adventure books.

The boys' world is haunted by superstition and governed by biblical injunctions. When they visit the graveyard they fear ghosts and devils, but they encounter Injun Joe, Muff Potter, and Dr. Robinson robbing a grave. Joe plays the role of a melodramatic villain, killing the doctor and blaming the murder on the alcoholic Muff. Although ignorant enough of conventional Christian history to identify the first disciples as "David and Goliath," Tom and Huck are so conditioned by conventional morality that they expect Joe to be struck down by lightning for his lie. When he is not, the boys assume he has sold himself to the devil. Indeed, he is a demonic character seeking revenge against ordered society.

Tom and Huck run away with another boy, Joe Harper, to escape from the murder they have witnessed. They live in freedom on Jackson's Island, enjoying boyish adventures until conscience intrudes. Their imaginations governed both by books and standard morality, they want to be pirates without violating the biblical injunction against theft, and Tom feels guilty about the innocent Muff Potter's arrest. Presumed dead, the boys enjoy the center of the town's attention when they return for their own funeral. This return suggests a pattern of death and resurrection, retreat from society and reunion. Tom's return marks a greater sense of responsibility when, racked by conscience, he reveals what he knows of the murder.

Adventure now becomes a reality for the boys as they discover that Joe has hidden a fortune and is plotting revenge against the Widow Douglas. The treasure hunt and Tom's romance with Becky merge in a maze-like cave where Tom and Becky get lost and find Injun Joe hiding out with his stolen money. While Joe dies in the cave, sealed in by unwitting townspeople, Tom and Becky emerge to community recognition, and

Tom and Huck share in the treasure retrieved from the cave.

The book ends happily with a unified society freed of a menace. Huck finds a guardian in the Widow Douglas, whom he has saved from Joe, and Tom gains recognition for genuine heroism.

◆ Literary Qualities ◆

The mid-nineteenth century produced a number of books dealing with boys rebelling against conventional society, such as Thomas Bailey Aldrich's *Story of a Bad Boy* (1869). While Twain's book is a powerful and original addition to literature about young people, it retains some of the "literary" language of nineteenth-century fiction. Twain abandons these conventions in *Huckleberry Finn*, in which he permits the title character to tell the story.

The novel contains many qualities of the adventure story: villains menace the innocent, hide treasures in caves, and inhabit haunted houses; heroes rescue helpless victims, discover buried treasure, and gain recognition from the women they love and from their community. Twain also employs conventions of frontier literature, in which pranks disrupt the order of the church and school, and the ominous Native American seeks revenge.

◆ Social Sensitivity ◆

As in *Huckleberry Finn*, the characters in *Tom Sawyer* exhibit attitudes typical of the mid-nineteenth century, referring to black characters as "niggers," though not as frequently. The stereotypical villain, Injun Joe, derives from the frontier figure of the violent and vengeful Native American. These elements should be recognized both for their negative connotations and their historical significance. Twain's realistic representation of his characters' attitudes should not be mistaken for his own attitude. The controversy surrounding *Huckleberry Finn* has produced substantial evidence of Twain's integrity; he intended much of what he wrote to reveal the inconsistencies in his characters' beliefs.

◆ Topics for Discussion ◆

1. Twain prefaces the novel by stating that it is intended to "pleasantly remind adults of what they once were themselves," but much of the book deals with unpleasantness. Discuss the darker side of the book. How does Twain remind his readers of some of the fears and insecurities of growing up?

2. Twain is sometimes called a "realist" writer. Are Tom, Huck, and Becky accurate portraits of young people?

3. Discuss *Tom Sawyer* as an adventure book. Compare its plot with those of other books, films, or television shows in which young people are menaced by villains, search for treasure, and win community approval.

4. Does Tom change in the novel? Discuss ways in which he "grows up."

5. Discuss the setting of the book. How does each significant place help in telling the story? Are some places more memorable? Why? Read again the descriptions of the places you remember best. What details are significant?

6. Discuss Injun Joe. Is he a believable character? Why? Is he given any motivation for his actions? Is he extended any

sympathy? Compare him with villains in other stories.

◆ Ideas for Reports and Papers ◆

1. Tom Sawyer also appears in *Huckleberry Finn*. How does his character differ in the two books?

2. Twain claims that his portrait of Huckleberry Finn in this book is drawn from life. Investigate Twain's early life to see how he derived Huck and other elements of the story.

3. Compare the language of *Tom Sawyer* with that of its sequel. Choose a significant passage from each and compare vocabulary and tone. What differences occur as a result of Huck speaking for himself?

4. Compare *Tom Sawyer* to one of Twain's later works (other than *Huckleberry Finn*) in which Tom appears. Is the later story less effective? Why or why not?

5. Discuss Tom as a rebel. Which conventions of society does he accept? Which does he reject?

◆ Related Titles/Adaptations ◆

Huckleberry Finn, written as a sequel to this book, is usually judged to be a more profound and powerful work. Both pieces hold central positions in American literature.

Tom Sawyer and Huckleberry Finn continued to fascinate Twain, and he used them in a number of other, generally ignored works such as *Tom Sawyer Abroad* (1894), a fantastic adventure in a balloon, and *Tom Sawyer,*

Detective (1896), in which Tom solves a murder mystery. These continuations of the boys' adventures offer little of literary merit or interest to the contemporary reader. Twain wrote a play based upon *Tom Sawyer*, and the novel has appeared in a number of dramatic versions, none of which achieved great distinction.

Three films, all titled *Tom Sawyer*, have been made from the novel: a slow-paced 1930 version directed by John Cromwell and starring Jackie Coogan, Mitzi Green, Junior Durkin, and Jackie Searle; a 1973 film musical with songs by Richard M. and Robert B. Sherman, directed by Don Taylor, and starring Johnnie Whitaker, Celeste Holm, Warren Oates, Jeff East, and Jodie Foster; and a 1973 made-for-television movie directed by James Neilson and starring Josh Albee, Jeff Tyler, Jane Wyatt, Buddy Ebsen, and Vic Morrow. The book has become an American classic and continues to be reworked by illustrators and television animators.

◆ For Further Reference ◆

Anderson, Frederick, ed. *Mark Twain: The Critical Heritage*. New York: Barnes & Noble, 1971. This general collection of criticism of Twain's writing traces critics' views from the first publication of Twain's novels to recent times.

Blair, Walter, ed. *Mark Twain's Hannibal, Huck and Tom*. Berkeley: University of California Press, 1969. A collection of other works, most fragmentary, in which Twain uses materials from the Hannibal background.

Because none of these possess any great merit, they are interesting to contrast with his greater works.

Bray, Robert. "Tom Sawyer Once and For All." *Review* 3 (1981): 77-83. A review of interpretations of Tom's character.

Ferguson, DeLancey. *Mark Twain: Man and Legend.* Indianapolis: Bobbs-Merrill, 1943. A reliable, balanced, and readable biography.

Fetterley, Judith. "Disenchantment: Tom Sawyer in *Huckleberry Finn.*" *PMLA* 87 (January 1972): 69-74. A study of the change in Tom's character from *Tom Sawyer* to *Huckleberry Finn.* Conveniently reprinted in the Norton Critical Edition of *The Adventures of Huckleberry Finn*, edited by Sculley Bradley, et al. (2d ed. New York: W. W. Norton, 1977).

Hill, Hamlin. *Mark Twain: God's Fool.* New York: Harper and Row, 1973. A portrait of Twain's unhappy final years.

Kaplan, Justin. *Mr. Clemens and Mark Twain.* New York: Simon and Schuster, 1966. A controversial, though effective, biography stressing the duality in Twain's character.

Lauber, John. *The Making of Mark Twain.* New York: American Heritage, 1985. A fine short treatment of the experiences up to 1870 that shaped Twain as a writer.

Paine, Albert Bigelow. *Mark Twain: A Biography.* New York: Harper, 1912. A two-volume biography by the man Twain chose to write his life. Still a major resource.

Regan, Robert. *Unpromising Heroes: Mark Twain and His Characters.* Berkeley: University of California Press, 1966. Useful discussions of Tom and Huck.

Stone, Albert E., Jr. *The Innocent Eye: Childhood in Mark Twain's Imagination.* New Haven: Yale University Press, 1961. Examines the role of childhood in Twain's vision and treats the conventions of boys' books.

Wecter, Dixon. *Sam Clemens of Hannibal.* Boston: Houghton Mifflin, 1952. An insightful treatment of Twain's early life.

Henry J. Lindborg
Marian College of Fond du Lac

TRAITOR: THE CASE OF BENEDICT ARNOLD
Biographical Novel
1981

◆

Author: Jean Fritz, b. 1915

Major Books for Young Adults

The Cabin Faced West, 1958
Brady, 1960
San Francisco, 1962
I, Adam, 1963
Early Thunder, 1967
George Washington's Breakfast, 1969
Cast for a Revolution: Some American Friends and Enemies, 1728-1814, 1972

Stonewall, 1979
Traitor: The Case of Benedict Arnold, 1981
Homesick: My Own Story, 1982
The Double Life of Pocahontas, 1983
China Homecoming, 1985
Make Way for Sam Houston!, 1986
China's Long March: 6,000 Miles of Danger, 1988

◆ About the Author ◆

Jean Guttery Fritz was born on November 16, 1915, in Hankow, China, where her father, Arthur M. Guttery, was a minister and a missionary, working for the Young Men's Christian Association (YMCA). She spent over a decade in the Far East before returning to the United States, where she was educated at Wheaton College in Norton, Massachusetts. After college, Fritz worked for a time as a research assistant for the Silver Burdett Company in New York City. She worked briefly as a librarian in Dobbs Ferry, New York, in the mid-1950s.

Fritz began writing fiction early in life, but it was not until 1954 that she published her first novel, Fish Head. She quickly established her reputation as an excellent writer of books for young adults. Her specialty is historical biography, and she combines meticulous historical research with a lively style appropriate for young audiences, making figures from the past come to life in her well-paced narratives.

Fritz's work has been recognized by several educational and literary associations, including the Pennsylvania School Library Association and the Washington (D.C.) Children's Book Guild. Homesick, Fritz's autobiography, received the Christopher Award, the National Book Award, a Newbery Honor Book citation, and a Boston Globe-Horn Book Honor Book citation. Stonewall was named a Boston Globe-Horn Book Honor Book in 1979, and Traitor: The Case of Benedict Arnold as a National Book Award finalist in 1982. Washington and Jefferson College awarded Fritz an honorary doctorate in 1982.

Jacket illustration by Alan E. Cober for *Traitor: The Case of Benedict Arnold* by Jean Fritz. G. P. Putnam's Sons: New York (1981).

Fritz was awarded the Children's Book Guild Non-Fiction Award for "total body of creative writing" in 1978.

◆ Overview ◆

Fritz's account of the life of the Revolutionary War general Benedict Arnold presents a difficult subject objectively yet with great sympathy. Long the subject of disdain and criticism from patriotic Americans who know him as the man who made a failed attempt to turn West Point over to the British, Arnold is shown to be a man driven by a

need to succeed and to be recognized for his accomplishments. Fritz reviews the facts of Arnold's life with care, showing how the events of his childhood and turbulent teen-age years had lasting influence on the man whom George Washington once considered the finest soldier in the Continental Army. Her account also provides some insight into the lives of the men and women forced to choose between submitting to an increasingly oppressive regime of colonial government administered from across the ocean, or taking the drastic step of declaring independence from their legitimate, if ill-willed, ruler, King George III.

◆ Setting ◆

The events of *Traitor* span the years of Benedict Arnold's life, 1741-1801, centering on the 1760s, 1770s, and 1780s. Fritz begins with Arnold's early life in Norwich, Connecticut, and traces his career as a soldier in New England and Pennsylvania. Her account of Arnold's campaign north through New York to Canada in an ill-fated attempt to capture the British-held city of Quebec provides vivid descriptions of both the foreboding surroundings and the hardships of the soldiers who accompanied Arnold on the expedition.

◆ Themes and Characters ◆

Fritz uses the story of Benedict Arnold's life to illustrate several important themes about human behavior. First, she demonstrates that, even in times of crisis, one's character determines one's actions; people are in control of their own destinies, rather than

Self-portrait by Major John André in *Traitor: The Case of Benedict Arnold* by Jean Fritz. G. P. Putnam's Sons: New York (1981).

being mere pawns swept up by events beyond their control. Arnold's life serves, too, as an example of what can happen when a person's ego prods him or her to seek selfish ends; the consequences of such action can lead to personal failure and to social and political disaster as well.

Fritz relies heavily on character development to present her themes. The focus of her study is Benedict Arnold himself. She plays up the dominant personality traits of the American general: his bravery, which at times leads him to the extremes of foolhardiness, and his driving need for success and recognition. In a sense, Arnold appears as an Achilles-figure: like the Greek warrior in Homer's *Iliad*, he is shown to sulk when lesser figures refuse to grant him what he believes is his due.

With great subtlety, Fritz illustrates how Arnold's childhood experiences lead him to become the hero and the egotist who is indispensable to the Continental Army yet considered reprehen-

sible by the army's governing body, the Continental Congress. The son of a successful but spendthrift merchant, Arnold devotes his life to amassing a fortune after facing poverty as a teenager when his father goes bankrupt. Arnold's obsession with riches, coupled with his insatiable desire for fame, makes him highly susceptible to the British general Sir William Howe's offer to sell out the American forces at West Point in exchange for a handsome reward and a commission in the British Army, where Arnold believes his prowess will be better appreciated.

Fritz also provides a vivid portrayal of Arnold's wife, Margaret "Peggy" Shippen. Peggy is a Philadelphia belle whose attentions are courted by the British occupying forces in the American capital and later by the Continental officers who take over the city when the British withdraw. Peggy's own need for attention and her penchant for material goods contribute to her husband's fateful decision to betray his country. Fritz paints Peggy as a willing helpmate who schemes with her husband to outwit the Americans and who suffers in her own right when Arnold's scheme is foiled.

Other historical personages are introduced as they interact with Arnold. One sees Arnold's brief encounters with such figures as Ethan Allen; members of the Continental Congress; and the British major John André, the go-between who is arrested and hanged as a spy when the plot fails and Arnold escapes. Fritz vividly captures Allen's personal magnetism (which Arnold despises) and André's suave mannerisms without detracting from her focus on Arnold.

◆ Literary Qualities ◆

Fritz is a captivating storyteller, and the major strength of *Traitor* is the fast-paced plot line. She carefully selects anecdotes that highlight character traits in Arnold and the other historical figures she portrays. Fritz also uses setting effectively, especially in contrasting the hardships of the upstate New York wilderness with the opulence of Philadelphia. These contrasts help build sympathy for Arnold, who can be seen at times as a man with just grievances.

Fritz does not search for symbols to lend her narrative larger significance. Instead, she uses the familiar image of money as an emblem of Arnold's grasping for material satisfaction. Although Fritz makes no direct connections between the two men, lurking in the background of this portrait of America's most famous turncoat is the image of the world's most renowned traitor, Judas Iscariot, the man who betrays Christ for thirty pieces of silver in the Bible.

◆ Social Sensitivity ◆

Fritz provides a delicate balance between sympathy and condemnation in her portrayal of one of the most vilified figures in American history. She acknowledges the facts of history: Arnold got off almost scot-free, even though his plot failed; he received a British pension that supported him for the rest of his life; and he never returned to America to stand trial for his crime. Nevertheless, Fritz clearly shows the destructiveness of his vanity, bitterness, greed, selfishness, and insatiable need for recognition and praise. With some care, Fritz shows that Arnold did have cause for anger but that his overreaction to apparent insult and his overweening pride led him to commit acts that can only be described as despicable.

◆ Topics for Discussion ◆

1. How do Arnold's daredevil actions as a young boy relate to his behavior later in life?

2. Is it wrong for the Continental Congress to deny Arnold the promotion he feels he deserves? Does Arnold act responsibly when he learns of the decision?

3. Arnold believes that by turning traitor he can shorten the war, thereby becoming a hero of a different sort. What events lead Arnold to think this way? Where is he wrong in his reasoning?

4. Arnold joins the Continental Army of his own free will, and as a result his business suffers. He makes up his losses, however, by skimming funds from the money he receives from the

Continental Congress. How do you feel about his actions?

5. What kind of future would Arnold have had if he had been promoted? How might that have influenced the war and the formation of the Union following the conflict?

6. If the British had won the war, would Arnold have become the hero he wanted to be?

◆ Ideas for Reports and Papers ◆

1. Critics of Fritz's historical biographies contend that Fritz illustrates common human characteristics that can be seen in men and women of any period. What are some of the characteristics of Benedict Arnold that appear to be "timeless"?

2. In *Traitor*, Fritz defines two different types of heroes: the brave, dashing military hero that Arnold becomes during the war, and the rather different kind of hero he hopes to become after the war. How do these two types differ? Is one better than the other? What do these two definitions say about society in general?

3. Fritz begins her book by focusing on Arnold as a small boy, who lacks confidence and feels unimportant. Trace the change in Arnold from an obscure youth to the most infamous traitor in American history, showing how specific incidents bring out character traits.

4. Technically, the Americans who rebelled against the British were traitors. Discuss the differences between Arnold's betrayal of the American revolutionaries and the colonists' betrayal of the British government.

5. Jean Fritz has written many biographical novels for young adults. Select one other work and compare her style, format, methods of characterization, and themes to those found in *Traitor*.

◆ For Further Reference ◆

Ammon, Richard. "Profile: Jean Fritz." *Language Arts* 60 (March 1983): 365-369. An overview of Fritz's life and work, concentrating primarily on the series of brief biographies of the founding fathers and *Homesick.*

Fritz, Jean. "Acceptance Speech: Regina Medal Recipient." *Catholic Library World* 52 (July/August 1985): 21-25. Provides information about Fritz's writing process.

Laurence W. Mazzeno
Mesa State College

Ann Kelly
U.S. Naval Academy

A TREE GROWS IN BROOKLYN
Novel
1943

◆

Author: Betty Smith, 1896-1972

Major Books for Young Adults

A Tree Grows in Brooklyn, 1943
Tomorrow Will Be Better, 1948
Maggie-Now, 1958
Joy in the Morning, 1963

◆ About the Author ◆

Elisabeth (Betty) Smith was born in Brooklyn, New York, on December 15, 1896, to a family of German immigrants. Smith's father, John Wehner, died when she was still a child, and her mother, Catherine Hummel Wehner, later married an Irish immigrant, Michael Keogh. Smith's early life was shaped by poverty, and the immigrant experience she describes in many of her works has strong roots in her own life. She left school after the eighth grade to help support her family, working in factories, offices, and department stores. Smith loved stories and derived her greatest pleasure from reading books or acting in plays at the Williamsburg YMCA.

In 1924 she married George Smith and with him later moved to Michigan, where she studied literature and he studied law at the University of Michigan. Upon completion of her husband's law degree, Smith moved with him and their two daughters first to New Haven, Connecticut, where Smith studied at the Yale School of Drama, and later to Detroit, where she worked as a columnist for the *Detroit Free Press*.

After the marriage ended in divorce in 1938, Smith moved to Chapel Hill, North Carolina, where she studied drama rooted in folk culture. Smith was inspired to write *A Tree Grows in Brooklyn*—a fictionalized reminiscence of her early years in Brooklyn—by her examination of this regional type of drama and her exposure to the autobiographical novels of North Carolina native Thomas Wolfe. Published in 1943, the novel was an instant best seller that eventually was translated into twenty languages and sold more than six million copies.

The book's great popularity transformed Smith into an instant celebrity, wealthy enough to live off her writing. She continued to write plays but is best known for her four novels, three of which deal with her Brooklyn childhood and adolescence. In 1943 Smith married Joseph Jones, a newspaperman, but in 1951 this marriage, too, ended in divorce. The late 1940s and early 1950s

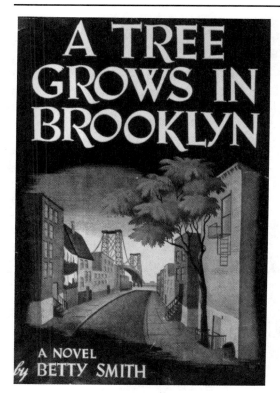

Jacket for *A Tree Grows in Brooklyn* by Betty Smith. Everybody's Vacation Publishing Company/Literary Guide of America: New York (1943).

she admired, Smith's writing is seldom pessimistic. She recognized the reality of grinding poverty, but her heroines are able to break free of the trap of poverty and limited education just as their author did.

<h2 style="text-align:center">◆ Overview ◆</h2>

Americans during World War II found *A Tree Grows in Brooklyn* inspiring. Set in a pre-war Brooklyn neighborhood populated largely by immigrants, the book held a nostalgic appeal for its first readers, reminding many of a battle over poverty already won. Others, especially the novel's first reviewers, savored *A Tree Grows in Brooklyn* as a respite from the often gloomy novels of other naturalistic writers such as Theodore Dreiser and James T. Farrell. Readers today might see the novel as a precursor of more recent young adult novels about sensitive young protagonists who face the conflicts and the delights of growing up. The book renders a vivid portrait of early twentieth-century life in Brooklyn: Francie cannot afford expensive pleasures but derives joy nonetheless from visiting the junk dealer, reading in the library, shopping for ground beef and soup bones, and walking more than forty blocks to school. Like Daniel Defoe's classic novel *Robinson Crusoe,* Smith's book offers a guide to survival skills, but in *A Tree Grows in Brooklyn* the skills are targeted for the streets of Brooklyn rather than the wilds of a tropical island.

were a difficult time for Smith; in addition to suffering the breakup of her second marriage, she incurred injuries in an automobile accident in 1952. Her two novels written during this time, *Tomorrow Will Be Better* and *Maggie-Now,* are less optimistic than *A Tree Grows in Brooklyn.*

A third marriage, to Robert Finch, seems to have been happy but ended with his death in 1959. Smith's final years were active ones; she acted, taught college, and produced numerous plays, another novel, and two volumes of autobiographical writings before her death on January 17, 1972. Unlike the work of the many naturalistic writers

<h2 style="text-align:center">◆ Setting ◆</h2>

A Tree Grows in Brooklyn is set in Brooklyn's immigrant neighborhoods. The novel opens in the summer of 1912

with eleven-year-old Francie Nolan sitting on the fire escape and looking at a Tree of Heaven in her backyard; it then moves back in time twelve years to the courtship of Francie's parents. The novel proceeds chronologically from this point onward, tracing the lives of Francie; her brother, Neeley; and their parents, friends, and relatives. The sights, smells, and sounds of Brooklyn street life permeate the novel, influencing Francie's moods and helping form her character during the nearly seventeen years covered in the story.

Francie's mother, Katie, a cleaning woman, tries to better her family's impoverished situation. She attempts to provide an education for her children with piano lessons and nightly readings of Shakespeare and the Bible, and even tries saving money to buy a home as her mother, Mary Rommely, advises her. Johnny's death does not break Katie's spirit, and five months after he dies she gives birth to a daughter, Laurie. At the end of the novel Katie plans to wed a wealthy, older policeman, Michael McShane. The marriage promises to yield both happiness for Katie and financial security for her family.

◆ Themes and Characters ◆

The most significant character in *A Tree Grows in Brooklyn* is Francie Nolan. A lonely child, Francie avoids close companionship with her peers. Although she is a talented writer and an excellent student, Francie drops out of school at age fourteen to earn money for her family. She later picks up credits in summer school and eventually passes a college entrance exam; she gradually opens up and forms closer relationships with people her own age through her work and her studies.

Johnny Nolan, Francie's father, dies at age thirty-four from alcoholism. A singing waiter by trade, Johnny has a dreamy sensibility that makes him a failure in the working world but a hero in the eyes of his children. Francie's younger brother Neeley, her sidekick in early childhood, comes to bear a striking physical resemblance to their dead father as he nears manhood. Johnny's romantic vision of Francie and Neeley allows them to imagine themselves as more than they are; his tragic example encourages them to achieve more than he ever could.

There's a tree that grows in Brooklyn. Some people call it the Tree of Heaven. No matter where its seed falls, it makes a tree which struggles to reach the sky...

Smith's book is populated by admirable female characters. Katie is depicted as the stronger partner in her marriage, and Francie as a better student than her brother. Katie's two sisters, Sissy and Evy, both serve as role models of sorts for Francie. Aunt Sissy has more street smarts than either Katie or Johnny. She deals effectively with the police, teachers who bully Francie, and a succession of lovers and "husbands." Aunt Evy, nowhere near as

A Tree Grows in Brooklyn

dramatic or amusing a figure as Sissy, is noteworthy in Francie's mind for taking over her husband's job successfully.

Several of Francie's teachers and a librarian also affect her development. The visiting music teacher, Mr. Morton, brings music into the lives of Francie and his other students, dubbing Dvorak's *New World Symphony* "Going Home," and teaching, with enthusiasm and delight, serious music to students unaware of the difficulty of what they are learning. Miss Bernstone, an inspiring art teacher who thinks best with charcoal or chalk in her hands, is similarly liberating.

In contrast to these teachers stands Miss Gardner, who dismisses Francie's writing as sordid, objecting to the absence of beauty in her descriptions of "poverty, starvation, and drunkenness." Asked by Francie to define beauty, Miss Gardner responds with a quote from the poet John Keats: "Beauty is truth, truth beauty," to which Francie replies, "those stories are the truth." Miss Gardner refuses to submit to Francie's reasoning, and Francie, in turn, refuses to turn in English assignments for the rest of the year. This conflict points up Smith's own conviction that naturalistic writing can reveal the truth without necessarily being sordid; Francie is angriest when she looks up "sordid" and finds that the dictionary defines the word as meaning "filthy," an adjective that hardly seems relevant to her description of her late father "wearing a fresh dickey and collar every day of his life and shining his worn shoes as often as twice a day." Francie knows that although truth is not always beauty, no falsehood can create beauty where there is none, and that, more important, beauty is neither the only nor the best standard by which to judge the value of life.

Lee Rhynor and Ben Blake both contribute to Francie's later growth and maturity. Lee cynically uses Francie, proposing marriage to her and then marrying another. He manipulates her, and although he ultimately does not get what he wants from Francie—a sexual commitment—he hurts her nonetheless. Francie's relationship with Ben lacks the passion that characterizes her relationship with Lee. She admires his success and compassion, but Ben does not allow himself to translate his need for Francie into sexual desire; he will not allow either himself or Francie to recognize his love and thus stifles his passion by denying it.

◆ Literary Qualities ◆

Smith uses a third-person omniscient narrator to relate her story. Thus, although Francie is the book's central character, Smith develops other characters, even the minor ones, by means of occasional internal monologues. When, for example, ten-year-old Francie and nine-year-old Neeley venture forth to win a Christmas tree—a process that involves "catching" unsold trees that are flung at them; children who fall down forfeit their right to the trees—Smith reveals the thoughts of the "tree man": "Oh...why don't I just give 'em the tree, say Merry Christmas and let 'em go?" After deciding reluctantly that he cannot grant the Nolan children any special favors, he throws a huge tree at them, and when they hold their ground he yells "now get the hell out of here with your tree..." At this point Smith shifts to Francie's perspective and has her realize that "he was really saying, 'Goodbye—God bless you.' " Smith's choice of narrative technique allows her to express an adult's perspective on events at times and a child's at others, yielding a rounded portrait of life in the Nolans' Brooklyn neighborhood.

The American novelists Theodore Dreiser and Thomas Wolfe were among Betty Smith's favorite writers. The relationship of her work to that of Thomas Wolfe is strong. For both writers, reminiscence seems to elicit an elation that idealizes in the present what was mundane in the past, and both make use of loose narrative structures and heavily autobiographical source material. Smith's symbol of the tree dominates her novel in the same manner that Wolfe's Blue Ridge Mountains dominate his landscape in books such as *Look Homeward, Angel* and *Of Time and the River*. But whereas Wolfe's mountains enclose lives and trap characters, Smith's tree represents growth and hope. Smith's work also resembles that of Dreiser in that it attempts to portray the plight of the working poor in early twentieth-century urban environments. But whereas in Dreiser's work—such as his best-known novel, *Sister Carrie*—protagonists are often caught in a naturalistic trap of character and environment, the characters in Smith's fiction often succeed in breaking free of the bonds of poverty.

◆ Social Sensitivity ◆

A Tree Grows in Brooklyn remains popular because of its optimism, its feminism, and its philosophical ties to more recent novels for young readers. Women are the strong characters in this novel. Even Ben Blake, who helps Francie in her studies, is flawed, although he is a tower of strength in comparison to the novel's husbands and boyfriends. Women in *A Tree Grows in Brooklyn*

succeed not only in traditional feminine roles, but in stereotypically masculine roles as well.

In comparison to most present-day realistic books for young adults, *A Tree Grows in Brooklyn* is relatively tame in its depiction of the difficulties and dangers of urban life. Perhaps the most disturbing episode occurs midway through the book when Francie is accosted by a murderer who has been terrorizing the neighborhood. The marauder exposes himself to Francie and attempts to drag her away. Katie shoots and seriously wounds the man, and although Francie seems to escape the incident with no psychological scars, her brush with sexual molestation and possibly with death may upset young readers.

Although she portrays the Nolans as a Catholic family, Smith does not make the subject of religion a focus of her novel. Smith's intent is to portray the insularity of various ethnic groups within the Williamsburg section of Brooklyn, but some readers may be offended by the attitude toward other religious faiths displayed by some members of the Nolan family. The characters do not demonstrate outright prejudice towards Jews, but their offhand references to "Jew women" and "Jewtown" suggest a divide between cultures not easily surmounted. Overall, however, *A Tree Grows in Brooklyn* is a deeply affirmative book that suggests that hard work and strong family bonds can effectively counter the hardships of poverty.

◆ Topics for Discussion ◆

1. What is the meaning of the novel's title? How does the tree function as a symbol throughout the novel?

2. Who seems stronger in *A Tree Grows in Brooklyn*, the male or female characters? Cite examples from the book.

3. What connection could be made between Francie's early writing—including the stories that her teacher rejects—and Smith's work in *A Tree Grows in Brooklyn*?

4. Neither Lee Rhynor nor Ben Blake seems to be the type of man that Francie wants. What kind of man does she want?

5. Many girls and women are traumatized for years by a rape attempt. Who or what helps Francie recover from an attempted assault?

◆ Ideas for Reports and Papers ◆

1. Betty Smith has said that she began writing *A Tree Grows in Brooklyn* after she read Thomas Wolfe's *Of Time and the River*. Read this, Wolfe's second novel, and compare it to *A Tree Grows in Brooklyn*.

2. Look up a definition of naturalism in a good dictionary of literary terms. How is naturalism defined? Is *A Tree Grows in Brooklyn* naturalistic? Why or why not?

3. What are Johnny Nolan's strengths and weaknesses as a father? What do you like about him, and what do you dislike about him? Is he a good father?

4. Francie loves yet resents her mother, Katie, because Katie seems to love Neeley more. Is Neeley Katie's favorite child? Is Francie's response to her mother's wish for Francie to work and Neeley to go to high school justified? What enables Francie to become independent of her mother?

5. Katie's reasons for marrying Johnny Nolan differ greatly from her reasons for marrying Michael McShane. Assuming that Katie loved both men, what is the difference in that love?

◆ Related Titles/Adaptations ◆

A Tree Grows in Brooklyn began as a play entitled *Francie Nolan* and a short story, "Death of a Singing Waiter." Smith eventually transformed the works into novel form in 1943, but this was not to be the story's final incarnation. The novel was made into a musical co-authored by George Abbot in 1951, a radio series that began in 1947, and a very successful film produced by Twentieth Century-Fox in 1945 and directed by Elia Kazan. James Dunn won an Oscar for best supporting actor in his film role as Johnny Nolan. Also included in the film's fine cast were Peggy Ann Garner, Dorothy McGuire, and Lloyd Nolan. A 1974 film version of the novel was directed by Joseph Hardy and stars Cliff Robertson, Diane Baker, and James Olsen.

Readers desiring to find sequels to *A Tree Grows in Brooklyn* in Smith's later work will be frustrated. Both *Tomorrow Will Be Better* and *Maggie-Now* are less expansive and more reminiscent than *A Tree Grows in Brooklyn*, and the heroines of both books are more beaten than victorious. *Joy in the Morning*, a story of married love set at a midwestern university, is more in the optimistic spirit of *A Tree Grows in Brooklyn*.

◆ For Further Reference ◆

Brockmann, Charles B. "In the Shadow of the Tree." *Carolina Quarterly* 2 (1950): 41-46. Brockmann elaborates on the symbol of the tree in the novel.

Gelfant, Blanche Housman. *The American City Novel.* Norman: University of Oklahoma Press, 1954. Contains a brief description of the urban experience as depicted in *A Tree Grows in Brooklyn.*

Prescott, Orville. *In My Opinion.* Indianapolis: Bobbs-Merrill, 1952. Contains an analysis of *A Tree Grows in Brooklyn.* Prescott was probably the most enthusiastic and powerful of the critics examining the novel when it first came out. As many readers have done, Prescott focuses on Francie, the heroine, whose spirit and struggles he admires.

Trilling, Diana. "Fiction in Review: *A Tree Grows In Brooklyn.*" *Nation* 157 (September 4, 1943): 274. Trilling's is an extremely negative view of Smith's novel. Her criticism of Smith on naturalistic grounds is enlightening, however.

Ziegfeld, Richard, ed. *Dictionary of Literary Biography Yearbook,* 1982. Detroit: Gale Research, 1983. Harriet L. King's perceptive essay on Smith is the best overall treatment of the author's life and work.

Craig W. Barrow
University of Tennessee at Chattanooga

THE TRUMPETER OF KRAKOW
Novel

1928

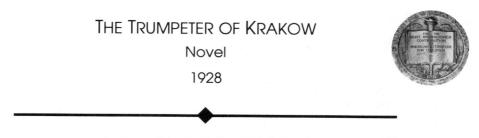

Author: Eric P. Kelly, 1884-1960

Major Books for Young Adults

The Trumpeter of Krakow, 1928
The Land of the Polish People, 1943, 1952

♦ About the Author ♦

Eric P. Kelly was born on March 16, 1884, in Amesbury, Massachusetts, attended his hometown high school and then Dartmouth College, from which he graduated in 1906. He then spent what he later described as "ten colorless, uneventful, and discouraging years" working for various Massachusetts newspapers. He also wrote short stories, two of which were finally published in 1916, ten years after his graduation from college.

By the end of World War I, in 1918, Kelly was in charge of the *Foyer de Soldat* (the French YMCA) at Quentin, France, where his duties included working with Polish soldiers in nearby regimental schools and supplying them with entertainment, athletics, and a canteen—a place they could relax, play cards, talk, and eat. Two years later, during the war between the Poles and Russian-backed Bolshevik forces determined to carry Russia's recent Communist Revolution into Poland (a war the Poles eventually won), Kelly was in Poland, serving in a traveling canteen near the front lines along the Bug River east of Warsaw. While there, he convinced the head chaplain of the Polish Army that the YMCA could do much good, and Kelly is credited with the organization's subsequent success in Poland.

In 1921, after the war, Kelly returned to Dartmouth College as an English instructor. He became a professor of journalism in 1929, and continue to teach until his retirement at age seventy, in 1954. During the 1920s, his interest in Poland continued to grow. In 1925-1926, he worked as a lecturer in American literature and institutions at the ancient University at Krakow in Poland. From that time on, as Kelly himself said, he exercised himself in every way he knew "to aid the cause of Poland in the modern world." He lectured on Poland in schools, colleges, and libraries from Maine to California. He wrote innumerable articles and books about the Poles and their history— many of them for young readers. The most famous of these, *The Trumpeter of*

Jacket illustration by Janina Domanska for *The Trumpeter of Krakow* by Eric P. Kelly. Macmillan: New York (1966).

Krakow, won the Newbery Medal in 1929.

During World War II, Kelly again contributed to the Polish cause by working through the U.S. State Department in Leon, Mexico, where he helped care for fifteen hundred Polish refugees. He was much honored for his work on Poland's behalf, receiving an honorary degree from the University of Krakow, the Polish Gold Cross of Merit, and the Pilsudski Medal. Kelly died on January 3, 1960.

◆ Overview ◆

The Trumpeter of Krakow plunges the reader directly into the exciting, turbulent, and darkly mysterious world of central Europe in the Middle Ages.

Poland was at the center of that world, and the Polish capital, Krakow, was at the center of Poland. *The Trumpeter of Krakow* is a fast-moving, adventure-packed story and, at the same time, a window into a world about which most people know relatively little.

◆ Setting ◆

Poland is the center of Eastern Europe in 1461-1462, the years in which the novel is set. In 1461, under King Kazimir IV, Poland embarked upon its Golden Age. United with Lithuania, the Polish kingdom stretches from the Baltic Sea in the north to the Black Sea in the south. The Germans along the Baltic, known as the Teutonic Knights, were defeated forty years earlier at the Battle of Tannenberg and are now sworn subjects of the Polish Crown. To the south, Polish control extends into Moldavia (the northeast portion of present-day Romania); to the east, the Poles and their Lithuanian allies control most of the Ukraine and present-day Byelorussia. The Tartars, who swept across the Ukraine and Poland a century before, have lost most of their power and are gradually retreating toward the area north of the Caspian Sea and central Asia. The Russian state, under Ivan the Great, is still limited to the small area around Moscow and has hardly begun the consolidation and expansion that will push its boundaries westward in the years to come.

As the center of this world, the Polish capital, Krakow, has become a vital crossroads for traders, bandits, scholars, German merchants, Cossack horsemen, and even renegade Tartars. Indeed, a half-Tartar, half-Cossack, known to some as Peter of the Button and to others as Bogdan the Terrible, is the book's chief villain.

The Trumpeter of Krakow takes place precisely at that moment when the medieval way of looking at the world is fading, and the early Renaissance way of thinking is making its way northeastward from Italy. It is the moment when medieval beliefs in a strictly ordered world threatened by dark mysteries is giving way to the new "humanism" of the early Renaissance. This new movement, sometimes called "Christian humanism," is a philosophy that sees not just scholars and church officials as capable of understanding the universe, but *every* individual as possessed of a God-given intelligence. Humanism is encouraging individuals to use this intelligence to make new discoveries, to explore new realms, and to cut through the dark shroud of medieval ignorance and superstition.

year-old son of Pan ("Master") Andrew Charnetski, a Polish landowner driven from the Ukraine by Tartar raiders. Joseph travels to Krakow, and through his eyes readers watch the broad sweep of medieval life; the crooked streets are filled with all levels of society—King's Guards, tradesmen, scholars and students, farmers, beggars, merchants, robbers, and ruffians. Through Joseph's eyes readers also see the magnificent monuments of Krakow—the Church of Our Lady Mary, the royal palace of King Kazimir Jagiello, the newly-built Clot Hall—as well as the narrow Pigeon Alley, bordered by three-story wooden buildings. Joseph's view also reveals the sinister activities of the night—the skulking cutthroats and thieves, the all-night student discussions and quarrels, the unruly mobs, the illegal duels, and, above all, the activities of the alchemists.

• Themes and Characters •

The Trumpeter of Krakow's guiding spirit, a scholar named Jan (pronounced "yon") Kanty, is a Christian humanist. Kanty represents a clearheaded, essentially optimistic and scientific view of life; he fights superstition, ignorance, mindless respect for authority, and the dangerous habits and fears such attitudes breed. A Renaissance scholar in the making, Kanty is a precursor of the famous Polish thinker Copernicus, whose assertion eighty years later that the sun, not the earth, is the center of the universe will radically change the way people see their world.

The novel presents these issues largely through the eyes of its central character, Joseph Charnetski, the fifteen-

...he wriggled beneath a dozen carts and past the flank of an outhouse near the church to take refuge behind a tree... Doubled up here, he waited until the watchman should pass...

Most of the novel's characters are moderately conventional: the brave father Pan Andrew; Joseph's dutiful mother; the wise and universally

Illustration by Janina Domanska for *The Trumpeter of Krakow* by Eric P. Kelly. Macmillan: New York (1966).

respected scholar Jan Kanty; the pretty and often-endangered Elzbietka, whom Joseph saves from a vicious dog and whom his family befriends; and the sneaking, duplicitous villain, Peter of the Button. As a character, the most interesting is probably Elzbietka's alchemist father, Pan Kreutz.

Pan Kreutz is a kind of Doctor Faustus, a scholar who is torn between using his knowledge of chemistry and physics to better understand the world and serve his fellow humans (the course Jan Kanty would have him follow), and using this knowledge to gain wealth and power. Just as Doctor Faustus is tempted by a devil, Mephistopheles, so Pan Kreutz is first tempted and then put under a hypnotic trance by the diabolical student Tring, who encourages Pan Kreutz in an increasingly crazed quest for the Philosopher's Stone, the magic stone that can turn baser metals to gold.

◆ Literary Qualities ◆

Kelly writes in an admirably clear, direct manner. His prose abounds with vivid physical description that provides a strong sense of the medieval world in which the novel is set. Particularly rich in this regard are some of the earlier chapters, rich panoramas filled with people and buildings as seen through Joseph's eyes. Kelly's characters speak a formal, slightly old-fashioned language, but this serves primarily as a reminder that this is a different world.

The Trumpeter of Krakow is a delightfully symmetrical book. It begins with a prologue that graphically tells the story of the famous historical "Trumpeter of Krakow," the young man who played the "Heynal" hymn hourly from the tower of the Church of Our Lady Mary during the Tartar invasion of 1241 and who broke off the song a few notes short of completion when struck by a fatal Tartar arrow. This prologue is balanced by an epilogue, which refers once more to the earlier trumpeter's heroism (a symbol of bravery against great odds throughout the book). This epilogue, written in 1926, when Poland was once again a free country for the first time in centuries, praises Poland's ability to survive oppression and stand as a model of national courage.

At the very center of the novel is chapter 7, "In the Alchemist's Loft," which draws into sharp focus the novel's major theme—the struggle between the enlightened use of knowledge for the good of humankind and the evil use of knowledge for the acquisition of power. It is in this chapter that the alchemist Kreutz finds himself caught between his basic belief in using his science for human good ("God has given me a mind that searches ever for the light, and I feel that I am doing His will when I seek the truths that lie about us on every hand") and his darker "other self" that is all too willing to listen to the diabolical Tring's hypnotic urgings ("Gold!...With this secret, you and I could become the very kings of the earth...armies would be at our disposal, and we could make every human being perform our will").

◆ Social Sensitivity ◆

On the surface, there is little material likely to offend anyone in *The Trumpeter of Krakow*. Kelly gracefully handles the unruly, potentially violent times he deals with; there are many moments of excitement and danger, but no killings or gratuitous violence. Kelly is a deeply moral writer; but for a book dealing with a highly religious people in a highly religious age, *The Trumpeter of Krakow* hardly mentions religion at all. Some readers might, with some justification,

find fault with the novel's primary female character, Elzbietka, who has been relegated to a passive role. But Elzbietka, like most of the novel's characters, is probably less important as a person than as part of a window through which a wonderfully vital and important age can be seen.

At a much deeper level, *The Trumpeter of Krakow* could be interpreted as a statement on issues that some people in the 1920s found controversial. In their attempts to better understand their times, many writers consulted the writings of Sigmund Freud, who was tremendously influential at the time. Kelly's own interest in the workings of the unconscious mind can be seen in his use of dreams (both Joseph and Elzbietka have powerful, almost surreal dreams in the course of the novel), his exploration of the unconscious mind (through Tring's manipulation of the alchemist Kreutz), and his consideration of the destructive effects hypnotic oppression can have on the human spirit (Kreutz is nearly destroyed by the end of the novel).

The 1920s also saw a renewed struggle between science and conventional religious dogma, a struggle highlighted by the Scopes trial of 1925, dealing with Charles Darwin's theories of evolution. Like many thinkers of his day, Kelly was obviously concerned both about the dangers of science run amok and about the dangers of religious closed-mindedness. His fictional scholar, Jan Kanty, at once a scientist and a morally responsible man, clearly represents the ideal middle position between science and religion—even though Kanty never talks explicitly about religion.

Kelly also addresses the disillusionment that World War I had brought regarding the humanist tradition. People in the 1920s wondered if there was any hope for humankind if human reason cannot control the darker human urges and the disastrous workings of progress gone awry. Kelly's answer is optimistic; he implicitly asserts that properly governed and given over to the service of others, human good will can prevail.

None of these issues—Freudian psychology, the struggle between science and religion, and humanism—is overtly dealt with in *The Trumpeter of Krakow*. But anyone who looks at the novel in connection with the times that produced it can see that such issues influenced its writing.

• Topics for Discussion •

1. What are the major encounters and events that influence Pan Kreutz's development, and what is the effect of each on his state of mind?

2. Compare Jan Kanty and Pan Kreutz (especially when Pan Kreutz is under Tring's influence). Does either man's philosophy prevail today?

3. Near the end of chapter 2 Joseph's mother says, "We will wait, for God is in the waiting." What does she mean by this?

4. Chapter 3 mentions that the book is set at a time "when children grew to be men and women often over a single night." What are the advantages and disadvantages of a world in which people are considered adults by the time they are fourteen or fifteen?

5. Are women given too small a role or is their limited importance justified by the times? Could you imagine a woman

as a hero in this world? Describe such a character.

6. In chapter 7, both Kreutz and Tring ask a number of questions. Has modern science answered them?

7. Tring is a great tempter. Where in the modern world are there temptations like those he offers to Kreutz? Is there anything in today's world that tends to "poison the mind" as Tring does?

8. What is the novel's climax or turning point?

9. In what ways does *The Trumpeter of Krakow* foreshadow or suggest explanations for the rise of totalitarian government that took over Europe during the 1930s, a decade after the book's publication?

• Ideas for Reports and Papers •

1. Research and report on the major national groups of the fifteenth century—Tartars, Poles, Cossacks, Teutonic Knights (Prussians)—that are mentioned in the novel.

2. Discounting modern medicine and conveniences made possible by modern science, compare life in Joseph's world to life in America today. Consider especially the fact that life in the crowded city forces Joseph to rub shoulders with all sorts of people. What are the advantages and disadvantages of this sort of close contact?

3. Study Copernicus, his discoveries, and his world. Is the world of the novel comparable to the world faced by Copernicus?

The Trumpeter of Krakow

4. Prepare a report on the history of astrology directed at isolating and listing the major astrological beliefs likely to have been current in 1461.

5. Research and prepare a report on alchemy, on medieval firefighting, or on medieval universities.

6. Learn something about Freud's and Jung's theories of the conscious and the unconscious and the meanings of dreams. To what extent do these theories accord with the view of the mind Tring seems to hold regarding Kreutz? There are several dreams described in the novel. How might a Freudian or Jungian explain them?

7. A struggle goes on within Pan Kreutz between two forces that might be called reason and unreason. Find examples of paintings from the 1920s—perhaps from the German expressionists and the surrealists—that reflect this same struggle between reason and unreason.

young people facing the difficulties of life in Poland during World War II.

Ernst Schoen-René
California State University, Chico

♦ For Further Reference ♦

Miller, Bertha M., and Elinor W. Field, eds. *Newbery Medal Books 1922-1955*. Boston: Horn Book 1955. Contains a brief autobiographical comment by Kelly on his work, followed by some reflections on his retirement. Also includes a kind of poetic tribute to Krakow and its lasting effect on the author, "The City that Sings."

Serraillier, Ian. *The Silver Sword*. 1956. Reprinted as *Escape from Warsaw*. New York: Scholastic, 1972. A well-known and much-praised account of

Eric P. Kelly

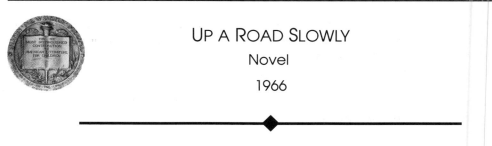

UP A ROAD SLOWLY
Novel
1966

Author: Irene Hunt, b. 1907

Major Books for Young Adults

Across Five Aprils, 1964
Up a Road Slowly, 1966
Trail of Apple Blossoms, 1968
No Promises in the Wind, 1970

The Lottery Rose, 1976
William, 1977
The Everlasting Hills, 1985

◆ About the Author ◆

Irene Hunt was born on May 18, 1907, in Newton, Illinois, the daughter of Franklin P. and Sarah Land Hunt. Educated in southern Illinois schools, she later obtained a bachelor's degree from the University of Illinois in 1939 and a master's degree from the University of Minnesota in 1946. From 1930 to 1945 Hunt taught French and English in the public schools of Oak Park, Illinois. After receiving her master's degree, she became an instructor in psychology at the University of South Dakota (1946-1950), and later served as a teacher (1950-1965) and then director of language arts (1965-1969) in the public schools of Cicero, Illinois. Since the mid-1960s, she has worked as a writer.

Hunt's writing career began with a much-praised historical novel about the Civil War period, *Across Five Aprils*. Her interest in historical fiction has continued in *Trail of Apple Blossoms*, a story of the American pioneer days, and in *No Promises in the Wind*, which details the times of the Great Depression. But the author will probably be most remembered for her honest and sensitive presentation of the maturing process of children—Julie Trelling of *Up a Road Slowly*, the runaway Grondowski brothers of *No Promises in the Wind*, and the battered George Burgess of *The Lottery Rose*.

Hunt's novels have all received critical acclaim, but perhaps the best-known is *Up a Road Slowly*, which received the Newbery Medal in 1967. *Across Five Aprils*, a close second in popularity, was sole runner-up for the 1965 Newbery Medal and received the 1964 Charles W. Follett Award and a 1965 American Notable Book designation. Hunt also received the Friends of Literature Award and the Charles W. Follett Award in 1971 for *No Promises in the Wind*. In 1974 she was a nominee for the Hans Christian Andersen Award, given for an author's overall contribution to literature for young people.

Up a Road Slowly is Julie Trelling's story, beginning when she is seven years old and her mother dies, and ending with her entrance into college at seventeen. Julie and each of the diverse members of her family must learn to adapt to life's sorrows through self-discipline and to derive pleasure from the simple joys of hard work, caring for others, and earning respect and love. Seven-year-old Julie feels abandoned on a very long and lonely road as she is forced to adjust to the loss of her mother and to the transition from a warm, enveloping home with her beloved older sister and father to a cold, stern living environment with a schoolteacher aunt in the country.

As Julie matures, she discovers that all people must walk their own equally lonely roads, many of which are beset with worse problems than her own. As Julie reflects upon the actions of adults and peers in her life, she begins to construct her own moral code based on the values of education, diligence, temperance, and compassion. *Up a Road Slowly* unites a fascinating story with a subtle but strong primer in ethics and proper behavior.

◆ Setting ◆

Although neither dates nor locales are identified, the setting appears to be a small midwestern community, perhaps in the late 1940s or early 1950s. Until her mother's death, Julie lived in the college town where her father, Adam Trelling, is a scholarly, overworked college professor. Because Professor Trelling feels overwhelmed with the responsibility of being a single parent, his two younger children, Julie and her nine-year-old brother, Christopher, are sent to live with their fifty-three-year-old spinster aunt, Miss Cordelia Bishop, and her older bachelor brother, Haskell, who lives in a renovated carriage house "out back." Until Julie's arrival, the home has seen little lighthearted pleasure, because Cordelia, in addition to teaching, has spent half of her life caring for her aged mother and two very old spinster aunts. Although Julie is initially apprehensive about living in the country, she grows to love her new home.

◆ Themes and Characters ◆

The novel is peopled with sympathetic characters, with two exceptions: Julie's high school love, Brett Kingman, whose attention to Julie is prompted by her willingness to write his English themes, and Julie's selfish, spoiled childhood friend, Carlotta Berry, who becomes pregnant by Brett. But, as Julie notes, the flaws Brett and Carlotta exhibit are largely traceable to poor parental guidance.

Aunt Cordelia leads a thoroughly proper, refined, self-disciplined life, which she devotes entirely to the welfare of others—her mother and aunts, her students, and Julie. As Julie matures, she learns that her aunt's proper demeanor and strict rules are not signs of coldness. Instead, they are Cordelia's method for coping with a life that does not allow for close friendships and, in her own words, "completeness in love." Beneath Cordelia's firm, unyielding exterior is a warm, sensitive, and loving person. As Julie develops her capacity for love, first for Aunt Cordelia and much later for Uncle Haskell, all three lives become more complete.

Haskell Bishop plays an important role. Intelligent and sometimes charming, Haskell is also an "alcoholic and pathological liar." For decades, Haskell has lied about the impending publication of the great novel he pretends to be writing and about the purpose of his twilight walks with a golf bag full of empty whiskey bottles that he "buries" in shallow graves. His life changes when, at sixty-five and after years of a dissipated, selfish life, he is asked by Julie to critique her short stories. He expends much effort in showing her how to improve her writing skills. Because of Julie, Haskell experiences one of the finest satisfactions in his life—the joy of helping someone he loves and of being loved in return.

Cordelia and Haskell are diverse and well-rounded characters, but it is Julie Trelling who seems most likely to step from the page into life. As she matures from an impetuous child who unintentionally hurts others and herself with her outbursts, she learns that living by rules, being a good student, and giving to others lead to happiness for herself. She also discovers that excelling in school and rejoicing in the beauty of nature and the wisdom of poets are not enough to make a person complete. She perceptively recognizes that a conductor, during a brief train ride, gives her some of the best advice she has ever received. When Julie weeps on the return trip from Laura's house because her sister has put her husband into "first place" above Julie, the conductor advises Julie to make herself "loved and needed in the Number Two, or Three, or Four spot." Through the death of Aggie Kilpin, the mentally retarded, dirty, and odorous child whose friendship she has rudely rejected, Julie learns humility and tolerance. And through her shared love with Danny Trevort, she learns

Jacket painting by Don Bolognese for *Up a Road Slowly* by Irene Hunt. Follett: Chicago (1987).

what it means to be "complete," as described by Cordelia.

Up a Road Slowly suggests that a child's maturation to virtuous adulthood is difficult for both the child and the adults who love the child, but Julia's story shows that education, generosity, and self-discipline may lead to happiness.

♦ Literary Qualities ♦

Up a Road Slowly projects a tone of warmth and innocence as it depicts a world where the positive aspects of life are emphasized and the ugly side of reality is usually suppressed. When Carlotta Berry leaves town to live with a relative, her pregnancy is a hushed event, and although it is understood, it is not discussed. No characters are portrayed as being truly evil, not even Brett Kingman; at worst, they are misguided. Even Aggie Kilpin, a victim of poverty, is beautiful in death, as Julie comments, because her body has been washed and the surface dirt cleansed away. Julie learns this symbolic wisdom from Aunt Cordelia; the teacher's mature outlook enables her to see through to Aggie's soul and disregard the dirt.

Uncle Haskell, a lying alcoholic and the pariah of the Bishop family because of his bad habits, is nonetheless described in glowing terms as being "slender and supple; when he walked it was as if he heard an inner music that delighted him down to his heels." Julie and her brother Chris observe that Uncle Haskell keeps cases of bottles of a "beautifully colored red-gold liquid" bearing the English translation of "*Le Vieux Corbeau*" in his basement, but despite the melodious French name that Uncle Haskell invents for it, the sparkling liquid is actually "Old Crow," a cheap, potent alcoholic beverage. Symbolism and effective imagery emphasize positive aspects of people and nature as well as soften what might otherwise be interpreted as ugly realism. Hunt's gentility of diction, poetic descriptions and metaphors, and use of mature vocabulary enable the story to affect the reader both intellectually and emotionally.

◆ Social Sensitivity ◆

At the center of this novel are serious subjects such as death, alienation, poverty, alcoholism, and teen-age pregnancy, but none of these is treated as more than a slight, temporary discomfort. For example, when Julie's mother dies, Julie forgets her quickly, and her father remarries after a few years. Additionally, the novel is subtly moralistic. Socially acceptable people have only transitory problems that can be solved with dedication to proper values. Problems are the fault of the individual, never of society, and it is taken for granted that ethnic minorities do not live in town. In spite of these observations, however, the life that Hunt portrays in *Up a Road Slowly* did exist in many small midwestern towns during the 1940s and 1950s, and many older readers can identify with the novel's small-town atmosphere. In this light, the book is true to a bygone era and reflects a time when life, at least on the surface, may have appeared to be simple and uncomplicated.

◆ Topics for Discussion ◆

1. Although Cordelia Bishop has only a high school education, she is very successful in preparing students like Jonathan Eltwing, Julie, and Danny for winning scholarships to prestigious universities. What types of learning responsibilities would those successful students have accepted that some students might consider unusual today?

2. What particular character traits would Aunt Cordelia need to develop in order to be happy with her adult life?

3. In what ways do Julie and her friends entertain themselves in an era before television and sophisticated toys?

4. Julie is angry when Jonathan Eltwing calls her "little Cordelia." Why does he call her that? Would she have responded differently to this statement when she was older?

5. Why does Aunt Cordelia place so much stress upon herself and Julie following self-imposed guidelines for daily routines?

◆ Ideas for Reports and Papers ◆

1. Irene Hunt also wrote *The Lottery Rose*. In what ways are *Up a Road Slowly* and *The Lottery Rose* very different in their portrayals of people and life? What might account for these differences?

2. Imagery plays an important role in allowing the reader to understand and sympathize with characters. Where is imagery used particularly effectively in bringing the reader inside the lives of Julie, Cordelia, and Haskell?

3. Uncle Haskell is a very different person at the end of the book than he is when he first appears. What specific experiences cause him to change?

4. Aunt Cordelia has very firm ideas about a young adult's personal behavior and interaction with adults. What are the strongest lessons she teaches Julie? What techniques does she use to teach Julie these lessons? Of these lessons, which would still be valuable today, and why?

5. Several lines of poetry written by Edna St. Vincent Millay and Sara Teasdale are quoted in this novel. How does this poetry extend the meaning of the story?

◆ For Further Reference ◆

Evory, Ann, and Linda Metzger, eds. *Contemporary Authors*, New Revision Series. Vol. 8. Detroit: Gale Research, 1983. Includes a short biographical sketch that covers Hunt's personal and career highlights.

Gelhardt, Lillian. "Review." *Library Journal* (February 15, 1967): 894. Gelhardt calls *Up a Road Slowly* "a top-flight" novel for girls because it presents "a description of the conflicting pressures of Julie's maturing years" and reveals "the insights about their elders that will never fail to intrigue young teenagers."

Hopkins, Lee Bennett. *More Books by More People.* New York: Citation Press, 1974. The reprise of an interview with Hunt contains reminiscences that help in understanding the biographical background of her writings.

Kirkpatrick, D. L., ed. *Twentieth Century Children's Writers.* New York: St. Martin's Press, 1978. Provides information about Hunt's life and writings.

"Review." *Horn Book* (February 1967): 72-73. This review of *Up a Road Slowly* praises Hunt's ability to see "the characters more clearly than most of us see people" and sees the novel as one which allows readers to "exorcise...guilt feelings for unkindnesses committed during the struggle to grow to maturity."

June H. Schlessinger
University of North Texas

VIVA CHICANO

Novel

1970

Author: Frank Bonham, b. 1914

Major Books for Young Adults

Burma Rifles, 1960
War Beneath the Sea, 1962
Deepwater Challenge, 1963
The Loud, Resounding Sea, 1963
Honor Bound, 1963
Speedway Contender, 1964
Durango Street, 1965
Mystery of the Red Tide, 1966
Mystery in Little Tokyo, 1966
The Ghost Front, 1968
The Nitty Gritty, 1968
Mystery of the Fat Cat, 1968
The Vagabundos, 1969
Viva Chicano, 1970
Cool Cat, 1971

Chief, 1971
The Friends of the Loony Lake
   Monster, 1972
Hey, Big Spender!, 1972
A Dream of Ghosts, 1973
The Golden Bees of Tulami, 1974
The Missing Persons League, 1975
The Rascals from Haskell's Gym,
   1976
Devilhorn, 1978
Forever Formula, 1979
Gimme an H, Gimme an E, Gimme
   an L, Gimme a P, 1982
Premonitions, 1984

◆ About the Author ◆

Born in Los Angeles on February 25, 1914, Frank Bonham attended Glendale College and served in the army during World War II before devoting himself to a writing career. A prolific writer, Bonham has published hundreds of short stories for magazines such as *McCall's* and the *Saturday Evening Post*, dozens of western novels, and numerous television scripts, particularly for popular western shows of the 1950s and 1960s.

Bonham's early books for young adults were adventure tales, but in the 1960s he became interested in the problems of juvenile delinquents and the life of minorities in American cities. He visited juvenile offenders in jail and began to write novels for young people about minority youths growing up in urban environments. These books, which include *Viva Chicano*, are known as Bonham's Dogtown novels.

◆ Overview ◆

The growing concern over the resurgence of street gang violence in the Los Angeles area makes *Viva Chicano* even more significant today than it was at its publication in 1970. Current press coverage of California's gang violence reveals the same problems portrayed in *Viva Chicano*.

Because he bases his works of fiction on firsthand experience with young people and the adult professionals who deal with them on a daily basis, Bonham's stories ring true. Keeny Durán, the protagonist of *Viva Chicano*, is clearly a composite of many troubled youths trying to maintain their pride and individuality in a hostile environment. Keeny's dilemma transcends both time and place, demonstrating that the understanding needed to make headway against gang mentality has not changed over the years.

Other writers have proposed a variety of theories about and solutions to the gang problem. Bonham's unique approach maintains that only when society puts aside ethnic analyses and examines each individual gang member as a potentially valuable member of society will a gradual resolution be achieved.

◆ Setting ◆

Viva Chicano is set in the 1960s in a sprawling ghetto, known as "Dogtown," of an unnamed California city modeled after Los Angeles. Ironically, the "Mexican-American district" of Dogtown, where Keeny lives, is called Happy Valley. Even the most energetic attempts toward beautification fail in the climate of despair and decay that pervades Happy Valley.

◆ Themes and Characters ◆

Seventeen-year-old Joaquín Durán, nicknamed "Keeny," is a confused youth who struggles, despite the hopelessness of his environment, to preserve his instinctive hunger for success. The ugliness and neglect prevalent in the landscape have distorted Keeny's view of life. For Keeny, family life consists of a succession of criminal stepfathers, and the educational system reflects the management of cynical bureaucrats.

In such a climate, even the good intentions of Mr. Baker, the perceptive social worker, are unlikely to change the course of a boy's life. Indeed, Keeny's own view of life convinces him that he is trapped like a rat and that there is no point in struggling to overcome his lot and make something of himself. Keeny's efforts to better his environment and himself are quickly squashed by reality.

Because of Keeny's criminal record, which dates back to when he was seven years old, the authorities are overly suspicious of him. When his little brother Armando falls from a window while Keeny is baby-sitting, the police and the neighbors assume that Keeny pushed him. Even though he is innocent, Keeny becomes a fugitive from the law. Part of the juvenile delinquency problem, according to Bonham, is that once teen-agers are found guilty of a crime, they are treated as criminals forever. Keeny challenges such treatment at the book's conclusion.

The central thrust of Bonham's narrative is that there is another side to Keeny that, to outside observers, is overshadowed by his criminal record. As Keeny recalls his father, who died when the boy was only six, the memory stirs within him a vague sense of self-worth. Keeny's growing pride in his Mexican heritage, called *la raza*, eventually emerges through a fantasy provoked by a life-sized cardboard display dummy of Emiliano Zapata, the Mexican revolutionary and folk hero. As

Bonham's involvement with youthful offenders in the Los Angeles area resulted in several other Dogtown novels, including *Mystery of the Fat Cat, The Nitty Gritty, The Vagabundos, Cool Cat, Chief,* and *Hey, Big Spender!* These novels all argue for more understanding from authorities and more recognition of young people as individuals. Since 1972 Bonham has also written mysteries and other types of young adult fiction.

◆ For Further Reference ◆

De Montreville, Doris, and Donna Hill, eds. *Third Book of Junior Authors.* Chicago: H. W. Wilson, 1972. Includes a biographical sketch of Bonham with some remarks on his writing methods.

Kirkpatrick, D. L., ed. *Twentieth Century Children's Writers.* New York: St. Martin's, 1978. Contains a biographical and bibliographical sketch of Bonham with some critical commentary.

Varless, Jana. *Young Adult Literature in the 1970s.* Metuchen, NJ: Scarecrow Press, 1978. Discusses Bonham's endorsement of traditional values and his notion that violence breeds more violence.

Paul Ettenson
SUNY-Old Westbury

WALDEN

Nonfiction

1854

◆

Author: Henry David Thoreau, 1817-1862

Major Books for Young Adults

A Week on the Concord and Merrimack Rivers, 1849
Walden, or Life in the Woods, 1854
The Maine Woods, 1865
Cape Cod, 1866

◆ About the Author ◆

Henry David Thoreau was born in Concord, Massachusetts, on July 12, 1817. His grandfather, Jean, a French Huguenot, had come to Boston in 1773, taken part in the American Revolution, and become a shopkeeper on the city's waterfront until he moved to Concord in 1800. Thoreau grew up in Concord with his father, John Thoreau, one of the first American makers of lead pencils; his mother, Cynthia Dunbar, a nature lover and abolitionist; his older brother, John; and two sisters, Helen and Sophia.

Thoreau began his education at Miss Phoebe Wheeler's infant school. He attended public grammar school and, at the age of eleven, enrolled at the Concord Academy. From childhood he had been a rather isolated figure; at school he kept to himself and refused to play games, preferring to spend much of his time in the woods and fields around Concord. In 1833 he entered Harvard College, where he studied rhetoric and modern and classical languages. He graduated in 1837.

During the winter following his graduation from Harvard, Thoreau established a close friendship with the Transcendentalist writer Ralph Waldo Emerson, who became his literary mentor. Thoreau wanted to become a writer, and undertook various jobs in order to support himself while working on his writing. He taught public school in Concord for a short time, but quit after learning that his duties included flogging the pupils. In 1838 he started his own school; his pupils included Louisa May Alcott, the author of *Little Women*, and two of her sisters. After the school closed in 1843, Thoreau tutored the children of Emerson's brother, William, on Staten Island, New York, until 1844. Thoreau was at times a surveyor, a carpenter, a house painter, and a mason.

Thoreau's friendship with Emerson led to his involvement with the Transcendentalist Club and the subsequent publication of his poems and essays in the Transcendentalist magazine *The Dial*. Thoreau also lived at times in Emerson's home, and it was on Emerson's property near Walden Pond that he built his famous cabin, the scene of his Walden experiment from July 4, 1845, to September 6, 1847. The friendship would cool in later years, but Thoreau remained a Transcendentalist all of his life. Except for occasional trips to Maine, Cape Cod, and Canada, Thoreau spent most of his brief life in Concord. Few writers have identified themselves so closely with their home region, and he became an authority on the history of Concord and the surrounding area. Thoreau's first book, *A Week on the Concord and Merrimack Rivers*, was a complete failure. *Walden* fared somewhat better, but much of its success came after his death. Throughout his career Thoreau presented his essays as public lectures and only later revised them for publication. Thoreau died in Concord of tuberculosis on May 6, 1862.

Soon after Thoreau's death, the publishers Ticknor and Field reissued both *A Week on the Concord and Merrimack Rivers* and *Walden*, and published *Cape Cod* and *The Maine Woods*. *Walden* has remained in print ever since and has appeared in nearly two hundred editions. Millions of copies have been sold, and the book has been translated into every modern language.

◆ Overview ◆

In *Walden* Thoreau records both his experiment in self-sufficient natural living and his ideas about nature, human society, and the proper way for people to live. In a series of essays, linked by themes and the progression of the seasons, Thoreau describes building his own cabin and living alone in the woods beside Walden Pond. The result is a blend of Transcendentalist philosophy, autobiography, biting social commentary, and superb nature writing that is unique in American literature. As modern life has become increasingly urbanized, complex, and isolated from nature, Thoreau's insistence that people should simplify their lives and interact with nature has appealed to a growing number of readers.

◆ Setting ◆

The setting of *Walden* is integral to its themes, although Thoreau did not set out to write a book about nature. He wanted a quiet place to write, so he secured Emerson's permission to build a cottage on his land near Walden Pond. The pond was only a mile from Thoreau's mother's house and within walking distance of town. Thoreau moved there in early July of 1845.

Thoreau's first tasks, as recounted in *Walden*, relate to his survival—planting a garden so that he can sell the produce for money to build his cabin, then building the cabin, and finally winterizing it. He meticulously records this work in his writing and reflects on its meaning. What evolves during the two years that Thoreau lives at Walden Pond is a book about humankind's relation to nature, and how self-sufficiency makes individualism possible.

◆ Themes and Characters ◆

Since *Walden* is, on one hand, a sort of spiritual autobiography, Thoreau himself is its central character. The narrator of *Walden* resembles Thoreau in many ways, but is also a distinct narrative persona. The real Thoreau was a much pricklier personality than the sunny tone of the book indicates. Thoreau as narrator is an apologist for Transcendentalist beliefs and for the rights of eccentric personalities to live as they choose. But privately, as entries in his personal journal have indicated, Thoreau did not always feel that nature held the answer to most social and spiritual problems.

> *I see young men, my townsmen, whose misfortune it is to have inherited farms, houses, barns, cattle, and farming tools; for these are more easily acquired than got rid of.*

The Transcendentalists believed that the human mind had sources of knowledge—such as conscience or an inner light—that were independent of or transcended the senses. Emerson became the foremost thinker among those who endorsed such views, and helped found the Transcendentalist Club, a loose, informal group that often met at his house in Concord. Like other members of this club, Thoreau believed that humans were basically good, and that nature was benign and favored humankind. By keeping themselves pure, and through a close relationship with nature, people could perfect themselves and grow in the knowledge already granted them through the inner light. Thoreau set out to live according to this philosophy when he moved to Walden Pond.

In *Walden*, Thoreau's most attractive characteristics emerge when he shows his genuine love for the world around him, treating even the tiny fish in Walden Pond with affection. But his attitude toward humans is less tolerant and loving; he is least attractive when he preaches to the poor people he meets near Walden. His attitude toward the Irish workmen he meets is self-righteously condescending, and none of the other people mentioned in the book are given more than sketchy treatment. Even Emerson, who owned the land the cabin sat on and who occasionally visited Thoreau, is never mentioned by name. Thoreau is interested primarily in his own consciousness and its development while at Walden.

Thoreau considers life a great gift bestowed upon humans, and he is distressed that people do not make proper use of it. He cannot understand why people enslave themselves by devoting much of their time to the attainment of material things when nature offers so much for nothing. Thoreau's reflections on the proper way of living constitute a major theme of the book. Thoreau believes that people should reap the benefits of nature by purifying themselves, forsaking false values, and seeking to become attuned to the spirit pervading the natural world and themselves.

Self-discovery is another theme in *Walden*. At the beginning of the section entitled "Higher Laws," Thoreau says that he has found in himself "an instinct toward a higher, or, as it is named, spiritual life, and another toward a primitive rank and savage one, and I reverence them both." Thoreau wants to develop spiritually, but at the same time he realizes that a degree of wildness is essential to human growth.

◆ Literary Qualities ◆

Unlike his mentor, Emerson, Thoreau has a sense of organic form, and as a result *Walden*—in contrast to many of Emerson's essays—is more than a collection of brilliant, briefly stated ideas. Thoreau revised the book at least seven times after writing the first draft during his stay at Walden. As usual, sections of it were tried out on audiences at his lectures, and rewritten according to their reactions. *Walden* is Thoreau's best book, for it displays his keen insight and his skill as a prose stylist.

Thoreau's actual stay at Walden lasted two years, two months and two days. The book presents a single year, beginning in early spring 1845, when he starts work on the cabin, and ending the following spring after the ice has melted on the pond. The chapters are carefully linked to assure continuity. Thoreau employs metaphors with a skill that makes his work a prose poem surpassing the traditional poems he wrote during his lifetime. The pond itself is a central metaphor, its purity a standard to which all humans should aspire. Metaphors suggesting rebirth and renewal are frequent, and express Thoreau's almost missionary zeal.

Thoreau's imagination reworked his experience into an American myth. He drew freely from other sources, especially his journals, in his revisions of *Walden*. His account of his life and thought at Walden Pond struck a strong responsive chord in the American consciousness. Although Thoreau often sounds like a sage in his pronouncements, he was essentially a writer, and most critics now agree that *Walden* should be considered a piece of imaginative literature rather than an autobiography or nature book. Thoreau, who never read novels, not even those of his friend Nathaniel Hawthorne, would not have liked this conclusion. But in *Walden* he created a Henry David Thoreau quite different from the one who spent those two years by the pond.

◆ Social Sensitivity ◆

Thoreau considered himself a reformer, and he genuinely wanted to change human lives for the better. He was distressed by the poverty he saw in the Concord area, but was convinced that the answer to poverty was not philanthropy. Thoreau felt a personal responsibility for the poor but believed that the inner person had to change before gifts or donations would do any good. So he preached to those poor people he met on his walks.

"We need the tonic of wildness..." Thoreau says in the chapter of *Walden* entitled "Spring." He was a pioneer conservationist who insisted that the primitive, wild side of human nature required the wildness of nature as a counterpart. He predicted that the exploitation of the West was inevitable once the business interests of the country realized that they could obtain resources there. He admits in *Walden* that he has a grudging admiration for the energy of commercial enterprises, but feels that it is energy applied for all the wrong reasons. At the end of the section of the book called "The Ponds," he says to his contemporaries: "Talk of heaven! Ye disgrace earth."

For a book that, on its surface, seems like a sentimental discussion of human interaction with nature, *Walden* has stirred deep resentment and critical attack from both individuals and governments. Critics who have disliked *Walden* object to Thoreau's belief that the individual rights of human beings take precedence over all other considerations. For Thoreau, society, no matter how benevolent, is a threat to the self-sufficient individual; Thoreau is dogmatically independent. When combined with his other views of society, particularly his support for "civil disobedience" in which he believes people may justly break "bad" laws, his idealism has both inspired and thwarted revolutionary movements.

◆ Topics for Discussion ◆

1. Why do you think the essay "Economy" is by far the longest chapter in *Walden*?

2. What does Thoreau hope to achieve at Walden Pond?

3. Which do you prefer, the sections of the book devoted to Transcendentalist philosophy or those in which Thoreau describes the living things around his cabin? Is his idealism ever completely absent anywhere in the book?

4. What kind of reading does Thoreau recommend? Why does he dislike newspapers?

5. Thoreau praises solitude, but insists he is not a hermit. Is this contradictory?

6. What famous event in Thoreau's life is mentioned briefly in the concluding paragraph of "The Village"?

7. Why are such detailed descriptions provided in "The Ponds"? What symbolic value do they have for Thoreau?

8. What is a paradox? Does Thoreau make good use of paradoxes in *Walden*?

9. In his descriptions of the various seasons at *Walden*, which season does Thoreau seem to prefer? Why?

◆ Ideas for Reports and Papers ◆

1. Seven centuries before Thoreau, a Japanese philosopher, Kamo Chomei, carried out an experiment similar to Thoreau's by living in a cabin in the woods. Compare *Hojoki*, Chomei's account of his stay there, to *Walden*. *Hojoki* is included in the *Norton Anthology of Oriental Literature*.

2. Thoreau was fond of reading religious books such as the *Bhagavad Gita* and *Dhammapada*, Hindu and Buddhist scriptures, respectively. What use has he made of ideas derived from these sources in *Walden*?

3. Thoreau's *Journals*, written between 1837 and 1861, contain many of the ideas that he worked into books such as *Walden*. Compare the writing in the *Journals* to that in *Walden*. How is it similar or different?

4. Thoreau's first two books, *A Week on the Concord and Merrimack Rivers* and *Walden*, both involve water, rivers and ponds. Compare the two books. How is the imagery the same? How does it differ?

5. Compare the books of a modern nature writer such as Edward Hoagland or John McPhee to Thoreau's *Walden*.

How do the approaches differ? Do these more recent books feature an underlying philosophy such as transcendentalism?

6. Compare Annie Dillard's Pulitzer Prize-winning book, *Pilgrim at Tinker Creek*, to *Walden*.

◆ Related Titles ◆

A Week on the Concord and Merrimack Rivers, like *Walden*, mixes observations of natural phenomena with discussions of their symbolic significance. *The Maine Woods* and *Cape Cod* read more like pure travel literature. In these last two books Thoreau encountered forms of nature not easily reconcilable to his faith in an external world friendly to man. In *Cape Cod* he describes the purely destructive force of a storm at sea. In *The Maine Woods* he writes of climbing Mt. Katahdin, New England's second highest peak; he reaches the summit, possibly only the sixth person ever to do so, and is shocked by what he finds there: a grey, barren expanse, strewn with rocks and totally indifferent to human existence. Thoreau's confidence in a benign nature did not outwardly change, but a reading of his *Journals* reveals that he sometimes continued an adherence in his published books to ideas that he had privately abandoned.

◆ For Further Reference ◆

Anderson, Charles R., ed. *Thoreau's Vision: The Major Essays*. Englewood Cliffs, NJ: Prentice Hall, 1973. Includes most of Thoreau's better short pieces and provides a good analysis of Thoreau's essays.

Bridgman, Richard. *Dark Thoreau*. Lincoln: University of Nebraska Press, 1982. Provides a different perspective on Thoreau's writings based on a close study of his imagery. The violence of many images in the works seem to Bridgman to indicate a deeply pessimistic, possibly even a pathological personality.

Harding, Walter. *The Days of Henry Thoreau: A Biography*. New York: Alfred A. Knopf, 1965. Regarded as the best biography of Thoreau.

Matthiessen, F. O. *American Renaissance*. London: Oxford University Press, 1941. Matthiessen first convincingly demonstrated Thoreau's skill in writing *Walden*. After nearly fifty years this work remains one of the best books on the classic nineteenth-century American writers.

Pillai, A. K. B. *Transcendental Self: A Comparative Study of Thoreau and the Psycho-Philosophy of Hinduism and Buddhism*. Lanham, MD: University Press of America, 1985. Drawing extensively on *Walden*, Pallai, a native of India, shows a close parallel between Thoreau's thinking and that found in traditional Indian religion.

Wagenknecht, Edward. *Henry David Thoreau: What Manner of Man*. Amherst: University of Massachusetts Press, 1981. A good, brief study of all aspects of Thoreau's career as a writer.

Karl Avery

THE WALLS OF WINDY TROY
Biography
1960

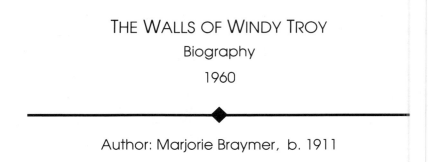

Author: Marjorie Braymer, b. 1911

Major Books for Young Adults

The Walls of Windy Troy, 1960
Atlantis: The Biography of a Legend, 1983

◆ About the Author ◆

Marjorie Elizabeth Braymer was born on March 21, 1911, in Chicago, Illinois. From 1930 until 1940 she worked in New York City as an editor and manuscript reader for film companies. She then returned to the Midwest and in 1943 graduated from Ohio State University with a degree in education. In 1944 she returned to New York to obtain a master's degree from Columbia University Teachers College, and from 1960 to 1961 studied at Stanford University.

Braymer has lived in California ever since 1945, when she launched a two-decade teaching career at Sequoia High School in Redwood, California. She also worked as an editor for Addison Wesley Publishing Company in Palo Alto, California, between 1965 and 1967. Braymer's writing has garnered many awards. She won the Vandewater Poetry Prize at Ohio State University in 1943, and in 1960 was honored with the *New York Herald Tribune*'s Spring Book Festival Honor Book Award for *The Walls of Windy Troy*. This book was also chosen as an American Library Association Notable Book in 1960.

◆ Overview ◆

The Walls of Windy Troy, a biography of the German archeologist Heinrich Schliemann, has all the appeal of an old-fashioned novel in its description of a poor boy's rise to prominence as a result of hard work and keen intelligence. Braymer skillfully weaves together the fascinating archeological story of the discovery of the site of ancient Troy and the equally astonishing story of Schliemann's life. Schliemann's obsession with Troy, launched when he is only eight years old, provides young readers with an impressive example of determination. Not only does he have an early sense of his life's mission, but he is also patient enough to devote more than three decades to amassing the wealth necessary to achieve his goal. An amateur archeologist whose deductions about the site of Troy earn him the

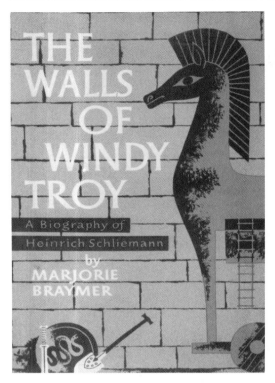

Jacket design by Enrico Arno for *The Walls of Windy Troy* by Marjorie Braymer. Harcourt, Brace and World: New York (1960).

businessman. Schliemann moves to California in 1850 to clear up his late brother's estate and to capitalize on the booming gold-rush economy. After his return to Russia, the scene shifts in 1866 to Turkey, where Schliemann digs for the site of ancient Troy. He hypothesizes that the city lies near the village of Hissarlik, and succeeds in unearthing layer upon layer of settlements, dating back to the Bronze Age. In 1874 Schliemann moves his operations to Mycenae in Greece, where he hunts for the tomb of the Greek warrior Agamemnon. An epilogue capsulizes the advances in archeological theory since the time of Schliemann's death and places his discoveries in the context of those that have followed.

◆ Themes and Characters ◆

Heinrich Schliemann is the only character of significance in *The Walls of Windy Troy.* When he is nine years old, his mother dies; meanwhile, his father, a minister, becomes implicated in a murky scandal concerning misappropriation of church funds. With his mother dead and his father preoccupied, Schliemann is sent to live with his uncle, the pastor Friederich Schliemann of Kalkhorst. But when Schliemann turns fourteen, the pastor concludes that his nephew has had enough schooling. Schliemann becomes a grocer's apprentice in Fürstenberg, a small village about a hundred and fifty miles from Hamburg, where he works for five years until a barrel falls on his chest, damaging his lungs. Let go by the grocer, Schliemann journeys to Hamburg and books passage on a ship to Venezuela. When the ship runs aground off the Dutch island of Texel, the

ridicule of the community of professional archeologists, Schliemann is an underdog figure who eventually proves triumphant over his doubters.

◆ Setting ◆

Heinrich Schliemann lived from 1822 to 1890, but *The Walls of Windy Troy* covers his early childhood only briefly, through use of flashback. The biography opens with Schliemann's visit to Hamburg at age nineteen in search of a job. The book follows him to Holland and eventually to St. Petersburg, Russia, where he becomes an established nineteen-year-old Schliemann is left destitute, but instead of returning to Hamburg he moves to Amsterdam and launches the business career that eventually makes him one of the wealthiest men in Europe.

Schliemann's most impressive traits are his diligence, his quick mind, and his remarkable imagination. Introduced to Homer's tales of the Trojan War as a young child, Schliemann decides to prove what most scholars doubt: that Troy was an actual city and not just a mythical spot conjured up by poets of old. One of the most amazing—and inspiring—of Schliemann's traits is his facility in learning foreign languages. Spanish, English, Dutch, Russian, Greek, Turkish, and other languages become part of the intellectual armament with which Schliemann attacks the worlds of commerce and archeology. Schliemann apparently never succumbs to sloth, nor does he ever reveal any inclination to squander the money he makes on luxury items. Had he not been correct in his intuitions about Troy, he would appear today as he did to many of his contemporaries—a clever eccentric victimized by his monomania.

Of all the stumbling blocks in Schliemann's life, it is his personal life that at first troubles him the most. He works hard to make his fortune, sustained by the thought that someday he will marry Minna, a childhood friend with whom he once shared the dream of finding Troy. But when in 1848, at the age of twenty-six, he finally feels capable of supporting a wife and writes a letter of proposal to Minna, he learns that she has married someone else. It seems typical of Schliemann's singlemindedness that he could go for so long assuming so much about a woman whom he has not contacted in years. Gradually reconciled to life without Minna, he

Photograph of Heinrich Schliemann reprinted by permission of F. A. Brockhaus Verlag for *The Walls of Windy Troy* by Marjorie Braymer. Harcourt, Brace and World: New York (1960).

decides in 1852 to marry Catherine Lyschin, a native of St. Petersburg. Catherine proves more interested in clothing and fashion than in traipsing around the Turkish countryside digging up potsherds, and as a result, the couple is divorced in 1869. Less than a year later, Schliemann marries seventeen-year-old Sophie Engastromenos, a quiet, learned Greek woman who becomes his companion in all of his enterprises. Schliemann courts Sophie by quizzing her on her knowledge of Homer; it is her fluent recital of Homeric verse that wins his heart. Thus

The Walls of Windy Troy

Schliemann's final choice of a wife proves contingent on her compatibility with his obsession.

Braymer does not develop many of the book's secondary characters in great depth. Neither Minna nor Catherine receives more than a passing reference, and Sophie never comes to life on the page. A few vignettes cast light on minor characters: Wendt, a ship broker in Hamburg, is depicted as a kindly person who goes out of his way to help Schliemann; Hermann Niederhöffer, a drunken student, recites the *Iliad* in classical Greek and fires young Schliemann with a desire to learn the language of Homer; and Simonsen, captain of the Venezuela-bound ship that capsizes off the coast of Holland, treats his destitute young passenger in a friendly way. But these people appear briefly and then disappear, always leaving Schliemann alone on center stage.

♦ Literary Qualities ♦

The Walls of Windy Troy is carried along smoothly by a sequence of highly dramatic scenes, well imagined and well presented: the young Schliemann encountering the student who recites Greek, appealing to Wendt for help, being shipwrecked, and working his way up the business ladder in Amsterdam; the adult Schliemann traveling to California, learning that his goods have survived a devastating fire in the Black Sea port of Memel, and discovering ruins at Hissarlik and Mycenae. The biography resembles a Victorian story of great expectations completely fulfilled, although not necessarily within the lifetime of its protagonist. Braymer avoids painting an overly rosy picture of Schliemann's career as an amateur archeologist, acknowledging that at the time of his death he still faced heavy criticism from scholars who deemed his conclusions rash and unfounded. Braymer writes that "[Schliemann] went too fast and he destroyed some evidence that it would be useful to have. He rushed into print with theories that could not be proved." A century after his death, Schliemann is regarded as a pioneer of modern archeology, but Braymer's incorporation of critical commentary makes *The Walls of Windy Troy* a balanced and thought-provoking biography for young adults.

An appealing literary feature of *The Walls of Windy Troy* is Braymer's effective use of epigraphs. Each of the twenty chapters begins with a quotation well chosen to foreshadow the theme of the chapter. Chapter 1, for instance, opens with Athena's remark to Telemachus in book II of the *Odyssey*: "That journey you have wanted so much to make will not be postponed any longer. For I am such a good friend of your father that I shall furnish you with a swift ship." And in the narrative that follows, the ship broker Wendt—an old friend of Schliemann's father—arranges for passage to Venezuela on the brig *Dorothea*. Appropriately, all the epigraphs are drawn from Homer's chronicles of the Trojan war and its aftermath, the *Iliad* and the *Odyssey*. The introduction to chapter 15 is from Virgil's *Aeneid*, another epic work about a survivor of this great conflict.

The Walls of Windy Troy is structured symmetrically around its twenty chapters. The first ten chapters follow Schliemann's life before he goes to Troy. This section of the book ends with the great fire on the docks at Memel; Schliemann makes a fortune because his goods are miraculously spared when those of every other merchant are consumed by flames. Chapter 11 introduces the second half of the story and opens with Schliemann in Greece, "standing in the strong sunlight of Ithaca," home of the Greek hero Odysseus. Chapter 20 closes with Schliemann's burial and is followed by an epilogue that evaluates Schliemann's contributions to archeology. Thus the first half of the book treats Schliemann's long years of amassing the wealth needed for his undertaking, while the second half relates how he applies his funds toward his excavations at Mycenae and Hissarlik. Overall, the book is clearly written and dynamically presented. Although not a prerequisite for reading the book, a familiarity with the events of the Trojan War will enhance a reader's enjoyment of the biography.

◆ Social Sensitivity ◆

Schliemann's attitude toward the women in his life may prove offensive to some readers. A man obsessed with finding the original site of Troy, Schliemann is depicted as having a somewhat proprietary air toward women. Throughout his life, Schliemann set goals—the acquisition of language skills, the accumulation of wealth, the discovery of ancient tombs and cities—and almost invariably succeeded in his pursuits. Braymer portrays Schliemann's quest for a suitable wife as no different from his other quests. Schliemann's assumption that Minna will be his for the asking, despite their fourteen-year separation, points up the often self-centered nature of his thinking. Singleminded determination made Schliemann a great success in business and archeology, but initially less successful in his personal life.

At one point Braymer writes that Schliemann "could have had his choice of beautiful and eligible women in half a dozen countries, but the lesson in disillusion that he had learned from Catherine had taught him what he valued most highly in a wife." Although "what he valued," namely intellectual curiosity, is a positive trait, Braymer's phrasing reflects a certain level of conceit on Schliemann's part and almost dehumanizes the "eligible women." When Schliemann finally forges a happy marriage with Sophie, she is depicted as always in her husband's shadow. According to Braymer, Sophie is happy to "cook the kind of food he liked." An intelligent woman, Sophie nonetheless assumes a stereotypically docile role in the partnership: "Sophie did not write. She had babies...She read Greek to him. She listened." Braymer never questions Sophie's dedication; this bias in the narrative in many ways reflects the inequalities inherent in many nineteenth-century marriages, but readers may wonder whether a woman of Sophie's intelligence was truly as satisfied with her subservient role as Braymer depicts her.

The two primary sites that Schliemann excavates—Troy and Mycenae—hold great importance in the history of Western civilization. In general, *The Walls of Windy Troy* fosters an appreciation of the magnificence and lasting impact of ancient Greek culture, but it is worth noting that in one instance Braymer allows a note of condescension toward non-European cultures to enter her narrative. Speaking of Schliemann's visit to Panama City, prior to his excavations of Troy, she writes, "He allowed himself to wonder how long it would be before he could start his search for a ruined city incalculably more important and imposing than this one."

1. Although Schliemann is a remarkably capable and self-sufficient person, he sometimes benefits from good luck and the kindness of strangers. Explain the role of good luck in his life. What help does he get from others?

2. What are the crucial events in young Schliemann's life that motivate him to devote his life to the discovery of the site of ancient Troy?

3. Summarize Schliemann's experience in Russia. Why does he go there in the first place? What are the most important events of his life in Russia?

4. Why does Schliemann go to America? Is he successful there? Describe his experience in California.

5. How do Minna, Catherine, and Sophie in turn influence Schliemann's career? What is Sophie's value to him as a colleague?

6. Why does Schliemann shift his excavations from Hissarlik to Mycenae? What does he hope to find in Mycenae?

• Ideas for Reports and Papers •

1. Find out when the Trojan War was fought and who fought it. What are the major sources of our information on Troy? What are some of the theories concerning Homer's authorship of the *Iliad* and the *Odyssey*?

2. After reading the epilogue, evaluate the success of Schliemann's research. In what ways was he wrong in interpreting what he found and in what respects right? In what ways have his discoveries influenced the course of archeology over the last century?

3. Write an essay about Schliemann's most important character traits and how they helped him to succeed.

4. Read *Agamemnon*, a play by the Greek dramatist Aeschylus, and evaluate Schliemann's discoveries at Mycenae in the light of this hero's role in Greek history.

5. How would you describe Schliemann's approach to learning a new language? Could his methods be readily incorporated into schoolroom teaching? Pretend that you are a language teacher whose job it is to teach English to young students, and draw up a study guide along the lines of Schliemann's methods.

• For Further Reference •

Ceram, C. W. *Gods, Graves, and Scholars: The Story of Archaeology.* 2d ed. New York: Alfred A. Knopf, 1978. Contains two fascinating chapters on Schliemann's efforts at Troy and Mycenae.

Ludwig, Emil. *Schliemann: The Story of a Gold-Seeker.* Boston: Little, Brown, 1931. The standard biography of Schliemann, primarily of interest to adult readers.

Frank Day
Clemson University

WALT WHITMAN: BUILDER FOR AMERICA
Biography
1941

◆

Author: Babette Deutsch, 1895-1982

Major Books for Young Adults

Heroes of the Kalevala, 1940
Walt Whitman: Builder for America,
 1941
It's a Secret, 1941
The Welcome, 1942
The Reader's Shakespeare, 1946

Tales of Faraway Folk, 1952 (with
 Avraham Yarmolinsky)
More Tales of Faraway Folk, 1963
 (with Avraham Yarmolinsky)
I Often Wish, 1966

◆ About the Author ◆

Babette Deutsch was born in New York on September 22, 1895, and lived there most of her life. She graduated from Barnard College with a bachelor's degree in 1917, and published her first volume of poetry, *Banners,* in 1919, beginning a literary career that continued for more than half a century. In 1921, she married Avraham Yarmolinsky, a scholar of European literature. She collaborated with Yarmolinsky on translations and anthologies of Russian and German authors. Their partnership started with a translation of Alexander Blok's *The Twelve* in 1920, and continued with two anthologies, *Modern Russian Poetry* (1921) and *Contemporary German Poetry* (1923), and a translation of K. Chukovsky's *Crocodile* (1931). At the same time, Deutsch was establishing a reputation as a poet, publishing *Honey Out of the Rock* (1925), *Fire for the Night* (1930),

and *Epistle for Prometheus* (1930). During the 1930s she worked as a critic and an editor, and in 1933 she became a lecturer at the New School for Social Research in New York City. Her poetry was neither experimental nor accomplished enough to elevate her into the first rank of American poets, but the professional qualities of her work were universally admired, moving Marianne Moore to note the "depth, range, straightness" that contributed to her "commanding stature as a poet." In addition to her poetry, Deutsch's studies *Potable Gold: Some Notes on Poetry and This Age* (1929) and *This Modern Poetry* (1935) established her as a widely respected critic. The novels *A Brittle Heaven* (1926), *In Such a Night* (1927), and *Mask of Silenus: A Novel about Socrates* (1933) demonstrated her ability to write in a variety of literary forms.

Deutsch continued to collaborate with Yarmolinsky during the 1930s, assisting him in editing a 1936 edition of

Photograph of Walt Whitman (c.1877) by Phillips and Taylor, now in the Charles E. Feinberg Collection, reprinted in *Walt Whitman: Camden Conversation* by Walter Teller. Rutgers University Press: New Brunswick, NJ (1973).

collaborated on an edition of Shakespeare, *The Reader's Shakespeare,* designed for young readers. During the 1950s, she and Yarmolinsky adapted a collection of folktales called *Tales of Faraway Folk* (1952), which was followed by a similar collection for young people in 1963. She was an honorary consultant at the Library of Congress from 1960 to 1966, and served in several national literary organizations during the 1960s. Her *Coming of Age: New and Selected Poems* (1959) was combined in some reviews with Robert Lowell's *Life Studies,* an indication of how seriously her work was taken. When she published her *Collected Poems: 1919-1962* (1963), critical response suggested that her work was an important, if not major, element in the American poetic tradition. The final volume of her work, *The Collected Poems of Babette Deutsch,* was published in 1969, shortly after her single volume of poems for younger readers, *I Often Wish.* She died in New York on November 13, 1982, seven years after the death of her husband.

Alexander Pushkin's works. As World War II drew closer, public interest about other nations was growing in the United States, spurring her to write her first book for young people, a version of the Finnish national saga called *Heroes of the Kalevala.* Her wide knowledge of poetry provided the background for a book on Walt Whitman for young readers.

Deutsch translated Rainer Maria Rilke's *Poems from the Book of Hours* in 1941, and became a lecturer on poetry at Columbia University in 1944, a position she held until 1971. She and Yarmolinsky translated Alexander Pushkin's *Eugene Onegin* (1943) and

♦ Overview ♦

Ernest Hemingway maintained that American literature began with *Huckleberry Finn,* but if he had narrowed the category to American poetry, he would have had to acknowledge the primacy of Walt Whitman. "It was you that broke the new wood," Ezra Pound once said in grudging acknowledgment of a poet he disliked but whose extraordinary originality he recognized. While some excellent poetry had been written in the United States before Whitman's publication of *Leaves of Grass* on July 4, 1855, it was essentially British in form, style, and diction. Whitman pointed this out in a letter to Ralph Waldo Emerson in 1856, when he declared that "old forms, majestic and proper in their own lands here in this land are exiles," and set for himself the epic task of creating a body of poetry that would capture the spirit, values, and character of a still newly emerging nation.

To do this, Whitman attempted to locate and employ the poetic qualities of ordinary American conversation, a goal in agreement with Henry David Thoreau's contention that "poetry is nothing but healthy speech." Whitman created an open stanza that expanded the possibilities of conventional metric organization, and he developed a long, flowing line that established rhythms beyond the limits of rhyme and standard meter. He used a particularly American vocabulary that led to the formation of an American "voice," eliminating the gulf between a poetic performance and an audience that had to be "educated" to appreciate the poet's song. He understood the power of poetry as sound, connecting his work directly to the vitality of an oral tradition that tapped an energy long lost to a print-dominated literary culture.

But Whitman was more than just a strikingly original poet. Even before the publication of *Leaves of Grass*, he had begun to think of himself as an artist who could express the full range and vitality of American cultural and political experience. This visionary ambition became his operating principle at a time when European models in the arts were still dominant in the United States, and it enabled him to claim artistic equality for the American experience. He saw his poetry as releasing and directing the forces latent in an untapped national consciousness. Because he believed that the ordinary citizen of the republic had an open, easy, accepting, and generous character unspoiled by artistic pretensions, he described and wrote for the "common man" and believed his poetry demonstrated that this commonality was the basis for heroic individuality. In a direct challenge to the vestiges of puritanism in American social life, he extolled the senses and praised the physicality of experience, believing as Emerson did that human beings were a part of the natural world and that nature was an example of God's bounty. At a time when the issue of slavery threatened to dissolve the Union, Whitman tried to show what was most valuable in American democracy. His mighty image of a confident, open-hearted, and great-spirited human on the threshold of an open road leading outward to the entire "kosmos" (as he spelled it) still stands as an emblem of what is most inspiring in American life.

◆ Setting ◆

Born in 1819, Walt Whitman lived until 1892, witnessing during the course of his life the progression of nineteenth-century American history and helping to define the timeless elements of American culture through his poetry. Because Whitman was a poet deeply sensitive to his environment and often inspired by a striking image of the city, the sea, or some region of rural America, Deutsch frequently pauses in the narrative to focus on particular places that influenced his poetry. She shows him as a very young child among the crops and animals on a farm in Long Island, and then shows him, at age five, moving to the city, where the crowds, wagons, factories, and warehouses of the growing metropolis fascinate him. As his family moves from one home in Brooklyn Heights to another, the names of the streets themselves evoke the flavor of the history of the old city. Whitman learns to appreciate the tremendous variety of urban life, and when he spends summers on Paumanok (the old Native American name for Long Island), Deutsch presents the landscape as a field for sensory experience. As an apprentice journalist, Whitman begins to develop a sense of the magnitude of creation during long walks by the seashore.

Near the beginning of his career as a newspaperman, at age twenty-two, Whitman is interested in every facet of city life, and attends lectures and the theater whenever he can afford the time and admission. One of his favorite forms of recreation is to ride trams and ferries while seated next to the driver or pilot. Deutsch shows Whitman absorbing the colors, sounds, and smells that will enter into the physical imagery of his poetry.

As a young person interested in the world beyond his native Northeast, Whitman begins to travel to other areas of the country. Deutsch indicates how each part of the country he visits adds to his increasingly epic conception of the United States. Travels to New Orleans, the Midwest, and then to Washington, D.C., during the Civil War, give Whitman a sense of the tremendous diversity of American life, which he praises in his writing as a source of national strength. In the later part of his life, although generally restricted by his declining health, Whitman visits Kansas, Colorado, Quebec, and New England, finding in each place something to excite him, either in the landscape or in the style and pattern of the lives of the people he meets. The summers Whitman spends on a farm near Camden, New Jersey, during his last years reunite him with details of the natural world through the cycles of seasonal growth and decay that he observes. When Whitman becomes unable to leave his home on Mickle Street very often, Deutsch draws the reader into his room to create the mood of his final days. The world of mid-nineteenth-century America, which was always an important part of Whitman's poetry, is shown through his eyes and ideas.

◆ Themes and Characters ◆

Deutsch's goal in her biography of Whitman is to connect the important incidents of his life to the formation of his creative intelligence in order to explain how the poet acquired and developed his abilities as a writer. Opening the book with a description of his early life on a Long Island farm close to the sea, Deutsch introduces the members of Whitman's family as distinctive characters, each of whom affects the young boy in a crucial way. His maternal grandmother is a sea captain's daughter who likes to tell stories of seafaring men and their adventures; a great-grandmother (who died before he was born) still lives in family legends as a strong, independent woman; and his paternal grandmother is a Quaker who may have sparked Whitman's interest in that gentle, tolerant religion.

Whitman's father is a carpenter, large and rough-hewn, quick-tempered and hard-working but never particularly successful. When the family moves to Brooklyn so that Whitman's father can seek work in this rapidly expanding borough, Whitman is as captivated by the "swarming crowds" of New York City as he had been by the natural world he knew on the farm. The narrative, to this point, is organized around the accumulation of experience; as Whitman reaches his twenties and begins to work in the newspaper business, these early experiences are concentrated into the first stages of poetic expression.

Whitman's fascination with the multiplicity of city life forms the foundation of his belief in the great diversity of democratic life in America. At age twenty-seven he becomes the editor of the *Brooklyn Daily Eagle*; already sympathetic to the cause of the underdog, he is moved by speeches in support of women's rights and the rights of labor. His political sympathies draw him to hear abolitionist speakers, and while he is still uncertain about his feelings on the abolition of slavery, he becomes convinced that the new states admitted to the Union must be free.

Deutsch suggests that by 1850 Whitman's earliest poems have begun to form in his mind. Moving from one newspaper job to another, Whitman makes entries in his notebooks that eventually grow into the poems of *Leaves of Grass*. Deutsch suggests that Whitman's driving ambition—to become the poet of the people—leads to his creation of a voice that is direct, simple, and clear, a voice that he thrusts upon an indifferent public in 1855. *Leaves of Grass* catches the ear of Ralph Waldo Emerson, the philosopher-king of American letters. Emerson responds to Whitman's gift copy of *Leaves of Grass* with his famous salutation to a poet "at the beginning of a great career." Delighted with Emerson's compliment but stung by some very negative reviews, Whitman writes and publishes pseudonymous reviews to enlighten the world about his own talent. From this point on, Whitman's life is devoted to his writing and to the promotion of what he writes.

In 1860, just before the Civil War, two crucial events occur in Whitman's life. He visits Emerson in Concord, Massachusetts, and then sees Abraham Lincoln—already a proto-heroic figure for him—in New York. When war breaks out and his brother enlists, Whitman's life reaches a turning point; the poet travels to Washington, D.C., to care for wounded soldiers after his brother is injured in battle.

Whitman's effort as a "wound-dresser" and comforter for injured soldiers enables him to be both witness to and participant in a crucial event in his country's history, but it also wrecks his physical health. For the remainder of his life, he gradually declines in strength until he reaches the near-helplessness of his final days.

Whitman suffers a stroke in 1873 and spends the rest of his life struggling with sickness, poverty, and some public enmity. He continues to revise *Leaves of Grass*, publishing a centennial edition in 1876 and working toward a final edition. His stature as a poet and public figure increases toward the end of the century as the country rapidly expands and a strong nationalistic spirit arises. Printers are able to rush a few copies of the last edition of *Leaves of Grass* into Whitman's hands just before he dies in March of 1892.

◆ Literary Qualities ◆

One of the strongest features of Deutsch's biography of Walt Whitman is its extensive selection of more than 100 pages of his poems "arranged so as to present his own life-story." This section of the book is followed by a chapter-by-chapter listing of the poems that correspond, in Deutsch's view, to particular periods in the poet's life. Even for a poet as open and personal as Whitman, to assume the direct autobiographical equivalence of poetry and the poet's life is questionable, but Deutsch's choices are certainly useful as a guide to correspondences between incident and art. She used the material on Whitman available in 1940 to try to tell the story of the poet's life and work, whenever possible, from the perspective of the subject himself. Deutsch often uses the rhythms and images of Whitman's own writing to try to convey the mood of his thinking. Frequently, she depicts Whitman's responses to an especially important aspect of his world by directly interjecting an appropriate line from his poetry. Although Deutsch occasionally takes this technique into the realm of speculation, she is rarely far from the essential outlines of Whitman's life.

The other prominent feature of her work is an attempt to explain how Whitman's singular style of composition developed. To do this, she attempts to locate its origins in specific moments of perception in the course of the poet's life. Some of her speculation is sound, such as her observation that the "rough music at the station, the shouts of the newsboys, the rich brogue of the Irishwomen peddling peaches" influenced Whitman in his creation of poetic language that expressed the varieties of interesting speech he heard around him. She notes that he began to experiment with "loose unrhymed cadences" and that he was interested in breaking down "the barriers between verse and prose." She also draws interesting conclusions from early notebook entries, interjecting parenthetical asides amid Whitman's assertions.

In some cases, Deutsch tends to oversimplify, claiming that Whitman "broke all the rules. For one thing, his lines did not rhyme. They were almost as formless as prose," a statement that ignores the long breath lines and intricate rhythms that Whitman orchestrated into new but hardly formless measures. But for the most part, her main points— that nature served as a source of inspiration; that Whitman saw God in every object of creation and that this led him to embrace existence; that he took America as his ultimate subject and identified his destiny as a poet with his country's destiny; that he saw the "poet as prophet" of a new age—are helpful in understanding Whitman's poetry and some of the motivating factors behind its production.

◆ Social Sensitivity ◆

Casual references to "darkies" and "pickaninnies" early in the book indicate the unconscious use of racist language that even a sensitive and unprejudiced person might employ in Whitman's own time as well as in the 1940s without realizing the effects of such words. Most of the narrative, however, is quite sensitive to the evils of slavery and racial intolerance. A greater problem involves Whitman's sexual inclination. Even today there are some readers who are offended by Whitman's open celebrations of physical desires and feelings. Deutsch handles Whitman's sensually oriented poems tastefully, but generally avoids the issue. She has either decided to totally ignore any aspect of the poet's homosexual tendencies or else has completely accepted the story—regarded as historically accurate in the early twentieth-century—that Whitman's work was heavily influenced by a mysterious, unknown "beloved" who might have been secretly married to the poet or the mother of his children. Recent scholarship has not corroborated this tale, nor has it entirely discredited it. But to understand Whitman's poetry, it is crucial to realize that the type of love he expresses is not dependent on a response to any specific attraction. Rather, it is an encompassing ardor for what he admires in humanity: a predisposition to love and understand, to extend compassion and appreciation for all, including the unconventional and the unknown.

◆ Topics for Discussion ◆

1. Show how Whitman's boyhood on a farm on Long Island introduces him to the natural world. What other experiences in his life contribute to this interest?

2. Discuss Whitman's relationship to his immediate family. How do actions and decisions of other family members influence his work?

3. Whitman admires many people. Examine his attitude toward Abraham Lincoln, Ralph Waldo Emerson, and Elias Hicks.

4. How does Whitman use the sea in his poetry?

5. What images of the city occur in Whitman's poetry?

6. What kind of a picture of America does Whitman develop from his travels throughout the United States?

7. Examine Whitman's career as a journalist. What effect does this career have on his poetic style?

◆ Ideas for Reports and Papers ◆

1. Connect a particular poem to an incident in Whitman's life and show how Whitman used his experience as a foundation for poetic expression.

2. Examine Whitman's concept of democracy and show how he supported "democratic" virtues in his work.

3. Discuss Whitman's experiences in the Civil War and examine the poems that emerged from this aspect of his life.

4. Analyze any one of Whitman's poems in depth, or describe the major features of Whitman's poetic style in depth.

5. Trace the development of Whitman's reputation as a poet from the publication of *Leaves of Grass* until his death. Explain positive and negative responses to his work.

◆ Related Titles ◆

Readers who enjoy Deutsch's discussions of Whitman's work might also be interested in reading her *Poetry in Our Time: A Critical Survey of Poetry in the English-Speaking World, 1900-1960* (1963) or her *Poetry Handbook: A Dictionary of Terms* (1974).

◆ For Further Reference ◆

Allen, Gay Wilson. *The Solitary Singer: A Critical Biography of Walt Whitman.* New York: New York University Press, 1967. The first critical biography to connect the poet's life to his work. Comprehensive if not always penetrating.

Bedient, Calvin. "Walt Whitman." In *Voices and Visions*, edited by Helen Vendler. New York: Random House, 1987. An excellent, appreciative essay which places the poet and his work in the context of American poetry and thought.

Davenport, Guy. "Whitman." In *The Geography of the Imagination*. Berkeley, CA: North Point Press, 1981. An exceptionally imaginative and empathetic essay that captures the sensibility of the poet and sets it within the cultural context of Whitman's times.

Kaplan, Justin. *Walt Whitman: A Life.* New York: Simon and Schuster, 1980. Winner of a Pulitzer Prize and a National Book Award, this fine biography combines research with perceptive, revealing commentary.

Zweig, Paul. *Walt Whitman: The Making of the Poet.* New York: Basic Books, 1984. Very thoroughly researched and well-organized coverage of the period in Whitman's life between his employment with the *Brooklyn Daily Eagle* and the first publication of *Leaves of Grass.*

Leon Lewis
Appalachian State University

WATERLESS MOUNTAIN

Novel

1931

◆

Author: Laura Adams Armer, 1874-1963

Major Books for Young Adults

Waterless Mountain, 1931
Dark Circle of Branches, 1933
Cactus, 1934
Southwest, 1935
The Trader's Children, 1937
Farthest West, 1939
In Navajo Land, 1962

◆ About the Author ◆

Laura Adams Armer was born on January 12, 1874, in Sacramento, California. Her family moved to San Francisco when Armer was young, and she attended public and private schools there until the age of sixteen, when she was forced to continue her schooling at home because of ill health. Because San Francisco was an ethnic melting pot, Armer became infatuated at a young age with the various customs and traditions to which she was exposed.

In 1893 Armer enrolled at San Francisco's California School of Design and studied art under Arthur Matthews, a teacher and mentor who advised her against formalized systems of academic training. In 1902 she married Sidney Armer, a fellow artist who also studied under Matthews. The Armers' only child, Austin, was born in 1903, and Armer dedicated much of the next twenty years to being a mother and a homemaker.

In 1923, accompanied by Paul Louis Faye, a family friend, the Armers vacationed in northern Arizona's Navajo land; because she had brought with her printed translations of Navajo songs, as well as other books about Navajo lore, many Navajo came to visit her out of curiosity. The Navajo were impressed with Armer's painted reproductions of their sacred paintings, and Armer was impressed with the richness of their culture.

Armer returned to Navajo land in 1925, and with the help of Lorenzo Hubbell, a white trader, and Herbert, a Hopi, she set up camp at the base of the Blue Canyon cliffs that she described as a "painter's paradise." Eventually she became so well known and accepted among the Navajo that she was permitted to witness ceremonial dances that even Navajo women were not allowed to see, but only after she told the men to think of her as an artist rather than as a woman.

Armer's heart and imagination were captured by the beauty, legend, mysticism, and people of the Navajo land. In 1928, with the assistance of Lorenzo and Roman Hubbell, Armer produced *Mountain Chant,* a film about a Navajo ceremony featuring an all-Native American cast. Along with Armer's reproduction of Navajo sand paintings, *Mountain Chant* premiered at New York City's American Museum of Natural History in September 1928. Three years later, Armer published *Waterless Mountain,* a young adult novel based on her experiences among the Navajo. The book won the 1932 Newbery Medal. Armer's next book, *Dark Circle of Branches,* is the story of Na Nai (Navajo for "he who creeps"), an old medicine man born without any feet whom Armer often visited. Armer went on to publish books about other cultures as well, including *The Forest Pool* (1938), a book for young children about a Mexican boy. *The Forest Pool* won the 1939 Caldecott Medal for the best American picture book. One year before her death on March 3, 1963, Armer published an autobiographical account of the time she spent immersed in the Navajo culture entitled *In Navajo Land.*

◆ Overview ◆

Many books about Native Americans, such as Shannon Garst's *Crazy Horse,* Brent Ashabranner and Russell Davis's *Chief Joseph,* and Dee Brown's *Bury My Heart at Wounded Knee,* focus on the cultural clashes and inevitable wars between Native Americans and white settlers. While these stories are historically accurate and often depict the human side of the Native Americans, their main purpose is to detail the bloody clashes. On the other hand, Armer's *Waterless Mountain,* like Jim Kjelgaard's *Wolf Brother* and Dyre W. Doughty's *Crimson Moccasins,* falls into a category of books that focus on Native American life, folklore, and religious beliefs, providing insight into a rich culture. Because Armer lived among the Navajo and increased her understanding of their culture through research and firsthand experience, her work demonstrates a strong grasp of the Navajo perspective. Armer's novels are set in the 1920s, after the major cultural clashes and battles had taken place, and this setting enables her to focus on the Navajo's daily life and their stoic attempts to carry on tribal ways despite the onrush of twentieth-century technology and development.

◆ Setting ◆

Waterless Mountain takes place in the 1920s, a time that coincides with the author's visits among Arizona's Navajo people. The Navajo, as well as the other Native American tribes, have clashed culturally with the white world and have suffered from these clashes. In *Waterless Mountain,* for example, Armer alludes to the Navajo's "Long March" of the 1860s, when the United States government exiled them to Fort Sumner, an ordeal related in Ruth Roessel's *Navajo Stories of the Long Walk Period* and in Scott O'Dell's novel *Sing Down the Moon.* Armer's main purpose, however, is to detail the simple pleasures of Navajo daily life, especially their close bonds with the land itself. Armer also alludes to twentieth-century inventions that intrude upon the Navajo way of life: the airplane, the automobile, and the steam locomotive. Even the segment in which Younger Brother and the white boy join each other hints of the white world's eventual incursion into Navajo land and life.

At the same time, Armer's primary setting is the Navajo land with its beautiful mountains, canyons, and sage brush. Armer's depiction of this setting not only conveys an accurate sense of the land itself, but it also complements the story's main thrust: the rites-of-passage theme as Younger Brother matures and moves toward becoming a Navajo medicine man who is one with the land, the animals, and the universe.

Illustration by Sidney Armer and Laura Adams Armer for *Waterless Mountain* by Laura Adams Armer. David McKay: New York (1975).

◆ Themes and Characters ◆

Through the characterization of her protagonist, Younger Brother, Armer develops the rites-of-passage theme in *Waterless Mountain*. As the novel opens, Younger Brother is eight years old and lives with his family—Father, Mother, Elder Brother, and Baby Sister. These generic names suggest the universal aspects of the family unit. Younger Brother's duties as an eight-year-old include taking care of the family's sheep herd. While tending the sheep, he observes the birds and beasts, wind, clouds, rain, and rainbows. He also forms mystical bonds with the bees that eat jam from his lips, the Deer People that sing and dance for him, and the Pack Rat that trades treasures with him. When Younger Brother grows up, he will be a medicine man, and to prepare him for this role, his medicine man uncle tells him Navajo legends about the First Man and the First Woman, the Spider Woman who teaches the First

Woman how to weave Navajo blankets, and the Turquoise Woman and her husband, the Sun Bearer.

When Younger Brother is twelve years old and has his own pony, he leaves home as part of his initiation to adulthood and travels west in search of the Turquoise Woman and the Sun Bearer. This journey increases his knowledge and enriches his perspective by introducing him to the outside world. At the same time, the journey increases both his appreciation of his home and his desire to become the tribe's medicine man. When he returns home, he knows the location of the tribe's lost deerskin masks that were hidden in a cave before the Navajo began their "Long March" in 1863.

The members of Younger Brother's family are not important to the plot line, but Armer uses them to round out her picture of Navajo family life and traditions. Father is an excellent silversmith who fashions turquoise jewelry and thus provides insight into Navajo beliefs about the mystical qualities of turquoise. Mother is a skilled weaver of rugs and thus reflects the influence of the Spider Woman legend. Elder Brother teaches Younger Brother about hunting and Navajo lore.

She called to the Sun to ask him how she was to cross the water to her island home, and he sent a gorgeous rainbow for her to travel on.

The Big Man, the white man who operates the trading post, is the Navajo's friend whom they respectfully call "Grandfather." When Younger Brother first meets the Big Man he senses the man's friendly nature and thinks that the Big Man may be a medicine man whose power is in his blue eyes. In addition to taking Younger Brother on his first airplane and automobile ride, the Big Man also accompanies Younger Brother on his excursion into the modern world and to the Pacific Ocean. Within the plot's larger construct, the Big Man's characterization represents the white man who admires and respects the Native Americans. In a sense,

too, he may be a fictional combination of Armer, Paul Lewis Faye, and Lorenzo Hubbell. At the same time, with his automobile, airplane, adding machine, and trading post, the Big Man also symbolizes the intrusion of the twentieth century upon the Navajo's life and world.

◆ Literary Qualities ◆

Waterless Mountain belongs to the universal literary tradition of the rites-of-passage story that traces an adolescent's acquisition of knowledge about himself or herself and the world. In *Waterless Mountain,* the rites-of-passage motif fuses with the journey motif, during which the questing hero or heroine experiences a separation, a series of adventures, and a return. Younger Brother's separation occurs when he begins his journey in quest of the Turquoise Woman. During his journey, he experiences different adventures—his meeting with the white boy during the sand storm, his encounter with the renegade Cut Finger, the tragic flood at the camp called Beautiful Under the Cottonwoods, and the strange, marvelous inventions in the white man's twentieth-century world. When he returns from his quest, he has matured and gained knowledge about himself and Navajo traditions. Complementing these exciting adventures are the Navajo legends that Armer weaves into the narrative—the legends about the Deer People, the Spider Woman, the Pack Rat, the Sun Bearer, and the Turquoise Woman. While providing deeper insights into Navajo life and beliefs, these legends also explain how and why Younger Brother moves toward becoming a medicine man.

Another valuable literary quality of *Waterless Mountain* is its vivid imagery, derived from Armer's painting background and her firsthand experience of living among the Navajo. Whether it is a thunderstorm with "evil serpents of lightning across the sky," a girl's skirt that is "the color of the garnets on the ant hills and trimmed with a finger-wide band of deep blue," or the landscape's vivid blues, browns, greens, golds, and yellows, Armer's descriptions carry the reader into Navajo land and life.

◆ Social Sensitivity ◆

Unlike many books about Native Americans, *Waterless Mountain* does not dwell on the social issues surrounding the conflicts between the white and Native American cultures. Armer acknowledges the existence of such conflicts and mentions the tragic Navajo "Long March," but her primary purpose is to celebrate the vitality of the Navajo culture, not to emphasize events that undermined it. She shows Younger Brother and his people pursuing a traditional way of life as the twentieth-century technology that threatens traditional ways lurks in the background of the narrative. Younger Brother's interactions with the white characters who appear in the narrative suggest that Armer, perhaps idealistically, hoped that her novel would stand as an example of how white and Native American cultures could live in harmony if each tried to understand the other. Some readers, though, may find Armer's depiction of the Big Man somewhat disturbing, for the Native Americans occasionally seem to be too dependent on this benevolent white man.

◆ Topics for Discussion ◆

1. *Waterless Mountain* contains insights into Navajo customs and traditions. Discuss the importance of one or two of these customs or traditions.

2. *Waterless Mountain* also contains insights into the Navajo's religious beliefs. Can you draw any parallels between Navajo religion and other religions that you are familiar with?

3. In terms of the novel's plot and theme, discuss the role and significance of the following characters: the Big Man; the white boy whom Younger Brother meets during the sandstorm; Cut Finger; and Elder Brother's wife.

4. In terms of the novel's plot and theme, what is the significance of Younger Brother's encounter with Yellow Beak, the Pack Rat, and the Soft-Footed Chief?

5. Younger Brother gains important knowledge from his experiences during his journey west. Which experience do you think he learns the most from? Why?

6. After the Big Man and Younger Brother and his family have been in the white man's world, the Big Man says, "Yes, we must all go back. We do not belong here. There is too much noise and too much heaping of goods." What does this mean and how does it also apply to Younger Brother's newfound knowledge?

7. Before she became a writer, Laura Adams Armer was a painter, and in *Waterless Mountain* her prose descriptions create vivid images. Pick one of your favorite descriptions from the novel

and read the passage aloud. What makes it an effective passage?

8. Because she lived among the Navajos and learned their language, customs, and traditions, Armer's narration has an insider's point-of-view. Discuss several scenes in which the insider's point-of-view is evident.

9. The entire narrative of *Waterless Mountain* points toward Younger Brother's return home and his help in finding the lost tribal masks. What gives him insight into the masks' location, and how does finding the masks emphasize his role as a future Navajo medicine man?

♦ Ideas for Reports and Papers ♦

1. Prepare a report about turquoise. Discuss where it is found in the United States, what colors it has, what the Navajo use the stone for, and what they believe about this gemstone. What is the significance of turquoise in *Waterless Mountain*?

2. Prepare a report about Navajo sand paintings. Discuss the colors that are used, the subject matter of the paintings, and the paintings' legendary or religious significance.

3. Prepare a report about Navajo rugs—how they are made, what colors are used, what figures are depicted, and what the figures represent.

4. Prepare a report about Laura Adams Armer's art career and paintings, describing her various subjects and explaining the critical response to her art.

5. Prepare a report about Armer's *In Navajo Land* and emphasize some of the interesting and exciting events she describes in this biographical account. What is her attitude toward the Native Americans? Is her tone explicitly or implicitly condescending?

6. Prepare a report about the Navajo medicine man, emphasizing the purpose of the medicine man, the process for becoming a medicine man, and the duties of the medicine man. Is the medicine man still a respected member of the Navajo community? How does his role compare to that of an American medical doctor?

7. Prepare a report about the ancient cliff dwellers who once lived in cliff dwellings near Younger Brother's home. Where did the cliff dwellers come from, and what became of them?

8. Prepare a report about the history of the Navajo's "Long March," emphasizing why they made the march, the hardships they endured on the march, and the final result of the march. Are Native Americans still oppressed in the United States?

9. Prepare a report on the traditional roles of men and women in Navajo society. How have those roles evolved? Are Navajo men and women still able to practice the rituals and traditions that once defined their identities? How has the influence of white culture changed these roles?

♦ Related Titles ♦

Like *Waterless Mountain*, *Dark Circle of Branches* focuses on a Navajo adolescent—Na Nai—as he matures, learns from his medicine man uncle and from life, and realizes that his destiny is to become a medicine man. Armer also addresses Navajo legends and the relationship between the white and Navajo world in this later novel, and devotes some narrative sequences to the place of the "Long Walk" in Navajo history.

Although *In Navajo Land* is an autobiographical account of Armer's experiences, the details she records echo some of the plot details from her fiction. This work of nonfiction describes ceremonial dances, cliff dwellings, and Navajo customs and traditions, and even includes a chapter on Na Nai.

◆ For Further Reference ◆

Amsden, Charles Avery. *Navaho Weaving: Its Technique and History.* Chicago: Rio Grande Press, 1964. This book provides interesting insights into an ancient Navajo art and includes photographs showing techniques.

Bleeker, Sonia. *The Navajos: Herders, Weavers, and Silversmiths.* New York: William Morrow, 1958. A valuable background for understanding Navajo life, customs, and skills.

Breed, Jack. "Better Days for the Navajos." *National Geographic* 114 (December 1958): 809-847. An easy to read account of the Navajo life in the 1950s, highlighted by excellent photographs.

Frisbie, Charlotte J., and David P. McAllester, eds. *Navajo Blessingway Singer: The Autobiography of Frank Mitchell, 1881-1967.* Tucson: University of Arizona Press, 1978. An account of one man's experiences as a Navajo ceremonial singer.

Gilpin, Laura. *The Enduring Navajo.* Austin: University of Texas Press, 1968. Readable text augmented with photographs of the Navajo land and its people.

Newcomb, Lois. *Navajo Folk Tales.* Sante Fe: Museum of Navajo Ceremonial Art, 1967. An interesting collection of folktales.

Roessel, Ruth, ed. *Navajo Stories of the Long Walk Period.* Tsaile, AZ: Navajo Community College Press, 1973. An interesting collection of stories about the "Long Walk" as recounted by individual Navajo.

Edward C. Reilly
Arkansas State University

THE WHEEL ON THE SCHOOL
Novel
1954

Author: Meindert DeJong, b. 1906

Major Books for Young Adults

Bells of the Harbor, 1941
Billy and the Unhappy Bull, 1946
The Wheel on the School, 1954
The House of Sixty Fathers, 1956
Along Came a Dog, 1958

The Singing Hill, 1962
Far Out the Long Canal, 1964
Journey from Peppermint Street,
    1968

◆ About the Author ◆

Born on March 4, 1906, in the village of Wierum (located in the province of Friesland on the north coast of the Netherlands), Meindert DeJong came to the United States with his family in 1914. In Grand Rapids, Michigan, where the DeJongs settled, Meindert attended Dutch Calvinist secondary schools and Calvin College. He later attended the University of Chicago but left without a degree. During the Great Depression, DeJong held many different jobs and began writing for children and young adults only at the suggestion of a local librarian. He published his first book, *The Big Goose and the Little White Duck*, in 1938.

After completing several more books, DeJong joined the U.S. Army Air Corps during the Second World War and served in China. Readjusting to civilian life after the war, he continued his writing career, and during the 1950s wrote a book a year. He spent several years in

Mexico during the next decade and wrote six books during this period. Returning to the United States, DeJong stayed for a period in Michigan before settling in North Carolina.

Many of DeJong's novels deal with a young person overcoming the difficulties of living in a world controlled by adults. The books often take place in a foreign land and often feature animals as important characters. *The House of Sixty Fathers*, which grew out of DeJong's World War II military experiences, is about a boy and his pet pig. *Journey from Peppermint Street* and *The Wheel on the School* are set in Holland. Maurice Sendak illustrated six of DeJong's books, including *The Wheel on the School*.

DeJong has received several prestigious awards for his writing. *The Wheel on the School* was awarded the 1955 Newbery Medal; *Journey from Peppermint Street* won the 1969 National Book Award; and *The House of Sixty Fathers* received the Children's Book

Award of the Child Study Association and was named a Newbery Honor Book. In 1962 DeJong won the International Hans Christian Andersen Award for his contributions to literature for young people.

◆ Overview ◆

The chief goal of *The Wheel on the School* is to illustrate how members of a community can work together and grow closer in the process of achieving a common goal. DeJong develops this theme in his tightly structured dramatic novel set in the Dutch village of Shora during the early twentieth century.

The routine business of Shora is interrupted after Lina, the only girl in the village school, asks why there are no storks in Shora. Since storks bring good luck, the village ought to have some of the birds nesting on its roofs, but for some reason the storks do not come. Lina's teacher encourages the class to ponder Lina's question, and before long the entire village—old people, parents, children, and even pre-schoolers—are involved in bringing storks and their good luck to the town.

◆ Setting ◆

DeJong establishes the setting in the opening lines of the novel. A fishing village on the North Sea protected by a dike, Shora is located in the province of Friesland. The village of Ternaard is located south of Shora, and the next village along the dike to the northeast is Nes. A canal road connects Shora to Hantum.

The novel's depiction of Dutch village life may at first appear out of step with the rushing modern world of rapid travel and instant communications. The story probably takes place around 1912, when DeJong himself could have been one of the pupils in the village school. At this time, before the two world wars, people in Shora dress as they have for centuries, wearing native costumes and wooden shoes. Almost no events from the world at large seem important in this small village, which depends on fishing for its livelihood. The sea and the sky provide topics of conversation that vary only with the weather.

◆ Themes and Characters ◆

The story begins and ends in the village school, but there is an important difference in the setting at the conclusion of the story: a wheel rests on the school for storks to nest in, and two waterlogged storks have been rescued to tenant the straw atop the wheel. DeJong explains how the children, their parents, and the old people of the village manage this feat, emphasizing what happens to a community when its members take joy in working together to achieve a common goal. Focusing on the children's points of view as well as their initiative, DeJong is primarily interested in the role that children can play as a force for action in the world, even this small world of the village.

On the Friday afternoon in spring that Lina reads her composition about storks, the students get immediate assistance from their teacher, but not in the form of action. He challenges their existing knowledge, asking them what they know about storks, and then asks them to exercise their curiosity: "Will you wonder why storks don't come to Shora to build their nests on the roofs, the way they do in all the villages around? For sometimes when we wonder, we can make things begin to happen." Grandmother Sibble III further fires Lina's imagination by telling her that when she herself was a child, storks nested in the village.

The next day, Lina and five boys undertake searches for a wheel. Jella is the biggest of the boys and husky for his age; Eelka is mentally swift, but physically slow and clumsy; Auka is "a nice, everyday boy"; and Pier and Dirk are twins who enjoy each other's company. A chapter is devoted to each individual search, ending with that of Lina, who finds a wheel in a most unlikely place with the help of the hearty village patriarch, Douwa.

Hunting for a wheel involves others, and the children's searches begin to connect people: Pier and Dirk encounter the legless Janus, who the children think is the meanest man in the village until he becomes a friend and helper. Eelka pulls the drowning Jella out of a canal. Auka meets a seller of pots and pans, the Tin Man, on the way to Nes. Through some clever maneuvering, Auka helps the Tin Man get a wheel for his wagon. In gratitude the Tin Man gives Auka a wagon ride back to Shora, where he and many other villagers work together to help Lina salvage a wheel for the school.

Putting the wheel on the school unites the community of Shora. Even people who seem to be outsiders, such as Janus and Douwa, are brought into the group. Friendships develop, especially between the young and their elders: characters give up prejudices about others, and together they overcome obstacles. Since no one seems to know exactly how to raise the wheel to the top of the school, the villagers learn through experience and achieve their goal through perseverance.

Illustration by Maurice Sendak for *The Wheel on the School* by Meindert DeJong. Harper & Row: New York (1954).

Two processes are central to the story—teaching and learning. After Lina reads her paper, the class starts on a quest for information, which turns into a quest for a wheel. Since none of the children has been involved in such a search before, the process of finding a wheel becomes an adventure. The book also shows that people can gather information from unexpected sources. Adults whom the children previously ignored suddenly seem important. For instance, Lina realizes that Grandmother Sibble III knows a great deal and is willing to share her knowledge. The old woman suggests that Lina must think like a stork, explaining that it is necessary to put oneself in the situation of others. The children learn that questions are important, even if they do not yield instant answers, and that dreams and wishes have value, too, but must be supported by actions. The villagers must find a wheel before they can hope for storks, and the teacher encourages the students to "look for a wagon wheel where one is and where one isn't; where one could be and where one couldn't possibly be." Instead of training the children to learn by rote or by example, the teacher encourages independent thought, curiosity, and creativity.

◆ Literary Qualities ◆

DeJong creates suspense by giving the children a goal that may appear unattainable. What seems a trivial matter at first becomes an all-consuming passion for them and for the rest of the village. Suspense is heightened further when DeJong shifts the action in times of crisis. For example, while Lina and Douwa wait to be rescued, the narrative suddenly jumps to the legless Janus, the teacher, and the boys who are trying to fish a wheel rim out of a canal. Similarly, the raging storm described near the book's end continues unabated for five days, forcing the village to wait to find storks.

The focal object of the story is, of course, the wheel, which begins to symbolize the effort that goes into finding it. All the children and some of the adults work as spokes that will support a hub—or central "dream"—around which they turn. This one dream seizes the imagination of the villagers and leads all of them to work together. The concept of the wheel also encircles the community, bringing the village inside its circumference. Perhaps it is this clearly developed symbol of a simple idea that makes The Wheel on the School so believable.

The novel's omniscient narrator concentrates on the children, telling what each one thinks. Because the narrator never provides similar insights into the adults' thoughts, the tale belongs to the children. The children's language includes American colloquialisms, making it easier for American readers to identify with the children of Shora.

Maurice Sendak's illustrations in The Wheel on the School give readers a clearer understanding of Dutch costume and dress. Ultimately, the book teaches a great deal about early twentieth-century Dutch culture through the subtle integration of text with illustration, but the plot itself is always more important than the details conveyed in either the pictures or the text. One interesting point is that there are no full-page pictures; therefore, all of the drawings are in close proximity to the parts of the text they illustrate. The drawings underscore the text rather than extend or overwhelm what DeJong has written.

◆ Social Sensitivity ◆

The children's goal of getting the wheel on their school becomes a project that includes the participation of the whole community—the aged, the disabled, the toddlers, and the middle-aged parents. The project provides everyone with a chance to do something important for the village and for themselves. If the children, with help from all the others, are able to achieve their goal, they can take pride in something they started. Teamwork is all-important, and the villagers have a collective sense that they are doing something for the common good. Even if storks are supposed to bring good fortune, it is not luck that unites the village, but rather the effort with which everyone—from legless Janus and ninety-three-year-old Douwa to the tots in the tower—contributes to the cause. The villagers are rewarded when they learn to tolerate one another's differences and to value and respect the contributions that each individual is able to make. DeJong stresses the importance of tolerance and cooperation, and *The Wheel on the School* teaches its readers a positive lesson as a result.

• Topics for Discussion •

1. Janus is thought of as the meanest man in the village, at least until the children get to know him. What general and specific ideas emerge from DeJong's treatment of Janus's character?

2. The teacher is an important person who helps transform the children's thoughts into action. Why do you suppose that DeJong never gives the teacher a name?

3. How do the children encourage adults to become interested in their project?

4. How important is the setting to the events of the novel? Could the story be elsewhere?

5. What have you learned from *The Wheel on the School* about the Dutch countryside and village life in the early twentieth century?

• Ideas for Reports and Papers •

1. One scientific method for solving problems is as follows: 1) select an area for research, 2) define the problem, 3) gather data, 4) organize and test data, 5) formulate a hypothesis, 6) test the hypothesis, and 7) accept or reject the hypothesis. Although this specific method may not have been the model the teacher had in mind, this process seems applicable to the way the children discover the solution in the book. Show how the villagers use each step in this process to bring storks to Shora.

2. Consult some nonfiction books about storks. How would an ornithologist—a scientist who studies birds—view the events in *The Wheel on the School?* How accurate is the information about storks? Consider, too, the superstition that storks bring luck.

3. The story begins on a Friday and concludes the following Friday. Explain what happens on each day and discuss the novel's structure.

4. Water plays an important part in the action of the novel. Why does DeJong use this one element so frequently? Are the repeated rescues at sea the only pattern DeJong creates from the ever-present water?

5. Trace how Lina, Jella, Eelka, Auka, Pier, and Dirk each contribute to the process of getting the wheel on the school.

• For Further Reference •

Cianciolo, Patricia Jean. "Meindert De-Jong." *Elementary English* 45 (1968): 725-730. Biographical and critical commentary.

Commire, Anne, ed. *Something about the Author.* Vol. 2. Detroit: Gale Research, 1972. Contains a brief sketch of DeJong's life and works.

DeJong, David Cornel. "My Brother Meindert." *Horn Book* 31 (August 1955): 247-253. Biographical information about Meindert DeJong by his brother.

DeJong, Meindert. "For the Love of the Word." *Horn Book* 60 (September/October 1984): 569-577. The author discusses his beginnings as a writer of children's books.

————. "Newbery Award Acceptance." *Horn Book* 31 (August 1955): 241-246. In his speech, DeJong talks about the writing of *The Wheel on the School*.

Kirkpatrick, D. L., ed. "Meindert DeJong." *Twentieth-Century Children's Writers*. 2d ed. New York: St. Martin's, 1983. Contains a bibliography of DeJong's writings and brief critical commentary.

Lindquist, Jennie D. "Review." *Horn Book* 30 (December 1954): 431-432. Short, positive review of *The Wheel on the School*.

Susan Garland Mann
Indiana University Southeast

David D. Mann
Miami University

WHERE THE LILIES BLOOM
Novel

1969

◆

Authors: Vera Cleaver, b. 1919
Bill Cleaver, 1920-1981

Major Books for Young Adults

By Vera Cleaver and Bill Cleaver:

Ellen Grae, 1967
Lady Ellen Grae, 1968
Where the Lilies Bloom, 1969
Grover, 1970
The Mimosa Tree, 1970
The Mock Revolt, 1971
The Whys and Wherefores of Littabelle Lee, 1973
Me Too, 1973
Dust of the Earth, 1975
Trial Valley, 1977
Queen of Hearts, 1978
A Little Destiny, 1979
The Kissimmee Kid, 1981
Hazel Rye, 1983

By Vera Cleaver:

Sugar Blue, 1984
Sweetly Sings the Donkey, 1985

◆ About the Authors ◆

Bill and Vera Cleaver, married in 1945, wrote seventeen books together. Although they won few awards, their books have consistently received high critical acclaim.

Vera Fern Allen Cleaver was born on January 6, 1919, in Virgil, South Dakota, and grew up in Florida during the Great Depression. William Joseph Cleaver was born on March 24, 1920, in Hugo, Oklahoma, and grew up in Seattle, Washington. Although neither finished college, they both put a great emphasis on self-directed learning, claiming to be "graduates of the public libraries of America." Bill Cleaver served as a sergeant in the U.S. Air Force for many years, and Vera Cleaver was a U.S. Air Force accountant in Japan and France. During the early years of their marriage, the Cleavers wrote stories for pulp and family magazines. It was not until 1967 that their first young adult novel, *Ellen Grae*, was published.

The Cleavers derived many of the themes of their novels from their childhood experiences and observations, and in many cases they were the first writers to deal with these subjects in books for young adult readers. Both authors moved frequently as children and were exposed to poverty, illness, and family problems. Vera was the fifth of nine children, one of whom was mentally retarded. Bill's parents divorced when he was five, and he was sent to a private school in British Columbia, Canada. Mental retardation and divorce or parental abandonment are discussed in several of the Cleavers' novels. Their novels also reflect the value that both authors, from childhood on, placed on education and literacy.

Nearly all of the Cleavers' books have appeared on "best book" lists of publications such as the *New York Times Book Review*, *School Library Journal*, *Horn Book*, and *Publishers Weekly*. Their books *Grover* and *The Whys and Wherefores of Littabelle Lee* were National Book Award nominees in 1971 and 1974. *Ellen Grae* and *Where the Lilies Bloom* appeared on the *Horn Book* Honor List and *Me Too* was named an American Library Association Notable Book. *Dust of the Earth* won the 1975 Lewis Carroll Shelf Award and the 1975 Golden Spur award. *Queen of Hearts* was a 1979 finalist for the National Book Award. It has been suggested that one reason the Cleavers have won no major literary award is that no one of their books can be chosen as exceptional; rather, nearly all are consistently excellent.

Before Bill's death, the Cleavers worked together as a team on each book they produced. Bill usually came up with the basic plot and story line. Vera then did the actual writing, filling in details, dialogue, and action, while Bill researched the subjects and people they were writing about. After her husband's death on August 20, 1981, in Winter Haven, Florida, Vera completed their last joint novel, *Hazel Rye*, and she has since written two novels on her own, *Sugar Blue* and *Sweetly Sings the Donkey*. These, too, carry on the Cleavers' tradition of serious literature for young adults.

◆ Overview ◆

Where the Lilies Bloom is about self-reliance in the face of terrible odds. In this book, four orphaned children struggle to stay together and avoid being put in an orphanage. There are many obstacles: poverty, the harsh winter weather, the threat of their father's death being discovered, and the possibility of losing their house. The family must also deal with internal conflict brought on by normal sibling rivalry, aggravated in this case by the fact that one sibling, fourteen-year-old Mary Call, is the designated leader and the others are supposed to do as she says.

Readers come away from this book, which shows a group of children overcoming enormous obstacles, with a feeling of empowerment. The novel seeks to educate readers about poverty and in so doing encourages them to feel more compassion for the poor. Most readers will come away with a renewed sense of family pride and an appreciation of the importance of closeness within a family.

◆ Setting ◆

Although a particular period is never identified, the descriptions suggest that the story is set in the North Carolina mountains during the late 1950s or early 1960s. In many ways time moves more slowly in the mountains, and modern-day conveniences, such as electricity, refrigerators, radios, and cars, are luxuries in this setting. The Luthers' poverty is revealed by the description of their home, a "woeful," "seedy," and "downright disgraceful" shack. The mountains and land around the shack, though, are beautiful, "the fairest land of them all," and this fair land produces the wild plants that allow the children to survive. The plants have beautiful names: mayapple, witch hazel, ginseng, goldenseal, stargrass root, and queen's delight. The book's title refers to the beautiful mountain landscape, as well as to the mountain hymn, "Where the Lilies Bloom So Fair." Nature provides a livelihood for the children but it also brings suffering with its winter blizzards, spring rain storms, and scorching summer heat. To a large extent, the whims of nature determine whether life will be comfortable or dangerous for the Luthers. The children must be ever aware of natural threats such as storms and poisonous snakes. The story revolves around its setting, and nature itself almost becomes another character.

Photograph from Radnitz/Mattel film production of *Where the Lilies Bloom*, released by United Artists, reprinted in *Where the Lilies Bloom* by Vera and Bill Cleaver. Signet/New American Library/ J. B. Lippincott: New York (1969).

◆ Themes and Characters ◆

Where the Lilies Bloom portrays poverty in a realistic light, neither glossing over its ugliness nor dwelling unnecessarily on any of its horrors. Mary Call Luther has promised her father that the family will never accept charity, so the four children must work for a living without letting anyone find out their father has died. Mary Call comes up with a plan: the family will become "wildcrafters," gathering and selling medicinal plants that grow wild in the mountains. Through extremely hard

work, cleverness, and some luck, the Luthers survive. As the book ends one feels that the Luther family will be fine, and probably closer and stronger than ever.

The central conflict in the story revolves around Mary Call Luther's feeling of responsibility for her family. Her sense of obligation to fulfill the promises she made to her dying father leads to her feelings of inadequacy and rebellion. She fights with her brother and sisters, who say she is mean and "hateful," and struggles with a part of herself that wants to run away from the entire situation. Mary Call is a strong character, made wiser than most fourteen-year-olds by her duties to her family and her sense of honor. As the narrative progresses, she senses her strength: she can win the fight against nature, provide for her family, and keep most of her promises to her father. Mary Call is a model of self-control and perseverance, and her character suggests that anything is possible for someone who has enough motivation.

The novel features several interesting and unusual characters. Romey Luther, the ten-year-old brother, is generally loving and mature for his age. Although rebellious at times, he "has none of the rough makings of a farm boy." Eighteen-year-old Devola Luther is a sort of mother to her younger siblings; she apparently suffers from a mental disability that makes her "cloudy-headed." Kiser Pease, one of the villains of the story, is really more comic than evil, with his yearnings for Devola, his superstitions, and his rotten teeth. Mrs. Connell (whom Romey calls an "old bat,") is the only truly evil character. She plagues the children with her criticizing, prying, and threats. She vows to make sure that the children go to "an institution for people like them" when Roy Luther dies. She takes a sad pleasure in tormenting the children with tales of her own childhood as an orphan, and in ridiculing their old, torn clothing and proud refusal of charity. Even her gifts are meant to hurt: she gives Ima Dean, the youngest sister, a bag of candy, a real luxury to a poor little girl. When the child opens it, however, she finds the candy is so "old and dirty" that "nobody could've eaten it."

The need for emotional, financial, and physical security, the need to fulfill appointed duties and promises, and the need for family unity and pride are the themes that run throughout this story.

Although most readers will not have experienced the level of poverty that the Luthers endure, they will be able to relate to the spirit of struggle and will rejoice in the triumph of Mary Call and her siblings.

♦ Literary Qualities ♦

Where the Lilies Bloom is a straightforward story, without many obvious double meanings, symbols, or mythic elements. It is narrated by Mary Call and, apart from occasional awkward phrases, which seem self-consciously "poetic," the writing is clear, smooth, and often beautiful. The Cleavers always research the geographic areas they write about, and as a result the colorful mountain dialect is authentic.

The Cleavers use humor to lighten what might otherwise be a very depressing narrative. Mary Call and Romey keep their wits about them, and they usually have some amusing observation about the people or situations confronting them. The scene in which Mary Call uses a mountain recipe to heal Kiser Pease of pneumonia—the recipe calls for the patient to be stripped and slathered with cooked onion slices—is very funny, although it also contains numerous references to the Luthers' poverty and to the possibility of Kiser's death. Romey, with his optimistic spirit, is often thinking of pranks. His most successful prank comes when he frightens Mrs. Connell away with a stuffed bear: "I like to died laughing, watching that old bird fly out of here," he says of his enemy, the "old bat." Throughout the book, even in the midst of the most serious situations, the authors include enough comedy that the reader never feels overwhelmed or hopeless.

Where the Lilies Bloom

Nature plays a symbolic role in the novel. It is portrayed as something that can be exquisitely beautiful or hatefully ugly, depending on the season and one's financial resources. As the Luthers' poverty moves them further and further away from a "civilized" lifestyle and toward a primitive way of life, they become ever more reliant on nature and more affected by weather. This move toward nature progresses slowly throughout the book. At first the Luthers try to save money by not using the electricity in their house. Then winter comes and the roof falls in, leaving a gaping hole in the middle of the house where snow and wild animals can enter. Near the end of the book the Luthers are so poor that they must move out of their shack and into a cave, like "troglodytes." As this move towards primitivism progresses, there is an identification of the Luther children with animals or birds. When winter comes, the rooster, pig, and cow are brought indoors, and the house becomes a stable. The cow eventually takes over Romey's entire room, and "the smell that came from it was not good and it was not now a laughing matter." When the roof caves in, Mary Call must fight a wild fox for the rooster. She wonders if the fox has approached a human habitation because it is so hungry it has lost its natural fear, or because Mary Call herself no longer looks like a human. Finally, Mary Call decides the family must move into a cave.

It is interesting to note that as they become more identified with beasts and nature, the Luther children withdraw more from the company of other human beings. Mary Call makes Romey refuse an invitation to the Graybeals' house, and later declines a ride with Mr. Graybeal during a rainstorm. Romey also uses an animal to frighten away

Mrs. Connell. Kiser Pease is, for the most part, the only person the children see, and his visits are often prompted by his desire to give animals to Devola; his gifts to her include a pig and a cow.

◆ Social Sensitivity ◆

Where the Lilies Bloom shows how ambitious, intelligent people can be caught in the downward pull of poverty by factors beyond their control, such as illness, a poor local economy, or unfair land division. The novel also explores the potential abuses of the tenant farming system. The Cleavers never blame the true victims of poverty, but they criticize people who abuse the welfare system.

Parents or teachers should discuss the Luthers' extreme views on charity with young readers. The Luthers feel that charity is "seldom of real service to those upon whom it is bestowed and those who receive it are always looked upon with suspicion, every need and want scrutinized." Readers should be asked to decide how realistic this attitude is and to examine their own attitudes toward receiving and giving charity.

Another social issue raised by the Cleavers is that of children's rights. The Luthers are threatened, in large part, because of their youth. If they were older, Roy Luther's death would not have to be kept secret, because his children would not face the threat of a foster home. In this book, adults are not portrayed as exceptionally wise, good, or dependable. Roy Luther has let himself be beaten by poverty and by Kiser Pease; Kiser has been selfish and greedy; Mrs. Connell is cruel and hateful. Mr. Connell and Miss Breathitt, the teacher, are the only admirable adult figures in the book. Readers might discuss the rights and protections that children should have. They should also talk about the qualities that make Mr. Connell and Miss Breathitt stand out as exemplary adults.

Where the Lilies Bloom also deals with the issue of mental disability. Devola is not incapable of learning, but she is slow and somewhat gullible. Naturally, Roy Luther is concerned about her future. However, in the process of insuring that she will be safe and provided for, he takes away her freedom of choice by forbidding her to marry Kiser. Parents or teachers might discuss the rights of the mentally disabled and ask if Roy's decision is justifiable.

4. Think about Mary Call's attitude about charity: that it demeans people and makes them smaller than they are. Do you agree with her? Why or why not? Is charity always demeaning? What is the difference, if any, between charity and kindness?

5. Have you ever tried to help someone, only to have that person snap at you? Have you ever done this to someone trying to help you? Mary Call's siblings get very angry at her, and at times she thinks of leaving them. What are the differences between Mary Call's fits of anger and those of her brother and sisters?

◆ Topics for Discussion ◆

1. At the end of *Where the Lilies Bloom*, Mary Call has broken two of her promises to Roy Luther. She has taken charity (Kiser's gifts of ham, a cow, a pig, and a radio) and she has let Devola marry Kiser. Furthermore, Kiser is Mary Call's great enemy, symbolizing everything that is unjust. At the end of the book, Mary Call is, in a sense, Kiser's child, because he has become her legal guardian. Does this mean that Mary Call has been beaten? Why do the authors give such a strong role to Kiser in the story?

2. Is it right for Roy Luther to put such a heavy burden on his fourteen-year-old daughter?

3. If Mary Call did not have her family to think of, she probably would react differently to Roy Luther's death. How does her sense of responsibility affect the choices she makes?

◆ Ideas for Reports and Papers ◆

1. Retell a chapter of the novel from the point of view of another character, such as Kiser Pease, Devola, Romey, Mrs. Connell, or Miss Breathitt.

2. Explore the developing characterization in *Where the Lilies Bloom*. For example, what does Mary Call mean when she says Devola is "cloudy-headed?" Does Devola seem cloudy-headed to you? Is she cloudy-headed at the end of the story? If not, what has caused her to change? Or you may want to focus on Kiser, who changes dramatically during the course of the story. Is he a better person at the end? What has brought about his apparent reformation? Is it a lasting change?

3. Discuss the animals and birds used as symbols in the story. Do they mean the same thing to Romey as they do to Mary Call or Devola? What about the lilies of the title, or spring?

4. Research mountain life in North Carolina today. Is wildcrafting still practiced? Is poverty still a problem?

5. Think back on a time when you had a very hard decision to make, and reflect on the steps Mary Call took in making her decisions. How did your decision-making processes compare with hers? How could reading about Mary Call have helped you in making your decision? Do you think she would have eventually made the same decision that you made? Why or why not?

movie differs somewhat from the book; Mary Call is not such a compelling and strong figure, and the odds that she fights against are not as great. While many details are changed in the movie, changes in characters are even more surprising. For example, Devola is not shown as being mentally retarded, just impractical. The raw poverty and misery portrayed in the book are missing from the movie. Still, the film offers striking images of the North Carolina landscape and the wildflowers.

◆ Related Titles/Adaptations ◆

Where the Lilies Bloom is followed by *Trial Valley*, which takes place two years later, when Mary Call is sixteen. It tells of Mary Call's two boyfriends, one a local fellow, the other a social worker from Virginia. It is also the story of Jack Parsons, a little boy Devola finds abandoned in the woods, who becomes very attached to Mary Call. Because she has been raising her own younger siblings, Mary Call does not want the added responsibility Jack brings. *Trial Valley* seems overwritten when compared to *Where the Lilies Bloom*, and is disappointing as a result. Its plot is thin and its characters are not as well drawn as those in *Where the Lilies Bloom*. Even Mary Call herself seems less vibrant. Still, *Trial Valley* is worth reading, if only to see the Cleavers' idea of how Mary Call, Devola, Romey, and Kiser change with age.

Where the Lilies Bloom was also made into a successful, full-length feature film in 1974. This MGM/United Artists production was directed by William A. Graham and starred Julie Gholson, Jan Smithers, and Matthew Burrill. The

◆ For Further Reference ◆

Carpenter, Humphrey, and Mari Prichard. *The Oxford Companion to Children's Literature*. New York: Oxford University Press, 1984. Contains a brief overview of the Cleavers' major writings.

De Montreville, Doris, and Elizabeth D. Crawford, eds. *The Fourth Book of Junior Authors and Illustrators*. New York: H. W. Wilson, 1978. Contains a helpful autobiographical sketch and a biographical sketch with a short bibliography of articles about the Cleavers.

Estes, Glenn E., ed. *Dictionary of Literary Biography*. Vol. 52, *American Writers for Children Since 1960: Fiction*. Detroit: Gale Research, 1986. Includes a thorough critical analysis of the Cleavers' writings.

Kirkpatrick, D. L., ed. *Twentieth-Century Children's Writers*. New York: St. Martin's, 1978. Includes a short discussion of the Cleavers' fiction and the prevailing themes, character types, settings, and tone of their works through 1977.

Senick, Gerald J., ed. *Children's Literature Review*. Vol. 6. Detroit: Gale Research, 1984. A thorough compilation
of biographical facts on both Cleavers.

*A. Abigail McCormick
Estill County (Kentucky) Public Library*

WILD ANIMALS I HAVE KNOWN

Short Stories

1898

◆

Author: Ernest Thompson Seton, 1860-1946

Major Books for Young Adults

Wild Animals I Have Known, 1898
The Trail of the Sandhill Stag, 1899
The Biography of a Grizzly, 1900
Two Little Savages, 1903
Animal Heroes, 1905

Biography of a Silver Fox, 1909
Rolf in the Woods, 1911
The Biography of an Arctic Fox, 1937
*Great Historic Animals, Mainly
    about Wolves*, 1937

◆ About the Author ◆

Born Ernest Thompson in South Shields, County Durham, England, on August 14, 1860, the author of *Wild Animals I Have Known* adapted the ancestral family name of Seton in 1901. After backing Prince Charles in the unsuccessful Stuart Rebellion of 1745, Seton's Scottish ancestors had fled south to England, where they became shipbuilders and shipowners. When the author's father, Joseph Logan Thompson, lost his merchant ships, the family immigrated to Canada in 1866. They lived for a brief period in Lindsay, Ontario, a small town surrounded by forests and an ideal site for a boy who had become fascinated with wildlife. They left the woods in 1870, but Seton had already learned many of the skills in woodcraft that would make him an acknowledged expert in the field. Seton discovered his artistic talent and began sketching birds and animals while a student in the Toronto public schools.

He studied at the Toronto School of Art from 1877 to 1879 and at the Royal Academy of Painting and Sculpture in London in 1881.

In 1882 he joined his brother Arthur, who was homesteading near Carberry, Manitoba, in south-central Canada. There he found in abundance the animals that fascinated him: wolves, grizzlies, moose, and buffalo. Seton traveled to New York City in 1883 in an effort to sell his sketches to publishers and artists. Some of his first sales were to Sacket, Williams & Betzig, lithographic publishers. Seton also won a contract to produce one thousand sketches for Century Publications' new twelve-volume dictionary, and he began selling nature stories to such magazines as *St. Nicholas*.

After a return to Toronto in April 1884, Seton again joined his brother in Manitoba. He shuttled between Carberry, New York City, Washington, D.C., and Paris for several years, studying and producing art. His *Birds of*

Manitoba was submitted to the Smithsonian Institution at the end of 1890, and in 1892 one of his paintings, "The Sleeping Wolf," was accepted and later hung for exhibition at the Grand Salon of Painting in Paris. Seton also continued to write, and in 1898 his first book of stories, *Wild Animals I Have Known,* was published. It quickly became a best seller and is now regarded as a classic.

In 1902 Seton founded the Woodcraft Indians, the first outdoor organization for boys. Later incorporated as the Woodcraft League, this organization was the forerunner of the Boy Scouts of America. Seton was chairman of the committee that established the Scouts in 1910, and he was soon installed as chief scout, a post he held for five years. In 1911 he was largely responsible for the publication of the first Boy Scout's Handbook.

In 1896 Seton married Grace Gallatin, a strong advocate of women's rights and an author of popular travel books. They had one child, Ann, who in the 1940s and 1950s became a best-selling writer of historical romances. In 1930 the Setons were divorced and Seton moved to New Mexico. He married Julia Buttree, his former secretary, in 1935. Seton died in Santa Fe, New Mexico, on October 23, 1946.

◆ Overview ◆

Most of Ernest Thompson Seton's books offer readers a unique perspective on the nature and habits of wild animals. *Wild Animals I Have Known* gives detailed descriptions of the lives of several animals by a skilled writer who has an artist's eye for precise detail. As a scrupulously scientific writer, Seton depicts the animals and their surround-ings with precision; as a romantic naturalist, he focuses on the drama and beauty of nature. Informative, lively, and moving, *Wild Animals I Have Known* enables readers to learn about life in the wilderness of New Mexico and Canada.

◆ Setting ◆

This book has several settings. Northern New Mexico is the background for "Lobo: The King of Currumpaw" and also for "The Pacing Mustang." Most of the stories have western Canada, Ontario, or Manitoba as their locale. One story—"Wully: The Story of a Yaller Dog"—is set in northern England. This tale opens in the Cheviot district of Northumberland and moves south into Derbyshire. All the stories take place during the 1880s or 1890s.

◆ Themes and Characters ◆

In all of his work Seton displays the poetic ability to imagine himself as another, non-human creature. In his prefatory "Notes to the Reader" in *Wild Animals I Have Known,* he explains, "Man has nothing that animals have not at least a vestige of, the animals have nothing that man does not in some degree share."

"Lobo: The King of Currumpaw," the first story in the book, is Seton's most famous animal biography. Lobo, a wolf, is a notorious predator that for five years has claimed the lives of cows and sheep almost nightly. The ranchers of northern New Mexico hire Seton to do what all other hunters have failed to do: trap and kill the beast. Lobo eludes all traps and baits, until Seton takes advantage of a force stronger than the wolf's cunning: his love of his mate. Seton kills Blanca, the white wolf, and using one of her paws, spreads her scent over an area of carefully laid traps. In the past Lobo has quickly detected such traps and sprung them. This time, following his mate's scent, he walks into them and is captured. As Seton depicts him, Lobo is a king who does not cease being royal, even in captivity. After one angry howl when he sees his enemies approaching the spot where he lies helpless, Lobo never speaks again. Chained in a field where it is hoped that he may lure others in his pack to their destruction, he does not call for their help. Next morning he has died. He refuses to live as a prisoner, and wills his own death. He has been a relentless destroyer, and has died heroically.

Silverspot, the hero of the second story, is the wisest member of a flock of crows that rests on Frank's Castle, a mountain near Toronto. This old chief teaches young crows the art of survival in a dangerous world. Silverspot, however, meets a tragic end in a confrontation with the crows' main enemy, the great horned owl. In telling Silverspot's story, Seton provides a brief dictionary of the sounds crows make when they communicate with one another.

Wild animal mothers are a favorite subject in Seton's stories. "Raggylug: The Story of a Cottontail Rabbit," describes the heroism of Molly Raggylug's mother, who lures the fox away from her concealed little ones. In "The Springfield Fox," Vix, a mother fox, carefully trains her cubs for their future lives as predators. When they are killed by a hunter, her grief is as intense as that of any human mother. "Redruff: The Story of the Don Valley Partridge" depicts a mother partridge and her brood struggling to survive against predators both animal and human.

Redruff's mother outwits and outmaneuvers a fox to defend her chicks. As he does in several other stories, Seton shows in "Redruff" how the animals communicate with one another.

Dogs are the subjects of two of Seton's stories. The first of these illustrates the unbreakable bond between a dog and his master. Seton raises Bingo himself, but the author's travels force him to find a new home for his pet. Years later, however, Bingo comes to Seton's rescue when Seton is caught in a trap and surrounded by wolves. When Bingo eats poisoned meat, he drags himself back to Seton's cabin, seeking help from his former master. Wully, the Yaller Dog, is also loyal to his owner, but begins slipping out nights to kill sheep on neighboring farms. Dorley, his master, has kill him after Wully is caught with the blood of his victims on his coat.

Next to Lobo, Seton's favorite character is the beautiful black horse in "The Pacing Mustang." This mustang exemplifies the determination of a wild creature to remain free; he paces like a racehorse rather than gallops, and for years all attempts to capture him fail. Like Lobo, he lives in northern New Mexico in the 1890s. Caught by an old wrangler called Turkeytrack, he is roped, branded, and herded to a corral when, in a final burst of strength, he escapes and leaps over a cliff, landing "a lifeless wreck—but free."

Seton maintains that animals can on occasion display some of the qualities most prized in humans: loyalty, courage, and resourcefulness. He wants his readers to recognize something of themselves in these wild creatures. His book makes the case that animals should be free to live their lives in their natural habitats without human interference.

Animal stories have delighted readers since antiquity, but the characters featured in them have often behaved like people dressed as animals. Aesop's fables, for example, were written to teach humans about morality, and the medieval "Beast Epic" satirized the society of the day. In Seton's stories, animal characters are allowed to be themselves. Seton believes animals lead lives as interesting as those led by most humans, and he carefully selects details to highlight the interesting features of his subjects' lives. For the most part, too, he avoids the cuteness that characterizes many animal tales, although he does use expressions such as "thimblefuls of down" and "sweet little 'peep, peep' " to describe baby animals. Seton conveys his love for all natural things in *Wild Animals I Have Known*, despite the fact that he sometimes casts animals in the role of villain for dramatic effect. The horned owl in "Silverspot," for example, is called a "murderer," and the foxes in "Redruff" are "vicious killers."

Seton sets his stories against the vividly described background of the American Southwest, the Canadian provinces, or the English countryside. He uses local dialects and characters to make his narratives more colorful, and effectively captures the speech of subjects ranging from cowhands to crows.

◆ Social Sensitivity ◆

Ernest Thompson Seton was an advocate of animal rights long before this issue became a popular cause. As Redruff struggles in the snare, for instance, Seton comments:

Have the wild things no moral or legal rights? What right has man to inflict such long and fearful agony on a fellow-creature, simply because that creature does not speak his language?

Seton hunted and trapped for many years, and was highly skilled at both pursuits. He came to maturity when the buffalo herds of the West were being slaughtered and other game animals were becoming rare. After a moose hunt in 1884, he looked down on the animal's corpse and in remorse vowed "that so long as they are threatened with extermination, I will never again lift my rifle against any of America's big game." Seton was very much a conservationist in 1898 when *Wild Animals I Have Known* was published, and the book reflects this attitude. One of Seton's lesser-known works is *Natural History of the Ten Commandments*, an argument that animals deserve protection in the Christian scheme of morality. Thus, although *Wild Animals I Have Known* depicts violence and death in the animal world, Seton handles his depictions of these incidents with grave sensitivity.

◆ Topics for Discussion ◆

1. Seton became famous for his wolf stories. Why do you think he was so fascinated with these animals? Do you find "Lobo: The King of Currumpaw" a convincing portrait of a great predator?

2. Is Seton a better writer when he describes small animals or when he describes larger ones? Is it more difficult to identify with rabbits than with wolves?

3. Does Seton prove his point when he stresses the intelligence of crows? What makes Silverspot a leader of his flock?

4. Are the people who appear in Seton's stories as well drawn as his animals?

5. Both Lobo and the Pacing Mustang are featured in stories with the old West as a background. Are these typical western stories?

6. Seton is the narrator in all of these stories and is a character in some of them. How does he present himself?

◆ Ideas for Reports and Papers ◆

1. Compare Seton's *Wild Animals I Have Known* to Sterling North's *Rascal: A Memoir of a Better Era*. How does the narrative presence differ in each? Which offers a more realistic depiction of nature?

2. Seton the artist may not be as well known as he deserves to be. Examine his paintings and his illustrations. Does his art reflect the same themes found in his writing?

3. Research the critical response to Seton's animal stories and write your own book review of *Wild Animals I Have Known*.

4. Read *Never Cry Wolf* by Farley Mowat and compare the depiction of the wolf family in that book to Seton's depiction of Lobo.

5. Write a short story about an animal you have known.

◆ For Further Reference ◆

Devlin, John C., and Grace Naismith. *The World of Roger Tory Peterson: An Authorized Biography.* New York: Times Books, 1977. Provides an interesting account of Seton's influence on Peterson, an artist.

Samson, John G. *The Worlds of Ernest Thomas Seton.* New York: Alfred A. Knopf, 1976. Includes samples of Seton's writings and his art, along with generally favorable commentaries on both.

Seton, Ernest Thompson. *Trail of an Artist-Naturalist.* New York: Charles Scribner's Sons, 1940. In this autobiography Seton gives an interesting if incomplete account of his life and accomplishments.

Seton, Julia M. *By a Thousand Fires: Notes and Extracts from the Life and Unpublished Journals of Ernest Thompson Seton.* Garden City, NY: Doubleday, 1967. Seton's widow edits and comments on passages from her husband's journals, which he kept throughout his long career.

Karl Avery

WILLIAM BLAKE

Biographical Novel

1960

◆

Author: James Daugherty, 1889-1974

Major Books for Young Adults

The Kingdom and the Power and the Glory: Stories of Faith and Marvel, 1929 (edited by Daugherty)
Their Weight in Wildcats: Tales of the Frontier, 1936 (edited by Daugherty)
Andy and the Lion, 1938
Daniel Boone, 1939
Poor Richard, 1941
In the Beginning, Being the First Chapter of Genesis from the King James Version, 1941 (edited by Daugherty)
Abraham Lincoln, 1943
An Outline of Government in Connecticut, 1944
The Wild, Wild West, 1948
The Landing of the Pilgrims, 1950

Of Courage Undaunted: Across the Continent with Lewis and Clark, 1951
Trappers and Traders of the Far West, 1952
Marcus and Narcissa Whitman: Pioneers of Oregon, 1953
The Magna Charta, 1956
West of Boston, 1956
The Picnic, 1958
William Blake, 1960
Walt Whitman's America, 1964 (edited by Daugherty)
Henry David Thoreau: A Man of Our Time, 1967 (edited by Daugherty)
The Sound of Trumpets: Selections from Ralph Waldo Emerson, 1971 (edited by Daugherty)

◆ About the Author ◆

James Henry Daugherty was born June 1, 1889, in Asheville, North Carolina, to Charles M. and Susan Peyton Telfair Daugherty. He spent his early childhood on an Indiana farm and in a small southern Ohio town. When Daugherty was about nine, the family moved to Washington, D.C., where his father took a government job. In addition to his public schooling in Washington, Daugherty attended the Philadelphia Art Academy for one year and studied in London during his father's two-year assignment there as an agent for the U.S. Department of Agriculture.

As important as his formal education were the lessons in storytelling Daugherty learned from his parents and his grandfather. From his mother, a native of Virginia, he heard songs and stories of the pre-Civil War South. From his father, a graduate of the University of Michigan, he heard the best of English and American literature, from Chaucer to Mark Twain. Daugherty's grandfather, meanwhile, told him tall tales about the frontier that had been handed down for several generations.

During World War I, Daugherty camouflaged ships and designed war posters for the U.S. Navy. He also worked on murals and illustrations for books and magazines. Shortly after the war, he became an illustrator for the Doubleday Page Company, and as his reputation grew, he worked for a number of book publishers, as well as for magazines such as the *New Yorker*, *Forum*, and *Golden Book*. During the 1920s he also painted murals in movie theaters belonging to the Loew chain. Later, as a part of President Franklin Roosevelt's New Deal, he painted murals in public buildings, including a high school in Stamford, Connecticut. His biographical novel *Daniel Boone*, which he both authored and illustrated, won the 1939 Newbery Medal, and his other biographies for young adults consistently garnered high praise. In 1971 a retrospective exhibit of his work was held in New York.

Daugherty's wife, Sonia Medvedeva, was also a well-known author of books for children and young adults. Their son, Charles Michael (Chris), continued the family tradition, writing young adult books that his father illustrated. In the 1920s the family moved to Westport, Connecticut, where Daugherty lived until his death on February 21, 1974.

◆ Overview ◆

In his foreword to *William Blake*, Daugherty not only introduces his subject, placing him in historical and geographic context, but also emphasizes the immense power of the human imagination, both as a source of artistic inspiration and as an essential ingredient in any fully realized life. Daugherty declares that, in the twentieth century, a time when it "seems we are getting nowhere faster than ever before," readers should take the time to look at remarkable pictures and read great poetry. Daugherty points out that Blake received little recognition in his lifetime and was considered by many to be a complete failure. Today, however, his work is priceless, his reputation ever-increasing. Blake's courageous battle to celebrate individuality and originality, and his victory for the power of the imagination, should prove inspirational for readers.

◆ Setting ◆

William Blake lived in London for most of his life, and consequently this city serves as the principal setting for Daugherty's biography. The book covers the time period between Blake's birth in 1757 and his death in 1827. The late eighteenth century was a time of great social change brought about by the Industrial Revolution; Daugherty depicts London as a rapidly expanding city, stocked with people who have migrated from the countryside to take advantage of newly created jobs. The city is a bustling and exciting place to live, and for Blake almost anywhere else seems too dull.

◆ Themes and Characters ◆

Daugherty's biography of William Blake is divided into five major parts, each headed by an epigraph, or brief quotation, selected from Blake's writing

Portrait of Blake by John Linnell (1820) reprinted courtesy of Fitzwilliam Museum, Cambridge, in *Blake* by Kathleen Raine. Praeger: New York (1971).

lying. His judgment is softened, however, when Mrs. Blake argues that children often have extraordinary experiences, and that their son's tale recalls visionary stories from the Bible.

Young Blake's wanderings around the teeming streets of London lead him into galleries and shops. Seeing the work of famous painters fuels his imagination and provides a storehouse of inspiration for him to draw upon throughout his career. His formal training in art begins with a four-year stint in drawing school, where he learns to sketch the human figure. He later is apprenticed to a famous engraver in London, in whose shop he masters the difficult technique of printing illustrations by means of copper plates, cutting tools, ink, and presses. Blake excels in his work, and at age sixteen begins his first major work, a series of engravings of the antiquities in Westminster Abbey. This task consumes five years of his life, during which time he absorbs the mysteries, spirit, and glory of gothic art.

The course of world history marks the maturing Blake; he is stirred by the events of the American and the French revolutions. Ideas about liberty and brotherhood greatly influence the young artist, and become a compelling theme that shapes his life and his work. Another central theme of Blake's work is that of childhood. The death of his beloved younger brother Robert—who lived with Blake and his wife, Catherine Boucher, for three years—inspires Blake to write poems about their happy times together, poems Daugherty describes as "simple and joyous verses about children, for children, written out of a child heart." Blake calls this collection *Songs of Innocence* (1789), and decides to assemble the poems into a book with each accompanied by an interpretive illustration.

to set the tone for what follows. Each of the book's twenty-six chapters opens with an excerpt from Blake's poetry or prose, and Daugherty quotes lengthy segments of the writer's work throughout the text. As a result, Blake's work is introduced to young readers and placed in a meaningful context.

Part One of the biography begins with Blake's birth in London on November 28, 1757, and describes his religious upbringing. His stern father's misjudgment of the sensitive and highly imaginative little boy is tempered by his mother's understanding. When the child tells his parents he has seen a tree full of angels, "the most beautiful sight I ever saw," his father accuses him of

Blake's poems in *Songs of Innocence* are written from the perspective of innocent children; the poems are spontaneous, ecstatic, unshadowed by reflective thoughts, and freely imaginative. With the help of his wife, he hand-paints each drawing and sews them individually into the bindings of the books. Blake uses a process called "relief etching" to illustrate *Songs of Innocence*; now widely employed by engravers, relief etching was a revolutionary technique for its time.

Blake's next illustrated volume of poetry, *The Book of Thel* (1789), is a mystical poem that tells the story of an innocent soul—the maiden Thel—who rejects the opportunity to live. *The Marriage of Heaven and Hell* (1793) follows, and here Blake's vision begins to darken, growing more complex and difficult to interpret.

Part Two of the biography covers the next seven years of the artist's life. When visions of biblical figures and long-dead English poets, including Geoffrey Chaucer and William Shakespeare, begin to appear to Blake, public opinion labels him a madman. His next major work, *Songs of Experience* (1794), is a sequel to *Songs of Innocence*, and differs from the earlier work in tone and voice. During the "innocent" stage of life the child is untouched by evil; he or she is joyous, peaceful, and filled with wonder. "Experience" introduces the child to the cares and responsibilities that bind people to earthly sorrow and pain.

In *Songs of Experience*, Blake unifies his political and social concerns. He attacks the social evils that imprison children of his day—especially child labor and slavery—and condemns the government for ignoring the suffering of innocents. The new work is printed together with *Songs of Innocence*, resulting in a pictorially beautiful and inspirational volume. Blake's most famous poem, "The Tyger," is included in this later collection, and stands as a companion piece to the earlier poem "The Lamb."

Part Three examines Blake's experimentation with a series of spiritual adventure stories that he calls his "Prophetic Books." These works feature characters from a mythological cast of his own creation, and describe struggles between good and evil, between freedom and slavery, and between imagination and the forces that would restrict it. The abstractions central to these works alienate whatever small audience Blake may have, and the chaotic energy of the action seems incomprehensible to most readers.

In Part Four of the biography, Daugherty documents the events of a period that the Blakes spend in Felpham, a village on the southern coast of England. Here, a misunderstanding between Blake and a British soldier escalates into a court trial against Blake, who is charged with sedition. Because England is at war with France, any resistance to government or to any representative of government is considered grounds for execution. Blake is found not guilty, but he never forgets this personal experience of oppression and the restraint of individual freedom; the vivid memories and images it evokes appear in both his poems and pictures that follow.

Part Five outlines the final years of Blake's life. Increasingly viewed as everything from eccentric to insane, Blake is forced by extreme poverty to sell his lifetime collection of prints. A few artists recognize his plight and collect money on his behalf. This aid enables him to begin his best-known work, a powerful group of water-color illustrations for *The Book of Job* (1825).

Blake's final years are peaceful and rewarding; he produces one of his greatest works, a set of illustrations for Dante's *Divine Comedy,* and dies peacefully on August 12, 1827.

◆ Literary Qualities ◆

Most critical writing about Blake is extremely sophisticated, a reflection of the complexity of the ideas expressed in Blake's own work. In contrast, Daugherty's relatively straightforward narrative serves as a useful introduction to the life and philosophy of a great artist whose work many young readers might otherwise have been too intimidated to approach. Daugherty utilizes short paragraphs, a suitable level of diction, and a carefully selected vocabulary. To keep his narrative moving smoothly, he does not rely excessively on dates or on other data more appropriate for historical texts. Daugherty does, however, include a wealth of information about the American and French revolutions and the major figures involved in these momentous events. Through his examination of Blake's life, Daugherty shows that both world events and individual personalities are affected by changing ideas about human values, society, and methods of government.

Daugherty also makes reference to many of Blake's contemporaries, ranging from scientists and inventors to other artists, both poets and painters. This material expands the "cast of characters" in the biography, and informs the reader of important movements in the sciences and humanities.

Daugherty goes so far as to contrive conversations between the people in Blake's life. His use of direct—although largely fictional—quotations gives the narrative a flow and informality that might appeal to young readers. Of particular note are the detailed scenes of Blake's childhood; Daugherty describes everyday experiences that both humanize Blake and set him apart as a special, gifted child. Daugherty places details about the complex life of his subject within the context of a world in transition. Blake's poetry, with its poignant call for social reform, echoes the era's revolutionary spirit. By appealing, as Blake himself did, not only to the five senses to evoke his word pictures, but also to the unfathomable realm of imagination, the biographer succeeds in reinforcing his text with the very qualities of his subject's art.

◆ Social Sensitivity ◆

Blake is considered by scholars to be one of the most original and radical thinkers in English history. His ideas about society and God remain controversial; people who cannot accept his vision of life often dismiss him as insane. The central element in Blake's philosophy is "four-fold vision"—four hierarchical stages of awareness, the highest of which permits direct communication with God and the afterlife. Blake vehemently believed that he had reached this fourth level himself; when he stated that he had seen angels in a tree or talked to his dead brother, he by no means meant that he had done so only in a symbolic sense.

Blake was also controversial in his unorthodox beliefs about the nature of God. He often said that every person had the potential to elevate himself or herself to the same level of divinity as Jesus. This idea ran counter to what most people held to be true, as did Blake's opinion of Satan. The accepted theology of Blake's time paralleled the sentiments of John Milton's famous poem *Paradise Lost.* In this poem, God is depicted as a wise, gentle deity, whereas his fallen angel, Satan, is rebellious and full of spirit. According to Blake, although Satan might be wrong about a lot of things, he is nonetheless striving to fulfill himself. For Blake, Milton's Satan is a seeker of truth, whereas his God is complacent. Blake said that Milton reversed the roles—that his character, Satan, really exemplified the traits of God, and that the repressive God figure was evil. Many people continue to reject Blake's idea.

Even though Daugherty's biography of Blake emphasizes the artist's originality and eccentricities, the book suggests that Blake—despite being unappreciated and little understood by his contemporaries—nevertheless led a happy, joyous, and fulfilled life. Fame and adulation were unnecessary to a person who gave personal witness throughout his long life to a passionate belief in freedom, both of the human spirit and its artistic expression. Although deemed by many a madman, Blake never wavered in his beliefs. An awareness of his strong sense of purpose, as documented in the story of his life, should inspire others to follow their individual convictions despite opposition, ridicule, or rejection.

♦ Topics for Discussion ♦

1. Even though many of his ideas appear to be impractical and eccentric, what does Blake have to say to present-day society?

2. Many people judged Blake's life a failure. In what ways is his life a success, despite the lack of tangible rewards?

3. Why is Blake driven to invent an entire mythological system? How do his reasons for inventing characters relate to his desire to invent new artistic techniques?

4. Why is urban life essential for Blake's artistic inspiration?

5. Because Blake lived in a time of revolutions, can his work be termed "revolutionary"? How?

♦ Ideas for Reports and Papers ♦

1. Although Blake was a highly original and inventive artist, he was influenced by the attitudes and styles of his time, if only by rejecting them. Research and report on "The Age of Reason" (also known as "The Enlightenment") in intellectual history. What were the characteristics of the pictures being painted by others during Blake's lifetime?

2. The image of Blake as a "lonely genius" is misleading. In what ways was he not a solitary, rejected figure?

3. To "synthesize" means to bring separate parts together into a whole. What is meant by the claim that Blake's ambition was to create a vast synthesis, poetic as well as pictorial?

4. What characteristics of Christianity are evident in Blake's work?

5. The twentieth-century father of psychology, Sigmund Freud, believed the mind was divided into three parts which fought against one another for domina-

tion. If any one of the parts became dominant, the mind became imbalanced, and this could lead to insanity. In what ways did Blake anticipate the teachings of Freud?

6. "Humanism" is a philosophy centered on humankind and human values, emphasizing human free will and superiority to the rest of nature. How can Blake be seen as a startling and powerful humanist?

7. Research other poets of Blake's time who were influenced by his work.

◆ For Further Reference ◆

Blunt, Anthony. *The Art of William Blake.* New York: Columbia University Press, 1959. The reader who would like to dig more deeply into Blake's work will find a fuller coverage of his unique art here.

Brownowski, Jacob. *William Blake and the Age of Revolution.* New York: Harper and Row, 1965. Well-known writer, artist, and television personality Jacob Brownowski emphasizes the momentous period of history in which Blake lived.

Gleckner, Robert F. *The Piper and the Bard: A Study of William Blake.* Detroit: Wayne State University Press, 1959. Emphasizing the contrary roles Blake assumed to introduce *Songs of Innocence* and *Songs of Experience,* this study provides additional material about Blake's poetic accomplishments.

Malcolmson, Anne. *William Blake: An Introduction.* New York: Harcourt, Brace and World, 1967. This general,

illustrated introduction puts Blake as man and poet within his times and provides a guide toward understanding his poetry.

Todd, Ruthven. "Introduction." In *Blake.* Laurel Poetry Series. New York: Dell, 1960. The introduction to this selection of Blake's poetry points out why he "stands out like a giant" of his time.

Maryhelen C. Harmon
University of South Florida

WILLIAM THE CONQUEROR
Biographical Novel
1959

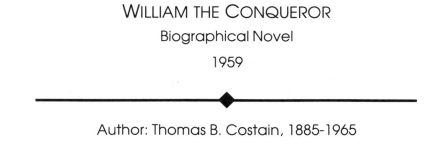

Author: Thomas B. Costain, 1885-1965

Major Books for Young Adults

The Mississippi Bubble, 1955
William the Conqueror, 1959

◆ About the Author ◆

Thomas Bertrand Costain was born on May 8, 1885, in Brantford, Ontario, Canada. He began writing novels while a teen-ager, and after publishing a mystery story left school to become a newspaper reporter. After nearly two decades of work as a journalist and editor, Costain moved to Philadelphia in 1920 to become associate editor of the popular magazine *Saturday Evening Post.* He tried to save enough money to become a full-time author, but lost his savings in the stock market crash of 1929. While serving as an editor for a film studio and a book publisher, he began work as a part-time novelist, retiring from publishing in 1946 to devote himself to writing. By this time, Costain had published his first three novels: *For My Great Folly* (1942), *Ride With Me* (1944), and *The Black Rose* (1945), which would later become a popular motion picture. All of these reflect Costain's usual technique of focusing his books on an important person or event from history.

Over the next eighteen years he produced many novels, the most famous of which was *The Silver Chalice* (1952), a story centering on the cup used at the Last Supper. This book, too, was made into a successful film. During this period Costain produced two histories of the Middle Ages, *The Three Edwards* (1958) and *The Last Plantagenets* (1962), and also wrote two books for young people, *The Mississippi Bubble* and *William the Conqueror.* Costain is best remembered as one of the finest historical novelists of the twentieth century. He died on October 8, 1965, in New York City.

◆ Overview ◆

A fictionalized biography of the French-born warrior-king who changed the course of British history, *William the Conqueror* tells the rags-to-riches story of an orphan who became one of medieval Europe's most powerful rulers. Drawing upon the few known facts about William's life, Costain uses both his skill as a novelist and his knowledge of history to paint a rounded picture of a man seemingly born to be a leader. Costain's account of William's life—his narrow escapes from assassination as boy, his training to become a knight, and his military campaigns in England and France—reads like an adventure story. All in all, Costain takes a familiar figure from history, breathes life into him, and shows the elements of character that made William a great king. Additionally, Costain informs his readers about the nature of life in the Middle Ages, describing the food, the clothing, and the uncomfortable living conditions that even the most powerful and wealthy individuals had to endure.

♦ Setting ♦

The biography begins in France in about 1038, as the aptly named Robert the Devil, Duke of Normandy, addresses his vassal lords. A successful leader who has maintained a relatively violence-free state, Robert is now determined to go on a pilgrimage to the Holy Land, presumably to atone for the sins that earned him his nickname "the Devil." Robert's nobles are aghast at the plan because they know that few people survive such a journey; the country needs a strong leader, and the nobles ask Robert to designate an heir. His choice of William—a young boy born illegitimately—shocks the company, but slowly and reluctantly they swear allegiance to their boy-lord.

At this time in history, nations as we know them really did not exist. Under the feudal system only the most powerful nobles could hope to rule. Normandy was really a confederation of smaller baronies—something like countries—whose leaders often feuded with and raided each other. The Norman barons wanted a strong leader to protect them not only from foreigners but also from each other. Most European battles and wars of the time were fought for the possession of land. Areas with fertile land were the most desirable, which is why William so wanted to conquer England. The story of William's life takes the reader from Normandy to Paris to Belgium and finally to England, providing a panorama of medieval Europe.

♦ Themes and Characters ♦

Costain's biography follows William's life from boyhood to old age, using examples from his life to highlight those qualities most desirable in a medieval ruler. From the first, William possesses unusual potential. He maintains icy poise as he accepts the allegiance of his father's followers, and he shows considerable presence of mind in evading attempts on his life before he is thirteen. As an orphan, but ward to the King of France, he undergoes training for knighthood, a status he attains at the unusually early age of fifteen because he is stronger and more skillful than his fellows in horsemanship and the use of weapons. Costain depicts William as a "fighter by nature"; no one else has the strength to draw his bow, and he can leap into a saddle in full armor, while most knights need assistance. William's most important leadership qualities are his skills in battle and his ability to lead soldiers, which he uses to his advantage in subduing the rebellious Norman barons and in pacifying and unifying his duchy by the age of twenty-one.

One of William's obligations as a ruler is to take a wife in order to produce heirs and thus establish succession to his throne. Because medieval kings' marriages are often arranged for political or military reasons, William's ideal wife would be a daughter of the king of

England, but Edward the Confessor—the West Saxon King who rules England from 1042 to 1066—has no daughters. William decides on Mathilda, daughter of the Count of Flanders. She, however, is not as eager to marry, and she delays the wedding for seven years. Eventually, they marry and have many children.

Through his portrayal of William, Costain shows that not all medieval rulers were absolute monarchs. William has to trick or cajole his allies into assisting him in his various campaigns. He persuades the King of France to assist in the pacification of Normandy, and he secures backing for his invasion of England by promising his followers large, prosperous estates if the venture is successful.

Costain does not, however, sugar-coat the life of his protagonist. William has many admirable qualities: intelligence, exceptional strength, and bravery. Few of his contemporaries match his level of education; most nobles are illiterate, but William can read, write, and apply mathematical principles toward the design of ships and castles. William is not, however, an example of ideal human virtue. He can be violent, cruel, arrogant, and covetous of others' wealth. Like many medieval rulers, he is relatively unconcerned with the plight of the common people. He is capable of destroying peasants' crops in an effort to defeat a ritual lord, or of starving a walled city into submission.

Despite William's personal flaws, his invasion of England in 1066 and its aftermath bring out many of his most impressive qualities. He shows his organizational skills in amassing his army and—thanks in part to luck—getting his fleet to the south of England. Here he establishes a beach head, defeating King Harold at the Battle of Hastings, and, finally, in his old age, consolidating his base in England. Although history has recorded him as William the Conqueror, Costain reports that he is more commonly referred to by his people as "William the Great."

◆ Literary Qualities ◆

Costain's technique is essentially the same in *William the Conqueror* as it is in his historical novels for adults. He performs exhaustive research into the background of his subject to find authentic details. *William the Conqueror* is filled with specifics, including technical terms for weapons, an analysis of military tactics, and descriptions of clothing styles. Costain even includes information about which social classes could use specific types of hunting birds. By blending general historical research with specific biographical fact, Costain enhances the realism of his settings and his action.

But *William the Conqueror* is also a fictionalized biography. Costain builds upon the few known details of William's life to create a vivid, believable character. Indeed, much of Costain's material must be described as speculative. Although Costain does not tamper with historical fact, he constantly introduces dialogue or internal monologues for which no evidence exists. As a result, *William the Conqueror* is not a scholarly work for professional historians, but rather a compelling portrayal of a great warrior-king intended to delight young readers while teaching them about a historical period.

◆ Social Sensitivity ◆

The feudal system was not democratic, and people were not treated as equals. Because one of Costain's primary concerns is accuracy of detail, his treatment of politics, religion, violence, and the relationships between men and women reflects the era about which he writes. As a result, some readers could fault him for being too nonjudgmental on matters of social concern. Although Costain does not emphasize the conflicts between church and state, he does note that William was excommunicated upon his marriage, but that the next pope lifted the decree. Costain is never brutally graphic, but he does reveal the violence of the period in his battle scenes, and England's Harold dies from an arrow through his eye. Women play a subservient role in this work: William's wife, Mathilda, is depicted essentially as an object whose primary role is motherhood; and William's mother is barely mentioned except in regard to her physical beauty.

♦ Topics for Discussion ♦

1. What kinds of obstacles does William have to overcome as a boy?

2. How are William's childhood sports related to his later career? How does Costain reveal William's unusual strength? What evidence reveals both his intelligence and his learning?

3. How does William gain the respect of his peers? Cite examples from his childhood and his adulthood.

4. How do ideas about marriage in the Middle Ages differ from modern ideas about marriage?

5. What different strategies does William use to defeat his enemies? Why

does he believe that he has a right to the throne of England?

6. Do you think William's sole motivation as a ruler is his own personal gain?

♦ Ideas for Reports and Papers ♦

1. Show how the events of William's first twenty-one years prepare him for his greatest exploit, the conquest of England.

2. Compare and contrast William with other rulers who appear in the biography.

3. Read one of Costain's other historical books, such as *The Black Rose* or *The Silver Chalice*, and compare his integration of historical fact and fictional speculation in that book to his technique in *William the Conqueror*.

4. Rewrite one of the scenes in *William the Conqueror* from the point of view of one of the nobles who served William.

5. Research and report on the Battle of Hastings and its impact on the course of British history.

♦ Related Titles ♦

Although Costain wrote no sequels to *William the Conqueror*, all of his other titles—both the novels and the histories—are appropriate reading for high school students. These books, with settings that range from the first century A.D. (*The Silver Chalice*) to the Napoleonic era (*The Tontine*), all feature interesting plots and provide readers with a sense of a specific historical period.

♦ For Further Reference ♦

Frederick, John T. "Costain and Company: The Historical Novel Today." *College English* 15 (April 1954): 373-379. Analyzes Costain's work in the context of other historical-based writing.

Martine, James J., ed. *Dictionary of Literary Biography.* Vol. 9, *American Novelists 1910-1945.* Detroit: Gale Research, 1981. Contains a biographical entry on Costain.

Van Gelder, Robert. "Interview with a Best-Selling Author: Thomas B. Costain." *Cosmopolitan* 18 (October 1947): 201. Costain discusses his method of writing historical novels.

James M. O'Neil
The Citadel

WIND, SAND AND STARS

Autobiography

1939

◆

Author: Antoine de Saint-Exupéry, 1900-1944

Major Books for Young Adults

Southern Mail, 1933
Night Flight, 1932
Wind, Sand and Stars, 1939
Flight to Arras, 1942

The Little Prince, 1943
Letter to a Hostage, 1950
The Wisdom of the Sands, 1950

◆ About the Author ◆

Antoine Marie Roger de Saint-Exupéry was a rare combination: a man of action who was also a man of thought. A professional aviator and a skilled writer, Saint-Exupéry is the author of some of the most highly regarded commentary on flying ever written. Born into an aristocratic family (he could trace his family name back to the fourth century) in Lyons, France, on June 19, 1900, Saint-Exupéry had one younger brother and three sisters. His family was not, however, rich; the death of his father in 1904 left the family in need of money. His maternal grandmother helped support the family, making it possible for Saint-Exupéry's sister to establish a home where Saint-Exupéry often visited at Agay in the south of France.

The most important event in Saint-Exupéry's youth was his rebellion against the strictness of his Catholic upbringing. He respected a disciplined way of life, but found it difficult to conform. Some scholars believe that many of his later actions (including his inability to settle down in one place and his thirst for adventure) were reactions to this early constraint.

During World War I, Saint-Exupéry was sent to Switzerland for safety; while there he learned of the death of his beloved younger brother, François, a loss from which Saint-Exupéry never fully recovered. Scholars have suggested that the shock of his brother's death helped turn the budding author (who, from childhood, had written poetry) more and more toward internal fantasies and philosophical speculations.

After receiving his college education at the Marist College in Fribourg, Switzerland, Saint-Exupéry—who had not proved a great scholar—was called up for military service. This event did not provoke the dismay that it usually does in young people. St.-Ex, as his comrades began to call him, looked forward to the challenge. He had been interested in the relatively new phenomenon of flight from childhood; military duty gave him the chance to join the French Air Force in 1921.

The aircraft flown in the early 1920s were exceedingly primitive; breakdowns were frequent, and forced landings had become expected events. Saint-Exupéry did not at first seem well-suited for a career as a pilot—throughout his life, he was notably absent-minded and sometimes even clumsy—but he tended to be cool in emergencies, and his colleagues learned to trust him with their lives. After several years with the French Air Force, he was hired as a commercial pilot by a company that later joined with several others to become Air France. His adventures with the airline are recounted under fictional guise in his novels, as well as in the autobiographical *Wind, Sand and Stars.*

His first book, *Southern Mail*, recounted the adventures and romances of a commercial pilot. Although *Southern Mail* did not meet with great success, his second novel, *Night Flight*, was well received. But it is the great French author André Gide, a close friend of Saint-Exupéry's, despite their differences in literary style, who is given credit for encouraging his fellow writer to stop writing novels and to use the form, at that time little employed, of the personal essay. The result, *Wind, Sand and Stars*—originally published in France as *Terre des Hommes*—won the prestigious Grand Prize of the French Academy in 1939. Saint-Exupéry continued to write until 1943, when he returned to his old squadron in North Africa. Although he had been grounded on account of his age and old injuries (most notably those resulting from a nearly fatal crash in Guatemala many years before), Saint-Exupéry was finally

Illustration by John O'Hara Cosgrave II for *Wind, Sand and Stars* by Antoine de Saint-Exupery. Reynold and Hitchcock: New York (1970).

allowed to make reconnaissance flights over southern France. On July 31, 1944, he failed to return from one of these flights. It is generally thought that he was shot down—an unverified account by a German pilot tells of an encounter with a plane similar to Saint-Exupéry's—but no one really knows the exact time or circumstances of his death. Such an outcome would probably have pleased Antoine de Saint-Exupéry, the world's supreme author about flight and, in many ways, always a man of mystery.

◆ Overview ◆

Wind, Sand and Stars is an adventure story that also contains thoughtful observations about flying and about the remote areas of the world that Saint-Exupéry visited in his travels. Since Saint-Exupéry was one of the pioneers of flight (he patented a number of devices that helped to advance the technology of aviation and to make modern aircraft possible), his observations about flying are of historical interest. The world view of this exceptionally philosophical man of action is well worth considering, for flying made him keenly aware of the bonds among people of different nationalities. Few writers have spoken of this solidarity better than Antoine de Saint-Exupéry. *Wind, Sand and Stars* was translated from French into English by Lewis Galantière, an American-born scholar and consultant who devoted much of his career to strengthening the ties between the United States and France.

◆ Setting ◆

The action of the book takes place from the mid-1920s through the 1930s. Saint-Exupéry describes his experiences as an aviator in places ranging from Europe to Africa to South America. He traces the topography of Spain field-by-field and farm-by-farm with his friend Henri Guillaumet before embarking on his first real flight for the Latécoère Company; he crashes in the Sahara Desert with his engineer Prévot during an attempted long-distance flight from France to Saigon; he visits the battlefields of the Spanish Civil War as a correspondent and observes the strength and the sadness of the soldiers there. Saint-Exupéry is a sensitive and observant traveler, and *Wind, Sand and Stars* derives its power from his insightful descriptions of the exotic sites to which his restless wings take him.

◆ Themes and Characters ◆

Since *Wind, Sand and Stars* is a series of reflections upon various incidents in his flying career, Saint-Exupéry does not introduce characters as one would expect in an ordinary novel. Nonetheless, his portraits emerge with accuracy and realism. The narrator himself becomes the principal character, a devoted pilot who believes that bravery without a deep consideration for one's duty and the welfare of others is hollow bravado. As a pilot in South America, he spends several years helping to open new air routes for the mail, and later for freight and passengers; he remarks that the letters he and his colleagues carry may be unimportant, but that the mail itself is sacred. To do one's duty regardless of personal safety is one of Saint-Exupéry's imperatives, and his friends Jean Mermoz and Henri Guillaumet emerge as heroes in his book for their admirable sense of responsibility.

In one of the book's most fascinating episodes, Saint-Exupéry tells of Guillaumet's crash in the Andes Mountains of South America. Lost in a region from which even the natives believe nobody can escape alive, Guillaumet displays great courage and, more important, an unshakable responsibility to himself, his wife, and the mail he is to deliver. At one point, when Guillaumet is almost sure that he cannot go on, he moves out of the probable path of future avalanches so that his body will be found and his wife will be able to collect his life insurance.

The sense of comradeship that marks the relationships between the author and nearly everyone he meets on the job becomes a vital theme of *Wind, Sand and Stars*. The French title, *Terre des Hommes*, or "Man's Earth," emphasizes the bond between human beings and the earth, and hints at the bond among people of all nations that is cemented by their common tie to the planet. Saint-Exupéry preferred the English version of the title, since for him it evoked a particular atmosphere that he wished to describe to others. It is a new earth that the pilot observes from the sky, gliding on wind, passing over sand, blanketed by overhanging stars. Here the pilot comes in contact with natural elements and forces; according to Saint-Exupéry, an airplane is "the means that helps one to analyze and discover the face and the secrets of the planet earth." Saint-Exupéry does not fly to escape the earth but to understand it; he concludes that the only true joy in life is to be found in the relationships one forms with friends and colleagues.

Along with Saint-Exupéry's focus on the need to rise above adversity and to make the most of human contacts, he dwells (especially in the later passages) on his attempts to find out what men will die for. In his meetings with soldiers in Spain, Saint-Exupéry constantly examines the reason that these men will fight, often against overpowering odds and in ghastly circumstances. While visiting the Madrid front, he happens upon a corporal lecturing a group of filthy and worn-out troops on the subject of botany. As the young corporal speaks about the fragile parts of the flower he is holding out to the gathering, Saint-Exupéry wonders what has impelled these men to attend such an unlikely event. He concludes that some force within them, some spirit, has urged them to stop being brutes for a time and to join up with "humanity." Saint-Exupéry then observes that only by being aware of the sacredness and sweetness of life can one be happy: "Only then will we be able to live in peace and die in peace, for only this lends meaning to life and to death."

◆ Literary Qualities ◆

A series of incidents loosely connected by the author's personal reflections, *Wind, Sand and Stars* places the reader in the cockpit with Saint-Exupéry as he recalls the early days of aviation. The book's central episode, Saint-Exupéry's plane crash in the Sahara, displays the author's highly developed powers of narration. Because radar has not yet been invented, neither Saint-Exupéry nor his mechanic Prévot have any idea where they are. Saint-Exupéry tells his story with suspense and animation, and the reader shares in his death thirst, sees the same mirages that appear on the horizon, and draws strength from his indomitable will to live. Saint-Exupéry's narrative skills are displayed in the book's briefer episodes as well.

Personal, philosophical ruminations connect the various chapters, but Saint-Exupéry is saved from moralizing by his poetic talent. His writing style has been justly praised for being both straightforward and remarkably evocative. His analogies are masterful and reveal not only his thoughtfulness but also the wide range of his experience. He compares a range of mountain peaks shrouded by heavy fog to a group of loose mines in the sea, and concludes that, just as the mines make navigation nearly impossible, so too do the unseen peaks, of unknown height, turn the whole sky into a danger zone. The layers of snow on certain mountains, as seen from the air, appear to Saint-Exupéry like large white scarfs. This figure of speech not only creates a clear visual impression, but also suggests a personification of the mighty mountains over which he flew.

Almost any scene viewed from the air can inspire a telling image for this flying poet. Saint-Exupéry describes the windy sea as a shattered mirror, "the crust of the earth...as dented as an old boiler," and a waterfall as a "braided column roaring over the rocks." Such images add substance to the text and make the reading enjoyable. Saint-Exupéry extends his use of picturesque language to his descriptions of human subjects, as well. He notices the clogs worn by a sergeant in a combat zone:

> "Enormous clogs, iron-shod and studded with nails, the clogs of a sewer-worker or a railway track-walker. All the poverty of the world was in those clogs. No man ever strode with happy steps through life in clogs like these: he boarded life like a longshoreman for whom life is a ship to be unloaded."

Readers familiar with Saint-Exupéry's classic fable *The Little Prince* will note that nearly all the important ideas in that earlier book are expressed in different form in *Wind, Sand and Stars*. Whereas *The Little Prince* is allegorical, *Wind, Sand and Stars* is autobiographical, poetic, and at times mystical. The need for human communication that drove the Little Prince to earth is the same bond that unites the mail carrier pilots in their dangerous profession, and the sense of responsibility to other human beings and the desire for a humane world is central to each book. Critics have noted that the fairy-tale quality of both *Wind, Sand and Stars*

and *The Little Prince* echoes the work of Hans Christian Andersen, Saint-Exupéry's favorite author from childhood.

◆ Social Sensitivity ◆

Wind, Sand and Stars is a book that stresses the importance of human bonds, and as such it stands as a positive and thought-provoking reading experience. Saint-Exupéry's delicate portraits, gentle sense of humor, and overarching regard for basic human dignity inspire respect for every character in his narrative. Readers may be put off by the author's use of a racial slur in chapter 7, but should be reminded that, inexcusable as the word is in present-day society, it was a popularly used—if unfortunate—term in the 1930s. Saint-Exupéry concludes the book with a biblically inspired phrase: "Only the Spirit, if it breathes upon the clay, can create Man." No technology is capable of creating a marvel to match that of human life. Even the airplane, a product of human intelligence, is ultimately secondary in importance to the people who fly it and who, in flying, gain a new appreciation for the world.

◆ Topics for Discussion ◆

1. Of the various aviators and other friends of the author, which seems to be the one Saint-Exupéry admires the most? Cite evidence from the text.

2. Do you agree with Saint-Exupéry's claims that only a special kind of person flies for a career? Remember that these early pilots used planes of a very primitive sort, by today's standards.

3. Which of the author's adventures do you find most exciting? What sort of courage was required of Saint-Exupéry in this particular episode?

4. Which features of Saint-Exupéry's writing style are the most impressive? Choose several examples of passages that you find especially striking, and explain what contributes to their effect.

5. What seems to be the author's final judgment about the nature of human life? Does he seem to be an optimist at heart or a pessimist, judging by his comments throughout the book?

◆ Ideas for Reports and Papers ◆

1. Most of Saint-Exupéry's flying was done between the two world wars, 1918-1937. What events during this twenty-year period helped to foster his interest in flying? What economic reasons spurred the fairly rapid development of aviation at this time?

2. In what ways might the original French title, *Terre des Hommes*, be a more accurate (from a philosophical viewpoint) indication of the thrust of this book? Why do you think the author, who was given a choice of a number of English titles, selected *Wind, Sand and Stars* over other possibilities, including a literal translation ("Man's Earth")?

3. All standard editions of the book contain a map showing the various routes along which Saint-Exupéry flew. Explain the vital importance for pilots, in the days before the invention of radar, to have a clear grasp of geography. Describe some of the topographical features with which these early pilots had to contend.

4. During the early years of the Second World War, Saint-Exupéry was deeply involved in both military and political activities. Were his efforts in these areas fairly successful? If he encountered difficulties, what was their source?

5. Saint-Exupéry often speaks in the book about the perils of flying at night. What solutions to this problem have been developed? What other developments in the science of aviation may have been inspired by such daring pilots as Saint-Exupéry and his colleagues?

6. Read the author's other major essay, *Flight to Arras*. In what ways is *Flight to Arras* more successful than *Wind, Sand and Stars*, and in what ways is it less so?

◆ Related Titles ◆

Two earlier works by Saint-Exupéry— the novels *Southern Mail* and *Night Flight*—deal with flying and the lives of fliers. Although inferior in quality to later productions, these books introduce themes which the author continued to explore for the rest of his life. The allegorical *The Little Prince*, a deceptively simple tale that also features charming illustrations by Saint-Exupéry, is the story of a little prince who leaves his home planet in search of companionship on earth. The most important of Saint-Exupéry's "essays," for those readers who wish to understand the philosophy of this man of action and ideas, are *Flight to Arras*, which tells of the author's experiences as a pilot during World War I; *Letter to a Hostage*, a wide-ranging piece, about the great days of the past and the difficult times of the war, that contains restatements of many ideas and convictions found in

Saint-Exupéry's earlier works; and *The Wisdom of the Sands*, a posthumously published collection of Saint-Exupéry's thoughts and beliefs.

◆ For Further Reference ◆

Cate, Curtis. *Antoine de Saint-Exupéry: His Life and Times*. New York: G. P. Putnam's Sons, 1970. This long study is probably the best English-language account of the life and milieu of Saint-Exupéry. The book explains a great deal about the art of flying during Saint-Exupéry's lifetime, and contains a fascinating set of photographs of Saint-Exupéry, his friends and fellow aviators, and the rudimentary aircraft in which they flew.

Migeo, Marcel. *The Story of Saint-Exupéry*. Translated by Herma Briffault. New York: McGraw-Hill, 1960. A fellow aviator and a friend of Saint-Exupéry's, Migeo tends to emphasize Saint-Exupéry's descriptions of flight over the philosophical content of his writing. Contains several helpful maps.

Richardson, Kenneth, ed. *Twentieth Century Writing*. New York: Newnes Books, 1969. The short entry on Saint-Exupéry focuses on the author's philosophy; the discussion is clear and pointed.

Rumbold, Richard, and Lady Margaret Stewart. *The Winged Life: A Portrait of Antoine de Saint-Exupéry, Poet and Airman*. New York: David McKay, 1953. A brief, authentic treatment of the subject's life and ideas. Includes a useful index and an excellent map showing the routes that Saint-Exupéry flew.

Smith, Maxwell. *A Saint-Exupéry Reader*. New York: Dodd, Mead, 1960. While this short volume is essentially a collection of excerpts in French for students of the language (it has an English glossary of French words at the end), it also contains an informative preface, in English, and useful introductory remarks to each selection, also in English.

Fred B. McEwen
Waynesburg College

Sister Irma M. Kashuba, S.S.J.
Chestnut Hill College

THE WITCH OF BLACKBIRD POND
Novel

1958

Author: Elizabeth George Speare, b. 1908

Calico Captive, 1957
The Witch of Blackbird Pond, 1958
The Bronze Bow, 1961
Life in Colonial America, 1963
The Sign of the Beaver, 1983

◆ About the Author ◆

A native New Englander, Elizabeth George Speare was born on November 21, 1908, in Melrose, Massachusetts. She now lives in Easton, Connecticut. For more than twenty years, she lived in Wethersfield, Connecticut, where the events of *The Witch of Blackbird Pond* take place.

After earning her bachelor's and master's degrees from Boston College, Speare spent some years as a teacher and mother before turning to research and writing full time. She was almost fifty years old before she published her first young adult novel, *Calico Captive*.

Speare is one of the few authors whose books have been awarded the Newbery Medal twice: *The Witch of Blackbird Pond* and *The Bronze Bow* were so honored in 1959 and 1962 respectively. Her latest novel, *The Sign of the Beaver*, was named a Newbery Honor Book and won the first Scott O'Dell Award for historical fiction.

◆ Overview ◆

In *The Witch of Blackbird Pond*, Speare creates strong and memorable fictional characters who interact with actual historical personages. The result is a vivid portrait of life in Puritan New England. Kit Tyler, a rebellious orphan who has grown up in Barbados, moves to Connecticut and is soon exposed to the restrictive rules of Puritan society. In her new home, she frequently finds herself in conflict with her Uncle Matthew. These domestic confrontations point up some of her conflicts with Puritan society at large, for Kit is temperamentally unsuited to following other people's rules. To survive she must curb her impulsiveness, and when she cannot she suffers "helpless rage." Kit's difficulties in adjusting to her new surround-

Elizabeth George Speare

The WITCH of
Blackbird Pond

Jacket for *The Witch of Blackbird Pond* by Elizabeth George Speare. Houghton Mifflin: Boston (1958).

ings culminate in her being tried on the charge of witchcraft.

♦ Setting ♦

The events of the tale begin in April 1687 and continue through the following spring. Wethersfield, the principal scene of the action, is several miles south of Hartford, Connecticut, near the banks of the Connecticut River. Historically, this is the time of the witch trials in Salem, Massachusetts.

The opening chapter introduces the cultural contrasts between the warm, friendly island life of Barbados and the cold Puritan society of Connecticut, where religion rules everything from parties and husking bees to courting. Kit sees constant reminders—"a pillory, a whipping post and stocks"—of the oppressiveness of Puritan New England. She must put away her colorful dresses brought from Barbados and wear the drab colors that are standard in Wethersfield. Before coming to America, she swam in the warm Caribbean waters; now she finds that swimming in New England is suspect and that the waters are as chilling as the society. Young people, Kit discovers, are to be seen and not heard in Puritan society, which is based on the premise that punishments are given in this world, rewards in the next world. The New England setting contrasts with Kit's former life and immediately introduces conflict into the story.

◆ Themes and Characters ◆

The granddaughter of Sir Francis Tyler, sixteen-year-old Katherine (Kit) Tyler is the novel's protagonist. Her encounter with Hannah Tupper, the title character, helps Kit to understand her own outcast position in this Puritan society, where she is torn between rebellion and conformity. Through her meetings with Hannah, Kit becomes more understanding, partly because Hannah functions as a surrogate mother. As a Quaker, Hannah is an outcast in the Wethersfield community. She appears different from others because she lives in the meadows near Blackbird Pond and practices a religion the others do not understand. Unlike the rigid Puritans of the town, she is genuinely kind and demonstrates a capacity for love, but the townspeople consider her a witch because she keeps cats. In the

past, Hannah was branded on the forehead when she and her now-deceased husband were banished from Massachusetts and forced to seek religious freedom in Connecticut.

Upon Kit's arrival in Wethersfield, she meets for the first time her uncle, Matthew Wood, a dour New Englander and the stern master of Kit's new home. Despite his forbidding nature, he and Kit finally gain a mutual respect, and he shows great courage during the witchcraft trial by defending his niece. Matthew's wife, Rachel, is the thin, gray-haired sister of Kit's mother, Margaret. Rachel and Matthew have two daughters, Judith and Mercy. A blue-eyed beauty, sixteen-year-old Judith is eager to get married, although Kit causes her to change her initial plans. Judith's younger sister, Mercy, is the most important member of the Wood family, the "pivot about whom the whole family moves." Mercy, whose extraordinary gray eyes are "filled with light," is crippled and must use crutches. It is from Mercy that Kit learns patience and endurance.

The Cruff family also plays an important role in the novel. Kit first encounters the family on the ship from Saybrook to Wethersfield, earning Goodwife Cruff's enmity by saving young Prudence Cruff's doll. Goodwife Cruff considers Kit an upstart and ends up accusing her of being a witch. Yet Kit is able to teach the neglected Prudence to read and write, something that neither of the girl's parents can do.

Three other significant characters are Nathaniel (Nat) Eaton, William Ashby, and John Holbrook. Nat is a friend of Hannah's and one of the first Yankees that Kit meets. The son of the captain of the *Dolphin*, the ship that brought Kit to Connecticut from Barbados, Nat is also an outsider in Wethersfield. On the other hand, Ashby at age nineteen seems to be an up-and-coming member of the Wethersfield community. He builds a new house and is appointed viewer of fences, a position similar to a town surveyor. The quiet Ashby has a romantic interest in Kit. Holbrook, a character who matures in the course of the novel, has come to Wethersfield to study theology with the Reverend Dr. Gersholm Bulkeley, a real historical personage. During the story Speare shows Bulkeley acting in his capacity as a physician as well as a theologian.

Other "real people [who] walk through the imaginary story" include Eleazer Kimberley, the schoolmaster who oversees the Bible class that Mercy teaches; Sir Edmond Andros, the Royalist governor; and Captain Samuel Talcott, the magistrate at Kit's trial.

Kit matures through her interactions with the novel's various characters. At first she is impatient and impulsive. When Prudence's doll falls overboard, Kit jumps into the water to retrieve it. On Kit's first meeting her Uncle Matthew, he asks if "just on an impulse" she left her "rightful home and sailed halfway across the world." For the easygoing Kit of the West Indies, patience seems to be an unattainable virtue. Because she must stifle her natural reactions, she is frequently angry. With the quiet influence of Mercy, she does learn to be more patient, although she is not entirely tamed by her year in a new country.

Interlaced with Kit's lack of patience is her pride in being the granddaughter of Sir Francis Tyler. Her family's prominence gives Kit an undue sense of superiority. Kit has done nothing to earn respect from others; she believes it is owed to her. But during the long New England winter, she learns a different sense of pride: self-respect and dignity for a job she herself has done well. After Kit has kept the household together during sickness, and after it is proved in court that she has taught Prudence to read, her achievements are evident. She has earned the right to feel an honest sense of accomplishment. When it comes time for her cousins to be married, she can offer gifts of her dresses "with love instead of pride." This change shows how much Kit has matured in the course of a year.

> With a bound she was over the side and had set foot on America. She stood taking deep breaths of the salt, fish-tainted air, and looked about for someone to share her excitement.

An important theme in the novel is Kit's painful lesson regarding loyalties. At first she cares little for the Woods; she thinks of Uncle Matthew as a tyrant who bullies her Aunt Rachel, and she notices that her cousin Judith is as proud as she herself is. Yet Mercy, the linchpin of the family, teaches Kit patience, then endurance, and finally loyalty. Furthermore, Uncle Matthew and Aunt Rachel demonstrate loyalty to Kit when they support her during her imprisonment and trial.

Upon first meeting Hannah, Kit gives unquestioning loyalty to the Quaker woman because Hannah demands nothing of her. But Kit proves that she has the capacity for true loyalty when she protects Hannah from the threat of mob violence. Learning the importance of mutual trust from her relatives and from Hannah encourages Kit to consider staying in New England. In the course of the book, she has discovered that people can be loyal whether or not they agree with one another.

One of Speare's outstanding achievements as a writer is her ability to create a strong sense of place. In *The Witch of Blackbird Pond*, the contrast between Barbados and New England highlights the distinct characteristics of the Connecticut setting. Speare sets up this contrast in the novel's opening chapter: "The bleak line of shore surrounding the gray harbor was a disheartening contrast to the shimmering green and white that fringed the turquoise bay of Barbados..." Throughout the novel, Speare associates drab colors, particularly gray and black, with Kit's new home, while she describes Barbados with colorful imagery.

The books valued by residents of each locale further underscore the differences between Barbados and New England. In Barbados Kit was encouraged to read imaginative works of poetry and drama, including works by William Shakespeare, Thomas Otway, and John Dryden. The Wethersfield colonists, on the other hand, shun writing that seems purely imaginative and emphasize books that establish codes of behavior, such as the Bible and John Bunyan's allegory *Pilgrim's Progress*. The *Accidence* is also considered worthwhile reading in Wethersfield for the rules of grammar that it sets forth. Speare uses these differences in reading preferences to create a sense of the social values of the two locales.

Wethersfield and Barbados represent the two sides of Kit's personality. When the novel begins, she has already developed the love of beauty and the appreciation of the imagination that Barbados represents, but she has not developed the capacity for hard work or the sense of individual achievement and well-earned pride that Wethersfield represents. By the end of the novel, she has developed both sides of her personality, and it is only then that she becomes a mature young adult.

• Social Sensitivity •

There is little in *The Witch of Blackbird Pond* that is likely to offend readers, though one reviewer has taken issue with the suggestion at the novel's end that Nat and Kit will marry, calling this conclusion a "sexist compromise." But Speare is writing about an age where even the most independent young women had extremely limited options available to them, and so it would be difficult for her to suggest another future for Kit without sacrificing the novel's historical authenticity. Furthermore, Speare implicitly criticizes the treatment of women in seventeenth-century New England by showing how charges of witchcraft were used to suppress independent women, who were perceived as a threat. The kind Hannah Tupper is persecuted not only because she is an independent woman, but because of her Quaker faith, and in this sense Speare's novel also criticizes intolerance of religious differences.

✦ Topics for Discussion ✦

1. Why does Speare load the first chapter with so many important characters? Are all the principal characters well drawn?

2. Does Kit react to situations the same way that a sixteen-year-old today would?

3. What might readers conclude about outcasts in this Puritan society? About the society's tolerance? How significant is group pressure in Puritan society?

4. What moral questions arise from the book?

5. What significance do you find in the characters' names?

6. What tension exists between Kit and Nat? Cite examples of increasing and diminishing tension.

✦ Ideas for Reports and Papers ✦

1. Explain Kit's process of maturation in the novel.

2. Is Speare's description of the Puritan society in New England historically accurate? What evidence can you find to support or refute its accuracy?

3. Hannah Tupper is a Quaker. Research and report on the Society of Friends, its beliefs, and its establishment in America. Does Hannah live up to Quaker ideals?

4. What was the political situation of the colonies in relation to England in 1687? Discover what the major political issues were and how each side viewed them.

5. "People are afraid of things they don't understand" is one of the themes of the book. Cite situations in the novel where this idea appears.

✦ For Further Reference ✦

Buskin, Barbara H., and Karen H. Harris. *Notes from a Different Drummer: A Guide to Juvenile Fiction Portraying the Handicapped.* New York: Bowker, 1977. Briefly treats the character of Mercy and her handicap.

Commire, Anne, ed. *Something about the Author.* Vol. 5. Detroit: Gale Research, 1973. Contains a brief sketch of Speare's life followed by her own remarks about her work.

Cosgrave, Mary Silvia. "Elizabeth George Speare—Newbery Award Winner." *Library Journal* 84 (April 15, 1959): 1291-1292. Brief biographical and critical commentary.

"A Feminist Look at Children's Books." *Library Journal Supplement* 17 (January 1971): 19-24. Charges that the novel is a "cop out" because a "sexist compromise is made" by setting up the marriage between Kit and Nat at the end of the novel.

Kingman, Lee, ed. *Newbery and Caldecott Medal Books, 1956-1965.* Boston: Horn Book, 1965. Reprints Speare's Newbery Medal acceptance speech for *The Witch of Blackbird Pond* as well as biographical commentary on Speare by Helen Reeder Cross.

Kirkpatrick, D. L., ed. *Twentieth-Century Children's Writers*. 2d ed. New York: St. Martin's, 1983. Includes a bibliography of Speare's writings and brief critical commentary.

Peterson, Linda Kauffman, and Marilyn Leathers Solt. *Newbery and Caldecott Medal and Honor Books: An Annotated Bibliography*. Boston: Hall, 1982. Brief plot summary with some critical commentary.

Senick, Gerald, ed. *Children's Literature Review*. Vol 8. Detroit: Gale Research, 1985. Excerpts reviews of Speare's books, including *The Witch of Blackbird Pond*.

Susan Garland Mann
Indiana University Southeast

David D. Mann
Miami University

WUTHERING HEIGHTS

Novel

1847

◆

Author: Emily Brontë, 1818-1848

Major Books for Young Adults

Wuthering Heights, 1847

◆ About the Author ◆

Emily Jane Brontë, born July 30, 1818, in Thornton, Yorkshire, England, moved with her family to the village of Haworth in Yorkshire when she was two years old. She spent most of her life in that small, isolated community, and died on December 19, 1848, at the age of 30. Emily's father, Patrick, a brilliant, eccentric Irishman, was the pastor at the parish church in Haworth. The Reverend Brontë, an avid reader and aspiring writer, never achieved the literary success of which he dreamed. But all six of his children inherited his love of reading, and four of them became published writers, with Emily and her older sister Charlotte each producing a critically acclaimed novel.

When Emily was just three, her mother, Maria Branwell Brontë, died, leaving the six Brontë children to the care of a maternal aunt, Elizabeth Branwell, a servant, Tabitha Ackroyd, and the Reverend Brontë. Aunt Branwell, a spinster, attempted to instill her own Calvinist principles in the Brontë children. Emily's early years in Haworth were spent composing poems and stories with her imaginative sisters and brother and wandering alone on the starkly beautiful moors surrounding the family home.

Emily's two oldest sisters, Elizabeth and Maria, died in a typhoid epidemic that spread through the Cowan Bridge School for Clergy Daughters. Charlotte and six-year-old Emily survived the epidemic and returned home, where Emily remained until she was seventeen. In the intervening years, besides absorbing the lessons of her natural environment, Emily educated herself primarily by listening to stories and poems recited by her father and Tabitha.

The Brontë family was not wealthy, and the children duly realized that they ought to consider means of supporting themselves in the future, lest the eventuality of their father's death deprive them of both social status and financial security. In order to prepare herself for a teaching career, Emily left home at seventeen for boarding school. Four months later she returned to Haworth, seriously depressed and physically exhausted by her efforts to conform to the rigid, arbitrary rules imposed at school. Two years later Emily left home again to teach at Miss Patchett's Finishing School in Law Hill, near the industrial town of Halifax. Again, after only six months, she returned home emotionally drained, faced with both her own depression and her brother Branwell's impending breakdown.

At age twenty-three, Emily attended school in Brussels, Belgium, with Charlotte. The sisters planned to open their own school eventually and had borrowed money from Aunt Branwell to get the necessary higher education. But despite her success in French, German, music, and drawing, Emily left Brussels nine months later upon the death of Aunt Branwell, and never returned. She was left to care for her brother, who was still losing his sanity, and her father, who was losing his eyesight.

In 1844, after a valiant effort to open a school that attracted not even a single pupil, the Brontë sisters decided to earn their living by writing. Charlotte accidentally discovered some of Emily's poems and was so impressed that she insisted Emily contribute them to a volume she was compiling. Though angered by Charlotte's invasion of her privacy, Emily reluctantly agreed. Since women's poetry was rarely published in those days, Charlotte, Emily, and their younger sister Anne contributed poems under male pseudonyms. The resulting volume—*Poems by Currer, Ellis and Acton Bell* (1846)—was partly financed by money Aunt Branwell had left the sisters. It sold only two copies but received good critical reviews.

Emily's *Wuthering Heights* seems to have been written in a burst of energy fired by financial need, emotional conflict over Branwell, and frustration at not being able to conform to any society outside of her own eccentric family. Published in 1847, *Wuthering Heights* sold fairly well, but many critics were outraged by the physical brutality it depicted. Emily Brontë died at Haworth on December 19, 1848, a year after *Wuthering Heights* was published, and just two months after Branwell's death.

◆ Overview ◆

Despite the book's sometimes implausible plot and often melodramatic characters, virtually all modern critics consider *Wuthering Heights* a masterpiece of world literature. Indeed, the novel convincingly argues that real-life situations actually seem implausible at times, and that real people often do behave melodramatically, especially when frustrated by the relentless imposition of restrictions made in the name of social progress. *Wuthering Heights* demands that readers fearlessly attempt to discover those qualities of human nature that, stripped of social pretense, are truly valuable. Furthermore, although the language of the novel is rich and the themes complex, it is perhaps the most immediately readable of all Victorian novels. Young adults sympathize particularly with the early trials of Heathcliff; with Hindley's jealousy of his unwelcome foster brother; and with Cathy's dilemma in choosing between the wildly passionate Heathcliff and the somewhat meek Edgar Linton. Sophisticated readers are further intrigued by the unfolding of Heathcliff's passions as an adult, and see him not only as a spellbinding character, but also as a symbol of momentous social reformation.

◆ Setting ◆

The setting of *Wuthering Heights* is a vital but contradictory force in the novel, as important as any of the characters. "Wuthering" is a Yorkshire dialect term for the roaring of the wind, a sound both inviting and frightening. Wuthering Heights, the mansion where much of the action takes place, is a harshly beautiful building that contrasts with the other major locale of the novel, Thrushcross Grange, a more conventionally attractive mansion several miles from the Heights. Between the two houses lie the moors—high, broad stretches of wetland covered with heather and filled with marshy bogs.

The events of *Wuthering Heights* occur during the late eighteenth and early nineteenth centuries. Rural Yorkshire was then an area where sheep were raised for wool mills. As England became more industrialized, competition for power between older landowning families, such as the Lintons, and clever upstart businessmen, such as Heathcliff, increased. Thus the place and time of the novel intensify the major conflicts inherent in its themes.

Jacket painting by Bob McGuinness for *Wuthering Heights* by Emily Bronte. Bantam: New York (1983).

◆ Themes and Characters ◆

The most basic theme of *Wuthering Heights* is that one must be true to oneself or suffer dire consequences. In marrying Edgar Linton, Catherine (Cathy) Earnshaw denies her true desires and consequently violates her love of the untamed, disinherited, uneducated Heathcliff; she later dies of a broken spirit. Furthermore, she seems to damage the lives of all the other characters in the novel. But although Cathy dies midway through the narrative, she remains a mighty presence throughout, not only reproaching those who would belie their true natures, but also driving Heathcliff's ambitions. Viewed from a broader perspective, Cathy's dilemma and its resolution (she chooses to wed the financially secure, well-bred Edgar, thereby motivating the bitter Heathcliff to seek higher social status) suggest a complex theme. Cathy's martyrdom to the dual, contradictory cause of social stability and social progress epitomizes the plight of middle-class women in Western culture. In the nineteenth century, middle-class women were held responsible for both the achievements of the men close to them and the well-being of their children, yet were denied the power to make decisions in response to the rapidly changing social conditions that influenced their ability to fulfill these duties.

As important as Cathy's role is, many critics view *Wuthering Heights* as Heathcliff's story. Outliving Cathy by another generation, Heathcliff overwhelms all other characters, sometimes physically but more often by force of his indomitable personality. From the moment he arrives at Wuthering Heights, a foreign-looking, dirty little orphan whom Mr. Earnshaw brings home from the city, he throws the family into contention. But Cathy and Heathcliff soon become loyal companions and champions of one another, and the two indulge in their love of the wild landscape by spending as much time as possible alone together on the moors. Their relationship becomes so strong and reciprocal that, at a major turning point in the novel, Cathy declares, "I am Heathcliff." Nonetheless, she chooses Edgar for her husband.

Heathcliff's mysterious origins and exaggerated passions suggest that he, like Cathy, is meant to play a role larger than that of the jilted, disenfranchised lover. The hold that Heathcliff eventually gains over the inhabitants of both the Heights and Thrushcross Grange marks him as the representative of a new social class. As such, his character, too, suggests the theme of society in transition demanding the sacrifice of individuality.

Most of the other characters play minor roles. Lockwood is the somewhat spoiled city boy who opens the narrative. Having come to the country for seclusion, his naive perceptions of his hosts provide some of the scarce comic relief in the novel. Ellen (Nelly) Dean—whom Brontë probably modeled after Tabitha Ackroyd—is the housekeeper and nurse at the Heights and later at the Grange. Nelly narrates most of the story, recalling events from memory. Her mixed emotions about Cathy and Heathcliff, whom she has known since they were children, highlight the contradictions inherent in the novel.

Hindley Earnshaw, Cathy's brother, serves primarily to motivate Heathcliff's lifelong desire for revenge. Hindley's spoiled and drunken character may have been influenced by Brontë's own brother, Branwell. Edgar Linton, heir of Thrushcross Grange, becomes Cathy's husband and the father of their daughter Catherine. Edgar develops from a shallow boy to a kind, loving husband and father, but his passion for Cathy cannot match Heathcliff's. Isabella Linton, Edgar's sister and later Heathcliff's wife, is little more than a stereotypical, foolish adolescent whose unrealistic notions of romantic love lead her into a disastrous relationship with Heathcliff.

The three characters whose lives become enmeshed in the second half of the novel are Hareton Earnshaw (Hindley's son), Catherine Linton (Cathy and Edgar's daughter), and Linton Heathcliff (Heathcliff and Isabella's son). With Heathcliff as diabolical director, these younger characters act out a weakened, distorted version of the triangle presented in the first half of the novel. Both through her portrayals of these characters and through her less passionate writing style in the novel's second half, Brontë expresses one of the novel's themes: social stability cannot tolerate extreme passion, yet without such passion, the world is a much less exciting place.

◆ Literary Qualities ◆

Wuthering Heights has confounded those critics who attempt to place it in any one literary genre. For its depiction of the intensely individualistic personalities of Cathy and Heathcliff, *Wuthering Heights* has been called the first truly romantic novel. Early in the novel, Heathcliff is an almost pure type of romantic hero; furthermore, Heathcliff's mysterious origin, the larger-than-life dimensions of Cathy's and Heathcliff's characters, and their unearthly love for each other give *Wuthering Heights* the status of myth. Brontë's treatment of time—the narrative moves from present to past to present again—gives the novel an epic quality. But its subject matter, the survival of romantic love and the survival of the family, place it at the crossroads between romantic poetry and the Victorian novel.

Brontë employs numerous points of view to relate her story; much of the book is filtered through the perspective of Nelly Dean, who tells the tale of the inhabitants of Wuthering Heights and Thrushcross Grange to an outsider, Lockwood. By using two relatively minor characters, Nelly and Lockwood, as her primary narrators and interpreters of the action, Brontë challenges her readers to evaluate the book and its principal themes from a multitude of viewpoints. Brontë's sophisticated and groundbreaking narrative technique has been elaborated on by later writers such as Joseph Conrad in his novel *Heart of Darkness* and Henry James in his short story "The Turn of the Screw."

◆ Social Sensitivity ◆

The basic plot of *Wuthering Heights* may seem to be a timeless love story, but the characters and situations reflect many of the real social problems of the late eighteenth and early nineteenth centuries. Women of the time were denied equal economic opportunity, and when Hindley disinherits Cathy Earnshaw, she feels compelled to choose Edgar over Heathcliff in order to secure her material survival. Similarly, Isabella is at Heathcliff's mercy partly because she has no economic security. Heathcliff's character, too, is better understood when one realizes that a young man with no family and no money had few options but to outwit those who did have established social status. Even Lockwood's condescending attitude toward his country hosts points up a social problem that became more acute as industrialization lured more people into the cities; during this social transition, communication and understanding between inhabitants of differing social milieus, economic classes, or educational levels became increasingly difficult. Hindley's early treatment of Heathcliff and the initial relationship between young Catherine and Hareton are variations on this theme of class conflict.

◆ Topics for Discussion ◆

1. Based on his reactions to his treatment by the inhabitants of Wuthering Heights, what kind of society is Lockwood used to?

2. Lockwood smugly accounts for Heathcliff's behavior by implying that Heathcliff is just like Lockwood himself. Does Lockwood "read" his host accurately?

3. Why does Lockwood give such a thorough description of Wuthering Heights?

4. Is Hindley's strong aversion for Heathcliff justified?

5. Emily Brontë is careful to emphasize the contrasts between Wuthering Heights and Thrushcross Grange. Aside from the obvious surface differences, what are the deeper implications of these contrasts?

6. Catherine Linton is particularly delighted when Hareton learns to read. What does her attitude toward his education imply?

♦ Ideas for Reports and Papers ♦

1. A major obstacle to Heathcliff and Cathy's romance is their lack of financial security. Report on the economic prospects for women in late eighteenth-century England.

2. The moors play a role in *Wuthering Heights* almost as important as that played by the characters. Give a detailed description of the characteristic environmental conditions of a moor.

3. Several of the themes of *Wuthering Heights* (for example, the powerful influence of the environment on human beings) are evident in Emily Brontë's poems. Read some of her poems in *Poems by Currer, Ellis and Acton Bell,* and compare the themes of the poems to those of the novel.

4. Compare and contrast the characters of Cathy Earnshaw and her daughter, Catherine Linton.

5. Catherine Linton tells Heathcliff that he is a "cruel man" but not a "fiend." Trace the development of Heathcliff's character in the novel and support or refute young Catherine's assessment of Heathcliff.

♦ Adaptations ♦

Wuthering Heights was adapted to the screen in a 1939 production directed by William Wyler and starring Merle Oberon, Laurence Olivier, and David Niven. The film covers the story only through chapter 17, but it includes strong performances, an excellent script, and Oscar-winning photography. A 1970 production, directed by Robert Fuest, stars Anna Calder-Marshall, Timothy Dalton, and Harry Andrews, and authentically captures the atmosphere and setting of the novel.

♦ For Further Reference ♦

Crandall, Norma. *Emily Brontë: A Psychological Portrait.* Rindge, NH: Richard R. Smith, 1957. An analysis of Brontë's relationships with the various members of her family.

Eagleton, Terry. *Myths of Power.* London: Macmillan, 1975. Eagleton places *Wuthering Heights* in its historical context and demonstrates how the disruptive social changes occurring in the early nineteenth century are reflected in the novel.

Gerin, Winifrid. *Emily Brontë.* Oxford: Oxford University Press, 1971. A thorough, informative biography of Brontë.

Winnifrith, Tom. *The Brontës.* London: Macmillan, 1977. A relatively objective biographical account of Emily Brontë and her siblings.

Mary Lowe-Evans
The University of West Florida

THE YEARLING
Novel

1938

◆

Author: Marjorie Kinnan Rawlings, 1896-1953

Major Books for Young Adults

South Moon Under, 1933
Golden Apples, 1935
The Yearling, 1938
When the Whippoorwill, 1940

Cross Creek, 1942
The Sojourner, 1953
The Secret River, 1955

◆ About the Author ◆

Marjorie Kinnan Rawlings was born in Washington, D.C., on August 8, 1896. Her father was an attorney in the U.S. Patent Office, but he also owned a farm in Maryland, where Rawlings gained her first love and understanding of the land. She attended public school, then enrolled at the University of Wisconsin, where she graduated Phi Beta Kappa with a bachelor of arts degree in 1918.

After working for a year as a publicity writer for the Y.W.C.A. National Headquarters in New York City, she married writer Charles A. Rawlings and moved with him to Rochester, New York. She served as an editor of the magazine *Home Sector* and wrote for the *Louisville Courier-Journal* and the *Rochester Journal.* From 1925 to 1927 she produced a syndicated verse column for United Features entitled "Songs of a Housewife." She also wrote fiction during these years, but was unsuccessful at finding a publisher for her stories.

In 1928, Rawlings purchased a seventy-two-acre orange grove at Cross Creek in north-central Florida. This frontier scrub country and its inhabitants fascinated Rawlings, who had separated from her husband, and prompted her to write "Cracker Chidlings: Real Tales from the Florida Interior," a collection of character sketches that appeared in *Scribner's Magazine* in 1931. Although these colorful sketches aroused criticism that she was giving a bad name to the citizens of the state, Rawlings continued to write about the Florida moonshiners and hunters, portraying their lives with authenticity. Her short story "Gal Young Un" (1932) received an O. Henry Memorial Award in 1933, the same year that her divorce was finalized. Her first novel, *South Moon Under,* was also well received.

Rawlings believed research to be essential to her writing, and would spend

Illustration by Edward Shenton for *The Yearling* by Marjorie Kinnan Rawlings. Scribner Classic/Collier Books/Macmillan: New York (1938).

weeks living in the backcountry, gathering stories and facts firsthand. *The Yearling*, a story of twelve-year-old Jody Baxter and his pet fawn, Flag, was partially inspired by her visits with an old man who took her bear hunting. This novel, considered the high point of Rawlings's career and an outstanding book for young people, won the Pulitzer Prize for fiction in 1939. The novel also won the Lewis Carroll Shelf Award in 1963.

In 1941, Rawlings moved to St. Augustine, Florida, with her second husband, Norton Sanford Baskin. She completed an autobiographical story collection, *Cross Creek*, and won a second O. Henry Memorial Award in 1945 for her short story "Black Secret." In 1947 she purchased a summer home in rural New York and used this setting as the background for the final novel published during her lifetime, *The Sojourner*. Rawlings died of a cerebral hemorrhage in St. Augustine on December 14, 1953. She is buried at Antioch Cemetery near Cross Creek. *The Secret River*, a posthumously published novel for young adults, was named a Newbery Honor Book in 1956.

◆ Overview ◆

The Yearling is a touching, suspenseful, and realistic story about a boy caught between love for his pet and responsibility to his family. The novel follows a year in the life of this playful and sensitive boy—a year filled with adventure and danger, loss and loneliness. The boy's experiences of sorrow, bitterness, and courage speak of what it means to grow up in a harsh environment.

◆ Setting ◆

The story of *The Yearling* takes place in the 1870s in the untamed wilds of inland Florida. The Baxter family has settled in a clearing of pines near the "scrub"—a deeply forested stretch of land enclosed by rivers, surrounded by marshes, and inhabited by hundreds of wild animals and birds. Here, isolated from their moonshiner neighbors and the world at large, the family leads a hand-to-mouth existence, fighting against the constant threat of bears, panthers, wolves, rattlesnakes, and inclement weather. Water is scarce and must be carried from a large sinkhole. Survival depends on hunting, both to provide food and to protect the crops and livestock.

♦ Themes and Characters ♦

The main characters in *The Yearling* are a lonely twelve-year-old boy, Jody Baxter, and his pet deer, Flag. For a year the two are inseparable, sharing adventures and hardships as they grow. But when Flag begins to eat the family's crops and must be shot, Jody panics and runs away from home.

Somewhere beyond the sink-hole, past the magnolia, under the live oaks, a boy and a yearling ran side by side and were gone forever.

Penny Baxter is Jody's honest and compassionate father. Understanding his son's pain and bitterness, he urges Jody to face his sorrow and go on with life "like a man." Life has not been easy for Penny, either. At one point in the novel he is nearly killed by a rattlesnake bite, and as a result he must accept declining health and strength. His wife, Ora Baxter, is a sharp and bitter "no-nonsense" woman. Of her many children, only Jody has survived.

The Baxters' nearest neighbors are the Forresters, who are rough and boisterous. One of the sons, Lem, is broody and sulky, quick to pick a fight and hold a grudge. In contrast, another son, Buck, is strong and generous: when Penny is ill from the rattlesnake bite, Buck offers to work his fields. The youngest Forrester, Fodder-wing, is Jody's special friend. Although physically and mentally disabled, Fodder-wing has a vivid imagination and a gentle, unique love of animals. When he dies, both the Forresters and Jody are heartbroken.

Grandma Hutto, with her laughing eyes and luxurious lifestyle, is another special friend to Jody and Penny. They treasure their visits to her cottage, where her nurturing provides comfort and security. Grandma's son, Oliver, is a handsome sailor in love with a girl named Twink Weatherby, and Jody resents the time Oliver spends with her. Lem Forrester, too, is jealous of the relationship between Oliver and Twink. He attacks Oliver, drawing the entire Forrester family into the brawl. When Penny and Jody come to Oliver's defense, they are soundly beaten, and Jody feels resentful and betrayed. And when Lem Forrester burns Grandma Hutto's house and she decides to move to Boston, Jody is again heartbroken with the loss.

The Yearling has another set of important characters—the animals. There is, of course, Jody's beloved pet fawn Flag, whose natural instincts become destructive to the family and cannot be tolerated if the family's food is to be protected. Some wild animals, like the dancing whooping cranes, are admired by the characters for their mysterious beauty. Others, like the deer dying from the plague, are mourned. And predators, such as the wolves and bears who destroy crops and kill livestock, are hated. Old Slewfoot, the vicious black bear with a missing toe, is an especially feared enemy. Penny and Jody hunt him with anger and revenge, believing his death to be their duty. The family's dogs, Julia, Rip, and Perk, are valued in proportion to their skill in hunting. Old Julia, who tracks and fights wild animals with a vengeance, is cherished, but Perk, who is not a good hunter, is traded to the Forresters for a gun.

The relationship of people and animals to one another and to the land is one of the basic themes of *The Yearling*. Issues of loyalty and betrayal, survival, death, and loneliness are raised repeatedly as the characters interact with nature. The central question is whether humanity must necessarily be in conflict with nature, or whether the beauty of nature can be reconciled with the cruelty of life. *The Yearling* shows that life is hard, that suffering and sacrifice are to be expected and accepted, and that the loss of innocence is an inevitable part of growing up.

◆ Literary Qualities ◆

The Yearling is an excellent example of frontier regional literature. The resilience and earthiness of the characters is vividly captured in a unique pattern of speech that the Florida natives refer to as "cracker" dialect. Because the Florida scrub and its inhabitants are depicted with almost journalistic precision, the reader is absorbed into the reality of the period and the authenticity of Jody's conflict. The straightforward style of the narrative and the well-constructed plot keep this action story moving, but Rawlings has also taken great care to develop the thoughts and personalities of her characters and to show the complex causes of their feelings and behavior. She evokes a

spectrum of moods, ranging from the security and peace of the innocent boy at the pool, to the utter despair of the young man who feels abandoned. Rawlings skillfully unifies thoughts, themes, and impressions to present a rich and intricate picture of Jody's world.

◆ Social Sensitivity ◆

Readers of *The Yearling* may be offended by Rawlings's portrayal of women. Ma Baxter, for example, is the one member of the family who is consistently cold and severe. Her son considers her insensitive, and her husband scolds her like a child. She is pictured as an overweight and unimaginative complainer, unable to tell a decent story, to appreciate pets, or to shoot properly. Penny, on the other hand, is Ora's male opposite: he is a tender and intelligent optimist who loves animals, tells marvelous stories, understands boys, and is respected for his hunting abilities. Other women in the story receive equally fixed treatment. Jody considers little Eulalie Boyles both a prime target for potato-throwing and, vaguely, a romantic object. Grandma Hutto and Twink Weatherby are admired or despised for their ability to attract men. And women of all types are categorized as "running in breeds."

The Yearling's treatment of a boy's maturation might also be seen as stereotypical. As the book opens, Jody is relaxed and carefree, at one with nature and confident that owning a pet will complete his happiness. By the end of the story he has grown to regard life as hard and lonely, has been thrust into the violent world of the hunt, and has been forced, in the name of survival and maturity, to betray and destroy that which he loves the most. The novel appears to suggest that a boy must kill to be a man, and that a man must base his actions on survival, not on love.

Readers should also be aware of glimpses of racial prejudice in *The Yearling*. If taken as legitimate pictures of the prevailing social attitudes for the region and time, these objectionable images can inform our understanding of the characters' actions and emotions.

◆ Topics for Discussion ◆

1. At the conclusion of chapter 1, Rawlings says: "A mark was on [Jody] from the day's delight so that all his life, when April was a thin green and the flavor of rain was on his tongue, an old wound would throb and a nostalgia would fill him for something he could not quite remember." What does she mean? How does this opening statement foreshadow the outcome of the book?

2. Ma and Penny Baxter have very different attitudes toward animals. How do their opinions differ, and why? How is this difference indicative of their contrasting attitudes about life in general?

3. Why are Penny and Jody so attracted to the sinkhole?

4. Why is Jody resentful of Oliver Hutto and the Forresters? Is this a justified bitterness? How does this resentment bear on his concept of a friend's duty?

6. When Fodder-wing dies, the Forresters and Jody are devastated. Why do they take his death so hard? How is Fodder-wing's name symbolic of the loss of the innocence of youth?

7. What role do food, appetite, and hunger play in Jody's outlook on life?

8. Why do you think Ma Baxter dislikes Grandma Hutto? Why is Ma Baxter usually so sharp and bitter?

9. Would it have been easier on Jody if Penny had forbidden him to have a pet deer in the first place, instead of letting him raise Flag and then forcing him to kill the deer? Why or why not? Why does Penny suspect all along that the pet might not work out? How does this affect your opinion of him as a parent?

10. At the beginning of the story Jody builds a flutter mill; at the end of the story he builds another. How does he feel about building and playing with each of these toys? How do Jody's responses reveal the changes that have occurred in his personality?

◆ Ideas for Reports and Papers ◆

1. Trace Jody's feelings and responses to the hunt throughout the year. What events influence his impressions of the various hunting experiences? How would you generalize Jody's overall attitude toward the relationship of beauty and cruelty in life?

2. How does Penny define stealing and cheating? How do his interactions with his neighbors and with animals illustrate his beliefs? How do his attitudes relate to the concept of "the survival of the fittest" and to the American tendency to justify humanity's dominion over nature?

3. Some critics believe that *The Yearling* teaches harmful values by its suggestion that a boy must kill in order to

become a man. Do you agree or disagree? Why? Could Jody have done anything other than shoot his pet? How have other books about boys and their pets, such as *Old Yeller,* by Fred Gipson, or *Rascal,* by Sterling North, handled similar situations?

4. Many of the characters in *The Yearling* respond to conflict by running away. Penny has "run away" from civilization's "intrusion on the individual spirit" and Grandma Hutto decides to move out of town rather than face the Forresters' brutality. Jody instructs Flag to protect himself from wild animals by insisting, "You jest run from everything," and Jody attempts to run away from his anger and sorrow after killing Flag. Compare the reasons used by these characters and others in the book to rationalize walking away from life's problems. Is running away an honorable way to face conflict? Why or why not? Can it ever be ultimately successful?

5. Rawlings is often categorized as a writer of frontier regional literature. What does this mean, and how is *The Yearling* an example of this genre? What specific techniques does Rawlings use in *The Yearling* to write in this style? How important are these techniques in relation to the themes of the story—are they necessary or a hindrance?

♦ Related Titles/Adaptations ♦

Many of Rawlings's other works examine characters, settings, and themes similar to those in *The Yearling. South Moon Under* describes a family of Florida moonshiners trying to cope with the uncertainties of daily existence in the scrub. *When the Whippoorwill* is a collection of stories about Florida and its people. It includes two prize-winning stories: "Jacob's Ladder," which tells of a girl living in the marsh with her common-law trapper husband, and "Gal Young Un," the story of an unhappy man who marries an older widow for her money, and then asks a younger girlfriend to move in with them. Another book, *Cross Creek,* is a collection of autobiographical sketches about central Florida; it contains interesting background material on how Rawlings's novels and stories were inspired.

In 1946 MGM adapted *The Yearling* into a motion picture starring Jane Wyman and Gregory Peck. Twelve-year-old Claude Jarman, Jr., won a special Academy Award as the finest child actor of the year for his portrayal of Jody, both Wyman and Peck were Oscar nominees for their acting, and the film was nominated for Best Picture. The film is sentimental and ironic, but the rustic dialect which seems to flow authentically in the book sounds artificial on the screen. Ma Baxter's character is softened in the film, and the simple wonder and beauty of nature, an integral part of the novel, is overwhelmed by elaborately produced scenes.

♦ For Further Reference ♦

Bellman, Samuel I. *Marjorie Kinnan Rawlings.* Boston: Twayne, 1974. This biography of Rawlings analyzes and evaluates her work.

Bigelow, Gordon E. *Frontier Eden: The Literary Career of Marjorie K. Rawlings.* Gainesville, FL: University of Florida Press, 1966. Includes a literary critique of Rawlings's work, provides an excellent discussion of her use of dialect, and explains Rawlings's conception of the Florida people.

Commire, Anne. *Something about the Author.* Vol. 1. Detroit: Gale Research, 1977. Contains a biographical sketch of Rawlings.

Van Gelden, Robert. "A Talk With Marjorie Kinnan Rawlings." *New York Times Book Review* (November 30, 1941): 2. This interview presents some of Rawlings's own comments and ideas about her work.

Rhoda Preston

YOUNG FU OF THE UPPER YANGTZE
Novel
1932

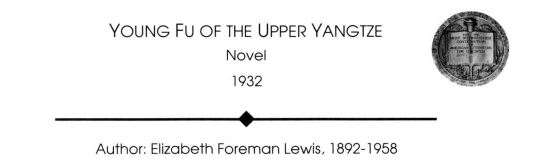

Author: Elizabeth Foreman Lewis, 1892-1958

Major Books for Young Adults

Young Fu of the Upper Yangtze,
  1932
Ho-Ming, Girl of New China, 1934
China Quest, 1937

Portraits from a Chinese Scroll, 1938
When the Typhoon Blows, 1942
*To Beat a Tiger, One Needs a
  Brother's Help*, 1956

◆ About the Author ◆

Elizabeth Foreman Lewis was born on May 24, 1892, in Baltimore, Maryland. She attended public schools there, and after graduation from high school studied art at the Maryland Institute in Baltimore. She continued her studies, particularly in religion and English literature, in New York City. In 1917 she was sent to China by the Methodist Women's Board. She served as mission treasurer in Shanghai, as supervisor of Chungking District Schools, and as a teacher at both the Huei Wen School for Girls and the Boys' Academy in Nanking. She was married in Nanking in 1921 to John Abraham Lewis, the son of a Methodist bishop. Lewis continued her work in China for a number of years, until illness forced her to return home to Maryland. For the better part of three decades, she devoted all of her available time and energy to speaking and writing about China, the country she loved so much and knew so well.

Young Fu of the Upper Yangtze was Lewis's first book and her most successful work of fiction. For this novel, Lewis received the 1933 Newbery Medal. Lewis's detailed descriptions of Chinese landscapes and characters contributed much to the success of this book and her subsequent works of fiction, all of them set in China. Her creative evocation of the Chinese land and people retains its place among the finest portraits of China in fiction for young adults. Lewis died in Arnold, Maryland, on August 7, 1958.

◆ Overview ◆

Although many things have changed on both the cultural and political fronts in China since this book was written, *Young Fu of the Upper Yangtze* remains a good introduction to the ancient and venerable civilization of "The Middle Kingdom." In her acceptance remarks for the 1933 Newbery Medal, Lewis said that she had "chronicled, rather than created" the lives of the characters in her novel. Good literature typically addresses questions of character and morality in a way that is timeless and universal, in a way that speaks to the human heart and the human condition everywhere. But good fiction also creates memorable, individualized characters, something that Lewis does admirably in *Young Fu of the Upper Yangtze.*

With its fast-paced action and adventure episodes, the novel also offers the fundamental pleasures of good fiction. Young Fu grows as a character as he deals with fire, floods, and bandits. Above all, the story presents solid, well-rounded characters who embody the values upon which the work is founded. Lewis does not preach these values; rather, she portrays Young Fu acquiring them through experience and through his relationship with the master craftsman Tang. Such qualities as courage, honor, dignity, truthfulness, generosity, compassion, and persistence are shown to be essential to anyone who truly wishes to mature beyond the apprentice phases of learning.

◆ Setting ◆

The story takes place during the 1920s in Chungking (now spelled Chongqing), a large city in southwest China's Szechuen (now spelled Sichuan) Province. Young Fu is a farmboy from a rural village in the hills; the novel opens with his move to Chungking at age thirteen and follows him as he discovers the wonders of this great, walled city with its narrow, winding streets and alleys. The busy life of the streets—the coolies, or load-bearing laborers, with carrying-poles balanced on their shoulders; the children playing games; the beggars; the shops of the craftsmen; the tea houses; the "foreign devils" creating a stir as they pass by— fills Young Fu's heart and mind with excitement. Just below the city walls flows the Yangtze River (or, as the Chinese call it, the Chang Jiang), and when it floods, the reader gets a powerful sense of its awesome force. The most memorable sub-setting of the novel is the coppersmith's shop, with the sound of hammers beating on anvils, chisels screeching on copper and brass, and workers chattering amidst the smoke of the fires.

◆ Themes and Characters ◆

Young Fu of the Upper Yangtze falls into a category of the novel known as the *bildungsroman:* a story of the growth and development of a young protagonist, or a tale of initiation. (*Bildung,* in German, means education, and *roman,* in French, means novel.) A novel of this type often involves an apprentice as the main character engaged in the learning process, and it often includes one or more figures who convey the important lessons to be learned. In this case, the master-apprentice relationship is literal and specific, since Young Fu is formally contracted for a three-year period of apprenticeship to Tang the coppersmith, a master craftsman. Their relationship, however, extends far beyond the formal working contract of master craftsman and trainee. In fact, since Young Fu's father died before the action of the story begins, it is clear from the beginning that Tang is a father-figure for Young Fu. Because of this story structure, Young Fu and Tang are the most important characters, and they are vivid, well-drawn, and well-rounded creations.

Tang represents, in one sense, the traditional virtues of China. He possesses a kind of wisdom and endurance founded on common sense, good humor, and hard work. In another sense, Tang represents the traditional virtues of any master craftsman in any society; one of the primary lessons he teaches Young Fu is summed up in the saying: "To be a good craftsman is an honorable estate." Tang can be a hard taskmaster, expecting the finest quality in all things, and he is capable of a hard bluntness when someone is lazy or dishonest. But he is always just. Wise, kind, and an expert artisan, Tang slowly transmits all of these qualities to Young Fu. The father-son relationship between these two characters, a spiritual fact throughout the narrative, is made legal in the story's ending through Tang's formal adoption of Young Fu. Thus the boy's apprenticeship involves more than lessons in copper- and brass-work; it is a moral apprenticeship as well, and a relationship of mutual respect, warmth, and love.

Illustration by Kurt Wiese for *Young Fu of the Upper Yangtze* by Elizabeth Foreman Lewis. Holt, Rinehart and Winston: New York (1973).

Another important character in the novel is Young Fu's mother, Fu Be Be. With her bound feet and her adherence to old Chinese superstitions, Fu Be Be represents one pole in the conflict between tradition and change, old ways and new, which stands as one of the books's central themes. But Fu Be Be is not a one-dimensional figure set up to demonstrate the shallowness of old-fashioned ways. She is a complex character, lovingly drawn by Lewis, and her compassion and humor are important guiding forces for Young Fu as he grows up. An important minor figure is Wang Scholar, the tattered but dignified teacher of Chinese classics who embodies the Chinese reverence for books and for the wisdom of the sages. Wang Scholar takes on Young Fu as a student,

without recompense, and teaches him to read and write and to respect the classics. It is important to realize that very few Chinese, at the time of this story, knew how to read and write; the Chinese written language, with its ideographs and complicated strokes, required long and intensive study. Still, although only a small percentage of the population was literate, all people held scholars and teachers in the highest esteem, and no profession evoked greater respect and admiration than that of scholar-teacher.

In a *bildungsroman*, true apprentices also learn from those characters who lack values and who illustrate negative traits. Many such figures cross Young Fu's path: the vicious soldier who murders a coolie; Young Fu's dishonest fellow apprentice, Small Den; and Wei the Revolutionary, who—as Lewis presents the matter—embraces an ideology (communism) that tramples on the rights of others and disregards fundamental human decencies.

Another way in which Young Fu learns is by evaluating his own actions. In the great fire and in the rampaging flood, he learns the meaning of courage and selflessness, the value of helping others. In the plague he learns the importance of compassion. He also learns through his own mistakes, recognizing his folly when he is deceived by gamblers or coerced into spending his mother's money on a gaudy, worthless wristwatch. He "loses face" several times, swallows his pride, accepts responsibility for his actions, and ultimately becomes a mature individual.

Lewis explores the role of superstition in Chinese life, relating it to the novel's overall pattern of contrasting "Old China" and "New China," tradition and change. Also related to this pattern is what might be called the "foreign devil" motif, which expresses the traditional Chinese distrust of all foreigners. According to this view, only evil can come from dealing with foreigners. In the course of the novel, Young Fu learns to discard this viewpoint because of his dealings with the yellow-haired foreign lady, a kind woman involved in missionary work. Another important secondary theme centers on the political discord of the times. Young Fu's China is ravaged by bandits and divided by contending factions and parties, warlords (*tuchuns*), Nationalists, and Communists. As the political tension grows and riots erupt in Chungking, Young Fu and the reader become more aware of the directions that "New China" may take. All in all, Lewis presents a balanced view of the

question, although it is clear that she regards the Communists—a group that she never identifies by name—as the most vehement and violent in their attacks on tradition.

Ultimately, though, what matters most in the novel are the values exemplified by such characters as Wang Scholar and Tang, the values that shape Young Fu and mark his maturity. These values—courage, honor, dignity, endurance, and compassion—are the only things that carry human beings through the world's great upheavals, of which China has seen more than its share in the past century.

◆ Literary Qualities ◆

In one sense, *Young Fu of the Upper Yangtze* is a fast-paced, action-packed adventure tale, and Young Fu himself resembles many another young hero of initiation-adventure fiction. Young and naive at first, he wanders the streets of a great city, which he sees romantically as a place of wonder. Then, when he witnesses violence and murder, the city becomes tinged with terror. His initiation into the ways of the world exposes him to certain classic situations reminiscent of other works of fiction: a great fire, during which he is first tested for courage; a "plague" of cholera and typhus, where, with people dying and falling gravely ill all around him, he responds with concern and compassion; a river voyage, during which he encounters bandits and reacts with poise and intelligence; a rampaging flood, from which he rescues an elderly couple; and an encounter with drug-smugglers, whose eventual capture results from his identification of their ring leader. Yet the novel is much more than the sum of its physical adventures;

the novel focuses on the central theme of any good *bildungsroman* —the moral growth to maturity of the young protagonist.

Young Fu of the Upper Yangtze features effective use of imagery and symbolism. Lewis evokes the physical reality of the streets of Chungking, for example, in poetic images: "The air was heavy with steaming sunshine, and cracks between the flagstones of the street hissed through the accumulated filth of ages, like miniature geysers." When Young Fu sees his first snowfall in the hills beyond Chungking, he is "bewitched under the spell of this white magic. Beautiful like white jade...soft, like silk in a cocoon." An old peasant tells him that snow is the "wintry breath of the Dragon." When Young Fu announces that he is going to carry buckets of the rare, marvelous snow into Chungking and sell it on the streets, he is warned not to do so, for his actions will offend the Dragon. He takes the snow with him anyway, and thus the snow is not only a vehicle for descriptive imagery but also a symbol of Young Fu's curiosity, wonder, and willingness to defy old superstitions.

Another striking stylistic feature of the novel is Lewis's frequent use of proverbs, such as "He who rides on a tiger cannot dismount when he pleases" and "You are like a man who sits at the bottom of a well and boasts about his knowledge of the world." These proverbs serve not only to give the flavor of Chinese folk wisdom, but to pinpoint the book's principal moral lessons, rendering in succinct form the knowledge that comes with maturity.

With any novel set in a foreign country, one of the greatest problems posed for the novelist is preserving idiosyncratic features of the original language while making "foreign" speech, written in English, sound natural and unstilted. Lewis succeeds admirably in this, especially through her use of idioms and sentence rhythms. In a preface to another novel by Lewis, *To Beat a Tiger, One Needs a Brother's Help,* no less an observer than Madame Chiang Kai-shek—wife of the late Chinese statesman—observed that Lewis is "especially successful in reproducing conversation" and the characteristically Chinese "half-serious, half-humorous banter."

◆ Social Sensitivity ◆

One issue that often crops up in fiction dealing with foreign cultures, especially those that are remote, non-Western, or impoverished, is a certain condescension on the part of the author. This condescension creates a distance between the reader and the characters and invites the reader to feel more privileged or somehow superior to the people of the story. *Young Fu of the Upper Yangtze* is free of any trace of such condescension; if anything, the sensitive reader—especially one from a more materially advantaged society than that depicted in the novel—may discover a spiritual thinness on the part of his or her own culture. Impoverishment, after all, is not just a matter of material possessions, but of morality and spiritual values.

Because Lewis herself was a teacher in China under the missionary auspices of the Methodist Church, another question that may occur regards the potential preachiness or possible Christian perspective of her fiction. Lewis's work avoids any overt traces of her Christian heritage; she does not write "missionary literature." In fact, although one of the novel's positive characters, the yellow-haired woman, is clearly associated with a missionary hospital, there are no specific references to Christianity. The net effect of the novel is to lead the reader to see the virtues and vision of Chinese civilization, and through that knowledge to understand a quote from the Chinese philosopher Confucius: "In the four seas all men are brothers."

◆ Topics for Discussion ◆

1. Discuss the principal lessons that Young Fu learns from Tang the coppersmith. How do the lessons concerning copper- and brass-work relate to more general lessons about conduct and character?

2. Although he is poor and fatherless, Young Fu feels that he is "favored by fortune." In what ways is he "favored"?

3. Tang tells Young Fu that one lesson he must learn before he becomes an adult is expressed in the saying: "The superior man finds pleasure in doing what is uncongenial." Why is this an important lesson?

4. Give examples from the text of conflicts between old customs and beliefs and new ways of seeing and doing things.

5. Compare and contrast Young Fu's view of foreigners with his mother's view of foreigners.

6. Several characters, such as Wei and the man who makes the speech in the tea house, are revolutionaries. Is there a disparity between what they say they want (freedom and justice) and their actions?

◆ Ideas for Reports and Papers ◆

1. A proverb is a wise saying, passed down over the years, expressed in brief, memorable form. Identify as many of the proverbs presented in the novel as possible. Analyze each in terms of the specific situations in which it is used in the novel and evaluate its validity in the context of modern American experience.

2. The novel presents many examples of tradition (superstition, foot-binding, and artisan-apprentice relationships) and examples of change (attitudes toward medicine, machines, and political revolt). Write a paper dealing with as many instances of tradition and change as you can find in the novel. Are the changes all for the good?

3. Various politicians and political parties are alluded to in the book, including Sun Yat-sen, Chiang Kai-shek, and the Nationalists. Do some research to find out who these people were and what the political situation was in China at the time of the book. How has the political situation changed since, and how has it changed over the past year? Are any of these changes foretold or hinted at in the novel?

4. Two years after writing *Young Fu of the Upper Yangtze*, Elizabeth Foreman Lewis published *Ho-Ming, Girl of New China*. This novel is concerned with a young girl growing up in circumstances similar to Young Fu's. Read this novel and compare various aspects of the two works. Note especially the differences between the expectations and prospects for girls and boys growing up in China.

5. Young Fu may be seen as a character of his time and place (China in the 1920s) as well as a character whose path

to maturity involves experiences valid in all times and places. Are his problems, mistakes, triumphs, and lessons significant today? How?

• Related Titles •

Everything Lewis published dealt with China; thus, in subject matter at least, all of her titles are related and shed further illumination on her best-known work, *Young Fu of the Upper Yangtze*. Very similar in tone and approach is *Ho-Ming, Girl of New China*, which is set in the same time period and is also a *bildungsroman*, a tale of a Chinese girl's growth toward maturity. Traditional Chinese gender-attitudes play a major role in this novel. Lewis's last novel, *To Beat a Tiger, One Needs a Brother's Help*, examines a group of sixteen Chinese boys living at the edge of Shanghai, the "city of despair." The "tiger" is extreme poverty, and these boys do everything they can to "beat" the tiger, to help one another survive. Once again, the political complexities and contentions of Nationalists and Communists figure importantly, but in this work the dominant historical factor is the Japanese invasion and occupation of China. As in her other novels, Lewis's work derives great strength from her creation of credible and compelling characters.

• For Further Reference •

Kunitz, Stanley J., and Howard Haycraft, eds. *The Junior Book of Authors*. New York: H. W. Wilson, 1951. Contains brief notes on Lewis's books, as well as a useful autobiographical sketch by the author.

Miller, Bertha Mahony, and Elinor Whitney Field, eds. *Newbery Medal Books: 1922-1955*. Boston: Horn Book, 1955. The section dealing with *Young Fu of the Upper Yangtze* contains brief commentary on the novel, a useful biographical sketch, and the full text of Lewis's "Acceptance Paper" for the Newbery Medal. Lewis's comments here are especially helpful for an understanding of her love and knowledge of China.

Sutherland, Zena. *Children and Books*. 7th ed. Glenview, IL: Scott, Foresman, 1986. Contains brief commentary on two of Lewis's novels.

H. R. Stoneback
SUNY-New Paltz

APPENDICES

APPENDIX A: NEWBERY WINNERS

Across Five Aprils
Newbery Honor Book
1965

Adam of the Road
Newbery Medal
1943

After the Rain
Newbery Honor Book
1988

Amos Fortune, Free Man
Newbery Medal
1951

And Now Miguel
Newbery Medal
1954

The Black Pearl
Newbery Honor Book
1968

Bridge to Teribithia
Newbery Medal
1978

The Bronze Bow
Newbery Medal
1962

Caddie Woodlawn
Newbery Medal
1936

Carry On, Mr. Bowditch is
Newbery Medal
1956

Daniel Boone
Newbery Medal
1940

Dear Mr. Henshaw
Newbery Medal
1984

Dicey's Song
Newbery Medal
1983

Dobry
Newbery Medal
1935

The Door in the Wall
Newbery Medal
1950

The Egypt Game
Newbery Honor Book
1968

From the Mixed-Up Files of Mrs. Basil E.
  Frankweiler
Newbery Medal
1968

A Gathering of Days
Newbery Medal
1980

Ginger Pye
Newbery Medal
1952

The Great Gilly Hopkins
Newbery Honor Book
1979

Homesick: My Own Story
Newbery Honor Book
1983

The House of Sixty Fathers
Newbery Honor Book
1957

I, Juan de Pareja
Newbery Medal
1966

Incident at Hawk's Hill
Newbery Honor Book
1972

Invincible Louisa
Newbery Medal
1934

Island of the Blue Dolphins
Newbery Medal
1961

It's Like This, Cat
Newbery Medal
1964

Jacob Have I Loved
Newbery Medal
1981

Johnny Tremain
Newbery Medal
1944

King of the Wind
Newbery Medal
1949

Lincoln: A Photobiography
Newbery Medal
1988

M.C. Higgins, the Great
Newbery Medal
1975

The Matchlock Gun
Newbery Medal
1942

Miracles on Maple Hill
Newbery Medal
1957

My Brother Sam Is Dead
Newbery Honor Book
1975

My Side of the Mountain
Newbery Honor Book
1960

Old Yeller
Newbery Honor Book
1957

Onion John
Newbery Medal
1960

Our Eddie
Newbery Honor Book
1970

Penn
Newbery Honor Book
1939

Rascal: A Memoir of a Better Era
Newbery Honor Book
1964

Rifles for Watie
Newbery Medal
1958

Roll of Thunder, Hear My Cry
Newbery Medal
1977

Roller Skates
Newbery Medal
1937

Sarah, Plain and Tall
Newbery Medal
1986

Shadow of a Bull
Newbery Medal
1965

The Sign of the Beaver
Newbery Honor Book
1984

Sing Down the Moon
Newbery Honor Book
1971

The Slave Dancer
Newbery Medal
1974

A Solitary Blue
Newbery Honor Book
1984

Sounder
Newbery Medal
1970

Strawberry Girl
Newbery Medal
1946

Summer of the Swans
Newbery Medal
1971

Thimble Summer
Newbery Medal
1939

To Be a Slave
Newbery Honor Book
1969

The Trumpeter of Krakow
Newbery Medal
1929

Up a Road Slowly
Newbery Medal
1967

Waterless Mountain
Newbery Medal
1932

The Wheel on the School
Newbery Medal
1955

The Witch of Blackbird Pond
Newbery Medal
1959

Young Fu of the Upper Yangtze
Newbery Medal
1933

*Note: This appendix lists Newbery Medal winners and Newbery Honor Books covered in volumes 1 through 3 of *Beacham's Guide to Literature for Young Adults*. All other Newbery Medal winners are covered in volumes 4 through 6 of *Beacham's Guide to Literature for Young Adults*.

APPENDIX B: TITLES GROUPED BY THEMES

Adopted Children/Foster Children/Orphans
Anne of Green Gables
The Great Gilly Hopkins
Jane Eyre
Oliver Twist
Pollyanna: The Glad Book
Rebecca of Sunnybrook Farm
The Secret Garden

American Dream
Abe Lincoln Grows Up
All-American
Amos Fortune: Free Man
The Catcher in the Rye
The Great Gatsby
Henry Reed, Inc.
Huckleberry Finn
Invisible Man
Journey Toward Freedom: The Story of Sojourner Truth
The Jungle
Lincoln: A Photobiography
Of Mice and Men
Onion John
Roll of Thunder, Hear My Cry
Samurai of Gold Hill
The Soul Brothers and Sister Lou
Tom Sawyer
A Tree Grows in Brooklyn

Art/Artists
American Painter in Paris
Cathedral
Cloudy-Bright
Dobry
From the Mixed-Up Files of Mrs. Basil E. Frankweiler
I, Juan de Pareja

Michelangelo
The Tale of Beatrix Potter
William Blake

Asian/Asian-American Experience
A Child in Prison Camp
Homesick: My Own Story
The House of Sixty Fathers
Journey to Topaz
The Master Puppeteer
Samurai of Gold Hill
Young Fu of the Upper Yangtze

Black Experience
Amos Fortune: Free Man
Anthony Burns
The Cay
Cry, the Beloved Country
Durango Street
Harriet Tubman: Conductor on the Underground Railroad
A Hero Ain't Nothin' but a Sandwich
I, Juan de Pareja
I Know Why the Caged Bird Sings
Invisible Man
Journey Toward Freedom: The Story of Sojourner Truth
Langston Hughes
M.C. Higgins, the Great
Native Son
Roll of Thunder, Hear My Cry
The Slave Dancer
The Soul Brothers and Sister Lou
To Be a Slave
To Kill a Mockingbird

Career Decisions

Albert Einstein
American Painter in Paris
Carry On, Mr. Bowditch
Dobry
Girl with a Pen: Charlotte Brontë
Great Ambitions: A Story of the
  Early Years of Charles Dickens
Hans Christian Andersen
Jacob Have I Loved
Shadow of a Bull
Spunkwater, Spunkwater!: A
  Life of Mark Twain
The Stone Book Quartet
Walt Whitman: Builder for
  America
William Blake

Child Abuse

Bridge to Terabithia
Good Night, Mr. Tom
Jane Eyre
Oliver Twist
Our Eddie
The Outsiders
Summer of My German Soldier

Class Conflict

Black Beauty
The Bronze Bow
Cloudy-Bright
Cry, the Beloved Country
Gandhi
Great Expectations
The Great Gatsby
Jane Addams: Pioneer for Social
  Justice
Josh
The Jungle
National Velvet
Of Mice and Men
Oliver Twist
Our Eddie
The Outsiders
The Power and the Glory
Pride and Prejudice
Queenie Peavy

The Road to Agra
A Tale of Two Cities
Viva Chicano
Wuthering Heights

Classical Greece/Rome

Alexander the Great
Caesar
Children of the Fox
Conqueror and Hero
The Eagle of the Ninth
The Mask of Apollo
The Walls of Windy Troy

Crime/Corruption

All the King's Men
Are You in the House Alone?
Black Jack
Cry, the Beloved Country
Durango Street
Kidnapped
Lord of the Flies
Master Rosalind
Native Son
Of Mice and Men
Oliver Twist
Otto of the Silver Hand
The Outsiders
Smith
Viva Chicano

Death

After the Rain
Bridge to Terabithia
The Bumblebee Flies Anyway
Cry, the Beloved Country
Davita's Harp
A Day No Pigs Would Die
Far Away and Long Ago
I Heard the Owl Call My Name
Of Mice and Men
Old Yeller
The Red Pony
A Separate Peace
Slaughterhouse-Five
The Sun Also Rises
The Yearling

Drug/Alcohol Abuse
A Hero Ain't Nothin' but
 a Sandwich
The Power and the Glory
Rumble Fish
That Was Then, This Is Now
A Tree Grows in Brooklyn
Up a Road Slowly

The Elderly/Aging
After the Rain
Good Night, Mr. Tom
Jacob Have I Loved
The Old Man and the Sea

Farming
Across Five Aprils
Caddie Woodlawn
A Day No Pigs Would Die
A Gathering of Days
Little House in the Big Woods
Of Mice and Men
Samurai of Gold Hill
Strawberry Girl
Thimble Summer

Father-Daughter
Relationship
Caddie Woodlawn
Davita's Harp
A Gathering of Days
Invincible Louisa
Little House in the Big Woods
Miracles on Maple Hill
Shelley's Mary
Summer of My German Soldier
To Kill a Mockingbird

Father-Son Relationship
Adam of the Road
Cry, the Beloved Country
A Day No Pigs Would Die
Dear Mr. Henshaw
Durango Street

A Hero Ain't Nothin' but
 a Sandwich
Incident at Hawk's Hill
Journey to an 800 Number
The Light in the Forest
My Brother Sam Is Dead
Onion John
Otto of the Silver Hand
Our Eddie
Rumble Fish
Samurai of Gold Hill
Shane
A Solitary Blue
Sounder
To Kill a Mockingbird
The Yearling

First Love
After the Rain
Anne Frank
Anne of Green Gables
Bridge to Terabithia
The Bronze Bow
Cloudy-Bright
Dinky Hocker Shoots Smack
Great Expectations
Jacob Have I Loved
M.C. Higgins, the Great
My Darling, My Hamburger
Summer of My German Soldier
Tom Sawyer

Frontier/West
Abe Lincoln Grows Up
Caddie Woodlawn
Chief Joseph
Crazy Horse
Daniel Boone
Ishi: Last of His Tribe
The Light in the Forest
Lincoln: A Photobiography
Little House in the Big Woods
Prairie-Town Boy
The Red Pony
Samurai of Gold Hill
Shane

Grandparent-Grandchild Relationship

After the Rain
Are You There God? It's Me, Margaret
Dicey's Song
Dobry
The Egypt Game
The Endless Steppe: Growing Up in Siberia
Heidi
I Know Why the Caged Bird Sings
Jacob Have I Loved
The Wheel on the School

Imagination

Bridge to Terabithia
Cathedral
A Day of Pleasure
Dobry
Don Quixote
The Egypt Game
From the Mixed-Up Files of Mrs. Basil E. Frankweiler
Hans Christian Andersen
Miracles on Maple Hill
Pollyanna: The Glad Book
A Room Made of Windows
The Secret Garden
Slaughterhouse-Five
The Tale of Beatrix Potter
Thimble Summer
William Blake

Immigrant Experience

Albert Einstein
The Bells of Bleecker Street
The Chestry Oak
Davita's Harp
Jane Addams: Pioneer for Social Justice
Journey to Topaz
The Jungle
Onion John
Our Eddie

Samurai of Gold Hill
A Tree Grows in Brooklyn

Individual vs. Societal Institutions

Are You in the House Alone?
Catch-22
The Chocolate War
Cry, the Beloved Country
Durango Street
Gandhi
I Am the Cheese
Invisible Man
Jane Addams: Pioneer for Social Justice
Journey Toward Freedom: The Story of Sojourner Truth
Madame Curie
Maudie and Me and the Dirty Book
Native Son
Never Cry Wolf
The Power and the Glory
The Scarlet Letter
To Kill a Mockingbird
The Witch of Blackbird Pond

Jewish Experience

Albert Einstein
Anne Frank
Are You There God? It's Me, Margaret
Davita's Harp
A Day Of Pleasure
The Endless Steppe: Growing Up in Siberia
Friedrich
Ivanhoe
Our Eddie
Summer of My German Soldier

Latino Experience

And Now Miguel
The Black Pearl
Durango Street
Viva Chicano

Learning Disability
Dicey's Song
Incident at Hawk's Hill
The Summer of the Swans
Where the Lilies Bloom
The Yearling

Medieval Life
Adam of the Road
The Black Arrow
Cathedral
The Door in the Wall
Ivanhoe
Men of Iron
Otto of the Silver Hand
A Proud Taste for Scarlet
  and Miniver
The Trumpeter of Krakow
William the Conquerer

Mental Illness
Black Jack
Catch-22
Good Night, Mr. Tom
I Am the Cheese
Our Eddie
Slaughterhouse-Five

Mentors
The Cay
Durango Street
I, Juan de Pareja
The Master Puppeteer
Men of Iron
The Old Man and the Sea
The Story of My Life
To Kill a Mockingbird
The Witch of Blackbird Pond
Young Fu of the Upper Yangtze

Mother-Daughter Relationship
Are You There God? It's Me,
  Margaret
The Birds of Summer
Davita's Harp
Dinky Hocker Shoots Smack
I Know Why the Caged
  Bird Sings
Pride and Prejudice
Roll of Thunder, Hear My Cry
The Tale of Beatrix Potter
A Tree Grows in Brooklyn

Mother-Son Relationship
Across Five Aprils
Alexander the Great
Good Night, Mr. Tom
A Hero Ain't Nothin' but
  a Sandwich
The Matchlock Gun
A Proud Taste for Scarlet
  and Miniver
Shadow of a Bull
A Solitary Blue

Native American Experience
Chief Joseph
Crazy Horse
I Heard the Owl Call My Name
Ishi: Last of His Tribe
Laughing Boy
The Light in the Forest
The Sign of the Beaver
Sing Down the Moon
Waterless Mountain

Nature
The Black Pearl
The Cay
A Day No Pigs Would Die
Eskimo Boy
Far Away and Long Ago
Incident at Hawk's Hill
Island of the Blue Dolphins
Miracles on Maple Hill
My Friend Flicka
My Side of the Mountain
Never Cry Wolf
The Old Man and the Sea
Rascal
Samurai of Gold Hill
The Sign of the Beaver

Sing Down the Moon
Thoreau of Walden Pond
Walden
Waterless Mountain
Where the Lilies Bloom
Wild Animals I Have Known
Wuthering Heights

Nonconformity
The Catcher in the Rye
Dobry
Don Quixote
Huckleberry Finn
Josh
Lord of the Flies
Onion John
Shadow of a Bull
Shelley's Mary
Summer of My German Soldier
The Tale of Beatrix Potter
Walden
Where the Lilies Bloom

Pets/Animals
Black Beauty
A Day No Pigs Would Die
Eskimo Boy
Far Away and Long Ago
Ginger Pye
Incident at Hawk's Hill
Island of the Blue Dolphins
It's Like This, Cat
King of the Wind
My Friend Flicka
My Side of the Mountain
National Velvet
Never Cry Wolf
The Old Man and the Sea
Old Yeller
Rascal
The Red Pony
Sounder
Waterless Mountain
Wild Animals I Have Known
The Yearling

Physical Disability
The Bumblebee Flies Anyway
The Cay
The Door in the Wall
The Eagle of the Ninth
Johnny Tremain
Our Eddie
The Road to Agra
Sounder
The Story of My Life
The Sun Also Rises

Political Conflict
Albert Einstein
Anne Frank
The Bronze Bow
Chase Me, Catch Nobody
Cry, the Beloved Country
The Endless Steppe: Growing Up in Siberia
Friedrich
Gandhi
Ivanhoe
Kidnapped
The Power and the Glory
The Silver Sword
A Tale of Two Cities
Traitor: The Case of Benedict Arnold
Young Fu of the Upper Yangtze

Poverty
The Birds of Summer
Black Beauty
Cry, the Beloved Country
Durango Street
Hans Brinker; or, The Silver Skates
A Hero Ain't Nothin' but a Sandwich
Jane Addams: Pioneer for Social Justice
M.C. Higgins, the Great
Native Son
Of Mice and Men
Oliver Twist
Our Eddie

The Outsiders
The Road to Agra
Sounder
Strawberry Girl
A Tree Grows in Brooklyn
Viva Chicano
Where the Lilies Bloom

Quest/Journey
Adam of the Road
The Black Pearl
The Catcher in the Rye
The Chestry Oak
Children of the Fox
Cry, the Beloved Country
Don Quixote
The Door in the Wall
The Eagle of the Ninth
Eskimo Boy
Footsteps
Heart of Darkness
The House of Sixty Fathers
Huckleberry Finn
I Am the Cheese
I Heard the Owl Call My Name
Ishi: Last of His Tribe
Laughing Boy
My Side of the Mountain
The Old Man and the Sea
The Road to Agra
Samurai of Gold Hill
Sing Down the Moon
Slave Dancer
Waterless Mountain
The Walls of Windy Troy

Racism
Amos Fortune: Free Man
Anne Frank
Anthony Burns
The Cay
A Child in Prison Camp
Cry, the Beloved Country
Durango Street
Gandhi
Harriet Tubman: Conductor on
  the Underground Railroad

A Hero Ain't Nothin' but
  a Sandwich
Huckleberry Finn
I Know Why the Caged
  Bird Sings
Invisible Man
Ivanhoe
Journey to Topaz
Journey Toward Freedom: The
  Story of Sojourner Truth
Langston Hughes
The Light in the Forest
Native Son
Roll of Thunder, Hear My Cry
Samurai of Gold Hill
Sing Down the Moon
The Soul Brothers and Sister Lou
Sounder
To Be a Slave
To Kill a Mockingbird

Redemption
Black Jack
A Christmas Carol
Great Expectations
The Great Gilly Hopkins
Heidi
Huckleberry Finn
I Heard the Owl Call My Name
Incident at Hawk's Hill
Jane Eyre
Miracles on Maple Hill
Otto of the Silver Hand
The Power and the Glory
The Secret Garden
A Tale of Two Cities

Religion
Are You There God? It's Me,
  Margaret
The Black Pearl
Cathedral
Cry, the Beloved Country
A Day No Pigs Would Die
A Day of Pleasure
Far Away and Long Ago

Friedrich
Gandhi
I Heard the Owl Call My Name
Our Eddie
Penn
The Power and the Glory
The Scarlet Letter
The Witch of Blackbird Pond

Revenge
The Black Arrow
The Bronze Bow
The Chocolate War
Great Expectations
Hans Brinker; or, The Silver
  Skates
Kidnapped
Lorna Doone
Master Rosalind
Otto of the Silver Hand
The Three Musketeers
Wuthering Heights

Romantic Love
Anne Frank
Don Quixote
Gone with the Wind
Great Expectations
The Great Gatsby
Ivanhoe
Jacob Have I Loved
Jane Eyre
Laughing Boy
Little Women
Pride and Prejudice
Sarah, Plain and Tall
The Scarlet Letter
Shelley's Mary
The Sun Also Rises
A Tale of Two Cities
That Was Then, This Is Now
The Three Musketeers
Tom Sawyer
A Tree Grows in Brooklyn
Wuthering Heights

Runaways
Black Jack
From the Mixed-Up Files of Mrs.
  Basil E. Frankweiler
Huckleberry Finn
Incident at Hawk's Hill
Thimble Summer
Tom Sawyer

School/Schoolteachers
All-American
Bridge to Terabithia
The Chocolate War
A Hero Ain't Nothin' but
  a Sandwich
Jane Eyre
Maudie and Me and the
  Dirty Book
Penrod
Queenie Peavy
Rebecca of Sunnybrook Farm
Roll of Thunder, Hear My Cry
A Separate Peace
The Story of My Life
Tom Brown's Schooldays
Up a Road Slowly
The Wheel on the School

Separation from Parent(s)
The Cay
Dear Mr. Henshaw
Dicey's Song
The Door in the Wall
The Eagle of the Ninth
The Egypt Game
The Endless Steppe: Growing Up
  in Siberia
Eskimo Boy
The Great Gilly Hopkins
Henry Reed, Inc.
The House of Sixty Fathers
Huckleberry Finn
Journey to Topaz
The Light in the Forest
Lord of the Flies
My Side of the Mountain
Otto of the Silver Hand

Queenie Peavy
Roller Skates
The Silver Sword
A Solitary Blue
The Summer of the Swans

Sexual Equality
Anne of Green Gables
Caddie Woodlawn
Children of the Fox
Girl with a Pen: Charlotte Brontë
Jacob Have I Loved
*Journey Toward Freedom: The
   Story of Sojourner Truth*
Madame Curie
National Velvet
The Witch of Blackbird Pond

Sexual Identity
Are You in the House Alone?
*Are You There God? It's Me,
   Margaret*
The Birds of Summer
The Catcher in the Rye
Jacob Have I Loved
My Darling, My Hamburger

Sibling Relationships
Across Five Aprils
Anne Frank
The Birds of Summer
Caddie Woodlawn
Dicey's Song
Incident at Hawk's Hill
Jacob Have I Loved
Little House in the Big Woods
Little Women
Meet the Austins
My Brother Sam Is Dead
My Friend Flicka
Pride and Prejudice
The Road to Agra
Rumble Fish
The Summer of the Swans
To Kill a Mockingbird
Where the Lilies Bloom

Single Parenthood
The Birds of Summer
Davita's Harp
Dear Mr. Henshaw
Dicey's Song
Durango Street
A Gathering of Days
Journey to an 800 Number
A Room Made of Windows
A Solitary Blue
A Tree Grows in Brooklyn

Social Pretense
All-American
Black Beauty
The Chocolate War
Dinky Hocker Shoots Smack
Don Quixote
Great Expectations
The Great Gatsby
Heidi
Huckleberry Finn
Invisible Man
Ivanhoe
Jane Eyre
Master Rosalind
National Velvet
Native Son
The Outsiders
The Pigman
Pride and Prejudice
Queenie Peavy
The Scarlet Letter
The Sun Also Rises
To Kill a Mockingbird
Tom Sawyer
The Witch of Blackbird Pond
Wuthering Heights

Sports
All-American
Bridge to Terabithia
*Hans Brinker; or, The Silver
   Skates*
Shadow of a Bull
The Sun Also Rises
Tom Brown's Schooldays

Unrequited Love
Don Quixote
Gone with the Wind
Great Expectations
The Great Gatsby
Ivanhoe
Jacob Have I Loved
A Tale of Two Cities
Wuthering Heights

Urban Life
The Bells of Bleecker Street
Black Beauty
Cry, the Beloved Country
A Day of Pleasure
Durango Street
Footsteps
A Hero Ain't Nothin' but
   a Sandwich
It's Like This, Cat
Jane Addams: Pioneer for
   Social Justice
The Jungle
Oliver Twist
The Outsiders
Roller Skates
Rumble Fish
Smith
The Soul Brothers and Sister Lou
That Was Then, This Is Now
A Tree Grows in Brooklyn
Viva Chicano
William Blake
Young Fu of the Upper Yangtze

War
Across Five Aprils
Alexander the Great
Anne Frank
The Black Arrow
The Cay
Chase Me, Catch Nobody
The Chestry Oak
A Child in Prison Camp
Children of the Fox
Conqueror and Hero
The Eagle of the Ninth

The Fighting Ground
Friedrich
Gone with the Wind
Good Night, Mr. Tom
The House of Sixty Fathers
Johnny Tremain
Journey to Topaz
Lord of the Flies
The Machine Gunners
My Brother Sam Is Dead
Pendragon: Arthur and
   His Britain
The Red Badge of Courage
Rifles for Watie
The Silver Sword
Slaughterhouse-Five
The Stone Book Quartet
Summer of My German Soldier
A Tale of Two Cities
Traitor: The Case of Benedict
   Arnold
William the Conquerer

Writers
Dear Mr. Henshaw
Girl with a Pen: Charlotte Brontë
Great Ambitions: A Story of the
   Early Years of Charles Dickens
Hans Christian Andersen
Invincible Louisa
Langston Hughes
Lantern Bearer: A Life of Robert
   Louis Stevenson
A Room Made of Windows
Shelley's Mary
Spunkwater, Spunkwater!: A
   Life of Mark Twain
The Tale of Beatrix Potter
Thoreau of Walden Pond
Walt Whitman: Builder for
   America
William Blake
Wind, Sand and Stars

GLOSSARY

A SHORT GLOSSARY OF LITERARY TERMS

◆

allegory: A metaphorical work in which characters and events represent abstract ideas and in which the story is usually intended to teach a moral. Hans Peter Richter's *Friedrich* is allegorical in that it is meant to teach the dangers of inaction in the face of evil and in that each character represents the attitudes of a particular segment of World War II German society.

allusion: A literary allusion is an indirect reference to other works of literature. For example, in Irene Hunt's *Across Five Aprils* the references to lilacs allude to Walt Whitman's famous poem "When Lilacs Last in the Dooryard Bloom'd." Through literary allusions, authors enrich their writing by drawing on earlier works.

analogy: The process of explaining one idea by comparing it to a dissimilar but usually more concrete idea. Metaphors and similes are types of analogies.

antagonist: An antagonist is anything that opposes a protagonist. Antagonists come in four forms: 1) a person 2) the natural world 3) society 4) a force or emotion within the protagonist (for example, Huck wrestles with his conscience in Mark Twain's *Adventures of Huckleberry Finn*, and Daniel learns to deal with his anger in Elizabeth George Speare's *Bronze Bow*).

bildungsroman: A novel that is primarily concerned with the coming of age of an idealistic protagonist. As such, the novel explores the conflict between the protagonist's romantic or even impractical outlook and the realities that he or she must eventually face. J. D. Salinger's *Catcher in the Rye* is an example of a *bildungsroman*.

biographical novel: A work in which the author presents the known facts of a real person's life. The author builds on this foundation to create fictional dialogue and descriptions of characters' emotions, and occasionally offers a psychological analysis of characters' motivations.

catharsis: The process by which a reader, moved to pity or fear by a work of literature, releases pent-up emotions and sometimes undergoes a change of heart. The term was originally applied to ancient Greek drama by Aristotle.

characterization: The process by which a character is developed in a narrative or drama. Often the character's personality is revealed through conflict or stress in the plot.

climax: The moment when the conflict in the plot reaches its peak of intensity and characters must face the consequences of their actions.

comedy: A literary work that is intended to please, amuse, and entertain, often by being funny. Comedies often have happy endings, but readers should remember that some comedy is grim or tragic, as in Joseph Heller's novel *Catch-22*.

coming of age: A theme in a narrative in which a young person takes a significant step away from childhood and into adulthood.

conflict: The struggle that results from the interaction of the protagonist and the antagonist.

critic: A person, often a scholar, who attempts to explain and evaluate works of literature or other art.

dialogue: Conversation between two or more characters.

didacticism: The practice of including clearly stated ideas, morals, sermons, or other forms of instruction in a literary work. Usually a didactic work is meant to teach its readers a moral lesson.

drama: Deriving its origins from theatrical presentations, the term "drama" in fiction refers to the actions that cause the climax. "Dramatic action" refers to a series of events leading to an inevitable outcome.

epic: A work of literature that celebrates a people's heroic traditions. Homer's *Iliad* is an epic about the war of ancient Greek heroes against the city of Troy. The ancient Greeks thought of the *Iliad* as the embodiment of the ideals of their society. By its narrowest definition, the epic is a narrative poem, but many prose works that celebrate a people's heroic tradition, such as the stories of King Arthur, are now called epics.

fable: A narrative that is intended to provide moral instruction, often featuring as main characters animals who speak and act like people.

fairy tale: A fanciful tale that usually employs magic and mystical creatures. Fairy tales are a subcategory of folktales.

fiction: A prose story that is produced from the imagination rather than from fact, although some works of fiction are based on historical or biographical information.

first-person narrator: A character who tells a story. This kind of narrator typically refers to himself or herself as "I." The first-person narrator tells the story from the *first-person point of view.*

flashback: A jump backward in the chronological order of the narrative, usually accomplished in literature through recollection or dream sequences.

foil: In literature, a foil is a character whose marked difference from another character, often the protagonist, highlights the other character's distinctive personality traits. Settings or events may also act as foils.

folktale: A story that usually has its origin in the oral tradition, having been passed on from one storyteller to the next by word of mouth. Folktales are often fanciful and romantic. The term "folktale" is also sometimes applied to short stories that imitate folktales, even though they were composed originally in written form.

foreshadowing: The process of hinting at the outcome of the story by placing literal or symbolic clues about what will happen before the events actually take place.

Gothic: A kind of literature that emphasizes the mysterious and grotesque. In popular fiction, this often takes the form of the horror novel, which emphasizes a frightening supernatural world.

hero: A character, usually a person or animal, who confronts a chain of potentially tragic events. In classical literature the hero, through his courage, integrity or nobility, may reverse the course of tragedy; other heroes risk or sacrifice their lives for some noble or divine cause. However, readers should remember that while heroes are often "good" people, they are not always so, especially in contemporary literature. Sometimes a hero begins as the villain but through self-discovery changes his view of life, as does Scrooge in Charles Dickens's *Christmas Carol*. The hero might also be unaware that he or she is acting heroically, thus becoming a naive or passive hero, such as Anne Frank or Anthony Burns. Usually a hero's actions result in an outcome that society considers "morally correct," but there is a body of fiction in which the "hero" works against society, as in Joseph Heller's *Catch-22*. This type of character is called an "anti-hero." In some regards even Huck Finn is an anti-hero.

historical novel: A work of fiction that uses historical facts as the basis for the story but adds imaginative material, such as dialogue.

imagery: The use of colorful description to produce vivid mental images. Often these images hold symbolic significance in the book, such as Holden Caulfield's "image" of children falling off a cliff in J.D. Salinger's *Catcher in the Rye*.

irony: The use of words to convey the opposite of their literal meaning. A reader's understanding of the characters and plot prepares him to understand that a statement is ironic. Similarly, a scene in a work contains "dramatic irony" when the words or acts of a character or group of characters have meanings that the characters do not perceive but which the audience or readers do understand. For instance, in Mark Twain's *Huckleberry Finn*, the reader knows that Huck and Jim's voyage down the river is taking Jim into slavery, while the characters believe they are escaping to freedom.

metaphor: A figure of speech that draws a comparison between two unlike objects. "His face is a bright red tomato" is an example of a metaphor.

moral: This is the lesson that a literary work—most often a fable or allegory—is meant to teach. Most literary works do not have explicit morals.

narrative: The narrator's account or interpretation of a sequence of events in a novel or short story.

narrator: The person who relates the events of a story. A first-person narrator refers to himself or herself as "I," and usually participates in the events of the story. A third-person narrator is usually not involved in the story and refers to all the characters as "he" or "she." An omniscient narrator is a third-person narrator who reveals the thoughts of the characters. A narrator who reveals the thoughts of just one character, usually the protagonist, is referred to as "limited omniscient."

novel: A long work of fiction that has both a main plot and subplots. It often, but not always, features many characters. A novel always builds to a climax, the moment when the characters must face the consequences of their actions.

novelette/novella: These terms are sometimes used to distinguish a short novel from a long novel or a short story. But a novelette or novella's length is not as important a characteristic as the number of characters it includes or the moment at which the climax occurs.

personification: A literary device by which human qualities are attributed to inanimate objects or abstract ideas. "The ocean crashed against the shore in a violent rage" is an example of personification because rage is a human emotion that oceans cannot experience.

plot: The actions that derive from conflict in a narrative or drama. In a novel, these usually build to one major climax. Novels that depend too much on plot and not enough on theme and characterization are considered inferior works of literature. Novels that contain a series of loosely connected plots are called "episodic."

point of view: In literature, this refers to the particular perspective of the narrator of the story. An omniscient narrator has a broad, all-knowing point of view; a first-person narrator has a much more limited point of view. A "shifting point of view" alternates the narrative perspectives of at least two characters.

protagonist: The main character in a work of fiction, biography, or other literary work. The protagonist can be the hero but does not have to be. Instead, the protagonist can be villainous and not at all heroic; he or she just needs to be the focus of the work. Sometimes the protagonist is not even a person but is instead an animal, a place, or even a building. For instance, in David Macaulay's *Cathedral*, the cathedral itself is a kind of protagonist because the book is about how the structure grows and changes during its construction.

satire: A literary work that ridicules its subject. It is often meant to inspire social or political change.

short story: A short work of fiction that is tightly focused on a central plot and a small number of characters. The climax always occurs at the end of the story, whereas in a novel it occurs about two-thirds through.

simile: A figure of speech that directly compares two dissimilar objects through the use of "like" or "as." One famous simile is "My love is like a red, red rose," by which the poet describes the qualities of a woman by comparing her to a red rose.

symbolism: The use of specific images, objects, incidents, names or places to suggest abstract ideas, such as love, faith, or wisdom. In Cynthia Voigt's *Solitary Blue*, the blue heron is a symbol that represents Jeff's withdrawal from people and his preference for the solitude of nature.

tone: The overall mood evoked by the narrative voice in the story.

tragedy: An account of a series of related events that end in catastrophe for the protagonist.

villain: The character who works against the good of the other characters or society. Often in fiction the protagonist is the hero and the antagonist the villain. In Charles Dickens's *Christmas Carol*, Scrooge begins as the villain and ends as the hero.

INDEX

INDEX

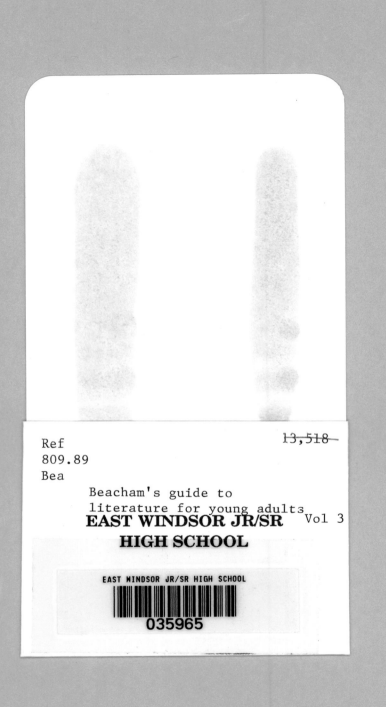